The Book of Rifles

An Illustration from the Original Millimete Manuscript. This is the earliest authenticated picture of a weapon using gunpowder. 1326 A.D.

The Book of
RIFLES

W. H. B. SMITH
and
JOSEPH E. SMITH

THE STACKPOLE COMPANY

Harrisburg, Pa.

Publisher's Foreword

The ability to shoot a rifle is an American tradition. Our country was established and its borders expanded westward by men with rifles in their hands. The rifle gave the settlers protection against marauding Indians and other foes, and was an important means of securing food for the pioneer family.

Skill in using the rifle helped our hastily recruited armies to win wars. Knowledge of the rifle and proficiency in its use are important factors in our national defense still, even in the nuclear age.

Hunting, individual competitive marksmanship, and interest in small arms have grown steadily during the past several decades. Many individuals, including business and professional men, have found hunting a real tonic and relaxation from the insistent pressures of high tension living, amid the wonders of nature in the great outdoors. Competitive shooting matches also provide relaxation and enjoyable tests of skill and coordination.

New developments in military rifles, both at home and abroad, have resulted in thousands of fine weapons becoming available for sale. Often they can be purchased at bargain prices. Some can successfully be converted to a sporter rifle to suit the individual shooter.

More and more persons, even those who have little opportunity for shooting, have found the collection of shoulder weapons and handguns a fascinating and ofttimes a profitable hobby.

Urgently needed was a reference work to identify and describe in detail the many kinds of rifles, both military and sporting. THE BOOK OF RIFLES, originally published in 1948 as *The N.R.A. Book of Small Arms: Volume II, Rifles,* is such a reference book. (Handguns are similarly covered in a companion volume, THE BOOK OF PISTOLS AND REVOLVERS, by W.H.B. Smith and Kent Bellah.)

The late W. H. B. Smith, internationally famous arms authority, provided the tremendous research effort and produced most of the material in the first editions of this book.

Mr. William Piznak furnished much important information, especially on rifles of Finland and Sweden and on recent developments world-wide.

Mr. Joseph E. Smith, noted small arms expert of the Army Materiel Command, has extensively revised and enlarged this new edition, and has added over two hundred photographs. Please see his "Preface to the Third Edition."

The publisher takes real pleasure in presenting this new Third Edition as the finest work of its kind in existence.

J. B. SWEET
Brig. Gen., USA, Ret.
Senior Editor

Preface to the Third Edition

Probably as the result of the large number of Americans who have had military service in the last twenty years; the very active programs of the National Rifle Association; the large number of gun magazines in circulation; and the large quantity of relatively low-priced, surplus, military rifles on the market today; there is currently a great deal of interest in the United States in small arms, particularly rifles. The Stackpole Company and I hope that this revision of BOOK OF RIFLES will prove of value both to those who have been interested in rifles for years and those who may be novices in the field.

Within the past twenty years we have seen the emergence of new and terrible weapons, nuclear and thermonuclear warheads, intercontinental ballistic missiles, supersonic jet bombers, etc. During this same period the rifle has continued to hold its place as the basic individual weapon of the soldier and marine. The place of the rifle in hunting and target shooting is taken for granted, but the terrible new weapons of mass destruction have tended to push military rifles out of public notice. The fact that all the major powers of the world and many of the lesser powers have equipped, or are in the process of equipping, their armies with new rifles points out the importance of the current and projected future role of the military rifle.

A great deal of information which was not readily available when the earlier editions of this book were published has been added to this edition. In addition the excellent material supplied by Mr. William Piznak in the second edition of the book has been integrated into the main body of the book.

I realize that even in this edition, it is possible some errors will have crept into some of the multitude of facts and figures contained in this book. The Stackpole Company and I will appreciate any correction a reader may care to send us. (I suggest you address your correction or comment to the Senior Editor, The Stackpole Company, Box 1831, Harrisburg, Pa.)

It is not unusual for the weights and measurements of rifles to be reported differently in various publications. There are several reasons for this situation. Most countries use the metric system of weights and measures. Differences in length and weights reported in various publications, can be the result of the number of decimal places used in converting the figure to English measurements.

Rifles of the same model having wooden stocks and handguards vary significantly in weight among themselves because of differences in the density and humidity content of the wood. Indeed, the same rifle may vary in weight from day to day due to differences in humidity. Another factor that must be considered in relation to rifle weights is that frequently publications, even detailed official manuals, do not indicate whether weights include sling, cleaning rod, or cleaning accessories in the stock. There will frequently be differences reported in muzzle velocities. As often as not, velocities given in various publications are really instrumental velocities (the velocity as taken by instruments at a set distance from the muzzle, usually 53 or 78 feet); instrumental velocities have to be converted to muzzle velocities by the use of various formulae.

I would like to acknowledge the great help of various individuals and organizations who have assisted me in the preparation of this revision directly or indirectly.

The following individuals and organizations of the U.S. Army Materiel Command have been of great assistance: Dr. Fred H. Carten, Mr. A. C. Bonkemeyer, and Mr. Thomas E. Cosgrove of the Research and Development Directorate, Army Materiel Command. Colonel Harrison H. Harden, Commanding Officer of the U.S. Army Foreign Science and Technology Center and the following personnel of that organization: Lt. Col. James C. Steele, Mr. J. J. Reen, Mr. Philip Valentini, Mr. John Parker, and Mr. L. C. Burden.

Mr. Joseph Penton of the Army Materiel Command Information Office, Mr. Thomas Nelson of Interarmco, and Mr. Ludwig Olson of the National Rifle Association have also been of great assistance. The Technical Intelligence Office of the Army Test and Evaluation Command at Aberdeen Proving Ground in the persons of Captain B. Painter and Mr. Howard Johnson have consistently cooperated, and my wife has had to cope with the translation of my terrible writing and rather mysterious notes into legible and intelligible typing.

The following arms manufacturers and arms dealers have been most helpful:
Fabrique Nationale, Herstal, Belgium
BSA Guns Ltd., Shirley Solihull, Warwickshire, England
J. G. Anschütz G.m.b.H., Ulm-Donau, W. Germany
Carl Walther, G.m.b.H., Ulm-Donau, W. Germany
Husqvarna Vapenfabriks AB, Huskvarna, Sweden
Hämmerli A. G., Lenzburg, Switzerland
Dansk Industri Syndicat, Copenhagen, Denmark
Interarmco of Alexandria, Virginia
Winchester Western Div. of Olin Mathison Corp., New Haven, Conn.
Colts Patent Fire Arms Mfg. Co. Inc., Hartford, Conn.

The opinions expressed in the revised sections of the book are my own. They are, for the most part, limited to pointing out what the advantages and/or disadvantages of a particular system might be. I have tried to be absolutely objective. My opinions do not represent the official opinion of the Department of the Army, the Army Materiel Command, or any other agency of the United States Government.

JOSEPH E. SMITH

Vienna, Virginia

Contents

APPENDIXES

PART I

The Evolution of Shoulder Arms

Chapter 1

THE ORIGINS OF GUNPOWDER AND THE GUN

GUNPOWDER

The discovery of gunpowder lies shrouded in the mists of time. We find ambiguous references in the writing of the ancients which the credulous and the romantic can use to prove—to their own satisfaction, at any rate—that almost *any* invention, including gunpowder, is a product of a dim and distant past.

In Virgil's *Aeneid* one can find mention of the attempt of Salmoneus to reproduce thunder; Valerius Flaccus can be quoted on the efforts of the Brahmins to do the same; Philostratus' *Life of Apollonius of Tyanaeus* says of the failure of Alexander the Great to storm India; "These truly wise men, the Oxydracae, dwell between the Rivers Hyphasis and Ganges; their country Alexander never entered . . . their cities he never could have taken, though he had led a thousand as brave as Achilles, or three thousand such as Ajax to the assault; for they come not out to the field to fight those who attack them, but these holy men, beloved by the gods, overthrow their enemies with tempests and thunderbolts shot from their walls." In Vitruvius, and in Plutarch's *Life of Marcellus* are statements which can be extracted to indicate that Archimedes was familiar with gunpowder.

The ancient Sanskrit records (notably those quoted in the Halhed translation of the *Gentoo Code* as printed by the East India Company in 1776 and alleged to date back some 500 years) and Oppert's *On the Weapons of the Ancient Hindus* published in England in 1880, are replete with allusions and out-of-context extracts which seek to establish a knowledge of gunpowder in India long before the dawn of European history.

French researchers in the last century endeavored to prove that the explosive was first brought to Europe by returning Crusaders who learned of it from the Arabs who, allegedly, had employed it in the year 690 A.D. at the Siege of Mecca.

While there is adequate evidence of the use of *inflammable* compounds by the ancients, there is no real evidence that gunpowder—particularly as a propellant—was known before the 13th Century.

On the contrary, there is a vast body of negative fact to make a case *against* gunpowder being used in very early times. Anna Comnena's work *The Alexiad,*[*] a history of the reign of her father, the Roman Emperor Alexius I, from 1081 to 1118 A.D., lists various Greek Fire formulas, but gives no evidence of a knowledge of a true explosive.

Another valuable piece of negative evidence is found in the account of one of the most remarkable—and most unknown—adventurer-ambassadors of all time: Giovanni di Plan Carpin. Carpin, a trained and experienced soldier thoroughly familiar with all the weapons of his day, was sent as ambassador

---

[*] An excellent English translation by Elizabeth Dawes of *The Alexiad* was published in England in 1928.

to the Court of the Great Ghengis Khan at Karakorum by Pope Innocent IV in 1246 A.D. Carpin was greeted by the Great Khan as a worthy friend and soldier; and during his stay he traversed the length and breadth of the Mongol Empire and was an observer of wars between the Mongols and the Chinese. Methodically he listed the types and classes of weapons he encountered—ballista and similar military machines, the sling, bows, Greek Fire, and he carefully described the burning of invested cities by hurling melted fat or tallow projectiles into them. He wrote a detailed account of the historic siege of Kai-Fung Fu. Yet nowhere in his original report does he intimate an awareness of any substance resembling gunpowder.

Hime, Oman, Guttman, Kohler and other researchers have written thick volumes exposing the errors of translation and belief which produced the early fables of gunpowder. Most of the legends of very early Arab firearms and explosives stem from translations of documents in the Escurial made by the Librarian, Michael Casiri, between 1760 and 1770; translations which have been proved incorrect. As to the claim that the fourteenth century monk Berthold Schwartz (or Bartholdus Niger) discovered gunpowder at Freiburg in Germany, even a cursory study of the record discloses that the legend is baseless. A Professor Lenz in 1840, seeking to claim the invention for Germany, reported an alleged entry in the *Memoriebook der Stad Ghant* for the year 1313 which translated read: "In this year the use of guns was first discovered in Germany by a monk." Here would seem to be clear proof of the Berthold Schwartz claim. But there are six copies of the *Memoriebook* known to be in existence. Five of these contain no mention whatever of the passage cited. The sixth copy when checked by M. Diegerich, the conservator of old records at Ghent, about 1906 also failed to disclose the passage quoted by Lenz under the date listed. However, in a transcript of the Ghent annals *for the year 1393,* a passage of somewhat similar nature is found. In some manner Professor Lenz may have confused the year 1393 with the year 1313. If we assume that this one transcript is accurate, the fact remains that *by 1393* firearms had appeared in every major corner of Europe, so that the Schwartz "discovery" claim would certainly not be valid.

Where, then, did gunpowder first appear *on the record?* In a manuscript first written in Greek by the unknown monk Marcus Graecus, which later appeared in expanded form in Latin under the title *Liber ignium ad comburendos bostes.*

This remarkable manuscript, while listing formulas for Greek Fire, also gives specific formulas for gunpowder *(ignis volans).* One formula is: "1 part quick sulphur, 2 parts willow charcoal, 6 parts saltpeter." Gunpowder made by this formula was too powerful for use in weapons made even in the 14th and the 15th Centuries. The *Liber ignium* lists 35 formulas altogether and also gives instructions for manufacturing rockets.

Hofer in his *Historie de la Chimie* gave the date of this manuscript as the year 846 A.D.; but later researches by Hime, Oman and others, and examination of the translations at the Bibliotheque in Paris, the Hof-und-Staatsbibliothek at Munich, and Germanische National Museum at Nuremberg, and at Oxford University have established that while some passages in the Graecus work are of classical antiquity, the sections dealing with gunpowder formulas were written about the middle of the 13th Century.

The next, or perhaps concurrent, references to gunpowder are in the manuscripts of the English monk Roger Bacon, the Spanish monk Ferrarius and the Bishop Albertus Magnus of Ratisbon.

The manuscript of Ferrarius is an unedited letter now in England in the Bodleian Library at Oxford addressed to an unknown "Anselm." The *Opus de mirabilibus mundi* of Bishop Albertus Magnus, like that of Ferrarius, is undated but Albertus Magnus is known to have lived between about 1193 and 1280. Inasmuch as the references to gunpowder in *Liber ignium* are believed to have been added to that manuscript about the middle of the 13th Century, and Bacon and Magnus were in communication with one another, there may be some connection between all three manuscripts. Obviously they all antedated the so-called "discovery" of gunpowder by the German monk.

In the *Epistola de secretis operibus Artis et Naturae et de nullitate magiae* which Roger Bacon wrote in 1248, and dedicated to William of Auvergne, Bishop of Paris, Bacon not only describes the ingredients of gunpowder and lists many of its properties, but actually recommends its military use as an explosive for the destruction of armies. This treatise is particularly noteworthy because Bacon does not claim to have invented the mixture, but speaks of it as something well known at the period of his writing and alludes to its use in pyrotechnics.

Where did Roger Bacon learn of gunpowder? We can do no more than guess. He travelled in Spain for a time when it was the home of a great culture and the seat of the outstanding universities. Among the authentic manuscripts in the Escurial at Madrid are a few treating of chemical formulas which might indicate a knowledge of gunpowder, though they are not explicit, as is Bacon's own work. Most notable of these are the formulas of Nedj-iddin Hassan Abrammah who died in 1295 and one credited to Yussuf-ibn-Ismail. It is important to note that while formulas such as these mention the ignition factor of saltpeter, they do not note any *explosive* applications of it. Since the subject was explored by the Saracens, many of whom were noted for their knowledge of alchemy, it is possible that Bacon gained some information from them, as is often claimed. However, since the Marcus Graecus manuscript was available with its gunpowder formulas about the year 1270, and the learned men of those days were principally churchmen, it seems more likely that Bacon's knowledge came through a study of the Graecus manuscript.

Millions of words have been written by enthusiasts, theorists, nationalists, scholars and religionists to prove that the invention was ancient Indian or Chinese, Italian or Saracen, German or Flemish, English—Russian and even Icelandic! All those theories are interesting. Many are possible. A few are even probable. But this brief summary covers the salient points of all that is *provable* of the origins of gunpowder.

THE ORIGINS OF THE GUN

Exactly when and where tubes were first used with a charge of gunpowder to hurl projectiles we do not know. In *The Alexiad* already quoted, we learn that bronze tubes were used to direct inflammable mixtures. The German

Zeitschrift für historische Waffenkunde among whose papers we find many of the outstanding research studies on early arms, states that Chinese annals for the year 1259 A.D. list the use of a "fiery powder" in bamboo tubes. Hollow tubes of wood wrapped around with hide, hemp or a similar winding and then loaded from the muzzle with alternate charges of powder and an incendiary ball are known to have been in use by the early Tartars and Arabs. These last mentioned devices operate on the system of Roman Candles, the fire at the muzzle communicating around each ball to the powder which launches it. It must be evident, however, that all such weapons were not actually guns but were, in effect, forerunners of the modern flame thrower. They were used to start fires, not to penetrate by projectile force.

German writers for years have pointed to the legend of the "discovery" of gunpowder by the monk Berthold Schwartz as evidence that the discovery of the possibility of projecting lethal balls by gunpowder was made in Germany. According to the favorite version of this tale, the monk was compounding gunpowder in a chemist's mortar with a pestle when it exploded and the pestle was hurled a goodly distance. From this accident Schwartz is said to have evolved the idea of projectile force from which came the artillery mortar. Schwartz may have had such an accident and it may have been the genesis of the gun idea in Germany but from the historical record we can establish that projectile firearms were known and used in Italy and in the Low Countries long before the time of Schwartz.

While the early Saracen records seem to show quite general use of stone-throwing cannon as early as 1247 in the defense of Seville, the projecting devices may have been mechanical engines rather than cannon with gunpowder. The earliest records whose authenticity can be satisfactorily established are those of Italian and Flemish origin, with the Italian apparently somewhat earlier than those of the Flemings.

Whether the handgun evolved from the siege or defense cannon, was concurrent with it, or was an entirely separate development, it is impossible to establish. One can make a case from fragmentary records to bolster any one of those conjectures; but invariably the weight of counterevidence is strong enough to prevent a positive decision. The earliest records seldom distinguish between heavy ordnance and hand guns. It is only at a later date that explicit descriptions, tapestries and drawings provide positive evidence about this phase of small arms evolution.

An excellent example of an undocumented statement being accepted as fact is to be found in the remark first made, apparently, by the German writer Auguste Demmin in his *Die Kriegswaffen* that the town of Amberg in Germany had a cannon in the year 1301. This claim was accepted uncritically by W. W. Greener in his book *The Gun* first published in 1880. Unfortunately, Demmin and Greener did not or could not document statements of this character. Their later statements about the very early manufacture of arms in Flanders also rest largely on undisclosed or unverifiable sources, and many have been seriously questioned by later researchers of the caliber of Oscar Guttman and Sir Charles Oman.

The first authentic contemporaneous illustration we have of a true cannon is in the famous *Millimete Manuscript*. The manuscript text is titled *De officiis regnum* and is a dedicatory address given by de Millimete to King Edward III on his accession to the throne in 1327 A.D. It is dated 1326. It is important to arms research because we know that Edward III was a military leader who tried to keep abreast of the war developments of his time, and that he was among the first to employ cannon on the field of battle. This manuscript is in the library of Christ Church College at Oxford, England. It has beautiful illuminations of cannon, but the decorations have no bearing whatever on the text of the manuscript! Whatever we learn we glean from the illuminations themselves. One of these vignettes shows a bottle-shaped cannon on a four-legged mount loaded with a huge "bolt" which projects from the muzzle. An armored soldier standing by the piece is firing it against a fortress gate at close range. From the tinting of the face of the soldier, some writers have suggested that the gunner was intended to be a Moor, indicating Saracen origin for the cannon—but this is guess-work pure and simple. The bolt (called "garrot" or "carreau") was adapted from projectiles used in earlier war engines such as the espringale; and was used in both hand guns and small ordnance of this and somewhat later times.

Some historians state that Edward III mounted two or three cannon on a small hill near Crecy, and that they played a part in the catastrophic defeat of the French.

From this point on, however, facts are easier to find. We still encounter the indiscriminate use of terms which may mean either heavy ordnance or hand guns (the Italians listing them as "bombardes," the Germans as "büchsen," the Lowlanders as "vogheleer" and the French as "quenon" or "canon"), but the Italian and French records in particular now begin to give specific descriptions often augmented by drawings and frescoes of great clarity. Small arms which can be verified as having been manufactured in these very early times do not exist but the text and pictorial records furnish a discernible pattern of the evolution of the hand gun.

Chapter 2

THE DEVELOPMENT OF SHOULDER WEAPONS

THE CANNON LOCK

The earliest positive data we have on the use of small arms comes from Italian sources. The first small arms, now called "Cannon Locks," were commonly of cylindrical form and had a length of about nine inches exclusive of the staff or pike to which they were affixed. They were made of cast bronze or brass or of wrought iron, some having chambers and some having straight bores. They actually had no "lock" but were ignited through a touchhole on top of the barrel. The muzzle commonly had a thick outer ring to strengthen it. The rear of the cylinder had a socket to receive the staff, which was fastened into place by leather or iron bands.

The crude powder of those days was truly a powder, granulation not then being known. A wad of soft wood was placed between the propelling charge and the projectile to give the gas pressure opportunity to build up, because the low saltpeter content of the compound coupled with the powdered form gave very slow combustion.

From a study of the tapestries and illuminations of the time it is evident that both balls and bolts were used as projectiles. The balls were of iron, lead or brass; while the bolts (quarrels or garros à feu) were similar to the crossbow missiles and were brass "feathered."

These first arms were usually "aimed" with one hand, the staff being held under the arm, while a lighted coal or a hot iron was placed against the powder in the touch-hole.

1324-1343 A.D.

In the early 14th Century, Italy was the most advanced and the best educated nation in the world. During that same period Flanders and Germany were busily engaged in developing all the appliances of war—the Belgians to sell them abroad, the Germans to use them for conquest.

The Italian records were the best organized in the world at that time, though the Germans were soon to outreach them.

The archives of the City of Florence for this period definitely establish that firearms were already in extensive use there. Since no invention is generally accepted immediately upon its appearance, the inclusion of firearms in a city's chronicles makes it reasonable to suppose that such arms had been experimented with and used at a much earlier date. However, for the record, here is the first account which can be positively checked: *Archivo de Florence*, reg. 23, *De riformagioni*, page 65, dated 1324.

In the year 1331, the *Chronicles of Cividale*, a town in the Province of Fruile in Venezia, made definite mention of "scolop." Three years later "sclopetus" was mentioned in the *Chronicon Extense* of 1334.

In 1340 Paolo del Maestro Neri began work on a series of frescoes in the church of the former monastery of St. Leonardo in Lecetto, a small town near Sienna, Italy. The actual receipt signed by the artist on completion of the work in 1343 is preserved in the Sienna Library, and in Jacopo Gelli's *Gli Archibugiari Milanesi* published in Milan in 1904 are photographs of the receipt and of the frescoes. These frescoes, still to be seen though peeling and badly weathered, show contemporary scenes of land and naval warfare. One panel shows very clearly the attack on a castle with the besiegers using cannon, while the defenders are firing back with bows and hand-cannons. These hand-cannon are true hand guns—metal tubes fastened to sticks but fired by one man with a lighted coal.

These hand guns are essentially the same as those illustrated in German manuscripts of 50 years later and English manuscripts of 100 years later. They offer definite proof, particularly when considered in connection with early Italian city records in Florence and Perugia, that the hand gun followed very closely, or paralleled, the development of the heavy cannon or "bombard." Many early writers on this subject were apparently led astray by incomplete historical research.

1364 A.D.

The *Chronicles of Perugia* for 1364 record a definite order for "500 bombarde." This last reference is of particular interest in that it is the largest single arsenal record of early days. It specifies that the bullets must penetrate any armor—quite an optimistic order for that day and age and for the arms and explosives then in use.

During the last century there were in Italy two hand guns which historians of great ability believed to be the oldest then extant. The first of these was thoroughly discussed by the German General Kohler in his comprehensive work on early arms *Entwicklung des Kriegswesens,* etc. It was of bronze, ornamented with a Greek cross and oak leaves, bore the number 1322 (believed to indicate the date of manufacture) and the letters PPPF. Kohler described it in his book published in 1887, though it had been described earlier (in 1847) by Count 'd' Arco who owned it at one time and also by the reliable Major Angelucci in his *Documenti inediti* published in Turin in 1869. This gun was stolen from the Monastery of St. Orsola at Mantua in 1849.

The second "sclopos" said to date from the early part of the 14th Century was a wrought iron piece having a very roughly finished barrel and shaft attachment which was understood to have been excavated from the ruins of ancient Monte Vermini castle in 1841. Assuming it to be genuine, this piece would date from at least 1341 A.D.

1347-1370 A.D.

While there are no English records yet found specifically dealing with hand guns at this period, there is ample proof of an extensive use of gunpowder. In the records for 1347 of Thomas de Roldeston, Keeper of the King's Privy Wardrobe, is an item covering the purchase of gunpowder at eighteen pence per pound. Later English records also detail powder purchase; but the hold of the longbow was so great on both the populace and the military of early days, that not until the Wars of the Roses (1455-85) do we encounter reasonably common mention of hand guns.

In France, Louis, duc d'Anjou ordered "four cannon at a price of three francs" in 1370. The original order is still in existence among *Les Titres*

Scellés Clairambault.

The very low price rules out entirely the possibility of the term "cannon" in this manuscript being interpreted as anything but hand cannon—a small metal tube attached to a staff for use by an individual.

The gunpowder of this period, ground to a very fine powder, had a slow rate of combustion and was very weak. Many of the earliest guns were made of strips of wrought iron poorly welded, hence only such a slow-combustion propellant could be safely used.

1380-1390 A.D.

The *Codex Germanicus 600* is an original manuscript entitled *Anleitung Schiesspulver zu bereiten. Büchsen zu laden und zu beschiessen* (Directions for Preparation of Gunpowder. How to Load Guns and Discharge Them.) It is in the Köngl. und Staatsbibliothek in Munich; and while early German authorities date it as far back as 1345, later and more thorough researchers place it in the period about 1390 A.D. As its name implies, this manuscript is an extensive and most important study of the explosives of the period and of their use. It is one of the best of several such treatises which have come down to us. It instructs that the barrel be loaded three-fifths of its length with powder, then rammed down; that a space be left between the charge and a soft birchwood wad or plug, and that the ball be loaded against the wad. The purpose was, of course, to improve combustion by allowing some air (oxygen) over the powder to compensate for the lack of oxygen in the closely packed powder.

During this period, and from then on, the record of the hand gun in contemporary manuscript, drawing and sample weapons becomes clearer. While other nations of Europe seem to have dabbled in or extensively used firearms sometime before the Germans, it is to German records, illuminations, tapestries, paintings and arms that we must now turn for most of our verifiable knowledge of the early arms.

Contemporary records are of definite value on firearms only when they are explicit. When the German "büchsen" appears in early records it may mean any type of ordnance or firearm. (Literally interpreted it reads "box.") But when in the *Vestenberg Inventory* of 1389 we find two "häntbuchsen" listed, there is no longer doubt. These häntbuchsen generally fired half or three-quarter ounce balls, and were held in the hands when discharged.

By this time the art of welding had been fairly well developed. One or two plates of steel were bent or rolled over a dorn (or mandrel) and welded into a tube the rear end of which was then sealed by forging. With the strength of barrel and breech increased by this improvement in metal working we find the proportion of saltpeter in gunpowder mixtures rising from 2 parts to 3 or 4 parts, with resultant improvement in combustion and pressures.

The Tannenberger Büchse, 1399

It is now that we come to the *Tannenberger Büchse,* probably the greatest single historical item in the field of early hand guns. This is the one existing hand gun of the 14th Century whose authenticity can be proved beyond doubt.

Vesta Tannenberg in Hesse during the 14th Century was the stronghold of a robber band whose depredations were notorious. The fortress was invested and stormed in 1399 and every effort was made to obliterate it. It was blown

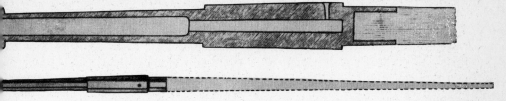

The Tannenburger Büchse, the earliest existing handgun, 1399.

up and so thoroughly destroyed that its destruction and the legends about it served through the following centuries to prevent it being rebuilt. Its very name was anathema; the fact of its ever having existed often was questioned.

Finally, in 1849, during the course of excavations at the site of the fortress, workmen unearthed fragments of several early hand guns and finally one complete weapon. The wood shaft fell to pieces when exposed to the air, an iron ramrod was still recognizable, and the bronze barrel itself had survived the ravages of time. It measures about 13 inches overall, weighs about 2¾ pounds and has a bore diameter of about 1.43 inches.

The rear section of the casting behind the breech is hollowed out to receive a wooden stock or staff. The inside of the barrel is of two dimensions. The smaller diameter section at the rear forms the powder chamber. It has a touchhole on top measuring about one-tenth inch diameter bored straight down with a shallow depression on the top of the barrel to hold the priming. This chamber section is necked down sharply in much the same fashion as our modern bottlenecked chambers. The casting is hexagonal on the outside with a reinforcing ring about the barrel muzzle.

The general design and construction of the Tannenberg hand gun is so superior to any other of its period of which we have a reasonably accurate description that for some time historians wondered if it did not indicate that the fortress had been rebuilt and again sacked at a later date than 1399. Intense research established that this was not the case. The arm authentically dates from before 1399.

The Hand Gun of the Burney Manuscript, 1469

One of the most famous authenticated drawings of the earliest Cannon Lock hand gun is that shown in the English *Burney Manuscript,* Number 169, Folio 127, at Oxford University. The Manuscript itself is in French, and like the earlier *Millimete Manuscript* has no bearing on or relation to the drawing. It is of value to the student of firearms development merely because its date cannot be questioned, and because the drawing ties in with the arms in the early Italian Neri frescoes, with the actual sample of the Tannenberg Gun, and with other original drawings of early periods such as the ones found in the British Museum Mss. (Sloane 2433) *Chroniques de Saint Denis.* That section of the *Burney Mss.* in which the noted figure appears is a French translation of Quintus Curtius made by Vasqua de Luchene, a Portuguese, in 1469.

The Kriegsbüch Bellifortis of Konrad Kyeser, 1400

This manuscript, *Codex Ms. phil. 63* in the Library of the University of Göttingen is reliably dated between 1396 and 1405. It covers in considerable

A Cannon Lock. Illustration from the Burney Manuscript, 1469.

detail the transition from Cannon Lock to Matchlock, and together with
Codex Mss. 719 at Nuremberg Museum Library and *Codex 734* in the Hof-und
Staätsbibliothek in Munich, marks the advance of the hand gun to the shoulder-
fired beginnings of the harquebus, the direct ancestor of the modern military
rifle.

Gradually we see the barrel length increased; the stock better proportioned,
squared off to give effective shoulder position and shaped at the grip to afford
a better hand grasp; a forestock evolves; the bores are drilled more carefully,
increasing the range and accuracy; the tubes are thicker and stronger to stand
heavier charges of more powerful powder mixtures; the metalwork is firmly
bedded and secured to the woodwork with tail screws; in all but the Spanish
forms, bent stocks appear; the flash pan has a cover to protect the priming
from damp and winds. Sights do not yet appear, because the priming is still
ignited by hand. The hook or "hak" to absorb recoil now appears and, except
for the mechanical firing of the priming, the first effective military hand gun,
the harquebus, has arrived.

Muzzle loading hand guns with several parallel barrels fired by match were
now introduced in Germany and France. Breech loading guns are listed in
Codex lat. 1390, now in the Library of Erlangen University. They are bulky
and impracticable, but they are forerunners of the modern types which had
to wait for the metallic cartridge case in the 19th Century before they were
successful. These guns weigh 20 pounds and more, but they mark a considerable
forward step in design.

Over-and-under guns, three barreled guns, guns shooting bullets of steel and of steel coated with lead; guns crude and guns exquisitely worked; guns to fire single balls—precursors of the rifle—and guns to fire several balls—ancestors of the shotgun; guns to be fired from the chest, from under the arm, from the shoulder—guns of every design possible under the technology then existing are to be found pictured in illuminations and tapestries, and described in manuscripts of unquestionable authenticity. Some of the guns themselves survived in the great Museums and collections of Europe at the outbreak of World War II.

By 1430 a new weapon appears in war—the Burgundians are employing a primitive form of Matchlock. The Cannon Lock will continue for yet a long time. But a new era is beginning—the Era of The Matchlock.

THE MATCHLOCK

It is impossible to ascribe a definite date or a definite country of origin for the first Matchlock, the lock which mechanically carried the fire to the priming and thereby made elementary gun sights practical.

Like all mechanical devices of importance, once the *principle* was established, copies and improvements and variations appeared in tremendous numbers. Moreover, the time in which we first encounter the Matchlock was an epochal period in the development of military might. It was the period when the old system of dependence on feudal levies for war was being replaced by armies of regular troops.

All of Europe was experimenting with and developing instruments of war. Every nation was on the alert for anything new which would save it from aggression—or help it in aggression.

Very early English records show a knowledge of hand firearms but it is not until 1471 that we find them of military importance, as introduced by Edward IV. It is to Henry VIII (1509-1547) that England is indebted for much of the early development of her hand firearms. The annals, order and inventories of his time, as well as many of the actual weapons used, have come down to us as understandable and detailed pieces in the mosaic of arms evolution. Henry VIII drew on all the development centers of the Continent for his knowledge, but most particularly from Flanders and Germany. He centered and developed a great arms industry at London in The Minories, a convent which was founded in 1293 and which Henry seized in 1539, promptly converting it to an arsenal. Stow, a contemporary historian, in a *Survey of London* written in 1598 testifies to the way this original arsenal had grown by the time he wrote. Very few of the important inventions of those early days were English; that country's conservatism being well evidenced by the fact that it was not until October 25, 1595, that an Order of Council instructed that all the "trained bands" must turn in long bows and arrows, to be replaced with "calivers and muskets." Various inventories list both bows and arrows in quantity until about 1635. Indeed the bow was not accepted as obsolete until 1638, when the official inventories dropped all mention of the weapon.

However, every development was duly reported and samples imported by Henry VIII and his successors.

The Zeugbücher of The Emperor Maximilian (1459-1519)

Across the scene now stalks one of the strangest and least known figures in history—Maximilian I, Emperor of the Holy Roman Empire, one of the most complex characters that even Germany has ever produced; a man whose influence on the period in which he lived, particularly with reference to military matters, and to the evolution of the Germany to come, has never been properly weighed.

Maximilian instituted great military reforms, the most notable being the establishment of the first standing army—the Landsknechte. A great huntsman, he was also an artillery expert of note. He was interested in every phase of small arms development.

The *Zeügbucher*—the *Arsenal Books*—of Maximilian, comprising nine huge, profusely illustrated volumes in their assembled form, are the outstanding record of arms developments to the year of his death, 1519. The entries run from the most learned and erudite by scientific minds of those days to the scribblings of unlearned smiths who forged and hammered out the actual weapons. The illustrations range from the most primitive to the genius of Dürer.

It is largely to these *Arsenal Books* that we must turn for a clear picture of the early period of the Matchlock, though the arms range from the Cannon Lock through many varieties of the Wheel-Lock. It must be remembered that there is never a *distinct* dividing line in the design and use of weapons. In primitive areas the Matchlock and the Flintlock are in use even in our own time.

The Serpentine

The first positive record of the "serpentine," the first Matchlock, occurs about the beginning of the 15th Century. The best known and authenticated of the early drawings is found in *Codex 3069* at Vienna (date 1411).

Very early attempts were made at designing the serpentine, as shown in *Codex 1390* (Erlangen) and *Codex 55* (Vienna), but these were merely anticipations of the successful matchlock of fifty years later.

The earliest and simplest Matchlock to see field use was the simple "C" type; followed by the elementary iron bar, bent to form a reversed "S", pivoted to the stock. The match was held in a split section at the top. To fire, the soldier aiming the piece pushed the serpentine with his left index finger, dropping the lighted match into the flash pan. This form is shown in *Codex Icon.* 22 (Munich) and in other contemporary 15th Century records. It is said by Hollinshed to have been in use in 1471 by Edward IV in his landing in Yorkshire at Ravenspur; while at the famous battle of Pavia its use enabled the Spanish to route the French army. It was issued to the English Yeomen of the Guard in 1485. A Swiss harquebus of the period of 1500-1510 of this general type still to be seen in Basle has a bronze barrel, front and rear sights and ramrod, as well as a needle for cleaning the touch-hole.

The Matchlock of Martin Merz

In the *Codex Germanicus 599* (Munich), dated 1475 A.D., attributed to Martin Merz, the most celebrated arms authority of that day, is illustrated and described a matchlock with many features generally overlooked until the end of the 17th Century. Curiously, its tremendous military potential was not grasped.

This arm had a right hand lock plate concealing a system of levers and springs. Pressure on a trigger was transmitted through a short sear to drop the cock carrying the match forward (most early matchlocks brought the cock back toward the shooter). This arm had both breech and muzzle sights (most early

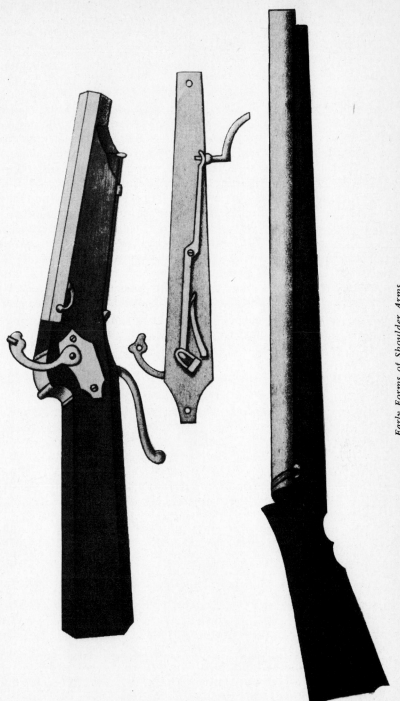

Early Forms of Shoulder Arms.

types had only a rear sight, if any). A needle for cleaning the touch-hole was attached to the forearm and an iron ramrod was carried in a socket below the barrel. (The iron ramrod was introduced in the field in 1698 by Prince Leopold I of Anhalt Dessaü. It contributed materially to his victory at Mollowitz in 1730.)

The Hackenbüchse

This type of arm made its initial appearance in Cannon Lock days but came into general military use only in the day of the Matchlock, and reached its highest form during the Wheel-Lock period.

The name probably derived from the "hak" (haken or harq), a spur projecting from below the fore-end, which served as a recoil block when hooked over a wall or against the forked stick on which the gun was usually supported when fired. This design was known as the *harquebus, hakbut, hackbut, arquebuse, archibuso* and by various other terms. The original hac (in French "à croc"), was much lighter than the "handgone" whose other names included demi-hake, halbehaken, handbüchse, handrohre (from the High German meaning hand-tube), bombardes à main, canons à main, sclopos, schioppi, schiopetto, escopettes, scopitus, etc.

In later pieces the "hak" or spur was eliminated but the name and its variants continued; a fact which seems to have confused numerous writers.

In *Codex Icon. 222* (Munich) is a drawing in detail of one of Maximilian's

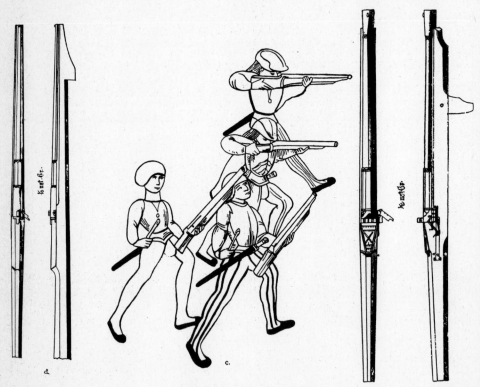

Early Hand Gun, 15th Century.

A Matchlock "Minute Man."

landsknecht firing a harquebus from the shoulder. The spur had by then gone from the piece, and no rest was employed. The lock is a serpentine dropping towards the firer.

Other Matchlocks

These included "standbüchsen," "scheibenbüchsen," and "zeilbüchsen," target guns, usually rifled, and fired from a rest; "pirschbüchsen," hunting rifles of large bore; "soldnerbüchsen" or infantry guns (an improved harquebus); and "langeröhr," a variety of long barreled harquebus.

Types of Locks

Viscount Dillon's *On the Development of Gunlocks*, Thierbach and Schön, and the *Nunnemacher Catalog* in America, afford detailed studies. Chronologically, the types run as follows:

Button Lock: This seems to be the earliest type in wide use employing springs and levers, not merely a pivoted serpentine. Probably German in origin, it is widely illustrated in the works of Maximilian's time. Pressure on a button on the outside of the lock plate released the cock (serpentine) which dropped into the flash pan. This was the most common military form until about 1520.

Pressure Locks: This most common and successful type of spring and lever matchlock was used long after better methods of ignition were developed. It was noted for its simplicity, consisting only of a cock, tumbler, sear and two flat springs. When the cock attached to the tumbler axle is pulled back it is caught by one end of the sear. Pulling the trigger releases the tumbler and allows it to revolve 90 degrees under spring force, bringing the lighted match down into the priming powder. Locks of this variety were manufactured in the Tower of London as early as 1521 by Cornelius Johnson.

Snap Locks: The "lüntenschnappschloss"—light snapping lock—also called the "schwammschloss"—tinder lock—was common on the Continent and is listed in many inventories from 1568 to 1596. Its name came from the fact that it carried a piece of tinder or match in a small tube in the jaws of the cock. The tinder was ignited by the soldier directly from a lighted match just before firing. Pushing the sear dropped the tinder under mainspring action into the pan. This lock is considered by some authorities to have been the forerunner of the snaphaunce. This lock was often used as a supplementary lock in conjunction with the standard Matchlock (and also with the later Wheel-Lock) as it was considered more reliable than either.

THE WHEEL-LOCK

We cannot be certain, but in its primitive form the Wheel-lock may have been the Dresden Monksbüchse—an elementary tube near whose touchhole was placed a piece of flint or pyrites with a rasp mounted alongside so that a push and pull on the rasp would shower sparks on the priming.

Neither can we be sure where, when or by whom the Wheel-lock was first introduced. The various accounts listing Johann Kufuss (or Kiefuss) as the inventor in 1517 are very hazily documented and he is placed at both Nuremberg and Vienna.

However, we have a large body of coincidental proof which indicates the date is nearly correct—perhaps a trifle late—and that Nuremberg was probably the place. Leonardo da Vinci, who died in 1519, wrote a description of the Wheel-lock and tells of shooting doves with it insisting, incidentally, that he used a single ball load, which would indicate a degree of marksmanship in keeping with his other fantastic abilities.

All the earliest forms of Wheel-locks still existing are of German origin. Many carry the Nuremberg stamp. Nuremberg Wheel-locks authentically dated 1541 are well known; and in the Nuremberg records for the year 1532 is an account of a letter from the Margrave of Brandenburg addressed to the Rath at Nuremberg calling for passage of an order prohibiting the use of this device by travellers. The ease with which firearms researchers can be misled is well illustrated by the fact that Luigi Collardo in an artillery treatise printed at Venice in 1586 mentions the Wheel-lock as a "new" German invention. The device had, by that time, been used for fifty years in Germany!

The early name for this lock was "feüerschloss", a name which spread to England where in an inventory of Edward IV we find "one chamberpiece with firelock"—that is, a breechloading Wheel-lock, a lock which threw fire. At a later date the term "feüerschloss" or firelock was transferred to the true flintlock; and at that time the Wheel-lock was listed as "rädschlosser". We know that the original Flemish-made breechloader of Henry VIII dated 1537 was a Wheel-lock as originally manufactured, though later converted to Matchlock.

It is evident that the spread of the Wheel-lock was rapid, its potential as a war instrument immediately recognized. Clumsy and complicated though it was, it again upset the world balance of power and revolutionized the art of war. Given the Wheel-lock pistol mounted men once again became the "strength of battle." The infantrymen with their slow-loading muzzle-loaders could not stand against the combination of speed, shock, and ability to maneuver and to kill at a distance; and no armor could withstand the loads now developed.

Revolutionary as was this mechanical striking of fire, it was still too complicated and costly for general use. The harquebus with Wheel-lock, the "rädschlossbüchse," though used as a mounted weapon, never achieved the success of the original Reiters' pistol, the one-handed "fauströhr" or fist-tube which was so deadly a close-quarters arm when first used by cavalry.

Types of Wheel-locks

The variety of these locks is almost beyond belief, and for even a general idea of them one must turn to the classic works of Oberst von Thierbach and Viscount Dillon already quoted.

The principle, of course, was fairly simple; though in working it out the lock often became a complicated mechanism of as many as eighteen parts. Basically it is a small steel wheel, with grooved edges, mounted in a frame. A chain or swivel and a strong spring are attached to the axis of the wheel. A spanner is fitted over the outer projection of the axis and is turned to wind or extend the spring. A piece of flint (originally the more fragile pyrites) held in the vise in the cock-head is pulled down until it rests on the circumference of the wheel, which enters the bottom of the priming pan. When the trigger is pulled the wheel is freed. As it spins in contact with the flint it showers sparks on the priming at the touch hole.

While there are any number of varieties, the structural changes are com-

German Harquebus, Circa 1600. Self-spanning.

paratively few. There is the outside wheel, the wheel with guard, the inside (concealed) wheel, the inner wheel with outside spring and chain, and double locks.

Special Features

The set trigger as we know the device, called the "stechschloss" or trigger-lock, developed with the introduction of the Wheel-lock. Because of the heavy trigger pull necessary to free the powerful spring, the mechanism of two triggers was developed. Pushing one when the arm was cocked permitted a very light pull on the other to release the mechanism. Here again we have difficulty in determining the time and place of the invention; for while many writers assign it quite definitely to Munich in 1543, there is an actual arquebus, reliably dated *1542*, in Paris which is fitted with set triggers.

Practically every form of safety lock in use today, both manual and automatic, was developed to lock the mechanism of the Wheel-lock against accidental discharge; while all the earlier forms of repeating and multi-barreled designs are also encountered as Wheel-locks.

Rifling became increasingly common, though it was far from standardized. The rifling in barrels of this period now in European and American museums varies from 5 to as many as 34 grooves.

THE SNAPHAUNCE—THE ORIGINAL FLINTLOCK

The cost, the need for constant attention and the general unreliability of the Wheel-lock, added to the popular recognition of the inherent desirable qualities of a fire-striking device, very soon brought about the introduction of the elementary Snaphaunce, the forerunner of the true flintlock which was to serve as a standard military arm for 200 years and more.

Again we are faced with the old questions of who, when and where in connection with its invention. And again no *positive* answer is possible. The term "schnapphahn" is Dutch for "snapcock"—probably indicating merely the snapping of the cock with its flint against the anvil to produce sparks. From its name and from such records as are available it seems probable it was of Flemish origin; but on the other hand it was claimed by Spain, and from very early times has been recorded in Germany as "der Spanische schnappschloss."

It first appeared about 1525 and was widely used in Spain, France and Italy and to a lesser extent in England and Scotland. It was not commonly used in Germany. Mechanically it is a rather direct descendant of the early German and Flemish "lüntenschnappschloss" (light snapping lock). Merely replacing the tinder or match in the jaws of the cock with a piece of pyrites, then providing a piece of steel against which the pyrites could strike to shower sparks, would convert one to the other. Pyrites, or marcasite, is a mineral combination of sulphur and iron used as a strike-fire since the days of Caesar's legions.

Quite evidently the Snaphaunce was invented not much later than the Wheel-lock, though the first recorded English mention of it is about 1580. Hewitt's *Antient Armour*, which is reliable when it is directly quoting contemporary records, cites a payment in 1588 to "Henry Radoe, smyth," for making one of the old pistols with Snaphaunce by the Chamberlain of Norwich; while the English *Hengrove Inventory* taken in 1603 lists 5 Snaphaunces.

The date of this *Hengrove Inventory* has been unquestionably established, yet Col. R. Schmidt, whose *Armes a feú portatif* is one of the classic works on arms, was very positive that the Snaphaunce was unknown prior to 1635. Scottish records show that the lock was in manufacture in that country as early as 1590. At the time of Schmidt's writing English research on the subject had not been effectively begun and he suffered from lack of detailed research facilities—which is another example of the reason so many arguments arise as to the authenticity of dated antique arms.

German Inventories

A tally of the entries during the year 1581 in the arsenal records of Dresden, Pleissenburg (now Leipzig), Sonnenstein (Pirna), Wittenberg and Zwickau shows that *three types* of locks were extensively used and stored at that time for military use.

Listed are 3160 röhre with tinder locks (schwammschlossen or lünten-Schnappschlossen): 74 "Spanish röhre" with Snaphaunce (fire striking locks, when literally translated); and 1384 röhre with Wheel-locks. Also listed are various multi-shot weapons and pistols—"fauströhrlein" at that period. The "röhre" was the German equivalent of the English "caliver"—a long barreled harquebus of uniform caliber.

Notes On Varieties of Guns of the Period (to about 1640)

Harquebus. This variety was the best known. The length was generally about 42 inches, weight generally 10 to 12 pounds after abandonment of the forked rest or "Swedish Swine's Feather" used with heavy early types. Balls, first of steel, then of copper, then of lead-covered steel and finally of lead, weighing usually from 1½ to 2 ounces were the customary missiles, though brass-feathered bolts were also used.

Other members of the harquebus family include: demi-hakes, short guns; double-hakes, using two matches operating from opposite directions; "Scharf-dunklen", 50 pound long range wall guns, the forerunner of the present anti-tank rifle; "viertelhaken", about 5 feet long and firing 4 ounce balls to considerable ranges; "strauhaken", having a bell mouth, the forerunner of the "streübuchse" (blunderbuss), the primitive shotgun with its scatter load.

In the *Tower Inventory* of 1547 "demy-hakes" are listed, while the harquebus itself is listed as "hole-hackes" (whole harquebuses) to distinguish it. In 1567 in St. Luc's *Discours sur l'artillerie* we find the French "arquebus á croc."

Musket. The name is said to have been derived from "moschetto"—the sparrow hawk. Be this as it may, early records bear out that it was used at an early date by the Venetians; and it is possible that the name may have come from the alleged inventor, an Italian gunsmith of Feltri named Moschetta.

The early musket differed from the harquebus in being larger and more powerful. It may have been used very early in the 16th Century in Italy and France. As used in France in 1573 it was fired from a forked rest, since it weighed 16 to 20 pounds. It fired 2-ounce balls and was used at ranges up to 200 yards. The comparatively light (16 lb.) Netherlands musket used balls weighing 10 to the pound—the original "10 gauge."

According to Brantome, Philippe Strozzi, Colonel General of Infantry under Charles IX of France, introduced the "mosquet" into French service in 1573.

The *Sir Thomas Ramsey Inventory* in England of 1577 lists "vi muskets with flasks and rests."

The Norwich (English) record of 1588 shows the purchase for troops of "xi Englishe musketts" and "xi playne muskets."

The *Wurzburg Inventory* of 1584 lists "musceten" as having been purchased two years earlier, together with "halbe-musketen" and "doppel-musketen".

Two ornamented wheel-lock muskets which were used by the guard of Elector Christian I (1560-1591) are in the Dresden Museum; they are dated 1589, were made at Dresden but have French-type stocks.

Probably the earliest *dated* muskets, however, are those at Dresden which were made at Suhl in 1570.

Sir Roger William in his *Brief Discourse of Warre* (1590) states that the recoil of Spanish muskets is less than that of others. The Spanish type had a straight stock, all other types being bent; and from Sir Thomas Kellie in *Art Militaire* (1620) we hear that "the barrel of a musket should be four feet long, and bullets twelve to a pound." (Was this the beginning of the 12-gauge shotgun mode?) The musket arrows, special quarrels fired from muskets, were used largely in sea engagements to pierce or set fire to sails; and in the *Tower Inventory* of 1589 we find listed "musket-arrowes, 892 shefe."

Caliver. One of the best authorities who can be quoted on the origin of the name "caliver" is Edmund York, an English officer with wide foreign-observer service, who wrote in 1588: "Before the battle of Mountgunter (Moncontour— October 3, 1569) the Prynces of the Religion caused seven thousand harquebuzes to be made all of one calibre, which was called "harquebuze de calibre de Monsieur le Prince." From this apparently evolved the French term "piece (or arquebus) de calibre"—meaning an arm in which the bore was standard so soldiers could interchange bullets.

The caliver was an improved harquebus, lighter and shorter than the musket. The related "curriers" or "currions" seem to have been first evolved in Spain.

In 1578 the *Tower Inventory* shows 7,000 calivers on hand, indicating the degree to which materiel standards had advanced.

In 1570 there is record in England of Thomas Rigges, caliver maker, receiving 50 pounds for making "100 calivers of old curriers, at 10 shillings each with furnishings"—from which it is evident that the currier commonly mentioned in records of those days was *not* the same as the caliver. Such then is the difficulty of *positive* identification of ancient arms.

Carbine. The origin of the term carbine is not positively established. In Gays' *Memoires pour l'artillerie* (1548) is the statement that the short arm used by the cavalry takes its name from the Spanish horse corps called "carabins." There is much other documentation of contemporary date for this belief.

However, the term is also said to have derived from having been used on small ships called "carabs"; while still others indicate that it came from a short weapon first used by Calabrian (Italian) troops. The theory of Spanish origination seems most logical.

THE TRUE FLINTLOCK

The true Flintlock, a practical combination of some of the principles employed in the snaphaunce with some used in the Spanish miquelet lock, ap-

Early flintlock—"transition type"—made by Samuel Depffer of Augsburg, circa 1660. The turning frizzen and dog catch are both primitive and complicated safety devices, so the gun could be carried loaded and primed. Both devices were replaced by the half-cock notch.

pears to have been developed in France about 1610. Practically all early German sources (which are the most numerous, detailed and reliable) credit the French with introducing the "batterie." This was the right-angle pan cover of steel which is struck and thrown back by the hammer, thereby exposing the priming in the pan below to the sparks which shower down as the flint in the head of the cock strikes and scrapes against the steel of the hinged pan-cover. The French term "batterie" and the American "frizzen" described the same thing.

Elementary as this device seems to us in these days, its perfection took years of experimenting in the shaping of flints, tempering of steel and counter-balancing of parts. Originally rather unreliable and always likely to misfire, under adverse conditions it nevertheless remained the most dependable ignition system known until the introduction of the percussion system some 200 years later. As late as the year 1935 flintlock arms were being made in Germany and Belgium for export to parts of Africa and Asia, a full list being pictured and described in the catalogs of the huge German arms and export firm of Gustav Genschow of Baden.

The Flintlock superseded the Matchlock in the British army about the year 1690. The popular name, "Brown Bess," was attached to it at a later date, probably from the combination of the brown-colored barrel (the Matchlock barrels seem to have been bright metal) and from the popular idea that it was introduced in the reign of Queen Elizabeth. Since Her Majesty died in the year 1603, the supposition is incorrect. Few early English arms show any marks of manufacture. However, during the reign of William and Mary (1680-1702) army weapons were usually engraved "W&M"; between 1702-1714 they were stamped "AR", indicating the reign of Queen Anne. In general, changes in the service Flintlock from the time of its introduction to its replacement by the percussion system are inconsequential. "Brown" Bess, for all the legends about her, was essentially just a handle for a bayonet. Rugged, simple, sturdy—at close quarters a terrible arm (when she fired!) this smooth bored musket fired a round ball weighing about fourteen to the pound.

For a clear and penetrating picture of the reliability and accuracy of the smoothbore flintlock, we can find no more effective description from a qualified source than that of Colonel Hanger of the British army, an outstanding and outspoken authority, writing in 1814. He wrote, "A soldier's musket if not exceedingly ill-bored (as many are), will strike the figure of a man at 80 yards, perhaps even at 100; but a soldier must be very unfortunate indeed who shall be wounded by a common musket at 150 yards, provided his antagonist aims at him; and as for firing at a man at 200 yards with a common musket, you might just as well fire at the moon and have the same hope of hitting your object. I do maintain and will prove, whenever called on, that no man was ever killed at 200 yards by a common soldier's musket *by the person who aimed at him.*"

The British Government conducted a series of flintlock vs. percussion lock tests in 1834 at the request of the Reverend Mr. Forsyth, accredited discoverer of the percussion principle. Six thousand rounds were fired under all kinds of weather conditions from six of each type of weapon. The score was 922 misfires for the flintlock—1 in 6.5 tries: The percussion missed 36 times or 1 in 166.

It required 32 minutes and 31 seconds average to fire 100 rounds from the flintlock, 30 minutes and 24 seconds for the percussion. The flint musket hit the target (size and range unspecified) 3680 times, the percussion 4047.

One more test tells the story of these early arms: In 1841 the Royal Engineers conducted tests on "Brown Bess." Depending on the elevation of the piece, they found it might carry anywhere from 100 to 700 yards. Curiously, the carrying distance of two muskets at the same elevation might vary as much as 300 yards. At 150 yards they could "by very careful shooting" hit a target "twice as high and twice as broad as a man," three times out of four shots. Beyond that distance, with the muskets vised in machine rests, the target could never be hit. Then "The mark was made twice as wide as before, but of 10 shots at 250 yards not one struck."

The French established arms factories at Charleville, Maubege and St. Etienne about 1717, and produced the "Charleville 1717," their first standard pattern, in that year. With only minor variations, this arm was in official use at the time of the introduction of the percussion lock in 1842, while one variant, the 1763 model, was used by portions of Washington's forces in the Revolutionary War.

Flintlock Breechloaders and Repeaters

As in all the previous stages of ignition development, breech-loading and repeating systems in all conceivable forms were tried again in the Flintlock period; and again the efforts failed because the breech could not be effectively sealed.

In Italy the famous Comminazzi produced hinged frame weapons loaded with "chamber pieces," steel inserts which were preloaded for insertion in the breech. Beautifully made pieces with side pivoting barrels dating from 1694 bear the marks of Aqua Fresca of Bargio. This latter type also had a self-priming device mounted to the cock or hammer.

All the older forms of double and multi-barreled designs; parallel barrels, over-unders with one or two locks, hinged breechblocks, forward sliding barrels actuated by levers, screw plugs actuated by triggerguard lever, revolving barrel and revolving cylinder, pepper-box designs, volley guns, multi-charge barrels with sliding rack firing locks—all these types were re-discovered or re-invented in this period.

American Flintlocks

The very early history of arms in America is obscure. The Pilgrims and the Puritans were generally armed with the cheap and already obsolescent Matchlock. It was not the habit of the princes or rich merchants of that time to arm the citizenry with up-to-date firearms. In 1628 the records of the Massachusetts Bay Company show the importation of some snaphaunce arms.

By the year 1700, however, firearms—including rifles—had reached a high degree of flintlock development in Europe and when the German settlers came to Pennsylvania they brought with them their national interest in weapons as target and hunting arms, as well as their skills in manufacture. The first of the long line of precision rifles which were to play so large a part in the history of our country began with the handicraft of these early German and Palatine Swiss newcomers, among the first of whom we have record being the brothers

A Kentucky Rifle, circa 1770. Made by J. Bender, location unknown.

Heinrich and Peter Leman who by 1732 were making fine rifled weapons.

The fascinating story of the evolution of these arms has been well covered in Henry J. Kauffman's *The Pennsylvania-Kentucky Rifle,* in J. G. W. Dillin's *The Kentucky Rifle* and in Ned Robert's *The Muzzle Loading Cap Lock Rifle.*

The original rifles introduced by the settlers were, of course, the short-barreled, large bore arms then popular in Europe, Flintlocks into whose muzzles the bullets were started with a mallet and which then had to be driven down on top of the powder charge by ramrod. The need for a lighter and quicker loading arm for the pioneers who were leaving the coastal towns and pushing into the wilderness brought an evolution in the European design. The barrel was lengthened from 40 to 45 inches, giving more complete combustion with the lighter ball, a longer sight radius and better balance. The stock of maple or walnut was extended the full length of the barrel to protect it somewhat in the rough and tumble of the pioneer's hunting, fighting and living. It was fitted for the ramrod. Blade or bead front and fine notch rear sights were fitted.

The name "Kentucky" by which all these early arms are known was given them because they were developed for and used by the settlers and "long hunters" who ventured into that area between the Cumberlands and the Mississippi River, all of which was at that time called "Kentucky."

While the early rifles averaged about .54 caliber and fired balls weighing about half an ounce, in a later period (1820 to about 1860) they were used extensively as small game arms and were often called "squirrel rifles." These arms used balls varying from 90 to as many as 200 to the pound, depending on the hunting ground and the game against which they were used.

Tests made in recent years by Remington of Kentucky rifles of .45 caliber loaded with 66.5 grains of black powder and firing a 137.5 grain ball showed muzzle velocities between 1500 and 1600 feet per second and muzzle energy of about 300 foot pounds. As to accuracy, Dillin says that the favorite target at 20 yards was the head of a tack; at 60 to 100 yards the head of a turkey; at 200 yards the body of the turkey. This was about the limit of accuracy, however, as *Freemantle's Book of the Rifle* points out that at 400 yards the best these rifles would do with regularity was hit an object the size of a horse.

The "Committee of Safety" Arms

The earliest truly official arms of the United States were those authorized by various committees set up in 1775 in the 13 colonies to provide weapons for the colonial militia units. Some 200 gunsmiths provided these weapons. Manufactured chiefly in Maryland, Massachusetts, Pennsylvania and Rhode Island, they were chiefly smoothbore muskets whose caliber varied from .72 to .80. They weighed about 10 pounds.

U. S. Military Flintlocks

The first official U. S. military musket was the Charleville flintlock, the weapon of the French Army. The Marquis de Lafayette arranged for the shipment of large numbers of these to us during the Revolution, and the 1763 model was used as the basis for American manufacture. The Springfield Armory was established and manufacture of these smooth-bores begun in 1795; and an improved pattern was put into production in 1797, which remained the standard.

A detailed list of the U. S. military types from 1795 to 1865, covering flintlocks and percussion locks is available in the compilation prepared by Claud E. Fuller from official Government sources and published under the title *Springfield Muzzle-Loading Shoulder Arms.* This together with Major Hicks' *Notes on United States Ordnance,* Major B. R. Lewis' *American Military Small Arms, 1775-1865* and Sawyer's works provide much more specific data than can be supplied in a book of this type.

THE PERCUSSION LOCK

For all practical purposes, the British court findings on the patents of the Reverend Alexander John Forsyth, Presbyterian Minister of Belhelvie, Scotland, legally confirm the popular idea that he invented the percussion system of discharging arms.

Forsyth lived and died in the little parish manse where his father served as minister before him, taking time out only for trips to London when he was developing his percussion system. He was an experienced hunter, a gunsmith, blacksmith and a chemist of ability. By his own account he was experimenting with detonation as early as 1793 (French scientists had recognized the existence of the principle as much as 90 years earlier but had made no application of it). In 1805 he startled his friends by building a gunlock which used mercuric fulminate as a priming. Lord Moira then induced him to go to London to work for a time in the Tower where better facilities for research would be available. Forsyth received a patent on the 4th of July 1807—three months after a politician who superseded his friend Lord Moira had decided the invention was useless and had ordered him out of the Tower! His invention was adopted by the British Army, but it was 1840 before the Lords of the Treasury grudgingly paid him the munificent sum of 200 pounds for his services—a reward which was increased by 1000 pounds because of public reaction in 1843, four months after the worthy inventor died.

Forsyth employed his fulminate priming compound first as a powder, then as caps placed between two pieces of paper as individual charges, and finally as caps in ribbon form to make automatic priming possible.

How old the discovery of detonation is we will probably never know, but we do know that Forsyth was among the first to *apply* the detonating principle to firearms ignition, and that without knowledge that others were working along the same line in his time. As a matter of fact, there is a tantalizing reference to detonation in Pepy's *Diary* of 11 November 1661, 130 years before Forsyth's experiments.

As early as 1808, Pauly, in Paris, was using his paper fulminating device fired by a needle piercing it—probably the forerunner of the muzzle loading needle gun designed by his employe, Nicholas Dreyse, the German who developed the principle of the bolt action lock a few years later.

Pauly's specification of 1816 is of historic interest because it clearly states the principle of effective breech sealing. It says, "A plug is so placed in the gun as to come between the charge of gunpowder and the movable breeching in all cases, and is formed of lead, copper, or such other ductile materials as will

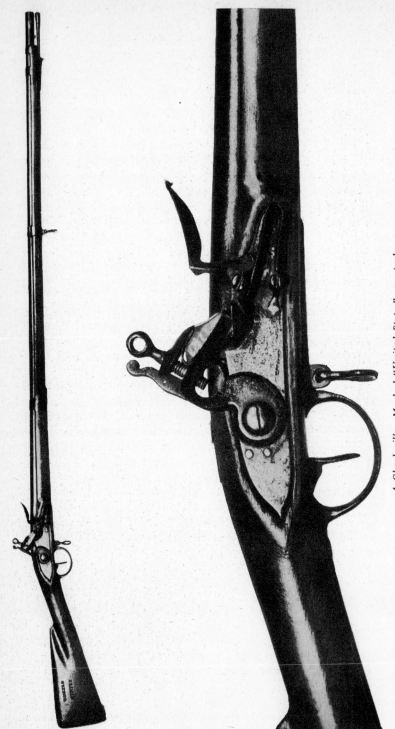

A Charleville. Marked "United States" on stock.

give way to the explosive force of the charge." Pauly understood the need but never worked out the ductile expanding case which was introduced by other Frenchmen, Lefaucheux in 1836 and Houiller in 1847. These developments were foreshadowed by the introduction in 1835 of the French Flobert cap. This cap, however, was evolved directly from the familiar copper primer cap. It did not use a powder charge, the explosion of the priming mixture being sufficient to propel the light, gallery or "salon" bullet. In other words, the Flobert cap, which is practically our "BB" cap of today, was a *cap* evolution in theory and design, rather than a breech sealing *cartridge*.

Just who first developed the copper cap cannot be positively decided, although the weight of evidence indicates that the one first generally used was that by the Englishman, Joshua Shaw working in Philadelphia in 1814. Colonel Hawker, one of the most prolific writers and bombastic sportsmen of that day made a backhanded claim to having invented it together with Joe Manton; other sources indicate it may have been developed by Joseph Egg who apparently introduced it into England; while a dozen less well known figures also sought to claim it.

In 1824 Berenger's patent covered percussion pellets fed from a magazine; a year later Joe Manton patented a revolving magazine primer; in 1834 Baron Heurteloup's continuous primer, a long tube of metal holding the fulminate which was fed forward and suitably cut by an edge on the hammer, was patented; in 1836 Egg's self-acting primer magazine was introduced. In 1845 Dr. Edward Maynard was granted a U. S. patent for his "tape primer," consisting of priming pellets embedded in strips of paper or linen so they could be fed automatically as the hammer was cocked.

Chapter 3
RIFLING AND EARLY REPEATING WEAPONS

RIFLING AND INTERCHANGEABLE BARRELS

The most thorough coverage of very early sights (fixed front and rear) appears in The Codex Mss. 1390 (dated 1500) at Erlangen University. Target shooting at a range of about 200 meters (!) is mentioned in an Eichstadt *Schutzenbrief* dated 1487.

Rifling. Rifling was developed early in the Matchlock era. Von Thierbach *(Die geschichtliche Entwicklung der Handfeuerwaffen)* located in a 1498 Leipzig account of a "Scheibenschiessen"—target match—an account of the development by one Caspar Köllner of Vienna of a process for cutting straight grooves lengthwise down the barrel.

From this account it would seem that rifling originated as a means of facilitating loading and cleaning—though this theory has been questioned by some authorities who fail to give as clear and documented an account as does von Thierbach.

Two statements are usually quoted about the discovery of curved rifling: (1) That of the German writer Fishart that it was originated by August Cötter of Nuremberg between 1500 and 1520; and (2) that of other researchers that it was originated by Caspar Köllner of Vienna in 1498. Neither of these claims has ever been proved.

However, we have some actual arms and some verified records which prove curved rifling to have been used late in the 15th or early in the 16th Century.

Major Angelo Angelucci in his classic coverage of early Italian arms *Catalago della Armeria Reale* (Catalog of the Royal Armory) published in Turin in 1890 cites a Turin inventory of 1476 listing "sclopetus unus ferri factus lumage," a firearm with spiral grooved barrel.

The Musée d'Artillerie in Paris has a rifled arquebus dated 1542; the Museum of Artillery at Woolwich has a barrel dated 1546 and another 1592. The *Nuremberg Chronicle* first lists rifled arms about 1578.

The third Baron Cottesloe (Thomas Francis Freemantle), writing about 1900 *(Freemantle's Book of The Rifle)*, pointed out that of 36 early rifled barrels of the 16th and 17 centuries then in the Woolwich Museum, only three had *straight* grooving. The earliest dated rifled piece known in England was brought there from Hungary in 1548. Dated 1547, it is spiral grooved.

The Zürich (Swiss) Arsenal inventories listed spiral grooved barrels in 1544, some of which are today in the Swiss National Museum at Zürich.

By 1563 spiral grooving was so well known and appreciated in Switzerland that a Berne archive for the year 1563 deals with complaints of shooters about the unfairness of allowing rifled barrels to be entered in shooting competition with smooth bores!

The first record we can authenticate concerning the military use of the rifle seems to be during the reign of Christian IV (1577-1648) in Denmark. Specimens of these rifles are still in the Arsenal at Copenhagen and one specimen dated 1611 is in Woolwich Arsenal.

Interchangeable Barrels. The principle of interchangeable barrels (Eisernem Laufe) was known and commonly practiced in 1500, as witnessed by detailed drawings in the *Arsenal Books* of Maximilian and other contemporary records, and confirmed by actual specimens in the German National Museum and in Basle, Switzerland. The barrels described in manuscript and found today usually are of bronze. Some had the familiar "hak". The system of mounting them to the stock was usually very simple and effective—a solid section behind the chamber fitting into a socket in the stock, while the front end was locked by the hak or a projection passing through a mortise in the fore-end which usually extended to within a few inches of the muzzle. Some were also fastened with tang screws.

REPEATING ARMS, MULTIBARRELED GUNS, AND BREECHLOADERS

Early in the 16th Century experiments with repeating arms were made in Germany, Switzerland and Italy by loading several charges down the same barrel from the muzzle, with heavy wadding between charges. The lighted match was dropped successively on individual touch-holes starting from the forward end. Flame jumping from the fired charge to those behind it made this system impracticable. (This idea was more highly developed in Flintlock days with a lock sliding on a rail on the right side of the breech; and was experimented with in Civil War days at Springfield Armory on percussion locks.)

Attempts at harquebuses with revolving cylinders were made during the time of Maximilian I (about 1500). Long barreled arms with cylinders which were locked by flat springs on top of the barrel to line up a chamber with the barrel were made in Germany and Italy before 1680. There are German specimens in the German National Museum; and Italian models date from 1697.

Multi-Barreled Guns. Double guns and the various types of "ladebüchsen" described under Cannon Locks were also made for Matchlocks. These were made in parallel and superposed designs.

Breechloaders. Some of the most remarkable breechloaders ever devised were developed in the time of Maximilian I. Henry the VIII of England, a friend of Maximilian, used breechloaders, some of which were made in Flanders for him, while others came from Germany.

The most famous of Henry's breechloaders is a harquebus still in the Tower collection. It is specifically mentioned in the Tower Inventory of 1547 and is

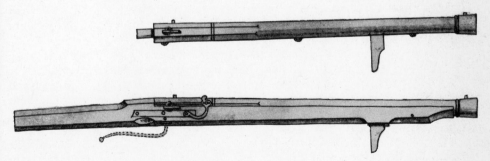

Early Hakenbüsche with interchangeable barrel reproduced from original illustration in one of Maximilian's Arsenal Books. Note that the barrels are fitted with both front and rear sights.

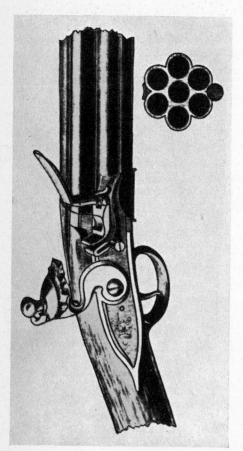

Early attempts at repeating weapons, using multiple barrels and locks.

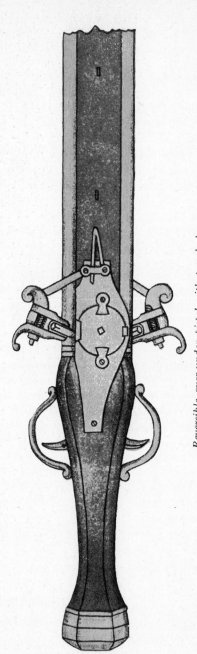

Reversible over-under pistol with two locks.

further dated by the fact that it bears Henry's initials, also a crowned rose supported by two lions, and the date "1537."

This remarkable arm has a 23 inch barrel so carefully bored that the greatest variation in any part of the barrel interior is .016 inch. It weighs about 9.5 pounds. Barrel caliber is .535 inch, while the removable steel cartridge chamber, measuring 2⅞ inches, is caliber .55. The arm has a brass front sight. It was originally a Wheel-lock, but was converted to Matchlock. (In the early days of the then new invention, the Wheel-lock was not found as reliable in general service as the Matchlock.)

When the arm was to be fired, the breechpiece was hinged up from the right and the cartridge chamber, loaded with powder and ball, was inserted and the breech closed. Priming was placed on the pan and when fired it flashed through a hole in the cartridge chamber to discharge the arm.

In the year 1866—over 300 years later—the British government paid prize money to the American inventor Jacob Snider for a system of altering the old muzzle loading Enfields they had on hand to permit breechloading. The system Snider sold the British is practically identical with that originated by the armorers of Henry VIII's time except that the breechpiece hinges to the left instead of the right. The Snider was successful because of the introduction of the brass case which would expand on firing and provide a breech seal against the gas. The Maximilian system failed because the powder and ball were loaded into a *steel* chamber or "cartridge" which was then inserted in the breech and which did not expand enough to seal the breech against gas escape.

Breechloading harquebuses and "röhre" (an improved and lightened harquebus) are pictured and described in authentic German manuscripts of the period 1570 to 1600; and examples of the arms themselves are in existence. These *Handbüchse mit Hinterlading* are generally hinged on the left to swing up from the right side and are often locked with a top bolt pivoted to the stock and spring supported. The flash pan is usually an integral part of the removable cartridge chamber and has a sliding cover to protect the priming from wind and rain.

While the earliest of these were Matchlocks, by 1580 both the Wheel-lock and the Snaphaunce had long been in use and specimens of breechloaders of this period often have combinations of two of these systems: matchlock and wheel-lock or matchlock and snaphaunce.

Evidence of the Italian efforts along these lines is found in the English *Westminster Inventory* of 1547 listing "380 Italian peces, guilte, without chambers, furnished with touche-boxes, etc; and 116 with chambers." Greenwich listed over 100 Italian matchlocks of this period. The records of Henry VIII for 1544 show the purchase of 1500 harquebuses from Brescia, Italy.

While Milan, Lucca, Pignerol and Brescia were all large centers of arms manufacture, no thorough and adequate research has ever established the types of arms made in those areas in early times.

For the further development of breechloaders in connection with the development of metallic cartridges, see chapter 4.

Pictorial Sources. Jost Amman's *Künstbüchlein* (1580-1597) is magnificently illustrated with detailed pictures of soldiers of his period and their armor and weapons. The matchlock with curved stock to fit the shoulder and permit better aiming was developed rapidly in Germany during this period and several of his drawings show all the details of loading, aiming and firing the early matchlock arms.

His work is equalled only by that of the immortal Albrecht Dürer, whose *Triumph of Maxamilian* (about 1520) is an outstanding work of art. Dürer illustrated many manuscripts on arms in Maximilian's time. Reinhart von Solms' *Kreigsbüchse* (1550-1560) is also noteworthy for its reliable data and drawings on arms of the period.

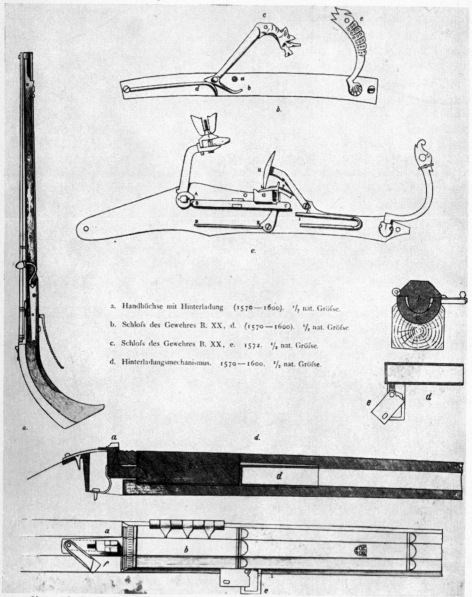

a. Handbüchse mit Hinterladung   (1570—1600).   ½ nat. Größe.

b. Schloſs des Gewehres B. XX, d.   (1570—1600).   ½ nat. Größe.

c. Schloſs des Gewehres B. XX, e.   1572.   ½ nat. Größe.

d. Hinterladungsmechanismus.   1570—1600.   ½ nat. Größe.

Sixteenth Century Breechloaders. From the Arsenal Books of Emperor Maximilian.

Chapter 4

THE DAWN OF THE METALLIC CARTRIDGE RIFLE

BULLET DEVELOPMENT

Between 1800 and 1850 the French had so advanced in the art of artillery firing that the military were forced to concede the necessity of greater range and accuracy for the shoulder arm.

When problems of exterior ballistics began occupying the attention of designers, it became apparent that the employment of rifling was a necessity if the required range and accuracy were to be obtained.

Up to this time the universal use of rifling had been prevented by the difficulty of ramming down the rifled barrel a lead ball large enough to take the rifling. With a clean barrel this was hard; with a fouled barrel it became impossible. The early American muzzle-loading rifles met this problem by the use of a greased patch around the bullet. In Europe between 1830 to 1840 much thought was given to designing a bullet which would enter the barrel easily but would then expand so as to fill the grooves of the rifling. Many different designs were produced, most of which disappeared as rapidly as they came. An early solution was that of Delvigne who made the powder chamber at the breech end of the barrel smaller than the bore, so that the ball when rammed down the barrel came to rest on the forward shoulder of the powder chamber. A few strokes of the heavy ramrod would then flatten the ball and expand it into the grooves. A somewhat similar expedient was that of Thouvenin, who placed in the middle of the powder chamber a post to support the ball so that it could be expanded by ramrod strokes. This was called the *carabine à tige* (gun with stem).

These devices and many others with a similar objective were superseded by the system named for Captain Minié. The Minié ball was an elongated lead bullet pointed in front and with a deep conical hollow in the base, which contained an iron cup. When the gun was fired this cup was driven forward and expanded the hollow base of the bullet into the rifling. Soon it was found that the iron cup was unnecessary as the bullet would expand anyway.

The simplicity and effectiveness of this system soon made all the others obsolete. The Minié (pronounced Mee-nee-ay) bullet became the principal rifle projectile of both the Union and Confederate Armies in the War between the States, and these so-called "Minnie balls" are still being dug up on the farms and battlefields of the South.

THE PERCUSSION BREECHLOADER—CARTRIDGE BEGINNINGS

The percussion period saw the usual experimental designs aimed at the production of breech-loading and repeating arms. Lacking proper metal cases to form an effective gas seal at the breech no really satisfactory weapons were produced. However, one advance in breech design, unrecognized as such at the time, did make its appearance. This was the introduction of the turn-bolt breech block by Nicholas Dreyse in his Zündnädelgewehr or Needle Gun in

1838. Except for one undated specimen in Paris in the Musee d' Artillerie, the Dreyse seems to mark the first application of this very simple locking system, a fact difficult to understand when we consider that the door bolt from which it evolved had been in common use for centuries. When the bolt was withdrawn, a paper cartridge was inserted. A primer was attached to the base of

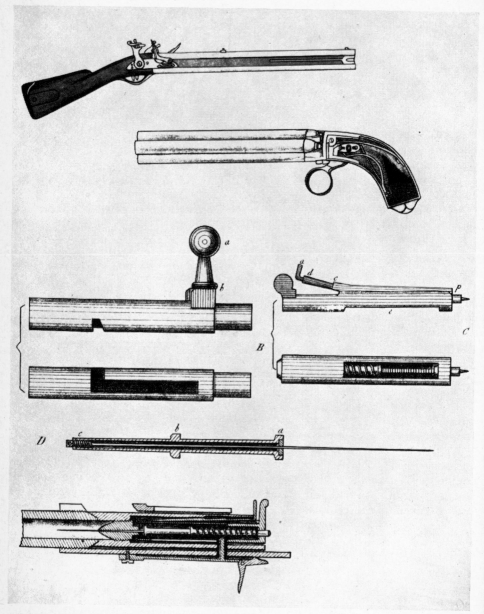

Top to bottom: Early Flintlock with set trigger and barrel sights. Early pepperbox. Details of the Dreyse Needle Gun.

the *bullet,* behind it was fastened the bag with the powder. A long needle inside the bolt functioned as the modern striker. When the trigger was pulled, the needle was driven ahead by its spring, its point passed through the powder and hit the primer ahead. The theory was that this placement of the primer would give more complete combustion of the charge. In this form the bolt action could not seal the breech properly because of the paper cartridges used; while the needle corroded rapidly and was subject to breakage.

The Sharps Rifles and Carbines

The really outstanding American breech-loading development of this period was the mechanism first patented in 1848 by Christian Sharps. This arm was the true forerunner of a tremendous line of dropping block actions, over forty of which were still in European manufacture at the beginning of World War II.

Originally designed in cap-lock days to be breech loaded with a paper cartridge, the design was carried on and modified into the metallic cartridge era. Even at the time of its introduction, it afforded a comparatively tight breech seal. The breechblock was lowered in its mortises in the receiver walls by action of the triggerguard lever. On closing the breech, the paper at the end of the cartridge was automatically cut by an edge on the top of the breechblock, thus enabling the primer to flash directly into the powder charge. In later models a knife-like blade was added to the block. The early types were also intended to be muzzle loaded in the event of excessive breech fouling, some models carrying ramrods for this purpose.

The Sharps was extensively used in the Civil War, and in its metallic cartridge form was the rifle which was responsible for the annihilation of the buffalo. It passed through many phases and alterations, all of which are discussed in Winston O. Smith's book *The Sharps Rifle.*

Three other designs of this period are worthy of mention because they represent the beginnings of the development of effective breech seals by the use of cartridges. The first was Gilbert Smith's .52 caliber Breech Loader patented in 1856 and made by the American Arms Co., Chicopee Falls, Mass., among others. Thirty thousand sixty-two of these guns were purchased by the Government during the Civil War, and the arm received considerable attention in Europe. It hinged at the breech somewhat in the manner of the common shotgun, the release being a small forward trigger within the triggerguard. It was loaded with a freak India rubber cartridge whose base was perforated to permit a common cap to be used on a vent to fire the powder. Some were later altered to the queer Crispin metallic cartridge. Over 13,000,000 of these Smith cartridges were produced during the Civil War.

The second of this group was invented by General A. F. Burnside. It used a special brass cartridge of conical type with a hole at the rear to permit the cap to flash through into the powder. Records show that 55,567 of these rifles and 21,819,200 cartridges were made in the original model.

The third was the Maynard. Like the Burnside and the Smith it was fired by percussion cap but used a freak brass cartridge case. The case had a rimmed base with a hole in the center to permit the cap to flash through. The barrel was hinged down for loading by pushing the triggerguard lever. The Maynard

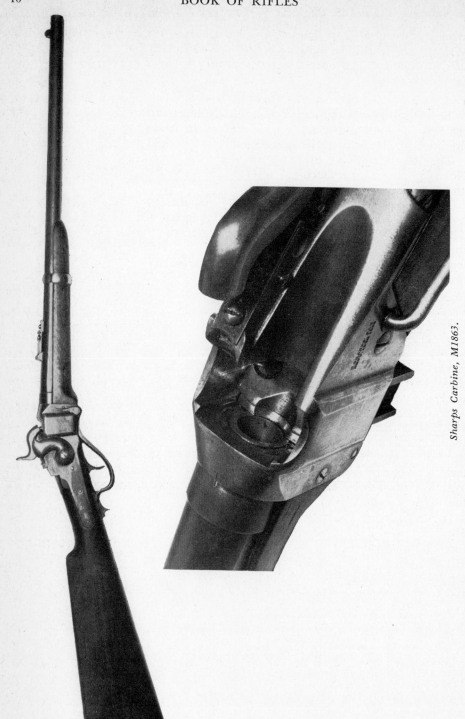

Sharps Carbine, M1863.

system was employed on later true cartridge arms. It was the invention of the Washington dentist, Dr Edward Maynard who earlier had invented the widely used Maynard tape-primer already described, a device still used in children's toy cap pistols.

The Jennings Rifle

The Jennings was the most important development of this era, for it paved the way for the transitional Volcanic which in its turn evolved into the rim fire metallic Henry rifle, the basis for the first Winchester rifle.

The Repeating Rifle of Lewis Jennings was patented December 25, 1849, No. 6,973. It was manufactured at Windsor, Vermont by the firm of Robbins and Lawrence.

The standard Jennings was equipped with an automatic pellet priming system, housed in a "pill-box" which might be mistaken for a Maynard tape container. The now familiar tube below the barrel carried twenty hollow conical bullets, the powder charge being in the hollow base of the bullet. This was a gravity loader, and the muzzle was elevated high enough to let the bullets slide back until the first cartridge to be fed dropped on the carrier which was operated by a ratchet through a ring trigger. The movement involved was about three inches each way.

This weapon is the earliest appearance of the below-barrel magazine in any arm commercially produced. It is also the direct parent of the toggle-locked breech in all its future developments. This fact has never been properly appreciated. While its toggle locking system is a far cry from that of its successor, the Volcanic, it is nevertheless the first use of this form of breech locking and we can trace its progress through a series of world famous designs.

This toggle principle as modified in the Volcanic was transferred to the Henry and then to the first Winchester. Hiram Maxim's first successful autoloader was an early Winchester fitted with a false butt with springs and a change in the leverage. From this experimentation developed the toggle-lock of the famous Maxim machine gun, an arm used by the Germans even in World War II. The British Vickers gun is an adaptation of this Maxim principle with the toggle inverted.

In the field of pistols the line of toggle development can also be traced. Hugo Borchardt, inventor of the pistol of that name which later developed into the widely known German Luger, was employed at Winchester for a time. His lock is an adaptation of the toggle-lock of the early Winchesters, the Luger toggle buckling up instead of down. Current Swiss machine weapons, notably the Furrer, also use a modification of the toggle principle; and even the American B.A.R. locks on a variant of this idea.

The Volcanic Rifle

The Volcanic Rifle represented a really important improvement in design with its introduction of the double-toggle lock joint (pat. 10535 of Smith and Wesson filed on Feb. 14, 1854). Tyler Henry, who had helped build the original Jennings rifle at the Robbins and Lawrence plant, was engaged to combine the Jennings and the Smith patents to produce the first Volcanic.

Originally introduced as the Smith & Wesson, and manufactured both as a rifle and as a pistol, at Norwich, Connecticut in 1854, the arm was taken over

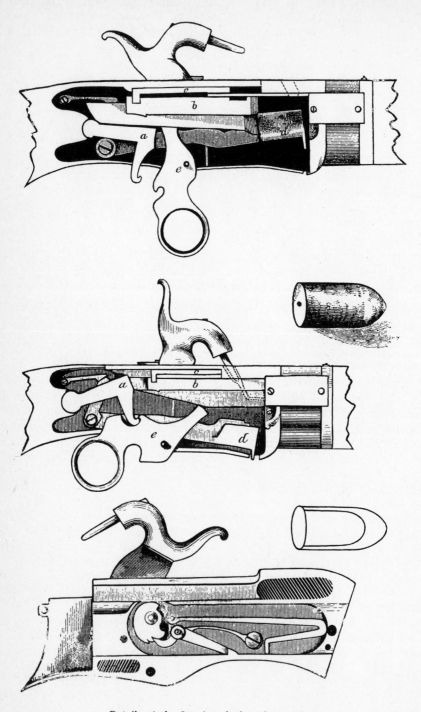

Details of the Jennings lock and cartridge.

by a corporation formed in July 1855 and renamed the Volcanic. In 1856 the company moved to New Haven, and Daniel B. Wesson soon left to found his own pistol company. When the company was thrown into bankruptcy in 1857, Oliver F. Winchester, one of the original stockholders, bought up the assets and formed the New Haven Arms Company.

The ammunition consisted of a hollow based conical bullet having a charge of black powder kept in place in the hollow by a cardboard disc containing the primer. Since there was no gas seal the system was unsatisfactory.

The Volcanic vanished from the American scene within six years after its optimistic introduction, but the toggle principle of breech action remains with us yet.

THE METALLIC CARTRIDGE

The Pin Fire Cartridge

Successful breech-loading systems were made possible only by the development of a cartridge carrying its own ignition and having an expanding case to serve as a breech seal. In its earliest form this successful cartridge was a "pin fire." The primer was inside the metal case head, but was not struck directly by hammer or firing pin; instead a metal pin jutted out from the side of the head of the case and the falling hammer hit this pin and drove it down into the primer to detonate the priming.

Pauly's experiments with sealing the breech by ductile metal discs led to further experiments in France by his successor, the Parisian gunsmith E. Lefaucheux, who also vastly improved Pauly's breech design. In 1836 Lefaucheux introduced a hinged frame breechloader which is the parent of our modern double barreled guns, though its locking mechanism was crude and inefficient. The new cartridge was made of paper with a metal base like the modern shotgun case, but with a pin projecting from the side of the case head. This pin was struck by the falling hammer and driven into the cap to fire the cartridge. The design was not sufficiently gas tight to be entirely satisfactory and it was not until the Frenchman, Houiller, produced his improved pin fire cartridge in 1847 that the problem was really solved.

The Houiller improved pin fire was immediately applied by Lefaucheux to his double barreled gun. The constant association of the gun and cartridge linked the two inseparably in the public mind; and the pin fire is known throughout the world today as the Lefaucheux System. Even in such authoritative contemporary works as the six volume *Etudes sur passe et l'Avenir de l'Artillerie* written by the Emperor Napoleon III and I. Fave and published from 1846 to 1871, we find pin-fire cartridges referred to generally as being similar to those in Lefaucheux sporting guns. Lefaucheux exhibited his shotgun with the improved pin-fire cartridge at the 1851 Exhibition in London.

The Rim Fire Cartridge

While Houiller's French patents touch on the rim fire principle, it is not on record that he did anything practical with the idea. Flobert, on the other hand, evolved the bulleted breech cap from the common percussion cap, and actually manufactured ammunition and arms to use it in the period between 1835 and

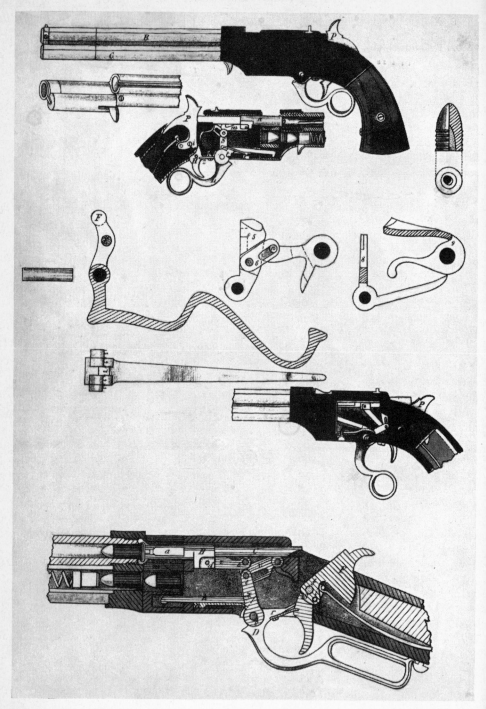

Upper: The Volcanic. Lower: The Henry which is evolved from the Volcanic, and which later became the Winchester '66.

1847. His patented muskets and pistols were entered in the Official Catalogue at the 1851 London Exhibition, under *France No. 215.*

Robbins & Lawrence of Windsor, Vermont had an exhibit of rifles and interchangeable parts (under *America No. 328)* at the same exhibit. Horace Smith, Daniel B. Wesson and B. Tyler Henry were all very intimately associated with Robbins & Lawrence at that time. It therefore seems quite probable that the founders of the Smith & Wesson arms company developed the first practical rim fire cartridge from Flobert samples obtained at this London Exhibition. The partners by devising a way to draw the cartridge cases at reasonable cost assured the immediate success of the rim fire cartridge. That was their great contribution. That original S&W .22 Rim Fire of 1857 is practically the same as the modern .22 Short.

On October 16, 1860 B. Tyler Henry was granted U. S. Patent No. 30446 for the Henry Rifle, the old Volcanic redesigned to shoot the .44 Flat Rim Fire Cartridge. Henry made no specific claims to being the developer of the rim-fire cartridge, but in remembrance of his efforts every Winchester rim fire cartridge from that day on has carried on its head the letter "H".

In their time the rim-fire rifles made history throughout the world. Limited today to "small bore" and "low-powered" weapons it was nevertheless the development of the breech-sealing rim-fire which opened up the whole vista of modern breech-loading small arms design.

The Center Fire Cartridge

As we have seen, Houiller in 1847 covered the *principle* of the center fire cartridge in his patent specification, but did nothing concrete about developing or marketing the improvement.

In 1852 the famous English gunmaker Charles Lancaster produced a center fire shotgun using a special cartridge which, while it was center fire in action, was not a forerunner of the successful center fire cartridge as we know it. It requires mention because so many foreign writers have listed it as the origin of the true center fire. It distinctly is not, as an examination of a specimen cartridge will at once disclose. It actually represented Lancaster's endeavor to overcome the failings of the unsymmetrical pin fire with its side-projecting pin.

The true ancestor of the modern center fire system is the French Pottet case, closely resembling the modern shotgun case, described in detail in Pottet's French patent of 1857.

English patent specification No. 2203 of the year 1861 covers the first widely used center fire cartridge case and was patented in the name of F. E. Schneider of Paris. G. H. Daw, a noted English gunmaker marketed this cartridge. When W. T. Eley produced a center fire cartridge under specification No. 880 of 1866, Daw promptly sued him. One of the little gems of cartridge literature is the 1867 pamphlet published by Daw entitled: *The Central-fire Cartridge before the Law Courts, the Government, and the Public, showing who has improved it, who has profited by it, and who ought to be rewarded for it.* Mr. Daw either didn't know or forgot to mention the Pottet principle. In any event, the suit was thrown out on the grounds that Schneider's was not a master patent; and a wide variety of modified center fire cartridges were promptly marketed in England.

EARLY CARTRIDGE CASE DESIGN AND THE BOXER AND
THE BERDAN PRIMERS

In the late 1860's the common American military type center fire cartridges were of the early "folded-head" design, resembling the common rim fire in outside appearance. The head of the case was reinforced by a cup-like piece of metal which was inserted through the mouth of the cartridge case and pressed down until the bottom of the reinforcing cup was snug against the inside of the head of the case. A pocket in the bottom of the reinforcing cup was loaded with the priming mixture before insertion in the case. Thus when the cartridge case had been assembled the priming mixture was held in its primer cup close against the inside of the center of the head of the cartridge. A vent led through the reinforcing cup from the primer into the main portion of the case and transmitted the flash from the primer to the powder. In order to fire this type of center-fire cartridge the firing pin had to indent the smooth head of the case and crush the primer pellet against the head-reinforcing element which served as an anvil. Such cases were expensive and ignition was none too reliable.

Colonel Boxer of the British Army in his time was honored for the development of the coiled brass case with its iron base head which made a perfect gas seal and started the trend to center fire metallic cartridge breechloaders in Europe. Meanwhile, in the United States breechloaders and repeaters of superior design were already in use with *rim fire* cartridges. Today the Boxer case is obsolete, but the Boxer primer was such an outstanding achievement that it is the type still universally used in America. Ironically, this primer invented by a British officer, is generally referred to as the "American type" primer. It is a simple metal cup containing the priming mixture and having its own anvil crimped in across the mouth of the primer cup. The primer unit is seated in the primer pocket in the head of the cartridge case. The primer flash travels through a single vent in the primer pocket into the interior of the cartridge case and ignites the powder. Aside from slight improvements in the quality of metal and in the form and method of crimping the anvil into the cup the "Boxer" primer remains unchanged even today.

Colonel Hiram Berdan of the U. S. Ordnance Department about 1870 developed a simple and cheap system of drawing brass cases and devised a new form of primer. This primer differed from Boxer's in that it did not have an integral anvil. Instead, the anvil was formed by a teat in the center of the primer pocket. Two small flash holes were provided in the bottom of the primer pocket, one on either side of the anvil, to carry the primer flash into the powder. These primers were in vogue in the United States for twenty years or more but are no longer generally manufactured for American consumption. Thus, the Berdan primer, designed by an American officer, is now the standard European type. The Boxer type primer, with its single, comparatively large flash hole has the advantage of being easier to push from the fired case, permitting simpler reloading. The case, with its simple primer pocket and single vent is somewhat simpler to manufacture. The open pocket and centrally located vent also seem to permit the use of higher intensity primers without the primer swelling or blow-back obtained with the Berdan type.

EARLY METALLIC CARTRIDGE BREECH LOADERS

In the 1860's and '70's the combination of American inventive and manufacturing genius first truly asserted itself. With the introduction of the metallic cartridge, the Sharps' locking system came into its own. Existing rifles were promptly converted to both rim and center fire types. Christian Sharps' original patent was granted in percussion days (September 12, 1848 to be exact), yet its essential locking system has come down through the years as one of the great basic locking forms.

The Sharps-Borchardt rifle in which the firing mechanism is inside the dropping breechblock (other Sharps used the familiar clumsy external hammer) was tested by a U. S. Ordnance Board in 1870 and a few were issued for field service. The famous Model 1878 of this design, made in a wide variety of styles and several calibers, is highly prized even today as the basis for single-shot actions. When the triggerguard lever is thrown down it lowers the breechblock, cocks the concealed hammer and ejects the empty shell. When the action is closed, the safety is automatically set; and a catch to the rear of the trigger must be pulled back to release it.

By 1881 when the life of the Sharps concern drew to a close, events in Europe were turning all military thought to the need for repeating arms. One repeating rifle, the Schneider, was produced on the dropping block locking system, but a lever action design is not suited to rapid prone shooting. The Sharps organization started manufacture of the Lee repeater, but because of financial troubles turned the arm over to Remington at Ilion, N. Y.

The long line of fine Ballard rifles, the Sims, the Stevens Ideal types, and the famous Winchester Single Shot developed by John M. Browning are all tributes to the original creative ability of Christian Sharps. All use comparatively minor variants of his original breechlock. In Europe dozens of small but fine gunmakers manufactured dropping block precision rifles up to the period of the Second World War; but in the U. S. only the Stevens found the market large enough to warrant production after 1920.

Henry O. Peabody of Boston developed the second great original locking system of the period, the basic patent dating from July 22, 1862 (No. 35947). This is the first arm to employ a breechblock hinged at the rear and above the axis of the bore. When unlocked by throwing the triggerguard lever down and forward, the front of the block falls below the line of the chamber to permit loading. This extremely powerful system had an advantage over the earlier vertical dropping block type in that the block could not be so readily jammed by an expanded case head. In 1862 it was submitted for military tests at Watertown Arsenal. As originally produced the Peabody used a .45 Rim Fire cartridge and was provided with an external hammer and an automatic extractor. While it was adopted by several militia units, the Peabody did not receive the attention in the United States which was accorded to it in Europe.

In January 1865 the Peabody was exhaustively tested at Springfield Armory together with 64 other rifles, and its performance was so outstanding that it was recommended by the Examining Board. By this time, however, the War had ended and the general lassitude and pinch-penny thinking which descends upon America after every war again halted Peabody. Like the British, all we could think of was how to convert our enormous stock of muzzle loaders cheap-

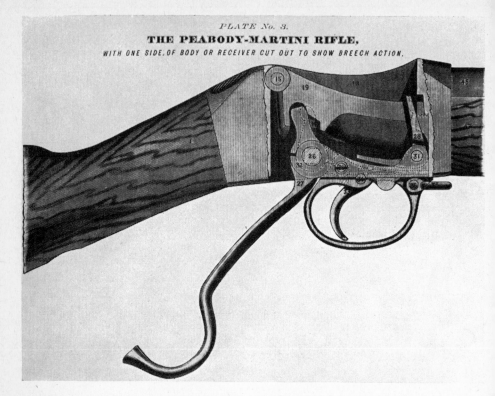

PLATE No. 3.

THE PEABODY-MARTINI RIFLE,

WITH ONE SIDE, OF BODY OR RECEIVER CUT OUT TO SHOW BREECH ACTION.

ly, we had no time for new designs. In that year Canada bought 3000 Peabodys in caliber .50-60 Rim Fire; and the manufacturers, The Providence (R.I.) Tool Company, were encouraged to seek foreign markets.

Turkey, Switzerland, Denmark, Roumania, Cuba, Canada, Mexico, France, Austria and Bavaria purchased Peabodys in varying quantities.

The Martini action now enters the picture. The Swiss turned the Peabody over to a master mechanic, Frederich von Martini of Frauenfeld, for modification. Martini's first modification was an elementary leverage arrangement which automatically cocked the Peabody hammer as the action was opened. His next modification, however, was the one which has completely submerged the name and fame of Peabody, the original designer. Martini dispensed entirely with the huge exposed hammer and substituted an internal lock within the breechblock. The result was a streamlined design retaining the Peabody breechlock but embodying the now famous Martini firing mechanism.

The Martini-Henry action resulted when Martini submitted this design to England for tests. It was slightly modified at Enfield and fitted with a barrel rifled on the English Henry system (Pat. No. 2802 of 1860 to Alexander Henry of Edinburgh). The bore is polygonal. Lands are formed at the angles, providing additional bearings for the projectile in its passage through the barrel. Unfortunately for Henry Peabody, the British adoption of the system under the name "Martini-Henry" was widely publicized, and even in America it was forgotten that Peabody had originated the action.

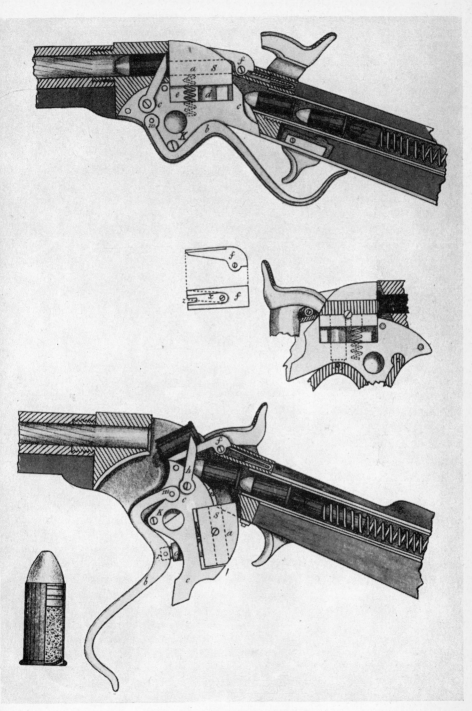

THE SPENCER ACTION.

Meanwhile in Bavaria the Peabody system was being modified more drastically than in Switzerland. J. L. Werder, director of a Nuremberg factory, was given access to the Peabody test which had been conducted by an Arms Commission for over a year, and in 1867 he introduced his modification which became famous as the *"Bavarian Lightning."* Werder recognized the military need for a rifle which could be rapidly manipulated from a prone position. Accordingly he modified the Peabody breechblock so that a *forward* thrust on a trigger-type lever within the triggerguard forward of the firing trigger would unlock the prop and let the front face of the block fall for loading. Pulling back a hammer-like cocking piece on the right side of the receiver cocked the arm, elevated the breechlock and locked the prop below its forward end. This breechlocking system is another Peabody variant, directly inspired, but again Henry Peabody received no credit.

The Francotte-Martini, in falling block *Field* (there is also a dropping block design in this type), the *Swinburne,* the *Stahl,* the *Westley-Richards* and a host of lesser known rifles in Europe quickly appropriated Peabody's breechlock—without acknowledgment of any kind. In recent years *the majority* of the precision single shot rifles made abroad—at least 21 types—used varying firing systems combined with the Peabody lock. With the one exception of the original German Aydt falling block in which the block is pivoted *below* the chamber, every falling block design made stems from the Peabody. In our own country even the once famous Spencer repeating shotgun locks on a modification of this principle, a fact which seems never to have occurred to the litigants in the suit of Bannerman (then owner of the Spencer patents) vs. Winchester over the right to make pump action guns.

The Spencer of 1860 was the first successful lever action repeater. This arm had a magazine tube in the buttstock. A semi-circular breechblock actuated by the triggerguard lever had both a falling and a rotating motion. When the breech was open, the magazine spring thrust a cartridge out and it was held against the face of the breechblock by a spring finger until chambered by a rearward movement of the lever. The hammer had to be thumb cocked. A magazine cut-off (Stabler's patent) was employed on later models to hold the magazine in reserve. Quick loading was achieved by the familiar metal tubes closed at one end used in shooting galleries today to quick-fill magazines.

The Henry of 1860 was the next lever action repeater. To load the magazine it was necessary to pull the coil magazine spring up into a muzzle part of the tube, which was then swung on a pivot to give access to the tube itself. Cartridges were inserted head first, the muzzle section was swung back, the coil spring released to provide pressure to push the cartridges back up the tube. When the triggerguard lever was swung down and ahead, it pulled the toggle jointed to it out of locking line. Continued motion of the toggle arm drew the breechbolt back in a direct line with the axis of the bore. The rear of the breechbolt pushed back and rode over the hammer which was caught and held by the sear. Further lever motion thrust ahead the carrier block on which the first cartridge had been forced from the magazine. As the lever was pulled back into rest position, it pushed up the center of the toggle causing the attached breechbolt to move forward and chamber the cartridge from the carrier. The carrier descended to receive the next cartridge from the magazine tube. The toggle joint was straightened out on final lever motion to support the breechbolt firmly against the cartridge case head, the extractors in its face gripping the case rim. When the lever was completely home, the trigger was in position to trip the sear when pulled and let the hammer fall on the firing pin in the breechbolt.

The very first Henry rifles fired a rim fire cartridge of .44-25-216 caliber. (This was later changed to .44-28-200.) While the *bullet* caliber was .44, the barrel was bored .42, then rifled with 6 grooves 0.005 inch deep. The "gain twist" rifling as used by Henry started at a breech rate of twist of 1 turn in 16 feet, and at the muzzle was 1 turn in 2.75 feet.

The original Henry was made only in one caliber and style, though the ornamentation varied greatly. This arm is marked "HENRY'S PATENT OCT. 16, 1860. MANUFACT'D BY THE NEW HAVEN ARMS COMPANY, NEW HAVEN, CONN." However, in 1866 there appeared the Henry Repeating Rifle and Carbine, Model 1866, carrying the King improvement—the now familiar spring side-loading gate. Pushing the bullet nose against the front of the gate pushed it in and permitted the cartridge to be forced into the magazine tube from the breech end. Repeating the action filled the magazine from the breech, a feature which disposed entirely of the loading objections to the Henry. These arms are seldom listed, and the Winchester records are hazy concerning them. However, collector's specimens exist, all bearing the barrel mark "HENRY'S PATENT OCTOBER 16, 1860" and also "KING'S PATENT MARCH 29, 1866." The side plates on these Henrys were standard but when the arm was re-named the *Winchester* later in 1866, they were bevelled only at the front to assist in removal without injury to the spring cover.

The Winchester 1873 (and its heavier model the 1876) was basically the same arm as the Model 1866 and the earlier Henry 1866 already described, except that the action was strengthened to handle the .44-40 Center Fire cartridge.

Marlin began manufacturing Ballards in 1875. In 1881 the first Marlin lever action repeater made its appearance. These were noteworthy in that day for their sturdy actions and their rifling. The breechblock locked against a solid ledge in the receiver. It was pushed back and down when the trigger-guard lever was operated. The barrels were deep grooved and enjoyed a high standing for accuracy and for giving a minimum amount of trouble from the black powder fouling. Following in the footsteps of the Winchester, the 1881 Marlin ejected through the top of the receiver. The Model 1881 with only minor changes was in manufacture in a variety of medium and heavy calibers until 1888, when it was replaced by another top ejector, the Model 1888. The Model 1889 was then brought out with the characteristic solid top and side ejection. The carrier was pivoted instead of rising vertically as in the Winchester '86.

The Winchester 1886 was a new design by John Browning which revolutionized lever action repeaters. This design ended the vertical carrier and the toggle-lock of the Winchester. Future locks, like the 1886, featured locking bolts riding up in mortises in the receiver walls and cuts in the sides or rear of the breechblock, the bolts being lowered and raised by forward and rearward action of the lever. In this form, which is carried through on other Winchester lever actions, the bolts are housed partly in the receiver and partly in the breechblock sides. In the 94 and other long cartridge models the lock rises behind the breechblock head. These variations are described under the Winchester arms in Part III.

The Winchester Model 1895 was another basic Browning patent. It differed from earlier lever repeaters in having a box magazine mounted in the receiver to handle long and pointed cartridges of the most powerful types then known. Because of the position of the magazine, the locking bolt was placed in the rear of the receiver behind the breechblock, being lowered and raised by lever action. A notch in the upper part of the locking bolt lets the hammer reach the firing pin when the action is closed. The Model 95 was an official U. S. Army weapon for a short time. It was used to some extent in W.W. I by Russia and occasionally by Russian partisans in W.W. II.

The Savage Model 1899 was tested in 1895 by the U. S. Navy Board. This arm employs a revolving box magazine which separates and protects the individual cartridges. Its really outstanding feature however (the revolving magazine had long been used in Europe) was its hammerless, enclosed-breech firing mechanism and its magnificently strong lock. This is the only lever action repeater locking system which compares with the turning bolt system for breechlock strength. The breechblock is a solid steel block fitted closely into the receiver walls. When the lever is thrown down and ahead, the entire bolt is first lowered out of the locking mortises and then drawn back over the top of the magazine well. When the lever is returned, the breechblock pushes a cartridge ahead to chamber, then is lifted into its receiver recess where its face is against the head of the cartridge case and the breech, while its rear rests against the solid metal of the heavy receiver.

Most Marlin, Savage and Winchester lever actions since produced are but modifications of those described above, and are discussed in more detail in Part III.

Slide Action repeaters are frequently called "pump" or "trombone" actions. We have already pointed out that early types of slide systems were patented in England to use impractical transition cartridges. In France and Belgium, too, the system was the subject of many early patents, none of which were ever manufactured.

The Spencer shotgun was the first successful slide action system. The system was later combined with a modified American Lee magazine to develop the unsuccessful Spencer-Lee rifle, an arm which received more attention abroad than in the United States.

Christopher M. Spencer and S. M. Roper (Roper had developed some rather impractical revolving guns earlier) worked together to produce an arm on which two patents were issued. This work was done in 1883-84. Patent 316401 covered: "Any magazine firearm having a piston breech, suitably connected to and in combination with an actuating sliding handle, situated forward of the receiver, and serving as a means for supporting the barrel, and provided with a path of reciprocation, in a line parallel with the axial line of the barrel." A perfect technical description of the slide action.

In 1884 Francis Bannerman of New York City formed a company to manufacture the Spencer Repeating Shotgun and manufacture was begun in a little plant in Brooklyn, N. Y. In all some 20,000 Spencer shotguns were sold.

By 1893 Winchester woke up to the possibilities in the repeating shotgun field, and when John M. Browning turned up with his original slide action shotgun, they promptly bought it up and put into production. The Browning, of course, functioned on the *principle* outlined in the Spencer patent, but most of the actual mechanics of operation were quite different. The two designs had slide actions and tube magazines in common; but feeding and locking were entirely different, the Spencer being actually a variant of the old Peabody falling blocklock, while Browning introduced a new tipping breechblock design from which stem most of the pump repeating shotgun and rifle locks since developed.

Bannerman promptly sued Winchester for infringement. Bannerman lost his suit and went out of the gun manufacturing business.

The Winchester Model 1890 rifle, another Browning design, is the original .22 caliber slide action repeater, differing only in lock design from his earlier shotguns. This hammer model repeater is the basis of all later Winchester hammer pump-action .22's. Later Winchester models of "hammerless" design resemble the action of the Browning hammerless shotgun.

Savage in 1903 introduced a slide action hammerless model whose outstanding difference from other types was the use of a detachable box magazine which in practice did not work out well. The 1914, 1925 and current models follow the pattern of the original but substitute the common magazine tube below the barrel.

The Marlin Models 20, 27 and 29, now discontinued, were standard pump types with tubes below the barrel. Their Model 32 was a hammerless type. The Marlin slide action rifles were a logical development of their Model 1892 shotgun. Unlike the other models which handled .22 Rim Fire cartridges, the Model 27 was chambered for .25 Rim Fire and for .25-20 and .32-20 C. F. cartridges.

Remington slide or trombone action rifles are made on the designs and patents of J. D. Pedersen, who also designed the Remington Model 1910 slide action shotgun. Besides the line of hammerless (enclosed hammer) .22's, the Remington line also manufactured this design as the Model 14½ in calibers .38-40 and .44-40 Center Fire, as the Model 25 in calibers .25-20 and .32-20 W.C.F. (both Models were discontinued), and as a medium powered (although it is called "high-powered") hammerless tube breechloading repeater in calibers .25, .32 and .35 Remington Rimless, a form still in manufacture.

Chapter 5

THE DEVELOPMENT OF BOLT ACTIONS

The United States

While the first successful metallic cartridge *bolt action* rifle was invented by Paul Mauser of Germany, it was not, as is generally stated, the 1871 Model adopted by the German Government.

Actually the first practical Mauser rifle design was the *Mauser-Norris* of 1867, the first patent for which was actually taken out in the United States on June 2, 1868. The patent number is 78,603 and the rifle was patented in the names of Samuel Norris of Springfield, Massachusetts and Wilhelm and Paul Mauser of Oberndorf, Würtemburg.

The two Mauser brothers were the legitimate inventors—Paul providing the designs and Wilhelm helping with the work. Norris was a European representative of Remington who had been so impressed with the new Mauser bolt action that he undertook to finance their venture. Norris, however, found himself unable to finance the new Mauser, and the brothers improved their design and sold it themselves to the German Army. On that slim thread hung the destiny of the Mauser—the most widely used and imitated design ever produced. If Remington, which then controlled most of the desirable foreign rifle business, had had the foresight to support Norris and underwrite the two Mauser brothers they might have changed the course of history. Espousal of Paul Mauser by the German Government led eventually to the most far-flung organization of arms interests in history. Even before the Mauser rifle was established, Remington hired Franz, another of the large family of Mauser brothers, who had emigrated to America. Paul and Wilhelm worked as a team but they had no business contact—and in later life little social contact—with their other brothers. The many legends linking Remington with the Mauser rifle stem from the employment of Franz by that company.

Every original good feature of the metallic cartridge turning bolt action design was developed by Peter Paul Mauser. He was the first to introduce the feature of cam-withdrawal of the firing pin (the British army had consistently refused to consider bolt actions to that time because of the danger of accidental firing with the pin forward). He introduced the first one-piece bolt and the locking lugs at the front end of the bolt (although in percussion days this feature had been used in the American Green rifle). He introduced escape vents to lead gas off safely in case of a blown primer or split case and the first successful built-in box magazine utilizing the strip-in charger was his. The rest of the Mauser story belongs to the European rifle history section.

In 1878 an Ordnance Board tested 29 arms with magazines, among which were 8 bolt actions. Out of these tests the *Hotchkiss* was adopted as the first official American bolt magazine rifle. The original Hotchkiss was manufactured in France (where the American inventor B. B. Hotchkiss was then living). When he showed the rifle at the Philadelphia Centennial Exposition in 1876, Winchester approached Hotchkiss to manufacture the design. The first U. S.

patent dates as far back as 1860, though modifications continued through 1878. By 1874 Hotchkiss had incorporated the idea of cocking on the lifting motion of the bolt handle. The magazine was in the buttstock. It had the additional excellent features of a magazine cutoff and a manual safety. Twenty-five hundred were supplied the U. S. Navy and 1500 to the Army. The actions were made by Winchester, the barrels and furniture by Springfield Armory. This arrangement permitted the use of Springfield-type bands, sights, and bayonets.

James Paris Lee was an American by adoption only. Born in Scotland in 1831, he was raised and educated in Canada before coming to the United States. All his designing and manufacturing, however, was done in this country after he became a citizen.

In 1879 Lee patented the "Lee U. S. Navy Rifle, cal. .45-70 Govt." This arm introduced the box-type magazine in the receiver, the type now standard in military rifles. That device seems simple at this late date, but its design completely revolutionized magazine rifles. It eliminated the slow-loading tube magazine; did away with the danger of accidental discharges in the magazine caused by the bullet of one cartridge striking the primer of the cartridge ahead of it in the tube; reduced the overall weight of the piece; simplified the clearing of feeding jams, and improved the balance of the arm when the magazine was fully charged. Lee also patented the box magazine in England, Belgium and Russia. Lee's magazines were also interchangeable as originally introduced.

His Navy Magazine Rifle was submitted to the Equipment Board in July 1879. Lee had arranged for manufacture at Bridgeport by a new concern consisting of the same officers as the Sharps Rifle Co. The backers, losing faith in the arms business, turned the manufacture over to Remington at Ilion. Lee went to work at that plant.

The Lee Model 1879 did not have a magazine cutoff. While originally made in .45-70 caliber and tested by U. S. troops, it was also made in .43 Spanish and was used by Spanish Civil Guards and in Cuba.

Lee later sued both Mauser and Mannlicher for alleged infringements when they introduced box magazines. However, a study of original foreign records discloses that Paul Mauser was working on the idea of several kinds of box magazines at the same time as Lee, and in all fairness it must be admitted that both Mauser and Mannlicher were apparently experimenting with the box design before they heard of Lee's magazine. It is possible, however, that the foreign inventors perfected their designs after a study of the Lee, which was tested openly in the U. S. and England before either the Mauser or Mannlicher box magazine was marketed.

In 1888 after three years of experimenting the British combined the Lee action with the Metford barrel and adopted the Lee-Metford Magazine Rifle Mark I.

Remington also made the Lee as a sporting rifle in several calibers.

In 1895 a Naval Board at Newport, R. I. adopted the Lee Straight Pull in caliber 6mm (.236). Pulling the bolt straight back unlocked the arm, ejected the empty case and cocked the action. Pushing the bolt straight forward, loaded the piece and secured the locking lugs in the receiver. This arm was assigned to Winchester for manufacture and 10,000 were delivered to the Navy. It was the first official U. S. *clip loader.*

The Chaffee-Reece rifle, offered by General J. N. Reece, was in 1882 recommended for test by an Ordnance Board. This was a tube magazine in butt stock design, loaded through a trap in the butt plate which could be opened only when the bolt was in open position. The arm had a cut-off for the magazine, and setting the thumbpiece at half-cock both set the safe and locked the bolt. One thousand were ordered manufactured at Springfield Armory in 1884, the Chaffee-Reece being the first U. S. Government made magazine rifle. Again fittings, sights and bayonets were the old Springfield Single Shot type. It proved to be too complicated mechanically to stand up in field service and was discarded.

The Krag-Jorgensen. In 1890, by which time every important nation in the world except ourselves had adopted magazine arms, another Ordnance Board was convened to consider magazine systems. Domestic and foreign designers submitted a total of 53 systems for consideration, and in 1892 the Board finally selected the Norwegian-designed Krag-Jorgensen as the basis for a new rifle, although even that went through five modifications before acceptance.

The Springfield. After using captured Spanish Mausers for tests, in 1900 and again in 1901 we developed experimental Mauser-types for rimless cartridges. When the first standard Springfield bolt action was manufactured at Springfield Armory in 1902, it was chambered for a rimless cartridge with a 220 grain round-nosed bullet similar to that used in the Krag. This rifle was first issued to troops in late 1904 and in 1905, as the Model 1903.

When the Germans introduced their famous pointed spitzer bullet in 1905, our Ordnance Department quickly seized on the design to improve the 1903 cartridge. Out of this development came the famous combination of the Model 1903 rifle rechambered for the 1906 ammunition having a 150 grain pointed bullet. The rifle itself, world famous as the "Springfield" is a close copy of Paul Mauser's best design, except that it combines a magazine cut-off with the bolt release, substitutes a two-piece firing pin for the one-piece Mauser, and can be manually cocked. Our Government paid the Germans $200,000 for manufacturing rights on the design, representing probably the best investment ever made in rifles.

The Enfield. Great Britain was experimenting with a Mauser-type rifle of .276 caliber when World War I broke out in 1914. American manufacturers were approached to mass-produce these arms chambering them for the standard .303 British caliber rather than risk an ammunition change-over to the .276. And so it was that when we entered the War in 1917 and found ourselves woefully short of Springfields and of manufacturing facilities for them, we arranged for the manufacture by Winchester at New Haven and by Remington at Eddystone, Pa. and Ilion, N. Y. of rifles of the British design adapted to our rimless .30 caliber ammunition. This became the "U. S. Rifle, Model 1917" (commonly known as the "American Enfield," Enfield being the English point of design) .

All modern American bolt actions fall into two classes, (a) small bore (.22 Rim Fire) types in which the bolt handle serves as the locking lug when turned down into the receiver (notable exception the U. S. rifle, caliber .22) ; and (b) large caliber and high power types which are *all* based on the Mauser system. These will be found described in Part III.

Great Britain

The Lee-Metford. In 1887 the British Arms Committee decided upon a Lee action and magazine with a Metford rifled barrel, the caliber to be .303 inch. This rifle was committed for manufacture in December 1888 as the Lee-Metford Magazine Rifle, Mark I. The magazine capacity of this first arm was 8 cartridges.

On January 19, 1892 the design of the original Mark I was altered for new sights, and was listed as the Mark I*.

In 1892 the Mark II was introduced. It had a double column magazine holding 10 cartridges, a simplified bolt, and several minor design improvements.

In 1895 the Mark II* was introduced. This was the same as the Mark II except that it had a safety catch at the rear of the bolt. Turning the catch up locked the striker and bolt from being opened.

The first **Lee-Enfield Rifle** was the L. E. Mark I of November, 1895. This arm was the identical with the Lee-Metford Mark II* except for the Enfield type of rifling and the sights.

The L. E. Mark I* differed from the Mark I only in doing away with the cleaning rod.

A **Lee-Metford Carbine** was introduced in 1894. It was the same as the L. M. Mark II* except for a barrel 9.5 inches shorter which was covered with a wooden handguard, front sight protected by wings on the nose-cap, no long range sights and a 6-round magazine.

The Lee-Enfield Carbine of 1896 had the same modifications as the Lee-Metford carbine and was otherwise the L. E. rifle.

The Short Magazine Lee-Enfields (S. M. L. E.) resulted from experience in the Boer War. The British decided to develop a short rifle which would serve the requirements of both infantry and cavalry. In the United States, Springfield Armory was working along the same lines as a result of our Spanish War experiences; while both Mannlicher and Mauser were also working along similar lines.

As the result of a Committee recommendation of 1900 and field tests in the following year, a new British arm was developed which was adopted in 1902. This short rifle was fitted with charger (clip) guides to permit use of the Mauser system of loading by stripping the cartridges down off the spring clip into the magazine. A double line magazine with capacity of 10 cartridges was employed to receive the contents of two 5-shot clips. A barleycorn front sight protected by horns on the nose-caps; new rear sights; a long handguard extending from the receiver to the muzzle (or nose) cap— those were the major additions. The bolt cover was omitted.

This "new" rifle had several of the basic defects of the old one. By this time every other nation had appreciated the Mauser lock principle: that the closer the locking lugs are to the point of immediate pressure (the face of the bolt), the greater the strength of the system. The Lee-Enfield lugs are on the bolt *to the rear* of the magazine. To some degree the Committee may have been influenced by the fact that the forward lugs on the bolt might require complete re-designing because of feeding trouble from the rimmed cases. This purely financial consideration resulted in the British Army being armed with comparatively low-powered rifles, using rimmed cartridges, which at best could never function as well as rimless, in a vertical box magazine where the rims may always be subjected to interlocking and consequent jamming. In December 23, 1902, this rifle was officially adopted, marking the first of the line of later battle-scarred S. M. L. E.'s, officially designated "Rifle, Short, Magazine, Lee-Enfield, Mark I."

The basic British rifle in World War I was the S. M. L. E. Mark III in caliber .303 with rim. The action is the modified American Lee with locking lugs far back on the bolt to the rear of the magazine well. The magazine may be loaded from strip-in clips through the action, or may be removed from the bottom of the receiver. The various "Marks" of this arm are given in Part III.

Pattern 1914 (Rifle No. 3 Mark I and I*). This is the .303 Mauser variant designed in England and made in the U. S. just before we entered World War I. The British used tremendous numbers of these rifles in both wars. As made by us in caliber .30-06 U. S. Government, it was known as the Model 1917 Enfield.

Rifle No. 4. This is the pattern developed in England after World War I. It uses the standard .303 rim cartridge. It is a modified Lee-Enfield designed for mass production and has the bolt system and the magazine system of the Lee-Enfield. A further modification for jungle use, very much lightened, is the Rifle No. 5.

Canada in 1905 adopted the Ross Straight Pull in caliber .303 British, a unique straight pull variant of the Mauser. Bolt lugs revolved to lock and unlock behind head of cartridge by cam action. Modified in 1910. Canada changed to the British S. M. L. E. during World War I.

European Developments

The first appearance of the successful metallic cartridge bolt action was not in Germany as is popularly supposed. Actually it appeared first in Switzerland. Frederic Vetterli's bolt action to handle a copper rim fire cartridge was produced several years before the great Paul Mauser began his successful experiments based on the Dreyse action.

The Swiss and a handful of Austrians saw the real opportunity presented by the bolt repeater. The virtues of the Lee vertical magazine principle was not then apparent. The late Henrys and the Winchester 1866 had a perfected below-barrel tube, rising cage carrier and side-of-receiver loading system, so the Swiss appropriated those features. The copper rim fire cartridge of .44 caliber had proven successful in America, so the Swiss developed a copper cased .41 Rim Fire of more efficient design.

The first **Vetterli** 10.4mm Rim Fire repeater was issued in 1867 but did not get into general production until 1869. New models were manufactured at Waffenfabrik Bern in 1871 and 1878, and the rifle was in official use until 1889. This first bolt repeater had a 12-shot magazine, fired a 313 grain lead bullet at a muzzle velocity of 1338 feet per second, and had a miximum range of about 3000 yards.

Switzerland adopted in 1889 the Schmidt-Rubin original Swiss straight pull rifle, an arm based on Major Rubin's rifle of 1883. The special revolving cam operated bolt has lugs midway on the bolt. The vertical detachable box magazine is of special design. Modified in 1911 and 1931.

The Fruwirth bolt action with tube magazine below the barrel, the invention of Ferdinand Fruwirth, an Austrian, was actually employed in quantity *before* *the Vetterli.* In 1869 it was adopted as the official Austro-Hungarian Gendarmerie rifle, and was issued in 1870. This 11mm arm had a bolt which turned down close to the stock and a hammer-like cocking-piece projecting from the rear of the bolt. Its use was limited to the Gendarmerie because by the time Fruwirth presented it, the Austrians had committed themselves to the manufacture of the Werndl single shot block rifle and were unable financially to assume another complete changeover.

The **Mauser** was the most important of the numerous single shot bolt designs introduced in 1870-1871. When Germany officially adopted it as the Gewehr 1871, the race was on. Holland adopted the **Beaumont** invented by a Dutch engineer, an 11mm caliber C.F. firing a 386 grain lead bullet at a muzzle velocity of 1476 feet per second. The one unusual feature of the Beaumont design was the use of a V-spring in the bolt handle to drive the striker instead of the conventional spiral spring.

Italy in 1871 adopted the **Swiss Vetterli** single shot in a 10.4mm caliber C.F. and manufactured it in her own arsenals.

Russia and Bulgaria in the same year adopted the bolt action Berdan II in caliber .42. This rifle fired a 370 grain lead bullet at a muzzle velocity of about 1440 feet per second. The Krnka quick loader, a device to hold 10 cartridges with heads up ready for instant grasping, was attached to the side of the Berdan II in battle use.

By 1873 **France** had the **Chassepot** modified for a metallic cartridge of 11mm caliber. Many of these conversions were made under the **British Kynoch** patent at Anston, England. In 1874 France adopted the **Gras** conversion, Chatellerault and St. Etienne being the large centers of manufacture.

A **Vetterli-Gras** combination was tested as early as 1874, but it was not until 1878 that the French made even a limited adoption of the repeating principle. In that year they issued the 11mm tube loader, bolt action **Kropatschek** to their Marine Infantry. The Kropatschek design was further improved by Gasser in Vienna, but by then the period of large caliber military rifles was nearing a close and the arm was not of any particular significance.

1878 saw **Russia** testing the impractical American **Evans** lever action stock tube repeater. The Archimedian screw feed principle permitted carrying the cartridges without points resting against heads, but the arm was otherwise of little practical value. Russia in 1891 adopted the "3-line" Nagant designed in Belgium with some contributions by Russian artillery Colonel Mosin. Turning bolt, box magazine, loaded with Mauser type clip. Slightly modified in 1910 and again in 1930 since which time it is known as the M. 1891/30. Caliber 7.62mm Russian.

1879 was a red letter year in rifle development for it saw not only the first American **Lee** vertical box magazine, the principle which was soon to revolutionize military rifle design, but also the introduction of the first revolving box magazine. The Austrian bolt action developed at Steyr Armoury in Austria by **Spitalsky** was the original European approach to the problem of maintaining balance in a magazine rifle while the cartridges were being expended; and of isolating the cartridges so there would be no danger of accidental firing. The Spitalsky, in which the cartridges in the receiver magazine circled around a revolving spool, was the forerunner of the Mannlicher, Schulhof, Savage and

Johnson types. It was, however, first perfected by Schoenauer and used by von Mannlicher.

In 1881 **Serbia** adopted the **Mauser-Milanovic** single shot bolt action in 10.15mm caliber, a backward step followed in 1885 by Portugal which adopted the **Guedes-Castro** single shot dropping block. **Portugal** adopted the **Mauser-Verguiero** in 1904 in 6.5mm Portuguese, and the 7.9mm German Kar. 98k in 1937.

In 1883 the **Mata** bolt repeater appeared, the first of a line of strange types designed to give a combination of large magazine capacity and yet retain a good balance. This type was fired by a thumb trigger. A vertical magazine pocket was provided inside the end of the butt, from which cartridges dropped to a transport rail below which ran to the receiver. This rail was moved on the endless chain system the length of one cartridge for each bolt stroke, thereby feeding a cartridge to the carrier which was also actuated by the bolt motion.

In 1888 Germany issued the Gew. 1888, with the "Mauser and Commission, Mannlicher Magazine System." This arm employed a modified early Mauser type bolt and the Mannlicher clip magazine system. The caliber was 7.92mm.

The next official model, the Gewehr 98, was the perfected Mauser with the built-in box magazine for clip loading, the forerunner of the American Springfield 1903. It introduced an improved 7.9mm cartridge which, as modified, was in use in World War II. Modified as the Kar. 98 and the Kar. 98k, it was the official German arm until the close of World War II. This weapon as modified in 1904 is the basis for every Mauser produced since that time, wherever made. It is the most important bolt design ever produced.

In 1882 the **Austrian Schulhof** magazine repeater appeared. This was a bolt action, thumb trigger arm. The side of the stock had a cover which was hinged up to expose 3 separate magazine compartments. The compartment at the small of the stock received 4 cartridges, the next compartment 5 and the last one 6. The transport rail below the compartments took 3 more cartridges, the carrier 1 more, and the chamber the final one. As the bolt was operated, cartridges fed down onto the transport rail starting with the end compartment. The rail kept the cartridges separated as a safety measure, and moved them ahead one cartridge length for each bolt stroke. This weird design was not successful. It was followed by another Schulhof bolt design having a revolving box magazine patterned after the Spitalsky.

In 1886 the first truly accepted **Mannlicher** design appeared, the wedge-locked straight pull rifle with the Mannlicher magazine system using the Austrian 11mm black powder cartridge. Austria adopted this as an official pattern.

The Austrian Mannlicher rifle of 1888 was only the 1886 pattern straight pull, wedge-locked, design altered from 11mm black powder to Austrian 8mm smokeless. These rifles were the first ever adopted to employ the Mannlicher magazine system in which the clip is loaded into the magazine well with the cartridges within it. When the last cartridge is chambered, the empty clip falls through the bottom of the receiver well.

The 1888 rifle was succeeded by the improved straight pull rifle with revolving bolt lock in 1895, following the introduction of the same design as a carbine in 1890.

Austria from 1888 on sometimes cross-manufactured with Germany on military designs, hence Mauser designs may be found with Austrian proofmarks. In 1914 Austria used a 7mm caliber Mauser to a limited extent.

In this same year of 1886 **France** introduced the **1886 Lebel,** the first of the smokeless powder bolt actions. This arm was a clumsy bolt action with tube below barrel, as undistinguished a rifle as even France has ever seen. But what the arms designers did not do, the French chemists more than made up for. The new smokeless powder wrought an immediate revolution in military arms design throughout the world. The French 1886 cartridge of 8mm caliber was the first small bore military cartridge officially adopted.

The **Berthier Carbine** adopted by **France** in 1890 was a bolt action using the Mannlicher clip magazine system, cal. 8mm. From 1907 the Berthier was issued in several styles. Essentially it is merely the carbine 1890 with a longer barrel. The design was made with both 3 and 5 shot magazines. The foregoing were the basic French rifles in both World Wars. Most models used the rimmed 8mm Lebel cartridge.

In 1934 a modified design was introduced with Mannlicher type turn-bolt action, but employing a staggered box magazine. The caliber was 7.5mm. In 1936 another model was introduced for this cartridge.

In 1887 **Norway** and **Sweden** officially adopted the undistinguished Jarman bolt action with tube below barrel, though it was several years before issue was complete. The tube held 8 cartridges of 10.5mm caliber, ballistics being about the same as other military arms of the period. This was merely the Jarman of 1880 with a tube below the barrel. The Krag-Jorgensen was adopted in 1894 by Norway, and the Swedes adopted the 1906 Mauser.

The **Italians** in 1887 adopted the *Vetterli-Vitali.* This arm was the Italian-made Vetterli bolt action mechanism built to take the Italian 10.4mm cartridge which was center fire (not rim fire as in the Swiss), and altered to take a fixed vertical box magazine. These rifles were made at Turin and at Terni. A magazine cut-off and a manual safety were provided. The queerly shaped box magazine design was a result of the spring type used. The magazine follower had a coil spring mounted below its center and this spring was seated in a projection at the bottom of the magazine. The Vitali magazine represented a modification of the Lee system. In 1891 the **Carcano M. 1891** was adopted in caliber 6.5mm Italian. This arm uses the Mannlicher magazine system, a turning bolt design of modified Mauser type, and a receiver designed by the Italian officer Carcano. While several carbine types were issued, no design changes were made from the time of introduction. As the M-38 the rifle was modified in 1938 to take an improved 7.35mm cartridge, but was issued only in limited quantity.

The Vitali box magazine modification was next applied to the Beaumont rifle in **Holland,** where it was called the 71/88. In 1895 the Austrian Mannlicher (also contract-made in Belgium) was adopted by Holland. This is not the Austrian Service straight pull type. It is a turning bolt design by Mannlicher using the Mannlicher magazine system. While this bolt system resembles the Mauser generally, it differs in having a detachable bolt head, with the two front locking lugs farther back than in the Mauser. The caliber is 6.5mm Dutch.

Chapter 6

THE DEVELOPMENT OF THE SEMIAUTOMATIC RIFLE

Before 1880

Just when or where the first inventor applied the forces of discharge to the task of reloading and cocking an arm, no man can positively say.

The authoritative official British *Textbook of Small Arms* (1929 Edition) considers that the automatic principle "appears to have been an English invention," on the basis of a fully authenticated entry in the records of the British Royal Society dated March 2, 1663. On that early flintlock day the record shows (see Birch's *History of the Royal Society*) that Sir Robert Moray, F.R.S., told the learned body that "there had come to Prince Rupert a rare mechanician who pretended . . . to make a pistol shooting as fast as could be presented and yet to be stopped at pleasure; and wherein the motion of the fire and bullet within was made to charge the piece with powder and bullet, to prime it and bend the cock."

It is true that no further mention of this remarkable arm has ever been unearthed by researchers, and that no weapon answering the description has come to light. But the entry is evidence that the automatic principle was grasped although its practical application was to be long delayed until the metallic cartridge made its appearance.

The March 4, 1664 entry in 'Pepys' *Diary*' may refer to either a repeating or a semiautomatic arm, as it is not explicit. It reads:

"There were several people trying a new-fashion gun brought by Lord Peterborough this morning, to shoot off often, one after another, without trouble or danger." No other contemporary record so far found adds to the information in this entry; but Pepys was quite a rifle enthusiast.

One can also point to the U. S. Patent No. 2998, dated 1863, of Regulus Pilon describing a system for recocking the hammer by barrel recoil; to the suggested gas-operated system of W. Curtis (U. S. No. 1810, year 1866); and to literally dozens of very early German, Austrian and Italian actual inventors' models of the early 70's. While all possess a modicum of historical value, their actual bearing on the later successful developments was practically nil.

1880-1885

The first practical approach to the semiautomatic rifle was made by an American, Hiram Maxim, in England. In 1881 and 1883 he worked out an elementary mechanical conversion for making a semiautomatic out of the Winchester 1866 and 1873 repeaters. These arms, it will be remembered, are locked by a toggle system operated by the triggerguard lever. Maxim worked out and patented a buttplate with a spring cushioned between it and the gun butt. In shooting, the buttplate rested against the shoulder while the spring thrust the rifle ahead in firing position. When the arm was fired the rifle recoiled and compressed the spring. A rod extending forward from the buttplate to the rear of the triggerguard, was brought sharply up against the triggerguard when the rifle recoiled. The triggerguard lever was thus pushed down a short distance. In the standard Winchester the length of that stroke would barely unlock the action. However, Maxim used a compound lever system within the receiver attached to the toggle levers. By this means a very short movement of the outside triggerguard lever was sufficient to (a) pull the toggle lock completely down; (b) thrust the breechblock all the way back to eject the empty and to cock and ride over the hammer. When the energy of the recoil had been spent, the spring between the buttplate and the rifle butt reacted. The entire rifle was thrust ahead. This forward movement of the rifle acted through the connecting rod to bring the triggerguard lever up into locked position, thereby loading and locking the arm.

This Maxim-Winchester received very wide attention in European military circles, and was applied to many Turkish Winchester .44's which may still be encountered abroad. The design went practically unnoticed in the United States. The design while interesting was not practical; but it was an early step by Hiram Maxim whose later machine guns changed the history of war.

In 1884 Maxim was granted his first basic patent for locked-breech, recoil operation. Since the patent applied to a machine gun, its consideration is not within the scope of the present book; but it requires mention as the first accepted use of the short-recoil principle which appears in reasonably successful rifles at a later date. Furthermore, the Maxim 1884 patent started a train of experiment and development—notably that of Mannlicher in Austria—which greatly speeded up automatic rifle design.

The Mannlicher 1885 is a short recoil action. It could be fired semi or full automatically. It was a crude looking shoulder arm with a pistol grip far forward. It has a pivoted accelerator operated by the barrel to give added flip to the breechblock as the barrel travel halts. It has a locking block which is cammed down and up on a block on the floor of the receiver to unlock and lock into recesses in the underside of the breechblock. It is cocked on rearward breechblock motion by a lever entering the breechblock and engaging with a cut in the striker. It has a recoil spring mounted in the receiver behind the breechblock. All these details are found in modified form in the Browning machine gun of 32 years later.

Browning did much of his work in Belgium where von Mannlicher's arms have been the subject of close study. However, Browning may never have seen one of the Mannlichers. Parallel development and honest duplication are commonly encountered factors in firearms, where little indeed is ever really new.

The developments of the next few years were entirely abortive. An early form of the long-recoil system of operation was outlined in the 1885 British patent specification of Schlund & Arthur; Paulsen's British specification for a gas piston operated revolver was along the lines of an arm still in the Museo de Armeria at Eibar, Spain, developed in that city in 1863; while attempts by various British and Continental gunsmiths to apply the automatic principle to the arms of the day, produced scores of freaks of no practical value.

Since 1885

With the arrival of smokeless powder in 1886 and the introduction of Swiss

Major Rubin's cupro-nickel jacketed bullet and its rimless solid drawn brass case, the semiautomatic rifle entered a new era.

Hiram Maxim was granted British patent specification No. 22859 in 1891. It reads in part "an arm which, though capable of being operated by hand, is provided with a simple and efficient automatic mechanism which the pressure of the powder gases in the barrel will operate to open the breech after a discharge, eject the spent cartridge and cock the firing pin, and re-close the breech on the insertion of a fresh cartridge in the chamber." The illustrations show clearly the application of his idea to the British Martini-Henry rifle system. It uses a short-stroke gas piston which however is entirely different in basic principle from that of the current U. S. Carbine M1. Gas taken off through a

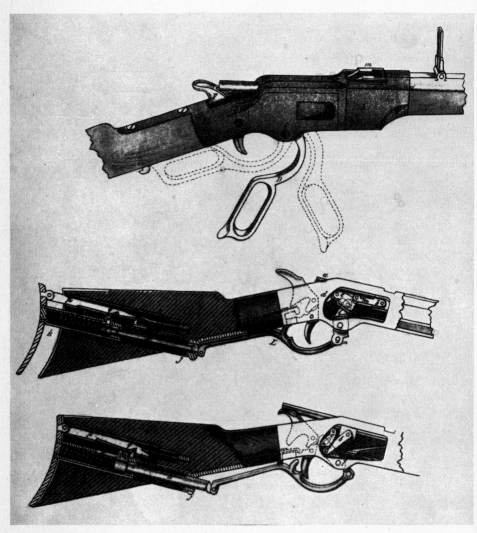

Hiram Maxim's first successful autoloader designed around an early Winchester.

barrel port close to the chamber drives a short piston which in turn operates the action. Maxim apparently did little or nothing with this principle.

Von Mannlicher in 1891 developed two new semiautomatic rifles, both operating on a modified version of the short recoil principle used in his 1885 type. The more successful was an arm quite modern in appearance even by today's standards. The recoiling barrel was mounted in a housing extending almost to the muzzle, a bolt handle projected from the right side to cock the arm and open the action, and the magazine was loaded with a standard Mannlicher 5-shot clip of cartridges. When the last shot had been fired the action was held open for reloading. The design was simple and quite efficient but it was never developed to such a degree of ruggedness and reliability as would make it suitable for military use.

John Moses Browning entered the field in 1889. The first Browning effort produced a lever rifle with a concave muzzle cap hooked up to a rod below the barrel which connected with the triggerguard lever of the rifle. When the arm was fired the forward blast of expanding gases behind the bullet pulled the cap and connecting rod forward thereby pulling the triggerguard lever and opening the action. (This principle was later utilized in the Danish Bang rifle of 1911, an arm brought to a high degree of perfection for U. S. Government tests by Captain (later Colonel) James L. Hatcher of the U. S. Ordnance Department).

Browning's second experimental model was a rifle with a small hole bored in the bottom of the barrel. Gas escaping as the bullet passed over the hole worked against a piston to operate a rod below the barrel which would function the lever mechanism. Out of this elementary design came the famous Colt Machine Gun, the "potato digger" of the Spanish American War. (The nickname derived from the fact that the gas blew a heavy hinged lever down at the front end to function the action, the lever cutting up the ground unless the gun was fired at the proper height.) By the time the famous Browning Machine Rifle of 1918 appeared, dozens of gas operated arms had been made, so we cannot honestly trace its derivation to these early experiments. Moreover, it must be stated that the Browning claim to "the first gas-operated automatic firearm ever invented" is not correct. The Eibar gas-operated revolver cited by the *British Textbook* has been definitely established as being correctly dated 1863, merely to mention one earlier type; while the French claims of the Clair Brothers who worked at St. Etienne, though discredited in many details, still can establish prior experimental gas types. John M. Browning was far too great an individual both as an inventor and as a man to need any undue claims made in his behalf; the record of his actual achievements is an unsurpassed milestone in successful arms development.

Von Mannlicher in 1893 came up with two semiautomatic rifles which he hoped would satisfy the military demand for a revolving bolt locked rifle. The first was an adaptation of his standard turning bolt magazine rifle modified for semi-automatic action. The customary bolt handle was first turned up to free the front bolt lugs from their recesses in the receiver, then was pulled straight back to eject. However, an extension to the rear of the bolt housed a powerful recoil spring which was compressed as the bolt went back. This coil spring was so designed that it exerted a twisting motion to the right to help keep the bolt closed. The barrel was firmly screwed to the receiver and did not recoil. The trick in the design was that the two forward bolt lugs were not the standard design which lock firmly in the receiver recesses. The dual lugs were cut to fit helical (or turning) grooves instead of the standard perpendicular grooves. In actuality, therefore, the breech was never actually locked—it was checked. When the cartridge was fired the thrust of the case against the face of the bolt was transmitted to the slightly curved lugs, and the turning motion started at once. Only the opposite torsion effect of the recoil spring tended to resist the opening. Once the lugs had turned down enough in the grooves to turn the bolt handle upright, the bolt was blown straight back to extract and eject, and to compress the recoil spring behind the bolt. The magazine spring fed a cartridge in line. The recoil spring reasserted itself and thrust the bolt forward to start a cartridge into the chamber. When the curved lugs hit the screw pitch in the receiver they turned the bolt into "locked" position.

The second rifle of this type was in effect the regular Mannlicher Model 90 straight-pull design with turning bolt, its lugs and grooves cut to compel the bolt head to start unlocking at the instant of firing as in the design just described.

These arms to all intents and purposes used the so-called "Blish principle" of our own day, a system which in theory provides a lock by adhesion at the instant of high pressure; but which actually is a "hesitation" device comparable to the common door check. In the 1920 to 1930 period a rifle on this principle was offered by General J. T. Thompson to the U. S. Ordnance Department, but was ultimately rejected. In 1928 the British found that the "Blish principle" was a chimera by the simple expedient of firing the Thompson submachine gun with its expensive "lock" and without it. No one could tell when the "lock" was in or when it was out.

Von Mannlicher in 1894 introduced two "blow forward" designs. Both the rifles embodied hesitation "locking" cams. The first of these rifles had an exposed hammer which required cocking for each shot. The breech was solid except for the hole through which the firing pin in the hammer nose passed. When the arm was fired, since the breech was solid, the force of the explosion forced the barrel forward, camming it first to the left in its casing. The barrel was pulled *off* the cartridge case which was then ejected. A heavy spring around the barrel was compressed. When the spring re-asserted itself, it drove the barrel to the rear picking up a cartridge from the magazine, and chambering it by forcing the head of the cartridge against the face of the standing breech as the barrel was revolved into its "hesitation" or "locking" threads.

The second arm of this design had a standing striker backed by a coil spring mounted behind the breech face, and the forward movement of the barrel served also to cock the striker.

Griffiths and **Woodgate**, two Englishmen, introduced in 1894 a short recoil rifle of simple design utilizing a barrel return spring around the barrel itself as well as an operating spring behind the bolt which served to close the action. The pivoted concealed hammer was operated by a V-flat spring. This design might have been better received at a later date, as it had many of the values of simplicity. Several other British specifications of this period cover automatic arms, but none achieved any importance.

Von Mannlicher in 1895 offered another rifle which had in it the essentials of greatness, but it was not until the perfection by John Garand of our M1 Rifle that the principles of the early Austrian master came into their own.

This 1895 had the following characteristics: (1) Gas operated locked breech. (2) Gas vent in underside of barrel leading to gas chamber to drive back piston positioned in tube below barrel. (3) Piston was hollow to receive operating spring, was bent at right angles towards the rear to form an operating rod; the rod section carrying the operating handle and cams to revolve the bolt. (4) Bolt was locked directly behind head of cartridge case, and was cammed up to unlock.

The arm differed from the Garand in that the bolt was cammed entirely up to the left on a hinge to open the breech; while in the modern arm the bolt is turned out of locking engagement and then driven back to ride over the hammer. (The Mannlicher 1895 had an exposed hammer which was cammed back to full cock by a sloping face on the bolt as it was raised). The Mannlicher was loaded through the top of the action with a regular Mannlicher clip which fell out the bottom of the receiver when the last cartridge was chambered. The Garand uses a modified Mannlicher clip which is loaded through the top of the action and which is ejected through the top as in Mannlicher's earliest design, when the last cartridge has been fired.

Mauser in 1898 introduced his first "Ruckstösslader mit beweglichem Lauf." This short recoil arm had a concealed hammer, standard Mauser box magazine, and an entirely new locking system. In this design twin locking cam levers are mounted in well extensions opposite the breech end of the barrel. Their surfaces lock into the head of the bolt when the action is closed, their tails engage the barrel. As the arm is fired the barrel and bolt recoil locked firmly together until cam faces on the locks hit sloping surfaces on the receiver housing and their forward surfaces are cammed out of bolt locking engagement. Thus the bolt is released from the barrel and moves to the rear, extracting the fired case and compressing the bolt return spring. The lock levers work essentially like a see-saw. These twin levers represent the earliest successful use of a locking principle which was modified to form the lock principle of the famous Russian Degtyarev LMG, and the lock of the gas operated rifles with which Germany ended the war—the rifles which came too late. (Meanwhile this locking principle has been further developed by Mauser himself, by Karl Brauning in the Netherlands and by Friberg and Kjellman in Sweden.)

Von Mannlicher's Model 1900 semiautomatic rifle was an interesting combination of design features. The revolving box magazine was loaded from a strip-in clip through the top of the action. The breech was solidly locked by a turning bolt. Gas was taken off quite close to the breech to drive back a short piston below the barrel. This short stroke piston had an angled prolongation which formed the operating rod. The unit had its own return spring. This rod section ran along the left side of the arm, and a cam stud on its forward end protruded through a cut in the left receiver wall to enter an opening in the body of the bolt. During initial movement of this piston-operating rod, the unit moved without affecting the bolt. However, as breech pressure dropped to safe limits, the cam stud on the operating rod hit a corresponding curved face in the bolt cylinder. This caused the bolt to rotate to the left out of locking engagement.

With the bolt unlocked, the operating cam stud was free to leave the bolt cylinder. The bolt continued back by itself and compressed the operating spring behind it, while it also ran over and cocked the pivoted hammer. Meanwhile, the separate return spring forced the piston back into place. The magazine spring revolved the spool to line up a cartridge for the closing stroke. At the appropriate point on forward motion, the curved cut in the wall of the bolt cylinder hit the cam face on the operating rod stud. This compelled the bolt to turn down and lock behind the head of the cartridge case.

Major Amerigo **Cei-Rigotti** of the 12th Italian Bersaglieri introduced in 1900 his interesting gas system. Compared with the standard Italian Carcano Model 1891 rifle design, the Cei-Rigotti weighs about the same but has the action further forward to protect the shooter. This is necessary since the bolt blows back and the handle shuttles in a straight line. Gas is tapped off into a cylinder on the underside of the barrel about midway along its length. The expanding gas drives back the piston which acts through a tappet to hit the operating rod of which the bolt handle is a part. Thus the bolt handle starts back in straight line until pressure drops. At that point a cam face on the attached operating rod acts on grooves in the bolt cylinder. The bolt cylinder rotates and turns its dual front lugs out of their locking seats in the receiver. The bolt then goes back in straight line with the operating rod. The action stays open when the magazine is empty. The box magazine was loaded from strip-in clips, some magazines holding 50 cartridges. In firing tests held at Rome June 13, 1900, the Cei-Rigotti delivered 300 rounds in one minute full automatic fire (the arm had a control switch affording both semi and full automatic fire). At the end of the 300 rounds of fire, the barrel was so hot the weapon could not be further used.

The essential gas operating principle of the Cei-Rigotti turned up in use by the Russians in 1936 and 1940 and in Germany in 1943 on semiautomatic rifles; the mechanism being mounted on top of the barrels instead of below.

Mauser introduced his "Ruckstösslader mit gleitendem Lauf" in 1902, a long recoil rifle to shoot the military cartridge. This arm was one of the forerunners of the Browning designed Remington automatic rifles. (Roth designed a long recoil military rifle in Austria as far back as 1899.) This was a box magazine, striker fired design. The cylindrical bolt was securely locked to the barrel by twin front locking lugs. The rifle barrel recoiled within a barrel casing when the arm was discharged. In this design the barrel traveled back locked to the bolt for the full length of the recoil stroke, then a separate barrel return spring pulled it forward. At this point an automatic catch held the breech bolt mechanism back. The barrel pulling on the bolt head caused the head to rotate until the lugs were freed. The barrel pulled forward off the empty case as it moved ahead. The case was ejected. The catch was then automatically released and the compressed spring behind the bolt drove it ahead to chamber a cartridge, rotate the bolt head and lock the action. Also in 1902 experimental work was done on gas operation using a muzzle blast cone. It was a failure then—as it was when tried in World War II on the 41 (M).

Winchester introduced in 1903 their first .22 semiautomatic rifle, an elementary blowback but still a design of outstanding worth. Its system of counterbalancing was sound enough to permit the principle to be applied in later years to the successful .32, .351 and .401 Winchester Self-Loading cartridges. These designs were developed by Thomas C. Johnson, a Winchester engineer whose name is too little known when one considers the success and ingenuity of his inventions.

Lieutenant **Friberg**, a lieutenant in the Swedish army invented about 1904 a short recoil rifle which did not receive the attention it deserved. Friberg died before perfecting the design, and the work was continued by **Rudolph Kjellman**, manager of the Stockholm Small Arms Factory. This rifle had the general characteristics of the Swedish 6.5mm Mauser, but was a short recoil arm locked by a perfected principle which disappeared until it turned up in the Spanish Civil War on the newly introduced Russian Degtyarev LMG. Germany, in a panic to supply huge quantities of low priced automatic arms as the war went against her, introduced a variant of this locking system in her famous LMG 42, and also embodied it in her Gew. 43 with gas operation.

In the Friberg-Kjellman we find for the first time the successful form of dual lever lock operated by the firing pin. Since the perfected type of this lock is covered in the later description of the German Gew. 43 and 41 (W) types, we do not need to describe it here. Upon its introduction it was explained with complete working drawings in the excellent Swedish "Tidskrift i Sjövasendet."

In 1904 Japanese Artillery Major **Nambu** and Infantry Captain Hino tested an automatic rifle before the Emperor, a description of the tests being given in issues of the German "Militär-Wochenblatt," of that year. The rifle was unsuccessful, but out of the experiments came the Japanese Nambu light machine gun.

Remington in 1906 introduced the Model 8, forerunner of the present Model 81, John M. Browning's long-recoil hunting rifle of medium caliber using rimless cartridges. Like the earlier Mauser 1902, this arm employs a turning bolt with dual lugs at the head. It is described in detail in Part III.

Soren H. Bang's rifle was tested in 1911 by our Ordnance Department and its performance was considered outstanding. The principle was originally patented by Hiram Maxim and constituted the basis of John M. Browning's first experimental semiautomatic rifle in 1889. A blast cone slid on the barrel at the muzzle. When the bullet passed out the muzzle the expanding gases pulled the cone (or cap) ahead a short distance. A rod leading from the cap to an appropriate lever below the barrel acted to throw the breechblock housing to the rear. Helical cuts on the inner surface of this housing acted on the opposing bolt surfaces to rotate the bolt out of locking engagement, then to carry it back for the ejecting stroke. The recoil spring closed the action and returned the blast cone to position for the next shot. While the Bang was the best of the auto rifles tested in 1911, its necessarily light weight barrel and its high production costs weighed against its adoption. It was tested again in improved form in the 1920s; and few army punsters ever knew how close they came to having "Bang" rifles issued to them.

France began active work on semiautomatic rifles with the Fusil B and Fusil C in 1911. Out of these experiments came the later St. Etienne rifles (popularly named for the Arsenal of manufacture and design) most noted of which were the M. 1917 and 1918. These arms were gas operated rotating bolt designs with box magazines. Clumsy and awkward, they were nevertheless weapons of consequence during World War I. They used the regular 8mm Lebel cartridge. The magazines were loaded with 5 shot clips resembling the Mannlicher style clips used in the French 1892 turn bolt carbines. The operating rod was a source of trouble, being completely exposed along the right side of the forearm.

From 1920 to 1930 further tests were conducted by our Ordnance Department on semiauto rifles. In 1920 the Bang rifle as modified and improved by Captain (later Colonel) **James L. Hatcher** was again up for trials. Lightened and strengthened, its lines considerably altered, the new model performed very well until a breakage occurred during the endurance tests. Withdrawn from the tests, it was recommended for further study. However, Hatcher was not allowed official time to work on the changes, and the Bang principle was allowed to drop.

John C. Garand introduced his primer-actuated semiautomatic in 1920. The Garand primer-operation system differed from any previously used. Before the turn of the century the Austrian inventor Roth had made rifles and pistols in which the action was primer operated, but they required special cartridges. Deep primer pockets were used in the special cartridges, and a very heavy striker was employed. When the arm was fired, the primer was blown back sharply against the striker. The striker, forced back inside the breechblock, was made to operate the unlocking mechanism. The unlocked breechblock then travelled back for the full recoil stroke. This design is essentially simple, requiring neither recoiling barrel nor gas port and piston.

Garand, realizing the impracticability of using special cartridges, designed a primer action for the regular service cartridge. The striker had a cup-shaped face which fitted over the primer. As the rifle fired the combination of primer pressure and gas pressure inside the case bulged the primer out against the striker. This blow pushed the striker back about .02 to .03 inch. This small motion was enough to actuate the lock. As the breech opened there was enough pressure still in the barrel to drive the action back its full stroke. Tests showed the system practical but the individual weapon as having certain structural weaknesses.

As a result of the showing made by this principle in an earlier design, Garand was hired by the Government and placed on the payroll at Springfield Armory to continue development of automatic arms.

J. D. Pedersen, another American arms designer whose name is not as well known as it should be, has to his credit such fine arms as the once popular M10 Remington shotgun and the M121 Remington line of slide action .22 repeaters; the High Power slide action rifles known as the M141; as well as the now discontinued Remington M51, and the famous World War I Pedersen Device. In view of his many successful firearms, Pedersen was in 1923 hired by the government to work at Springfield designing an entirely new semiautomatic rifle. Whereas up to this time all designers had been required to submit rifles chambered for the standard government cartridge, Pedersen, a great student of tactics, was allowed to design a new cartridge to go with his rifle to meet his advanced tactical ideas.

The Pedersen rifle was a "hesitation" rather than a true locked breech system. In general form the "lock" resembled the old Maxim and the Luger toggle systems in which jointed arms bend much after the fashion of the human knee. However, where the Maxim and Luger have recoiling barrels which are firmly locked to the breechblock by the toggles until the chamber pressure has dropped to a point where case extraction is easy, in the Pedersen the barrel was stationary. The toggle joint was a trifle above the center line of thrust to allow the recoil to function it. To prevent the buckling action from working dangerously fast, Pedersen used carefully designed cam surfaces in place of a straight hinge. These cam surfaces provided enough adverse leverage to slow the breech opening until reasonably safe limits had been reached. In designs of this sort, however, the action really starts to open, even though very slightly, at the instant of discharge. There is still enough pressure in the chamber to keep the walls of the cartridge case tight against the walls of the chamber. Extraction difficulties and ruptured cases result unless the cartridge cases are lubricated. Pedersen evolved a perfectly dry waxing process for the cartridges but there are many bona fide objections to the acceptance of a military weapon requiring lubricated cases and the Pedersen rifle was not accepted for this reason.

Despite the fact that his rifle was not acceptable, his cartridge, the 7mm (.276 Pedersen) was approved by the army for its eventual semiautomatic rifle; and arms entered in the the official 1929 tests were in this caliber, except for one Garand in the .30 government caliber. However, in 1931 the decision was made to hold to the original .30-'06 cartridge.

What is known to collectors as the **Pedersen Device** was one of the big ordnance secrets of World War I. Officially it was listed as "Automatic Pistol, Cal. .30, Model 1918" to hide its true nature.

The Pedersen device was a conversion to make a semiautomatic weapon of relatively low power but having considerable volume of fire out of the Springfield. It could be further converted to a full automatic with little difficulty. In form it was a complete receiver unit carrying a short rifled barrel and a blowback bolt mechanism which could be locked into the receiver of a Springfield or Enfield when the regular bolt was removed. The cut-off mechanism of the standard rifle was modified and served to lock the device in place. Its barrel was the exact length, size and shape of the regular rifle cartridge. When this device was installed, a special short .30 caliber pistol-type cartridge would chamber in it. A 40-round box magazine, double line, projected at a 45° angle to the barrel; and an ejection port had to be cut in the rifle receiver to line up with the ejection port in the device. Ejection was to the left. A trained operator could switch the bolt in his Springfield and install the Pedersen Device in about 15 seconds. Thus he had the advantages of the great power and magnificent accuracy of the Springfield for ordinary use plus the great speed and volume of fire of a 40-shot semiautomatic for short range work and in-fighting. At the close of the war it was decided that the additional weight, the danger of losing either the rifle bolt or the device, and a number of other military considerations outweighed the potential value of the Pedersen. The scheme was therefore dropped.

The 1929 Aberdeen tests quickly ruled out all experimental rifles except the Garand. However, MacArthur, Chief of Staff, disapproved the .276, so the Garand was developed for the .30-'06. In 1936 the Garand was officially adopted by the United States Army.

Julian S. Hatcher's *Book of the Garand* covers in detail the development and use of the Garand and other semiautomatic rifles.

Meanwhile only one important foreign design had been produced, despite considerable experimentation. That one was a gas operated rifle of trim lines and beautiful workmanship made in Czechoslovakia, which by the way, was in our 1929 tests in cal. .276 Pedersen. Its breechblock was a tilting block design. Officially known as the **Z. B. 29**, it was exported in some quantity. Most specimens to reach this country thus far have been rifles bought or captured in the Middle East. They were used to a limited extent in Ethiopia, and many bear the mark of the Lion of Judah.

Fortunately, **Germany** had been so wrapped up in the subject of light machine guns that her designers gave little heed to the semiautomatic rifle. It was only in 1940, when field reports of the effectiveness of the Tokarev used by the Russians brought home to them the value of that arm, that the Germans really gave attention to a new rifle. Mauser's abortive attempts at a recoil operated rifle, the success of the gas principle of the Krieghoff sporting rifle of 1936 and of the American and Russian arms, led Germany to consider the gas system. In 1941 the first clumsy attempts appeared—all using the blast cones over the muzzles to trap gas which rebounded to drive back operating rods along the barrels. All these rifles showed some characteristics of early Mauser designs in lockwork, receivers, locks or housings. Some were made by Mauser, some by Walther. The original issues, the 41M and 41W, are described later. By 1943 Germany had not only been sold on the value of the rifle, but had been further sold on the simplicity and ease of manufacture of the Russian gas system; and in that year she issued a crudely made but efficient arm, the Gew. 43 (later the Kar. 43 designation was applied to a slightly modified form). Adapting the Friberg-Kjellman locking system (which she was then using in principle on her LMG 42) to Russian gas operation, Germany turned out an arm which might have had a tremendous military future had it been made early enough to work the few bugs out of it, and to get it into the field in quantity.

Under the Czars **Russia** did little designing. With the coming of the Soviets a complete change occurred. A Small Arms School of real importance was set up, and out of it came the **Simonov** rifle in 1936, an arm issued as a semi and full automatic design. The gas system was simple and effective, but the wedge-locked breechblock was too complicated a design. The Russians found out their design weaknesses in the Spanish Civil War. In 1938 a new design, the Tokarev, appeared. This was followed by a modification in 1940. Russia has taken tremendous steps forward in rifle design.

In our own country, 1936 also marked the appearance of the first working model of the **Johnson** semiautomatic military rifle. Twenty-three models of this short-recoil rifle were made before production was started.

The Johnson earned the distinction of being the first really successful application of the short-recoil principle to a rifle. In 1940 differing schools of thought both in and out of the armed services clashed on the merits of the Johnson recoil operated as against the Garand gas operated rifle. By that time some 50,000 Garands were actually in use and the testing services had developed a large body of knowledge concerning the "bugs" likely to develop. Some important changes had already been made in the Garand. Granting some features of superiority in the Johnson design (notably the loading system) it was not practical to halt further production of the Garand at that time. The Garand was put into mass production at Springfield and a contract for manufacture was also placed with Winchester. The war record of the Garand more than justified all the hopes placed in the service adoption of a semiautomatic arm for the infantry.

Winchester offered in 1940 a new gas operated design to the U. S. Marine Corps for tests. The rifle used gas operation on the short stroke piston system of the later U. S. Carbine M1, which was also a Winchester design. Gas was taken off near the breech to drive the piston about .01 inch. The drive was transmitted to the operating slide which moved back to function the breechblock. The breechblock was rather like the famous old Savage rifle lock. It was a block lifted at the rear to lock. When in place it was supported by a wide steel surface behind the action opening. When fluted chambers were used, as in the Russian rifle design, extraction difficulties were minimized with unlubricated cases. The Marines did not adopt the rifle and it has not been put into production, though an improved form exists.

When it was decided in 1940 that a carbine would be a more efficient supplementary arm than the pistol for most troops the Ordnance Department selected a cartridge around which inventors were asked to build carbines within set specifications. Originally it was specified that the arm must weigh about 5.5 lbs., use a detachable box magazine up to 30-rounds capacity and fire semi or full automatic. Later the requirements were changed to semiauto only but a full auto also has since been adopted (the M2 Carbine).

The cartridge was practically identical with the original .32 Winchester Autoloading cartridge introduced in 1905 except for the use of a shorter and lighter bullet.

Auto-Ordnance Company, Harrington & Richardson, Hyde, Savage, Springfield Armory, Winchester and Woodhull submitted models. The Winchester locked-breech design was chosen, its locking action being very like the Garand, its gas operating system being the short-stroke used in the Winchester 1940.

The Winchester carbine was adopted and christened the **U. S. Carbine Caliber .30 M1.**

In **Germany** as the war neared its end several new designs in carbines appeared. The **M.P. 43** was actually the first "assault rifle" that was mass produced. It was a locked breech arm operated by gas. The magazine capacity was 30 cartridges. The cartridge was particularly noteworthy, as the German approach to its design was radically different from our own. The original case head and rim of the 7.92mm rifle cartridge was retained, the case was bottle-necked but shorter than the standard rifle case. The Spitzer (pointed) bullet design was retained, as was the caliber, but the bullet weight was reduced to about 125 grains. The cartridge was a big improvement ballistically over our own carbine cartridge.

After World War II many new semiautomatic and selective fire rifles were produced. They are covered under their countries of origin.

NOTE ON SOURCE MATERIALS

There are few books in English dealing in any way with even a small percentage of the evolutionary rifle forms just discussed. In view of that fact, this work seeks to consolidate all the essential data any average reader might reasonably want to know about them.

Before World War II the records of these weapons could be found in German, French, Spanish, Italian or Portuguese in most of the great libraries and museums abroad. Today few even of those sources are intact or generally available, while the magnificent private collections of the Continent have as a group been scattered or destroyed.

Of the literally hundreds of books and manuscripts consulted to form the foregoing digest, most were made available to me by foreign officials and collectors before the outbreak of World War II. The only titles of value available in America even at the Congressional Library are in German or French; and it is noteworthy that the authors of those works could find little material of value written in our language except on some strictly American developments.

The classic works of the period are *Die Geschichtliche Entwicklung der Handfeuerwaffen* by German Colonel von Thierbach and the *Allgemeine Waffenkunde für Infanterie* of the Swiss Colonel Schmidt. These works bring the subject up to the period of about 1885-1890. Colonel Schmidt's work also appeared in French as *Les Nouvelles Armes a feu Portatives*. The lesser works of French Commandant Jules Bonecque, especially *Les Armes a feu portatives* (Volume I published in 1894, Volume II in 1905 and Volume III in 1911), also deal in some detail with the arms of 1890-1910 in Europe in particular—very little consideration being given to U. S. developments.

Foreign service magazines of that period, notably the French "Revue d'Artillerie" the German "Militär Wochenblatt" and the Italian "Rivista di Artiglieria," carry many detailed accounts—often with excellent drawings—of arms of the time.

Among the libraries to which access was obtained for the preparation of the foregoing material were those used by Colonel Rudolph Schmidt in the writing of his classic works. Out of 83 sources which Schmidt considered important enough to quote for reference, only 1 was in English: (*Report of the Chief of Ordnance. Magazine Guns. 1878/81.* Secretary of War. Washington, D. C.) Furthermore, in the course of an exhaustive survey of the actual Mauser factory records dating to 1938, the only accounts published in English concerning Mauser history which the company felt were accurate or important enough to recommend were a minor item in the British magazine "Arms and Explosives" and a fine historical article by Col. (then Lt.) G. B. Jarrett in "Army Ordnance Magazine" in 1928.

PART II

Types of Rifle Actions

Chapter 7
SINGLE SHOT RIFLES

A single shot rifle, as its name implies, is a weapon having no mechanism for loading cartridges into the chamber from a magazine. It must be manually loaded for each shot.

Hinge Frame, Standing Breech

This type of rifle falls into two general classifications:

(*a*) Those of the original Maynard type in which pushing down the finger lever which forms the trigger guard releases the barrel at the breech, permitting the muzzle to hinge down from the fore-end for loading and unloading. In recent years only the discontinued Stevens low priced rifles in .22 caliber (of Marksman #12, and the Crack Shot #26 types) selling for a few dollars each have been manufactured in this design. The earlier Stevens "Pocket Rifles" utilizing the tip down barrel were unlocked as in the similar type of Stevens pistol. Pushing in a barrel release stud on the left side of the receiver permitted the breech to be hinged open. These designs all work loose in comparatively short order, and were never designed for use with powerful cartridges. The only quality American rifle of hinge frame construction currently made is the hammerless single shot Savage Model 219. This is actually a shotgun action fitted with a rifle barrel of .22 Hornet, .25/20, .32/20 or .30/30 Center Fire rim case caliber.

(*b*) The hinge frame type with top thumb lever, side thumb lever, or finger lever around triggerguard. These forms were widely manufactured in Europe and in England. They are based on the best European shotgun locking designs, such as the Greener, Purdey and Westley Richards. Arms of this type manufactured in England, and in all the gun centers on the Continent, may be encountered in any caliber, and may rank in quality from poor to excellent. They may be found with exposed hammer, concealed hammer, side lever hammer, or striker firing mechanisms. Arms of this general type have never been mass-produced for sporting or target use in the U. S.

Solid Frame, Dropping Breechblock

The basic design has many variants. Roughly they may be classified into:

(*a*) "high sidewall" receivers in which the receiver walls rise to the top of the barrel and completely support the breechblock at the moment of discharge.

(*b*) "low sidewall" receivers which do not reach all the way to the top of the barrel and which support the breechblock only to a point approximately in line with the bore.

(c) exposed hammers with a firing pin operating through the breechblock.

(d) "hammerless" with the firing mechanism in the breechblock.

All are lever-action. In some the lever is shaped to form the triggerguard. In some a separate lever is used, placed under the grip. In others a small lever is placed on the right side of the receiver.

The only rifles of this design in general production in the United States in recent years were the Stevens Walnut Hill line in .22 and .25 Stevens rim fire calibers.

However, the dropping block in its many modifications was a favorite with Austrian, German and Swiss gunsmiths before the outbreak of World War II.

In this general design the side walls of the receiver are mortised or grooved for the solid breechblock which slides in a vertical or nearly vertical plane, dropping down on movement of the opening lever to expose the chamber for loading. In some actions the extractor withdraws the cartridge only far enough to permit the head of the case to be grasped by the fingers and withdrawn by hand. In other actions the extractor is spring-actuated so that it mechanically ejects the empty case.

In the closing action of this breech mechanism, the face of the breechblock slides closely along the head of the cartridge case, and the breechblock is solidly supported against the shoulders of the mortise in the receiver in which the block travels. The best of these designs are provided with vents in the top of the breechblock to permit escape of gas in the event of a pierced primer or a blown head.

The German Aydt dropping block differs from the typical vertical dropping block rifle in that the actual breechblock is somewhat curved and has an extension hinged below and ahead of the chamber. When the triggerguard lever is lowered (this system may also be encounterd with side lever operation) it draws the breechblock down in an arc. The rear of the breech is so shaped that it provides a lock in the form of a somewhat curved wedge. This locking type has been widely used in connection with precision target rifles in all European countries, being a favorite of the fine Haenel gun factory in particular.

Flobert Rolling Block

The Flobert rolling block is one of the earliest of the breech loading designs. When the hammer is drawn back by the thumb, a pivoted breech piece having a projecting catch may be drawn back to expose the breech for loading. This design is generally used only with parlor cartridges or .22 Shorts. When a cartridge is inserted and the breech piece is pushed forward, pulling the trigger drops the hammer to fire the cartridge in the chamber. The breech piece may be pierced to permit the firing pin point of the hammer to pass through or the breech piece itself may carry an independent firing pin which is struck by the falling hammer. In any event, the breech closure in this design is very weak and is not intended for high powered loads. It will be found in European rifles usually of Belgian or French manufacture for the various types of 4mm, .177, 6mm and .22 cartridges and caps used in European indoor shooting. As late as the 1930s, both Remington and Stevens manufactured low-priced .22 RF rifles using this action.

Rising Block

The Belgian Flobert-Warnant lock is the only example of this design manufactured in recent years on a wide scale. When the hammer is cocked, the breechblock having two arms projecting forward along the sides of the barrel may be lifted. The arms are pivoted forward on barrel pins. Lifting the breech-block automatically operates the extractor.

Variations of this design used on German export arms carry the striker assembly in the breechblock. The cocking piece projecting from the rear of the breechblock is pulled back manually to cock the gun. These are customarily .22 caliber rifles or light European calibers.

Falling Block

The falling block action first successfully employed in the American Peabody and modified by the Swiss Martini is today manufactured only in England and on the continent. It is commonly referred to as the "Martini" action.

In this lever action design the breechblock is hinged high at the rear. When the lever is lowered, the front end of the block falls to expose the chamber. Modern actions of this type are of the "hammerless' type.

Expensive rifles of this type made by Francotte in Belgium and Vickers, B.S.A. and Greener in England have a removable breechblock which can be easily removed for cleaning. The Swiss Haemmerli is similar.

Bolt Action Locks

By far the most common design in modern single shot actions is the familiar turn-bolt action. The bolts may carry lugs for forward locking in expensive designs but in general a square shoulder at the base of the bolt handle serves as the locking lug when the bolt is closed and the handle turned down into its recess in the receiver. Scores of minor variants exist.

Chapter 8

REPEATING RIFLES

The term "repeating rifle" commonly means any rifle equipped with a magazine. The "repeater" may be of the lever action; slide, pump or trombone action; bolt action or semiautomatic type. The magazine may be of the tubular type placed either in the stock or under the barrel or it may be of the spool or box type built into the receiver.

Magazine Types

Tubular magazines. One advantage of the tubular magazine is that it provides the maximum capacity possible without spoiling the general appearance of the gun. It is the most efficient form for cheap "plinking" rifles.

The disadvantages of the tubular magazine are numerous.

(1) Slow loading. The cartridges must be loaded one at a time. They cannot be loaded from a charger clip. Galleries may use tube chargers.

(2) Dirt and failure to feed. Grit, lint, rust, gumming oil accumulations or accumulations of bullet lubricant are impossible to see and difficult to keep cleaned out of the long slender magazine tube. The long spiral magazine spring is under heavy compression when the tube is filled with cartridges but when only one or two cartridges are left in the magazine the spring is under relatively light compression and it does not require a very large obstruction to jam the cartridges in the tube—particularly if the magazine spring is an old one. When the magazine tube is exposed below the barrel it may be dented or bent just enough to cause the follower to hang irregularly and thus cause irregular feeding. The feeding may be poor when the gun is cold but may be all right when the gun has been warmed near a stove or by a hot noon-day sun.

(3) Danger of "didn't know it was loaded" accidents. For the reasons just mentioned it is possible to operate the action of a tubular magazine arm several times without any cartridge feeding out of the magazine. It will be naturally assumed that the gun is empty. However, the very next time the action is operated a cartridge may be chambered by having broken loose from the spot where it was jammed in the tubular magazine. Such occurrences are probably the greatest single cause of the tragic "I didn't know it was loaded" story. It is easy enough to open the action and see whether there are any cartridges in a box or spool type magazine but no such easy visual examination is possible with the tubular magazine.

(4) Danger of cartridge explosion in the magazine. Rimless cartridges with pointed bullets should not be used in the normal tubular magazine because the pointed bullet of the rearmost cartridge will bear against the primer in the cartridge ahead and a sharp jolt might fire the cartridge in the magazine. Some tubular magazines are designed with a "twist" effect so that the points of the bullets are held off-center in the tube and cannot impinge on the primer ahead.

(5) Change of balance. Obviously the center of balance of the gun will be much farther toward the muzzle when the underbarrel tubular magazine is

crammed full of ammunition than when only one or two cartridges remain in the magazine.

The action of the tubular magazine is simple. The cartridges are loaded into the tube one by one, steadily compressing the spiral magazine spring. Loading may be through a slot in the side of the receiver or in the lower end of the tube or, by withdrawing the magazine tube from its place in the stock or under the barrel it may be loaded by pressing the cartridges directly into the open rear end of the tube. When the loaded magazine is inserted in the gun the magazine spring presses the cartridges toward the action. When the action is opened, a gate or port at the end of the magazine tube opens and a cartridge is pressed onto or into the carrier or elevator which raises the cartridge into position in front of the chamber. As the action is closed the cartridge is pushed into the chamber ready to be fired.

Box type magazines. These magazines are built into the receiver of the gun. Basically they consist of (1) the magazine well which is the square-sided hole milled through the receiver from top to bottom immediately to the rear of the breech face of the barrel; (2) the magazine floor plate which is the steel plate that completely or partially closes the bottom of the magazine well; (3) the magazine spring which pushes the cartridges up into position for loading into the chamber; (4) the follower which is the steel platform mounted on top of the magazine spring. The follower is the platform on which the bottom cartridge of the stack rests in a box magazine. In all .22 rim fire weapons of the box magazine type the floor plate, spring and follower are all incorporated in the removable "clip" or box magazine which is loaded and then inserted into the magazine well where a magazine catch holds it in place. Several center-fire semi-automatic rifles use this same type of detachable box magazine. In most high-powered weapons various forms of clips or chargers are used to charge the magazine which is built into the receiver. In any case the fundamentals of the box magazine are the four features above mentioned.

Spool or Rotary type magazines. These are basically similar to the box type magazine. Instead of the horizontal follower on which the cartridges are stacked there are a series of concave troughs mounted radially around a spindle or spool. These troughs are so spaced that each cartridge rides in its own cradle. The spool is actuated by a coiled spring which is compressed as the cartridges are pressed into their troughs one after another. The magazine well is milled out with concave side walls and a concave floor plate to accommodate the rotary form of magazine. The rotary type magazine may be loaded by inserting single cartridges one after another or the cartridges may be stripped into the magazine out of a charger clip similar to those used for charging some types of box magazines. The rotary magazine is advantageous when rimmed cartridges are used. Each cartridge is carried in its own follower and it is therefore impossible for a loading jam to be caused by the rim of one cartridge locking over the rim of another. With modern rimless cartridges the simpler, less expensive box type magazine has almost eliminated manufacturers' interest in the rotary.

Krag-Jorgensen box magazine. This design is found only on the Danish, Norwegian and obsolete United States Krag service rifles. This design consists of a box below the action, having a bulky door or gate projecting from the right side of the receiver. The gate is hinged and has a projection to permit it to be turned out by the thumb to expose the magazine proper. (In U. S. and Norwegian design it hinges down; in Danish design it hinges out on a forward hinge.) Loose cartridges are dropped into the magazine, and the gate which contains the feeding arm is snapped up into place. A lever operated by a spring behind it in the outer wall of the gate acts to force cartridges ahead into line for feeding. (See Krag-Jorgensen under *United States* and also under *Denmark* for details of this action.) The sole advantage of the Krag-type of magazine is that it permits loading with individual cartridges while keeping the action closed. This is a theoretical advantage since it enables one to keep the chamber loaded ready for instant action and yet to reload the magazine to capacity at any time during battle use. It is impossible to speedily load this arm, since clips designed for it are necessarily cumbersome.

Harris box type magazine. This design was experimented with in England and will be found on a number of sporting rifles made abroad by custom builders. It is not used in the U. S. The Harris is fitted with a small thumb piece on the side of the fore-end which can be pushed down by the thumb to force the magazine follower down and compress the magazine spring. This permits cartridges to be dropped into the magazine through the open action instead of having to force them down against the pressure of the magazine spring.

Ross magazine. The original Ross rifles adopted by Canada for military use employed magazines with followers attached to a lever which was pivoted in the fore-end below the rear sight. The finger piece on the lever projected to the right. Pressing it down lowered the magazine follower and compressed the magazine spring. Essentially this was the Harris design.

Types of Repeating Rifle Actions

Following are the successful modern systems of repeating rifle actions.

Lever actions. The obvious feature of the lever action is the lever pivoted below the receiver, incidentally forming the triggerguard, which must be swung down and forward in order to open and close the action. Lever actions may employ either an exposed hammer or "hammerless" design. The magazine may be of the tubular, box or rotary type. The breechblock in lever action repeaters is an oblong steel block carrying the extractor and firing pin. It is locked and unlocked by the action of the operating lever. The breechlock in some models is locked into firing position by being solidly wedged between the face of the breech and the rear wall of the receiver. In other models square shouldered locking bolts are raised to engage in locking grooves cut into the side of the breechblock and into the side walls of the receiver. In neither case is the breechblock supported by locking lugs placed at the face of the block where the rearward pressure of the fired cartridge must be first absorbed. As a result of the elasticity of the steel in the breechblock and in the comparatively thin side walls of the receiver there is a great deal more "give" in a lever action than in the Mauser type of bolt action with bolt locking lugs at the head of the bolt.

The Winchester Model 88 lever action bolt is a rotating frontally-locked type and therefore suitable for high pressure cartridges.

Because of the long linkage required to handle cartridges of the .30/40 and .30/06 type the lines of most lever action rifles cannot be quite so clean around the receiver as the bolt actions and this has probably also caused many shooters to prefer the bolt type for the bigger, higher pressure cartridges, a good thing since most lever action locking systems are relatively weak.

Slide, "pump" and "trombone" actions. It is hard to understand why the popular term "pump gun" should have come to be so generally applied to the horizontally operating slide action instead of to the up-and-down operation of the lever actions but for some reason "pump gun" means slide action to practically all American shooters. "Trombone action" is the second most popular term used to refer to slide action weapons. Few shooters ever use the technical description which is "slide action."

The slide action is a simple, sturdy, solid-locking type of action with the one great defect of completely lacking leverage to aid in extracting fired cases. This, more than any other factor probably accounts for the fact that only one slide action rifle is made to handle medium powered center fire ammunition, all other "pump guns" are either .22 rim-fires or shotguns.

Most slide actions currently in production utilize the below-the-barrel tubular type magazine. They may be of either the exposed hammer or "hammerless" type.

The obvious feature of the slide action weapon is the "streamlined" appearance of its receiver and the slideable fore-end mounted around the tubular magazine. The operating rod or "action bar" extends from the fore-end or "slide handle" backward under the barrel through a slot in the receiver to the breechblock. A stud on the rear end of the action bar rides in a camming slot in the side of the breechblock, as the slide handle (fore-end) is pulled rearward the action bar lug is forced backward in its slot in the breechblock and the sloping slot cams the breech-block up (or down) thereby disengaging the locking lug from its seat in the receiver. As the rearward push is continued on the action bar the unlocked breechblock is moved rearward to extract and eject the fired case, cock the gun, and raise a new cartridge from the magazine. Moving the slide forward then pulls the breechblock forward and pushes the cartridge off the carrier into the chamber. The lug on the action bar comes up against the camming section of its slot and cams the locking lug into its recess in the receiver completely chambering the cartridge and locking the breech for firing. In some slide actions the breechblock is cammed upward at its forward end in order to disengage its locking lug. In some actions the breech block is forced downward at its forward end to unlock it. Regardless of operating variants the basic principle is the same—unlocking, extracting, reloading, relocking are all done by the "manpower" exerted on the sliding fore-end without the aid of the leverage afforded by the pivoted lever of the lever-action or by the carefully designed cam-and-lever system of the bolt actions.

Bolt actions. The obvious feature of the bolt action weapon is its low, cylindrical receiver snugly cradling the steel bolt, the handle of which projects to the right over the receiver wall—either in a straight, business-like fashion or in a graceful but sturdy curve hugging the stock just above the triggerguard. The bolt action, more than any other, bespeaks rugged, compact efficiency.

There are two principal types of bolt actions. The turn-bolt and the straight-pull type.

The turn-bolt is the more common type. Lifting the bolt handle rotates the locking lugs on the bolt cylinder out of engagement and starts cartridge extraction. Pulling the bolt handle to the rear extracts and ejects the fired case. The forward stroke strips a cartridge from the magazine and thrusts it into the chamber. Turning the bolt handle down engages the locking lugs in their recesses in the receiver and locks the action. In the straight-pull type, pulling the bolt handle straight back unlocks the action, extracts and ejects. Pushing the bolt handle straight forward reloads and locks the action.

The turn-bolt. In the field of turn-bolt actions the Mauser patterns have been most generally followed. These fall into two categories: 1) High power types in which the bolt cylinder is a one-piece unit bored out from the rear for insertion of the striker and having dual opposed locking lugs machined on the front end of the bolt cylinder. 2) .22 Rim Fire designs in which, because of the low power of the cartridges used, it is feasible to dispense with the forward locking lugs and to utilize a squared surface of the bolt handle where it turns down into a cut in the receiver as the locking element. (Note: Some target-grade .22s are front-lug locked as in the high power designs. Also, occassional rifles like the Savage-Stevens may have a single front lug; or in other designs a middle lug.)

In all Mausers designed after 1898 a third locking lug is provided on the bolt to the rear of the magazine. When the bolt handle is turned down this lug seats near the forward edge of the receiver bridge. It is intended as a safety feature in the unlikely event of the two front lugs failing to hold. Another very important characteristic of the Mauser design which is carried over into the best forms of American rifles is the system of gas vents provided in the bolt to relieve pressure in the firing pin hole in the event a ruptured primer or cartridge case allows gas to blow back inside the hollow bolt. Mausers and all good American types are also fitted with special features to prevent the firing pin from being blown back to injure the shooter in the event of such a cartridge failure.

Another outstanding characteristic of the Mauser bolt action design is the application of the camming principle to cocking and to the primary extraction of the fired case. In general this type of turning bolt action, operating on the principle of the inclined plane, will afford approximately six times the extracting power of the typical lever action rifle.

In actions of the Mauser design the extractor, whether over the rim of the case or in a cannelure, is grasping approximately 25% of the circumference of the head of the case. As the bolt turns, the extractor is held immovably *(except in Italian and Belgian 1889 types)* and as the bolt handle rides up the cam face or inclined plane of the receiver bridge and rotates the lugs out of locking engagement, it starts the entire bolt assembly back far enough to unfreeze the cartridge case from the chamber.

The system of cam cocking causes the lifting movement of the bolt handle to pull the firing pin back into the bolt body away from the primer; and to partially compress the mainspring. When the handle is turned down the camming motion completes the compression of the mainspring and cocks the piece.

The Remington 721 design is an advanced Mauser form. By utilizing a new spring extractor set into the bolt face, this design permits complete sealing of the case head.

The Danish Krag-Jorgensen system of single forward locking lug used in the

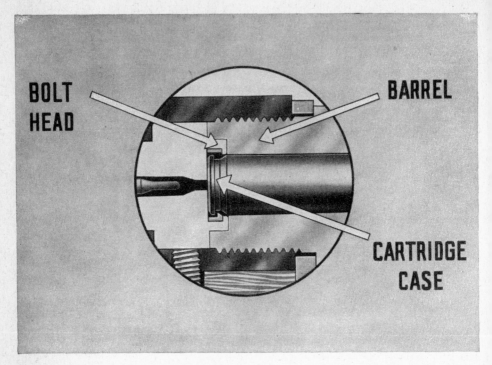

Bolt Head in Remington 721 and 722 is completely encircled and enclosed by the barrel. There is no extractor or ejector cut in the face of the bolt, as the design utilizes a spring-loaded plunger (as in the Garand) for an ejector; and a special spring extractor set into the face of the bolt itself.

While these features are remarkable for simplicity of manufacture and operation, and are new on commercial U. S. rifles, the principles themselves are old. The ejector system was old when it appeared on the Garand and the fully enclosed bolt head feature was used on .22 caliber French Army Trainer Rifles on the Lebel system as early as 1890. The extractor system was used experimentally by Krieghoff and by Simson in Germany, and a version of it occurs on some German and Austrian pistols. However, the effective combination of these features plus modern mass manufacturing methods make this new Remington a remarkable firearms achievement.

obsolete U. S. Rifle Model 1898 (Krag) was also used on the Danish and Norwegian service rifles.

The Austrian Mannlicher turning bolt is bored out from the front and has a separate screwed-in bolt head which compels placing the dual front lugs further back on the bolt cylinder than in the Mauser pattern. This construction permits manufacturing the bolt at lower cost than the standard solid Mauser one-piece design. However, as a result of this type of construction, the Mannlicher locking lugs are further back from the head of the cartridge case than the one-piece design. This requires a longer receiver for a given cartridge than the Mauser design. The two-piece bolt with its coupling devices is not as rugged as the one-piece Mauser. Except for some custom built rifles on Mannlicher actions, this bolt design is found only on Dutch, Greek, Hungarian, Siamese and Roumanian service Mannlichers.

The French service bolt (Lebel) and the Russian service (Mosin-Nagant) designs with dual lugs on a detachable bolt head assembled to the front of the bolt cylinder do not appear in other designs. The two are alike in principle but different in design. The British Lee bolt has a removable head and a single rear lug, plus locking support from a bolt rib.

Straight-pull bolts for high power arms are variants on a few basic patterns. The most successful pattern employs dual locking lugs which are turned in and out of their locking seats by the operation of feathers sliding in helical grooves as the bolt handle is moved forward and backward. Another less successful pattern employs a wedge type locking lug which is cammed in and out of engagement in its locking seat by the forward and backward motion of the bolt handle. Obviously two-piece bolts are essential to the mechanical operation of any straight-pull bolt design.

Typical of the wedge-type locking lug are the Austrian Model 1886 (11mm), the model 1888 (8mm black powder) and 1888-90 (8mm smokeless powder)—all the same rifles except as modified to take the cartridges indicated. These designs have two-piece bolts, the rear section sliding into a hollow in the front section. On the front section, a wedge is hinged to the underside near the rear. The bolt handle is a part of the rear bolt section. When the bolt handle is pushed forward the rear section of the bolt moves forward inside the cylindrical front section pushing the entire bolt assembly and chambering a cartridge. As the cartridge is chambered the hinged locking block on the underside of the forward section of the bolt is forced down into its seat in the receiver below it. A flange on the underside of the rear section of the bolt (the handle cylinder) forces the block into its locking seat.

Pulling the bolt handle straight to the rear starts the rear section (or handle cylinder) back and its flanged under piece raises the hinged locking block out of its receiver seating. From that point the complete bolt assembly travels straight back in the receiver guides.

This design does not give primary extraction. The jerking motion on the bolt handle, since it starts the rear section moving and then exerts a sudden pull on the forward locked section, assists extraction. However, this is the poorest of all the straight pull designs.

Typical of the more successful rotating locking lug patterns are the Austrian Cavalry Carbine Model 1890 and Infantry Rifle Model 1895.

In these designs, a bolt head bearing two opposed locking lugs at its forward end telescopes inside the rear bolt cylinder of which the handle is a part. The cocking, firing and extracting units are housed within the assembly. Two helical feathers inside the rear bolt cylinder work in appropriate grooves cut on the face of the forward bolt-head section. The bolt cylinder with the bolt handle attached can travel only in a straight line in the receiver guides. As the bolt handle is pulled back (the bolt head being securely locked in the receiver by its two locking lugs), the helical feathers inside the cylinder pulling back in the curved cuts in the rear section of the bolt head compel that unit to rotate. This disengages the lugs from their seats in the receiver. From this point the entire bolt assembly is free to travel straight to the rear. It will be seen that the turning motion is effected on the same principle as the common automatic screwdriver in which the handle is hollow and is equipped with feathers travelling in helical grooves in the shaft to which the bit is attached so that when pressure is applied to the handle the screw driver bit revolves.

The Canadian Ross rifle was an attempt to combine the straight-pull, sliding bolt sleeve idea with the strength of the Mauser dual locking lugs at the head of the bolt. The bolt proper is a single unit with dual lugs at the forward end. On late models the solid lugs were changed to the interrupted thread type of multiple lugs. The forward face of one lug was provided with a cam surface to aid primary extraction. A hollow bolt sleeve carrying the bolt handle enclosed the stem of the bolt proper.

The operating principle is the same as the Austrian Mannlicher. As the handle is drawn to the rear, curved ribs on the sleeve in contact with corresponding grooves on the bolt compel the bolt to revolve until its lugs are unlocked and then to travel back in a straight line with the bolt assembly.

The Swiss Schmidt-Rubin rifle is a rather complicated straight pull bolt having three main operating parts instead of two. It suffers from the fact that locking is done far back from the head of the cartridge case. The locking lugs are carried on a bolt sleeve which is mounted around the rear of the bolt. The third unit is an action rod to which the bolt handle is attached. This is inserted in the bolt assembly from the rear. The forward rim of the bolt sleeve bears against a flange on the bolt. At the rear the sleeve is held in place by a collar on the bolt.

A rearward pull on the bolt handle draws the action rod backward through the bolt assembly. A spur on the rod travels straight back in a straight cut in the locking sleeve for a short distance then comes against the helical portion of the slot, thereby rotating the bolt sleeve in the same basic mechanical fashion as in the Mannlicher and Ross bolts. The dual lugs on the exterior surface of the bolt sleeve are of course turned out of their locking seats and the entire bolt assembly then moves rearward to extract and eject the fired cartridge case. Forward motion of the bolt handle moves the bolt assembly ahead chambering a cartridge and rotating the lugs into their locked position.

The last Swiss straight pull rifle—the Model 31—has an entirely different type straight pull bolt. The bolt sleeve has been converted into the bolt proper and bears frontal locking lugs.

Occasional cheap arms may be encountered where a bolt is pulled out of locking engagement to the right, then drawn straight back to draw the breech mechanism to the rear.

Semiautomatic (Selfloading and Autoloading) Action Types

Most actions which the average shooter refers to as "automatics" are in fact semiautomatic actions. Real automatic actions are the type used in machine guns. Semiautomatic actions are divided into three basic types (1) Blowback, (2) Recoil operated, (3) Gas operated. Each of these basic types has one or more variations.

The blowback action is the simplest, cheapest and therefore most popular form of semiautomatic system for cartridges in the field of the .22 Rim Fire.

This design is inertia locked. In its most common form it consists merely of a relatively heavy breechblock, free to shuttle back and forth in the receiver, being driven to the rear by the thrust of gases within the barrel forcing back the head of the cartridge case against the face of the breechblock. The breech-block is driven forward by the recoil or operating spring which is compressed during the rearward movement of the breechblock assembly. A variant is the new British B.S.A. utilizing a radial moving block.

While this system is elementary, its successful employment requires a study of the ballistic and mechanical factors involved in order to insure proper timing.

At the instant of firing, when the highest pressure is generated, the expand-ing gas acting against the side walls of the case thrust it firmly against the chamber walls. The forward pressure starts the bullet down the barrel. The rearward pressure forcing the case head back against the heavy breechblock immediately starts the opening movement, although the movement is so slow in relation to the bullet travel that the bullet is out of the barrel before the breech has opened appreciably.

The resistance factors involved (the weight of the parts to be moved, friction, and the power necessary to compress the recoil spring) must be regulated within close limits for the specific type of ammunition employed. Slow timing may result in the breech assembly offering too much resistance to opening and hence jamming the rifle by not travelling back far enough to eject and reload. On the other hand fast timing in which the resistances are not heavy enough is also serious. The explosion may blow the action back so violently that the extractor may tear the head off the cartridge in trying to remove the case while it is still expanded against the walls of the chamber; the recoil will be unnec-essarily severe and the breechblock and receiver will take an unnecessary beating from the violence of the action.

All American made arms of this type are of good design and are reliable with the ammunition for which they are designed.

"Floating chamber" variants such as that made by Remington utilize a chamber long enough for the .22 short cartridge to blow some gas into a loose chamber joint. The chamber piece is thus blown back with the case, affording a greater area of thrust to drive the breeckblock back against forces normally too powerful for the cartridge to overcome. When .22 Long Rifle cartridges are used, their cases extend past and seal the chamber joint, the more powerful cartridge being "timed" to operate the action without benefit of added "floating chamber piston" power.

The so-called "delayed" or "retarded" blowbacks utilize various devices such as cams, screw-pitch lugs, curved or sloping surfaces in the receiver, etc., to prevent the breech opening as rapidly as with the straight blowback action.

A new type delayed blowback action was developed in Germany toward the end of World War II. This mechanism consists of a two-piece bolt. The front piece of the bolt contains two vertically mounted roller bearings. These bearings are cammed into grooves in the receiver by the forward movement of the firing pin, which is caused in turn by the forward movement of the rear portion of the bolt. The rear portion of the bolt is approximately four times the weight of the forward portion of the bolt. This action has been used successfully with high-powered cartridges. The neck and forward section of the chamber are fluted to ease case extraction. This locking system is used on the Swiss Model 57 assault rifle, the Spanish Model 58 assault rifle, and the West German G3 assault rifle.

Recoil actions. *In short recoil actions* the barrel and the breechblock are free to slide in horizontal guides for a short distance (about .375 to .750 inch) firmly locked together. When the gun is fired the barrel and breechblock recoil together until the barrel strikes a stop in the receiver and its rearward movement is halted. By this time the chamber pressure has dropped so that the cartridge case has released its grip on the walls of the chamber and extraction is feasible.

At this point, the operation of cam surfaces unlocks the breechblock from the halted barrel. The breechblock then travels straight back to extract and eject the empty case, cock the hammer and compress the recoil spring. When the breechblock completes its rearward travel the recoil spring drives it forward to load a new cartridge and to cam its locking surfaces into their seats in the barrel. Some types use strikers instead of hammers.

In the field of long recoil actions, the only successful rifle design is an American invention. Browning's first patents on his long recoil rifle were filed in 1900. A few years later the rifle was made in Belgium by F. N., European holder of Browning's patents. The original Remington Model 8, first introduced in 1906, was a slightly modified version of the Belgian. The modern version of this arm introduced in 1937 is known as the Model 81. The two designs differ only in detail. The European output never approached that of the Remington.

According to the official Browning history, John M. Browning first began work with the long recoil system of operation about 1900. Mauser and other European designers were working along similar lines at that time. While theirs used full power military cartridges and were not successful, Browning concentrated on *medium power sporting* cartridges and designed an excellent sporting rifle.

The short recoil action permits mounting the barrel in a very short housing but the long recoil system requires an extended barrel jacket or casing.

As the arm recoils on being fired, the breechblock (or bolt) locked to the barrel travels back through its housing for the entire length of the recoil stroke. This recoil stroke extends over the entire width of the magazine. At that point a catch engages the bolt and holds it firmly. The barrel return spring now asserts itself to draw the barrel ahead.

As the barrel exerts a pull on the bolt head (which is still locked securely to it), spiral grooves in the sides of the bolt compel the bolt to turn thus disengaging the locking lugs. The freed barrel is driven ahead and the extractor in the face of the still stationary bolt pulls the empty cartridge case out of the chamber. As the barrel reaches its forward position it trips a catch which releases the breechblock. The compressed recoil spring behind the breechblock now asserts itself to drive the block forward, chamber a cartridge and rotate the locking lugs into their seats in the rear of the barrel.

Gas operated actions are those in which a small volume of the expanding gases rushing down the barrel behind the bullet are allowed to expand into an auxiliary chamber where they exert force on a piston which in turn exerts force to unlock and open the action. The action is then closed and locked by a recoil spring compressed during rearward action movement.

Various mechanical hook-ups are utilized to lock and unlock the breechblock (bolt). Each will be described in its proper place as the individual rifles are covered in detail in Part III.

There are several marked differences in the design of gas operated actions. One is the long-stroke piston which usually takes off its operating charge of gas at relatively low pressures through a port near the muzzle or even through a muzzle cap. The operating rod is fastened to the piston stem and extends clear back to the receiver where it engages the breechblock or bolt. With this arrangement the head of the piston obviously has the same length of stroke as the operating rod must make in order to operate the action.

Another basic type is the *short-stroke* piston or tappet. With this type the operating charge of gas is usually taken off at relatively high pressures through a gas port in the barrel only a few inches forward of the chamber. The operating rod is not attached to the short stemmed piston (tappet) but is mounted just behind it so that as the piston is driven sharply to the rear the short piston stem delivers a powerful blow on the forward end of the operating rod. The force of this blow drives the operating rod to the rear and so operates the action through the same general type of mechanical hook-up as may be found in the long-stroke piston or other repeating action.

A type introduced with the Swedish Model 42 Ljungman rifle contains no piston; the gas is guided to the rear by a gas tube and pushes directly against the face of the bolt carrier.

PART III

The Modern Rifle

Detailed Descriptions

In the chapters that follow, the standard military and typical sporting rifles and the standard cartridges adapted to them are described in as much detail as possible.

The nations of the world are arranged alphabetically and the most prominent manufacturers are listed alphabetically under each nation.

In Europe, even more than in America, custom gun building has been widespread and many rifles having receivers stamped with the name of internationally famous makers are custom built, not standard factory models. For this reason there are thousands of rifles in the hands of sportsmen, collectors, and veterans which will vary in weight, length, caliber, or chamber dimensions from the data here given. This is unfortunate, but unavoidable.

For illustrations of typical rifle markings, see appendix XI.

Chapter 9

ALBANIA

(Shqiperia)

GOVERNMENT PLANTS: Repair and maintenance facilities.

PRIVATE PLANTS: Albania has no arms industry in the modern sense of the word. During the years of Turkish domination hundreds of "underground" gunsmithing establishments operated crude forges, lathes and rifling machines. As a result, guns made up of every conceivable combination of stock, barrel, sights and action may be found there.

PRINCIPAL MILITARY RIFLES: Albania is currently equipped with the Soviet 7.62mm SKS carbine. Older Soviet rifles such as the M1891/30 Mosin Nagant and M1944 carbine are also held.

Chapter 10

ARABIA

(Saudi)

GOVERNMENT PLANTS: Repair and maintenance facilities.

PRIVATE PLANTS: There is no integrated arms industry in Arabia. Manufacture and repair is generally confined to crude shops. Even the cheapest of weapons are usually imported.

PRINCIPAL MILITARY RIFLES: The most common official design is the U. S. cal. .30 M1 rifle.

All patterns of Mausers as described under Czechoslovakia, Germany and Turkey will also be encountered. Calibers are customarily 7.92mm German or 7.65mm Turkish.

Chapter 11

ARGENTINA

(Republica Argentina)

GOVERNMENT PLANTS: Pilot plants first built by German technicians. Production of some small arms of very good quality in government-owned or controlled factories. The FN "FAL" rifle has been made in a government plant.

PRIVATE PLANTS: See above.

PRINCIPAL MILITARY RIFLES: FN "FAL" in 7.62mm NATO; Mausers in 7.65mm. The cartridge is essentially the same as the original Belgian 7.65mm rimless. (See under F. N. *(Belgium)* for average ballistics.)

91

The following Mauser and Mauser pattern rifles and carbines are used:

(1) Argentine Model 1891. This is the first Mauser magazine rifle, having the protruding-box single-line magazine found in the Belgian 1889 and the Turkish 1890. Made in Germany.

(2) Model 1909: Made in Germany (principally by DWM) for Argentina and since WW II in Argentine government plant. This is essentially the German Service Gew. 98 but made in caliber 7.65mm.

Argentine 7.65mm Mauser, M1891 and M1909

M1891

Caliber: 7.65mm

System of operation: Manually operated bolt action

Length overall: 48.6"

Barrel length: 29.1"

Feed device: 5 round single column box magazine

Sights, front: Barleycorn
    rear: leaf

Muzzle velocity (w/spitzer-pointed ball): 2755 f.p.s.

Weight (empty): 8.58 lbs.

Bore diameter: .301"

Groove diameter: .311"

No. grooves: 4

Direction of twist: Right

Rate of twist: 9.8"

M1909

Caliber: 7.65mm

System of operation: Manually operated bolt action

Length overall: 49"

Barrel length: 29.1"

Feed device: 5 round staggered column box magazine

Sights, front: Barleycorn
    rear: tanget leaf

Muzzle velocity (w/spitzer-pointed ball): 2755 f.p.s.

Weight (empty): 9.2 lbs.

Bore diameter: .301"

Groove diameter: .311"

No. grooves: 4

Direction of twist: Right

Rate of twist: 9.8"

Argentine 7.65mm Mauser

Other Names 7.65mm Mauser

Type: Rimless, Necked, Centerfire

Overall Length: 3.06"

Average Wt.: 417 gr.*

Type Powder: Nitrocellulose

Approximate Chg.: 39.5 gr.

Type Primer: Both Boxer and Berdan.

BULLET

Type: Jacketed, Round Nose

Diameter: .311"

Weight: 212 gr.*

Length 1.20"

CARTRIDGE CASE

Length Overall: 2.09"

Length Head to Shoulder: 1.75"

Length of Shoulder: .10"

Length of Neck: .24"

Diameter at Rim: .474"

Diameter at Base: .470"

Diameter at Neck: .340"

Diameter at Shoulder: .425"

BALLISTICS (approximate)

Muzzle Velocity: 2066 f.s.

Normal Pressure Level: 39,000 lbs./sq. in.

Notes: *1. Later cartridges are loaded with a 154 gr. bullet as are the Turkish and Peruvian 7.65mm Mauser cartridges.

2. Powder and primer types vary with country where loaded.

EARLIER OFFICIAL BREECHLOADERS: Remington rolling block single shot Model 1875 rifle and Model 1879 carbine, 11mm (.433) Spanish. (See under *Spain.*)

Argentine Mauser Model 1909. Manufactured in Germany by DWM and Mauser and after WW II by Argentine government plant. Caliber 7.65mm rimless. General characteristics are those of the German Gew. 98.

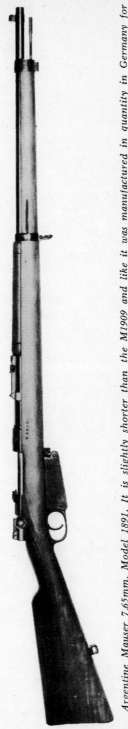

Argentine Mauser 7.65mm, Model 1891. It is slightly shorter than the M1909 and like it was manufactured in quantity in Germany for the Argentine government.

Chapter 12

AUSTRIA

(Oesterreich)

GOVERNMENT PLANTS: None currently manufacturing small arms. See German Intelligence Code List in appendix X for list of wartime plants in Austria.

PRIVATE PLANTS: Steyr-Werke A. G. was the outstanding manufacturer. This organization was founded by Josef Werndl, developer of the early Werndl breechloader. Steyr manufactured all forms of Mannlicher straight pull and turn bolt rifles. In recent years manufacture was concentrated on Mannlicher-Schoenauer rifles and carbines, hammerless double shotguns, small bore bolt actions both single shot and repeaters, and military rifles of the highest grade. The quality of steels, care given to finish and fitting, and the general excellence of Steyr arms has always been consistently high. This concern is now known as Steyr Daimler Puch A.G. and is manufacturing the sporting Mannlicher Schoenauer carbine and rifle again. Steyr has also manufactured the FN "FAL" rifle for the Austrian Army. This rifle is covered under "Belgium."

Military rifles from Steyr bearing the stamp "Oesterreich. Waffenfabrik-Ges." indicate manufacture before or during the opening stages of World War I. Many of these were converted before World War II from 8mm Austrian to 7.92mm German, principally by the Yugoslavs.

Hundreds of small organizations building custom-made rifles and shotguns flourished in all parts of Austria before World War II. The range of calibers and actions, as well as the general specifications of the arms preclude listing here. None have any characteristics which separate them from the standard systems described in this book, except for the inevitable experimental types never made in quantity.

PRINCIPAL MILITARY RIFLES: The Austrian Army currently uses the FN "FAL" rifle in 7.62mm NATO caliber. The Model 1895 rifle, Mannlicher straight pull 8mm, and its carbine form are no longer used.

Austria-Hungary officially adopted a 7mm Mauser design in 1914, but because of the production requirements of the war the design was shelved.

In 1930 the M 1895 Mannlicher Stutzen (Short rifle) was converted to take the then-new M 1930 (M.30) 8mm cartridge which by agreement the Hungarians adopted as the 31M cartridge in 1931. These are readily recognized by a capital "S" stamped on the top surface of the barrel between the receiver ring and the rear sight. In addition, the rear sight leaf was changed so that it was graduated in meters, and a higher front sight blade was used. When modified to fire the M30 cartridge the M95 Mannlicher Stutzer will not fire the M93 8mm cartridge for which it was originally chambered.

Note: Under an interchange policy with both Mauser and the German High Command Steyr tooled up for all varieties of German service rifles. This company supplied Mexico and the Balkans with Mauser patterns when the German factories could not take the orders. The Steyr name and proofs may thus be encountered on the German Gew. 88 and any of its commercial alterations and also on the Gew. 98 in most of its forms.

Model 1895 Rifle (and 1890 Carbine)

This is a straight pull rifle with Mannlicher design magazine, a form modified from the Model 1888-90.

The bolt is of two-piece design. The bolt cylinder carries the handle and is hollowed out from the front to receive a rotating bolt head, and from the rear to permit insertion of the cocking piece and striker assembly.

The bolt cylinder has side ribs which permit only forward and rearward travel in corresponding receiver grooves. The manual safety works in a cut in the rear left side of the bolt cylinder, opposite the handle. The cylinder is reinforced at the rear, the lower part of the reinforce being cut away to receive the cocking piece stud.

Two curved ribs are machined inside the middle section of the bolt cylinder. As the handle is pulled or pushed, these ribs work against corresponding grooves cut in the rear of the bolt head causing the head to turn for unlocking and locking.

The bolt head has two opposed cam shaped locking lugs which engage in seats in the receiver ring. Cam surfaces on the lugs working against opposing receiver surfaces provide primary extraction.

The rear portion ("tail") of the bolt head is turned down to fit inside the bolt cylinder and is machined with the two curved grooves necessary to provide the turning motion. A small groove leads out of each large groove. The top small groove is at the front end. When the bolt is open the rear small groove is at the right side. These small grooves are necessary to permit the extractor to function.

The extractor is a long flat spring with a specially shaped claw. It lies in a guide groove inside the bolt cylinder. A nib on the extractor tail travels in the long grooves in the bolt head. When the bolt goes back this nib rises out of the top groove, and as the bolt head turns it falls into the side groove. At this point the extractor claw is positioned around the right locking lug, and as the bolt goes back the lug carries the extractor and case along with it. On forward bolt thrust the claw grips the cartridge rim insuring proper positioning in the chamber. This extractor operating system provides a non-rotating extractor which will work in straight pull fashion with a rotating bolt head. The alternative would be a rotating extractor which would require milling away more of the rear face of the chamber thereby reducing the area available to support the head of the cartridge case.

The striker and its spring are inserted in the long bolt head from the rear. A plug is then screwed in. This plug has a hole which permits the rear of the striker to pass through, while its forward surface provides a rear compression point for the mainspring. A forward collar on the striker supports the mainspring at the front end.

When the striker and mainspring have been assembled inside the bolt head the unit is inserted in the front end of the main bolt cylinder. The cocking piece is then inserted in the rear of the bolt cylinder, and is screwed into the threaded rear end of the striker. There is a groove in the left side of this cocking piece for the manual safety bolt.

The cocking piece has an upward projecting thumb piece to aid in cocking without opening the action. (On the 1890 the cocking piece is provided with a knurled head.) On its underside is the customary cocking stud which is caught and held by the sear. A cam stud on its left side forces the cocking piece back out of sear engagement when the manual safety is applied. At this point the safety bolt passes between the front end of the cocking piece and the rear end of the bolt cylinder to block the forward movement of the firing pin.

The sear is of peculiar construction. It consists of two separate pieces mounted on a single pin. The upper section acts as a nose. It and the sear spring are mounted in the lower sear section. This two-piece design serves as a safety. When the bolt is pushed forward, a projection on its underside moves over the front part of the sear and prevents it from rising. This makes it impossible for the sear nose to be lowered, hence a trigger pull cannot free the striker until the bolt is fully closed and the locking lugs engaged. At that point the bolt safety projection has moved ahead and cleared the sear body. Moreover, when the trigger is pressed the sear body is raised behind the bolt safety projection, thus blocking any rearward movement of the bolt cylinder.

The ejector is a small piece pivoted to the front end of the sear body. The forward end of the sear spring acts against the ejector.

The trigger is a bell crank lever which is not pinned. It rests in its receiver slot and is supported by sear pressure. A hook at its upper forward end makes sear contact. Dual projections at its top rear end rise through a cut in the receiver and halt the rearward bolt travel, serving as a bolt stop.

The magazine must be loaded with the clip top side up. The clip is inserted with the cartridges and forms part of the magazine operating system, the spring-driven follower working through the cut in the bottom of the clip. The clip is held in the rifle while there are any cartridges in it by the

Austrian Model 1890 and 1895. M1890 has round head on cocking piece. Otherwise same design.

Top Line: Bottom view of bolt cylinder, bolt head and screw plug. The two projections at the forward end of the bolt cylinder work in undercut grooves in the receiver. When they hit the trigger projections, rearward bolt travel is halted. The rear projection on the bolt cylinder is the sear disconnector. The projection moves over the forward end of the sear as the bolt is forced ahead, and prevents the sear nose being lowered by trigger pull except when action is fully forward. In that position the sear body can rise behind the disconnector when the trigger is pulled. The sear body then blocks rearward movement of the bolt cylinder until the trigger is released.

The dual front lugs on the bolt head are slightly cam cut. The slit in the bolt head is to accommodate the ejector as the bolt is retracted. Plainly shown is one of the two spiral grooves in the "tail" of the bolt-head which impart the rotating motion to the bolt head as the bolt cylinder is forced forward or backward. The firing pin and mainspring are inserted in the rear of the bolt head and plug is then mounted over projecting pin and screwed into place. The assembly is then inserted into bolt cylinder from the front end and the cocking piece is screwed onto the rear of firing pin.

Second Line: Cocking piece and firing pin (striker). The stud on the underside of the cocking piece is engaged and held by the sear on the forward bolt thrust. The Model 1895 has rising projection at the end of the cocking piece instead of the round, knurled, head.

The collar at the forward end of the striker serves as forward compression point for the mainspring, the rear compression point being the base of the screw plug.

Third Line: Extractor.

Fourth Line: Loaded Mannlicher clip and mainspring. Note construction requiring insertion with top side up otherwise the forms vary somewhat, clips with cutaway side walls being common.

Fifth Line: Top view of bolt assembly. Extractor is around right hand lug as rearward bolt travel begins and when bolt is removed from receiver. The side ribs on the bolt cylinder work in receiver grooves, and together with the lower bolt cylinder projections they guide the rearward and forward straightline travel. The manual safety is seen at the rear of the bolt cylinder opposite the bolt handle.

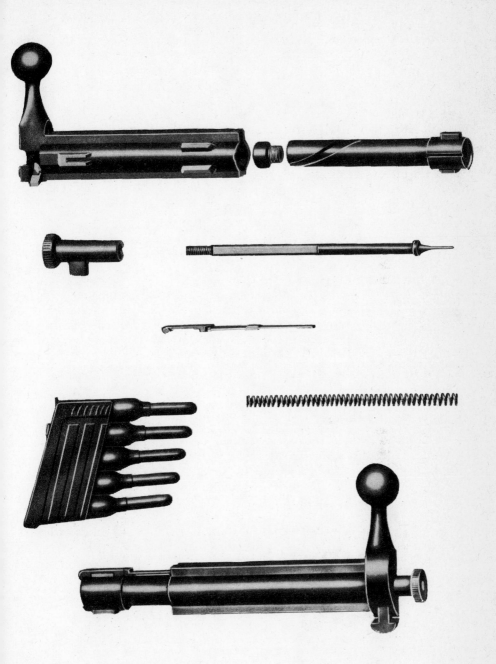

Austrian M. 1895 Rifle and Carbine. Model 1890 Carbine is essentially the same except for shape of cocking piece.
    Left side view with all parts at rest. Recoil block is seen bedded in stock forward of front guard screw. Rear section of magazine is open
at bottom to permit empty clip to drop out. Clip release catch is in forward curve of triggerguard.
    The striker and mainspring in bolt head are held by the screw plug through which the rear of the striker shaft passes, and has the cocking
piece screwed to its end. The downward projecting cocking stud is engaged by the sear nose.

    The sear is a two-piece unit with both pieces pivoted on the same pin. The ejector is pivoted to the forward end of sear body and is ac-
tuated by coiled sear spring. The trigger is not pivoted on the customary pin, but is held in a receiver groove by the sear. Dual projections
rise from the top of the trigger into the boltway to act as the bolt stop.

pressure of the follower on the bottom cartridge, and by a pivoting spring clip catch.

The stock is of one piece design with modified pistol grip and no handguard. The front sight is of the blade type mounted in a stud brazed on the barrel. The rear sight is of the ramp type with open notch.

Operation

Loading: (1) Pull bolt handle back as far as it will go to open action. (2) Insert a clip of cartridges in the magazine well and press the clip down until the clip catch engages it. (3) Thrust bolt straight forward to fully closed position.

Opening the Bolt: Pull the bolt handle straight to the rear.

The extractor, pulled back by the right bolt lug, carries the empty case back. The ejector point, forced up by its coil spring, enters a cut in the bolt head. Ejection is to the right, where the receiver side is cut away.

Bolt travel is halted when the stop projections on the underside of the bolt cylinder hit the projecting trigger "horns."

Unloading: A full clip or partially full clip may be removed by opening the bolt and pressing forward on the clip release which is on the forward inside surface of the triggerguard. This releases the clip catch and the pressure of the follower forces the clip and its cartridges out the top of the receiver.

When the last cartridge has been chambered, the empty clip falls out the bottom opening.

WARNING: Never lower the cocking piece on a loaded chamber. When it is down the firing pin protrudes.

Disassembly: (1) Pull bolt back. (2) Pushing trigger forward, hold it and withdraw bolt assembly. (3) Unscrew and withdraw cocking piece. (4) Pull bolt head assembly forward out of bolt. (5) Unscrew plug at rear of bolt head unit and withdraw striker and mainspring. (6) Snap extractor out. (7) Remove front and rear triggerguard screws. (8) Withdraw triggerguard and magazine unit. Springs, follower arm and follower may then be removed. (9) Punch out sear and ejector pins and remove two-piece sear with spring, ejector and trigger. (10) Remove bands and take receiver and barrel out of stock.

Austrian Model 95/24. This is a modified version of the straight pull Model 95, but redesigned to handle the 7.92 Mauser Rimless. Receivers are marked STEYR M95, rolled into receiver ring. Beside the "95" is hand stamped "/24". The same straight-line magazine system is used, but receiver is milled with clip slots for stripping from the Mauser clip. Magazine is altered with a non-removable filler clip to hold the stripped rimless cartridges in single file. Clip opening at bottom is closed with new guard assembly, same outlines as 95. Mauser rear sight. This is a factory made modification with bolt head designed for rimless cartridge and apparently was a rebuilding job on used actions. They were plentiful during the war.

These rifles were apparently used by Greece and probably were originally war reparations turned over by Austria to Greece. Another conversion of the M1895 to 7.92mm is marked M95M. These rifles were used by Yugoslavia. There are two conversions of the M1895 short rifle to the 8x56R cartridge. The Austrian conversion is marked with a large "S" on the top of the barrel while

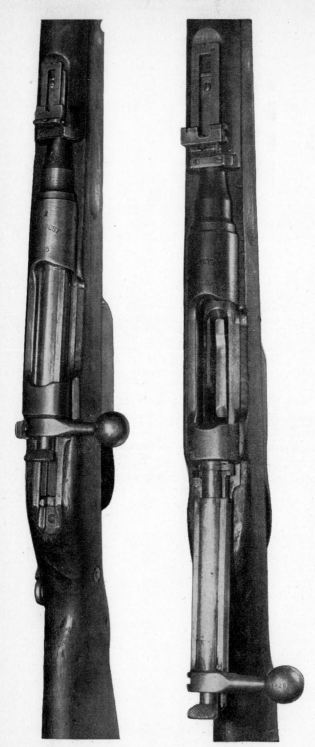

Austrian M1895, action closed and open. In upper picture bolt stop projections on top of the trigger can be seen. When the action is open, pushing the trigger lowers these stops and permits the bolt to be withdrawn from receiver. The upper picture is the M1895 Carbine, with sling swivel on side and short leaf sight.

Lower picture shows action ready for loading. A straight forward thrust on the bolt handle will force the assembly ahead, rotating the bolt head into locking engagement when the bolt lugs reach the entrance to their cam grooves into the receiver ring. Lower picture is M1895 Rifle.

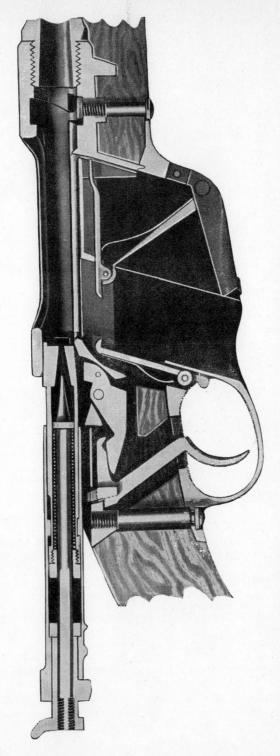

Austrian Models 1895 and 1890, right side view with action open and empty ready for loading. When a loaded clip is inserted and forced down into the magazine, the follower is depressed between the clip walls, exerting upward pressure on the bottom cartridge. The clip catch engages above the holding projection on the back of the clip to hold the clip in the magazine.

the Hungarian conversion is marked "H" on the barrel. A conversion of the M1888/90 to 7.92mm was believed to have been done for Greece. Markings on a specimen at the Aberdeen Proving Ground Museum show that the conversion was done in Belgium.

Model 1895 Mannlicher Stutzen (Short Rifle)

Caliber: 8mm
Overall length, without bayonet: 39.5"

Weight, without bayonet: 6.8 lbs.
Barrel length: 19.6"

Austrian Model 1895 Mannlicher

Caliber: 8mm
Overall length, rifle without bayonet: 50"
Overall weight, rifle without bayonet: 8.3 lbs.
Type of action: Straight Pull
Type of Magazine: Box—Vertical Column
Barrel Length: 30.1"   *No. Grooves:* 4
Bore Diameter: .315"   *Groove Dia.:* .329"

With bayonet attached: 59.5"
With bayonet attached: 9 lbs.
Type of bolt: 2 piece—Rotating Head
Capacity: 5
  Direction of Twist: Right
  Rate of Twist: 9.84"

Austrian 8mm Mannlicher Model 1893 Cartridge

Other Names: 8x50R Mannlicher
Type: Rimmed, Necked, Centerfire
Overall Length: 2.99"
Average Wt.: 437 grs.
Type Powder: Nitrocellulose
Approximate Chg.: 42.2 grs.
Type Primer: Berdan

BULLET

Type: Jacketed, Round Nose
Diameter: .323"
Weight: 244 grs.
Length: 1.25"

CARTRIDGE CASE

Length Overall: 1.98"
Length Head to Shoulder: 1.51"
Length of Shoulder: .20"
Length of Neck: .27"
Diameter at Rim: .551"
Diameter at Base: .490"
Diameter at Neck: .350"
Diameter at Shoulder: .462"

BALLISTICS (approximate)

Muzzle Velocity: 2030 f.s.
Pressure: About 42,000 lbs./sq. in.

Notes: 1. This cartridge has been the military cartridge in Bulgaria, Greece, and Hungary.

Austrian 8mm Model 30 Cartridge

Other names: 8x56R, Hungarian 8mm M31
Overall length: 3.02"
Average wt: 441 gr.
Approximate chg: 55 gr.
Type primer: Berdan
CARTRIDGE CASE
Length overall: 2.21"
Diameter at rim: .55"

BULLET
Type: Jacketed, Spitzer Pointed Boat Tail
Diameter: .323"
Weight: .208 gr.
Length: 1.35"

BALLISTICS
Muzzle velocity: 2,280 f.p.s.

Austrian Mannlicher Model 1888-90

Caliber: 8mm
Overall length, rifle without bayonet: 50.4mm
Overall weight, rifle without bayonet: 9.7 lbs.
Type of action: Straight Pull
Type of Magazine: Box—Vertical Column
Barrel Length: 30.1"   *No. Grooves:* 4
Bore Diameter: .315"   *Groove Dia.:* .329"

With bayonet attached: 60.2"
With bayonet attached: 10 lbs.
Type of bolt: 3 piece—depressed rear lug
Capacity: 5
  Direction of Twist: Right
  Rate of Twist: 9.84"

Notes:

1. When first issued in 1888, the then new 8mm cartridge was loaded with black powder. In 1890 the change to smokeless was made, calling for regraduation of sights.

2. The action of this model is the same as the Model 1886.

Austrian Model 1890 Mannlicher Carbine

Caliber: 8mm
Overall length, rifle without bayonet: 39.5"
Overall weight, rifle without bayonet: 7.1 lbs.
Type of action: Straight Pull   *Type of bolt:* 2 piece—Rotating Head
Type of Magazine: Box—Vertical Column   *Capacity:* 5
Barrel Length: 19.5"   *No. Grooves:* 4   *Direction of Twist:* Right
Bore Diameter: .315"   *Groove Dia.:* .329"   *Rate of Twist:* 9.84"
Notes:

1. This carbine is mechanically the same as the M. 1895 Rifle. The shape of the cocking piece, as shown in the photograph, and the barrel and furniture are the major differences in the two.

2. The drawings and description of the Rifle M. 1895 effectively cover the Cavalry Carbine M. 1890.

Models 1886, 1888 and 1888-90

These are straight pull rifles of a basic design quite different from the Model 95.

The bolt is a two piece type bored out from the front to permit insertion of the striker and mainspring. They are retained by a separate head which is screwed into the bolt. This head is locked by the extractor, a long spring claw in the right side of the bolt.

A swinging block is hinged to the underside of the bolt. This block is forced down into a cut in the receiver behind the magazine well to lock the bolt in firing position.

A rear section of the bolt is hollowed out to receive the bolt handle unit. A solid flanged projection on the underside of the bolt handle unit locks and unlocks the wedge as the action is operated.

The striker projects through the rear of both bolt and bolt handle unit. The cocking piece is screwed into the end of the striker.

The trigger is a bell crank lever attached to the underside of the sear. The sear is part of a long flat spring. The sear nose projects through a hole in the receiver tang.

Operation

Loading: Same as Model 95.

Firing: This rifle introduced the now common two-stage pull. There is no half-cock. The action can be cocked only by opening and closing the action.

Opening the Action: As the handle is pulled back it draws the striker with it. The flanged projection on the forward end of the cocking piece raises the hinged locking block out of receiver engagement. This block pressing back against the flange prevents any forward movement of the cocking piece. This holds the mainspring back. The extractor carries the empty case back until it hits a projection in the receiver bridge which serves as ejector. The bolt stop halts bolt assembly travel.

Closing the Action: The sear nose forced up by its spring arm catches the cocking piece stud. The bolt is thrust forward while the striker is held back, thereby cocking the mainspring.

The face of the bolt starts a cartridge forward. As the cartridge clears the clip, the extractor springs over its rim, guiding it the rest of the distance into the chamber.

Austrian Model 1888/90 Straight Pull rifle. Caliber 8mm Austrian rimmed. The bolt in this design is locked to the rear of the magazine way by a swinging wedge forced down into the receiver by action of the bolt handle.

Mauser 7.92mm Model 29 Rifle Made at Steyr and used by the Germans in World War II. It was known as the Model 29/40 in German service.

Austrian 11mm 1886 Mannlicher Straight Pull Rifle.

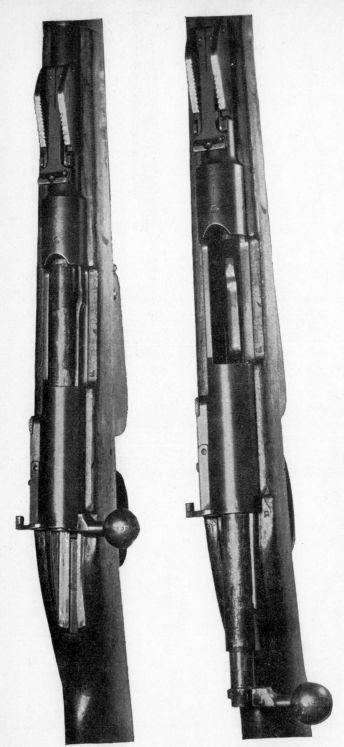

Austrian M1888/90, action closed and open. This design differs materially from the M95 and must not be confused with it.

Austrian M1888/90 converted to 7.92mm. This weapon bears proof markings indicating that the conversion was done in Belgium. It is believed that these rifles were used in Greece.

The flanged projection on the underside of the bolt handle unit forces the hinged bolt locking block down into the receiver cut and wedges it there.

If the thumb safety is turned, it forces a plate in front of the cocking piece to block forward movement. This safety may also be applied when the arm is uncocked, as a cut is provided in the handle unit to receive it.

Disassembly: (1) Pull out pivoted lever in left side of receiver and while holding it out withdraw the bolt. (2) Unscrew and withdraw cocking piece. (3) Pull out handle assembly. (4) Pry out extractor. (5) Unscrew bolt head. (6) Withdraw striker and spring. (7) Remove front and rear triggerguard screws. (8) Withdraw triggerguard-magazine assembly. (9) Remove bands and withdraw barrel and receiver from stock.

Austrian Model 1886 Mannlicher

Caliber: 11mm
Overall length, rifle without bayonet: 52″
Overall weight, rifle without bayonet: 10 lbs.
Type of action: Straight Pull
Type of Magazine: Box—Vertical column
Barrel Length: 31.7″   *No. Grooves:* 6
Bore Diameter: .433″   *Groove Dia.:* .445″

With bayonet attached: 61″
With bayonet attached: 10.8 lbs.
Type of bolt: 3 piece—depressed rear lug
Capacity: 5
  Direction of Twist: Right
  Rate of Twist: 28.5″

Notes:

1. These rifles were also issued with groove depth of .0079″ and with sights set in paces from 200 to 2300 (164 to 1886 yds.).

2. The Model 1886 officially introduced the Mannlicher "packet loading" system in which the cartridge clip is inserted in the rifle with its cartridges.

Earlier Official Breechloaders

In 1867 the Wänzl conversion of the muzzle loaders was introduced in Caliber .55 R. F. Cocking the hammer withdrew a bolt attached to the lower hammer face out of a recess in the breechlock. The breechblock was then lifted on a forward hinge for loading.

The first newly developed rifle as such was the Werndl, developed by the Director General of Steyr Armory. This was a turning block design. Adopted in 1873, it was modified and produced in quantity in the following year.

In 1886 the first Mannlicher was adopted, caliber 11mm.

Austrian Model 1868 Werndl Single Shot

Caliber: 11.2mm
Overall length, rifle without bayonet: 50.3″
Overall weight, rifle without bayonet: 9.7 lbs.
Type of action: Side rotating block
Barrel Length: 33.2″   *No. Grooves:* 6
Bore Diameter: .433″   *Groove Dia.:* .448″

With bayonet attached: 69″
With bayonet attached: 11 lbs.
Type of bolt: 1 piece
  Direction of Twist: Right
  Rate of Twist: 28.4″

Notes:

1. Specifications of the Werndl were subject to many minor changes during the years of its manufacture. Groove depths and sights vary in many specimen rifles.

2. The Werndl was also made as a carbine.

3. This weapon was named after Joseph Werndl, Director of the Steyr Armory at the time of its development.

Austrian 11.2mm M1868-1873 Cartridge

Other Names: 11.2x58R. 11.2mm Werndl

Type: Rimmed, Necked, Centerfire, Type A Base

Overall Length: 2.920"

Average Wt.: 656 Grains

Type of Powder: Black

Approximate Charge: 77.0 grains

Type Primer: Berdan (Two hole)

BULLET

Type: Lead, Paper Patched

Diameter: .451" (over Patch) . .433" (less)

Weight: 370 grains

Length: 1.063"

CARTRIDGE CASE

Length Overall: 2.28"

Length Head to Shoulder: 1.44"

Length of Shoulder: .14"

Length of Neck: .70"

Diameter at Rim: .618"

Diameter at Base: .545"

Diameter at Neck: .465"

Diameter at Shoulder: .538"

BALLISTICS (approximate)

Muzzle Velocity: 1440 f.s.

Pressure: About 28,000 lbs./sq. in.

Notes: 1. Cartridge assembled with a beeswax wad between two card wads behind the bullet.

Austrian Sporting Rifles

The Mannlicher-Schoenauer sporting rifles and carbines combine the Mannlicher turn-bolt with the Schoenauer rotary box magazine. The general mechanical design is the same as the Greek Mannlicher 1903 and 1903/14. (See under *Greece.*)

The actions were sold throughout the world by Steyr-Werke A. G. Many small British gunmakers and some of the larger German firms such as Haenel of Suhl barreled and stocked these actions to special order.

As a result, "Mannlicher-Schoenauers" may be found with any conceivable combination of caliber, sights, barrel lengths, stocking and engraving. Many have double set triggers; some have single set triggers.

Current Mannlicher-Schoenauer high power rifles and carbines made by Steyr Daimler Puch have the following characteristics:

CARBINE

Calibers: 6.5x54, 6.5x57, 7x57, 7x64, 8x57JS, .243 Win, .244 Rem, .257 Roberts, .270 Win, .280 Rem, .308 Win, .358 Win, .30-06

Length: 39"

Barrel length: 18.1"

Weight: 6.75 lbs.

RIFLE

Calibers: 6.5x57, 7x57, 7x64, 8x57JS, 8x60S, 9.3x62, .207 Win, .243 Win, 257 Roberts, .308 Win, .358 Win, .244 Rem, .280 Rem, .30-06

Length: 44.37"

Barrel length: 23.62"

Weight: 7.37 lbs.

A Magnum rifle is also made for the 6.5x68, 8x68S, and .458 Winchester Magnum cartridges. It has an overall length of 46 inches, and a weight of 6.83 pounds. The Mannlicher Schoenauer rifles and carbines can now be obtained with American type Monte Carlo stocks and rearward bent bolt handles.

STEYR .22 CALIBER RIFLES: Several different models of bolt action .22 rifles are made by Steyr Daimler Puch. The DeLuxe Model has a full stock similar to the Mannlicher Carbine.

Note On Mannlicher Calibers

The 8mm M-S cartridge in recent years was designated by Steyr as "8.2mm." As made in Europe it was also listed as 8 x 56 M-Sch. Please note that this cartridge when it can be inserted should never be used in Mauser rifles unless they are specifically chambered for it. The length of the Mannlicher case body is shorter than the 7.92mm (8mm) Mauser, permitting the M-Sch. cartridge to chamber too deeply in a Mauser rifle. This in effect produces dangerous tolerances between the head of the case and the face of the bolt.

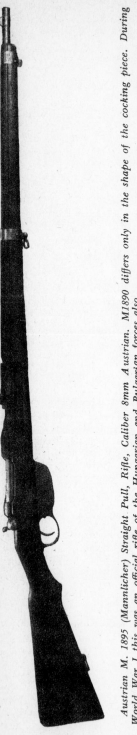

Austrian M. 1895 (Mannlicher) Straight Pull, Rifle, Caliber 8mm Austrian. M1890 differs only in the shape of the cocking piece. During World War I this was an official rifle of the Hungarian and Bulgarian forces also.

In caliber 8mm Austrian it saw extensive service in Eastern European War Theatres during World War II. These arms use a Mannlicher type clip. The magazine floor plate is slotted to permit the empty clip to drop out when the last cartridge has been chambered.

From 1924 on large numbers of these rifles were altered in Austria and in Yugoslavia to take the standard German 7.9mm cartridge. These conversions often have the date "24" stamped on the receiver near the original "95" model number. They can be positively identified, however, only by the alterations: (1) Mauser-type charger clip guides machined into the receiver. (2) Closed magazine bottom. (3) Insert-clip of straight line type sealed within magazine well to hold the heads of the rimless 7.9mm cartridges.

The M1895 Mannlicher must not be confused with the M1888/1890 which has a much weaker type of straight pull action.

Mannlicher-Schoenauer Sporting Carbine. Typical flat, turned-down bolt handle. Made in various calibers. Commonly encountered as shown with double set-triggers and full stock, but single triggers and half-stocks were also provided.

These rifles use the Mannlicher turn bolt action combined with the Schoenauer revolving box magazine. They may be loaded with single cartridges or from strip-in charger clips. They do not use the Mannlicher enbloc clips.

Austrian Mannlicher-Schoenauer Sporting Rifle. The bolt head is detachable in the Mannlicher turn bolt design. Lugs are at front end of bolt cylinder to rear of head, farther back than in Mauser design. The lugs are not visible in drawing, but location may be judged from position of their seats in the receiver ring. The cocking piece unit fits over the rear of the striker shaft and is held by a nut screwed on to the end of the striker.

Mainspring compression is completed as the bolt handle is turned down. At that point the sear holds the cocking piece nose, while the bolt is pulled forward as the locking lugs turn in cam slots leading to their locking seats in the receiver ring.

The rotary magazine detail shows loading with charger clip. In loading with individual cartridges, the magazine stop springs back as each cartridge is inserted, thus preventing any unwinding motion. The magazine follower spring is wound progressively tighter as each cartridge enters the magazine. Cartridges are never in touch with each other.

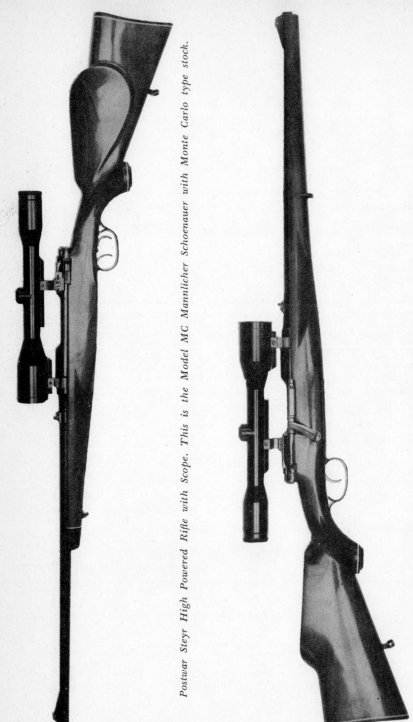

Postwar Steyr High Powered Rifle with Scope. This is the Model MC Mannlicher Schoenauer with Monte Carlo type stock.

Postwar Mannlicher Schoenauer Carbine with Scope; it is Model MC with Monte Carlo Stock.

Chapter 13
BELGIUM
(Royaume De Belgique-Koninkrijk Belgie)

Belgium has been a center for the development of all types of firearms throughout most of the period of recorded gun history. Much of the early equipment used in Germany and England came from there. Belgian factories have provided arms from the poorest grades (made during the 19th Century for South African, South American and Asiatic trade) to some of the finest modern arms manufactured.

GOVERNMENT PLANTS: Manufacture De L'Etat at Liege. None built or operated outright by the Government. All arms manufacture is government controlled.

PRIVATE PLANTS: Fabrique Nationale d'Armes de Guerre (commonly known as "F. N.") is one of the world's largest arms plants. This plant was founded in 1889 by a Liege (Belgium) Syndicate and by L. Loewe & Co. of Berlin to manufacture Mauser rifles for the Belgian government. After World War I, F. N. undertook large scale manufacture of Mauser rifles to supply markets formerly serviced by Germany. This firm is the manufacturer for Europe of John M. Browning's shotgun and rifle designs, and for most of Browning's pistol and machine gun designs.

Auguste Francotte of Liege, Anciens Establissements Pieper (Bayard trademark) and H. Pieper of Liege are the other outstanding Belgian names in the rifle world. Hundreds of small firms manufacture for custom or for export. It is not practicable to list them. None produce arms of unusual or noteworthy design; though all are reliable, since Belgium requires that all arms made there be Government proofed.

PRINCIPAL MILITARY RIFLES: F.N. cal. .30 M1949; F.N. 7.62mm NATO "FAL"; Mauser Models 1889, 1935, and 1936, Caliber 7.65mm. In recent years the F. N. Mausers have been withdrawn from service; these later types are all mechanically identical with the German Service rifle. Also British No. 1 and No. 4 Lee-Enfields were used after World War II.

Model 1889 Belgian Mauser

This is the basic Mauser one-piece bolt design from which all modern Mausers stem. It differs only in comparatively minor details from the later German types. Hence the design differences only need be pointed out.

The bolt has only the two forward locking lugs, the third safety lug did not appear on Mausers until 1896.

The end of the striker is threaded. Other Mausers use interrupted thread systems for attaching the cocking piece. The striker has a rib (instead of flat surfaces) to prevent it from turning within the bolt sleeve. The cocking piece stud rests in a notch in the rear of the bolt to prevent the sleeve from turning accidentally.

There is no safety flange on the bolt sleeve. There is a slight variation in the manual safety.

Belgian Model 1889 (Mauser) Carbine. Note barrel jacket and projecting box magazine which instantly identify this model. Caliber 7.65mm.

Belgian Model 1889 ready for loading. This is the first production model to use the strip-in charger clip. Cocking is completed on last inch of forward thrust, as sear holds cocking piece back.

Cross section shows straightline single column design magazine. This was used on all later production Mausers until the appearance of the double column staggered magazine in the Spanish 1892 Model.

Although discarded by all other armies, the M1889 design was kept in first line service by Belgium after World War I. These rifles were modified by the fitting of Model 98 type bolt sleeves and by the shortening of barrels. This model is called the M36.

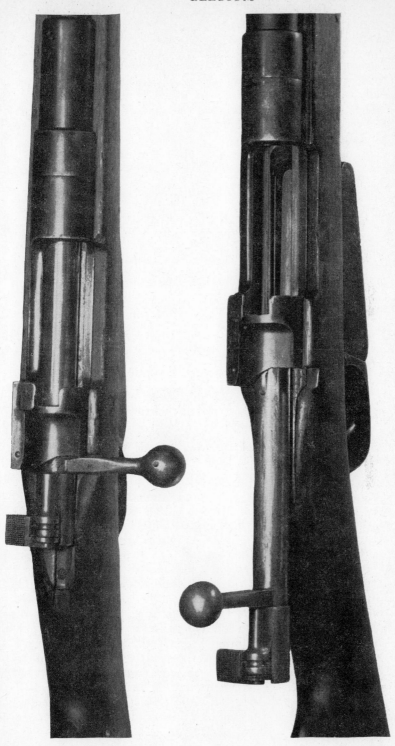

Belgian Model 1889 open and closed action. This is the first production form of the Mauser one-piece bolt design. This model does not have the rear safety lug found on later German Service arms. The Turkish M1890, Argentine M1891 and all other South American models of 1891 and 1892 closely resemble this bolt and magazine design, but do not have barrel jackets.

The extractor differs radically from all other Mausers. It is a short spring claw positioned in the bolt between the locking lugs. It turns with the bolt, a design which requires excessive chamfering of the rear face of the chamber decreasing the support for the head of the rimless cartridge.

The sear spring is positioned horizontally in the receiver.

The magazine is a single line vertical box which projects below the receiver. It is detachable. Two flat levers and two flat springs are used to feed the cartridges. The magazine side walls are of spring steel, cutaway and curved in at the top to retain the cartridges.

The barrel is lighter than later models and is fitted with a barrel casing for protection of the barrel and of the soldier's hand when the barrel becomes heated from rapid fire.

Loading: Standard for Mausers.

Opening the Bolt: Standard for Mausers, except for extractor action.

Closing the Bolt: Standard for early Mausers. Sear engages cocking piece stud when bolt has 1-inch farther forward travel. Cocking is on this last forward thrust, *not* on turning down the handle.

Belgian Model 1889 Mauser

Caliber: 7.65mm
Overall length, rifle without bayonet: 50"   *With bayonet attached:* 59.7"
Overall weight, rifle without bayonet: 8.1 lbs.   *With bayonet attached:* 9.6 lbs.
Type of action: Turnbolt   *Type of bolt:* 1 piece—Rotating Head
Type of Magazine: Detachable Box—Vertical Column *Capacity:* 5
Barrel Length: 30.7"   *No. Grooves:* 4   *Direction of Twist:* Right
Bore Diameter: .301"   *Groove Dia.:* .313"   *Rate of Twist:* 9.84"
Notes:

1. Fabrique Nationale de Armes de Guerre was originally founded to make this rifle. Today it is one of the world's greatest arms plants. These rifles were also made in Leige by Fabrique d'Armes de l'Etat. During World War I the M. 1889 was also made in the U. S. by Hopkins & Allen at Norwich, Conn.

2. CARBINE FORMS: The M. 1889 Carbine differs from the rifle only in shorter length and lower weight. Mechanically it does not differ from the rifle model.

Later Mauser Models

In the period between World Wars I and II, Belgian firms, notably F. N., manufactured Mauser rifles for distribution to nations throughout the world.

In accordance with common German practice, these arms were provided in calibers which permitted use of standard Mauser receivers and with slight changes in machining permitted interchangeability of parts. This was possible because of the original Mauser system of basing the 7mm, the 7.65mm and the 7.92mm cartridges on the same cartridge case head diameter and the same approximate case length.

All modern Mauser military rifles are based mechanically on the Mauser patents from 1893 when the Spanish Model was introduced through 1907 and on Belgian and Czech ordnance modifications instituted in 1924. The bolt heads on all these designs are the same. Only in the field of sporting Magnum and Short actions (which are merely oversized and undersized receivers and locking assemblies) does one Mauser vary particularly from any other *regardless of the country in which it is manufactured.* Magnum actions were built for sale to custom gunmakers throughout the world, who barreled and fitted them for ultra-powerful big game or "wildcat" cartridges.

Mauser rifles made by Fabrique Nationale d'Armes de Guerre are variously listed as the Models 1924, 1924-30 and 1930 in the export field. These rifles differ from the German and among themselves in the form of handguard about the barrel, projection of bolt handle, types of sights, thickness and weights of stocks, placing of sling swivels, types of slings and similar features which have little or no bearing on basic design or mechanical functioning or parts.

Post-war F. N. Sporting Mausers are basically the same mechanically, but are modified for U. S. sporting use in line with N. R. A. recommendations. These are also stocked in America and were formerly sold under the trade name of F. N.'s American rifle distributors, Firearms International Corp.

Model 1949 FN Semiautomatic Rifle

This weapon was developed prior to World War II but was not produced until after the War. In U.S. caliber .30 (.30-06), it was adopted by the Belgian Army. It has also been used by the Egyptian Army in 7.92mm and the Venezuelan Army in 7mm, among others. The weapon has also been made in selective fire, i.e., full or semiautomatic versions. This weapon was designed by Dieudonné Saive (pronounced like "save") of Fabrique Nationale, and the basic patents covering the weapon were filed in 1936. It has also been referred to as the Model ABL.

For the first time in its history Belgium adopted a semiautomatic rifle in the year 1951. Designed by Dieudonné Saive, the weapon became known throughout the world as the FN Semiautomatic Rifle, having seen service with the Belgian Army in Korea. In selecting the FN Semiautomatic Rifle for the army, the Belgians continued use of the .30-06 cartridge which had been adopted right after World War II.

M. Saive originated the design of the FN semiautomatic rifle, which was patented in 1936. Two years later by a strange coincidence—probably through the courtesy of the Patent Office—the Russian Tokarev was introduced, with a remarkably similar gas-operated bolt system which they perpetuated in their SKS semiautomatic rifle. For the second time in the Twentieth Century the Germans invaded Belgium and, as in World War I, M. Saive, like so many other patriotic Belgians, refused to work for the invader. At great peril to his life he escaped to England with the plans of his semiautomatic rifle, which impressed the British sufficiently to undertake development work and tests in 7.92mm Mauser. During his second exile in England, M. Saive contributed indirectly to the liberation of Belgium by assisting the British on important ordnance projects. However, it was not until M. Saive returned to FN in Belgium that the design was finally put into production.

In addition to Belgium, the FN semiautomatic rifle was also adopted in caliber .30-06 by the Grand Duchy of Luxemburg. Venezuela preferred it in caliber 7mm. Egypt purchased 50,000 in caliber 7.92mm. Approximately 160,000 were produced before the design was discontinued in favor of Saive's later adaptation, the celebrated FN NATO assault rifle. A limited number of FN semiautomatic rifles were produced for Belgium with a full automatic as well as the semiautomatic feature.

The gas-operated bolt system of the FN semiautomatic rifle functions as follows: When the weapon is fired, gas is tapped from the barrel near the muzzle.

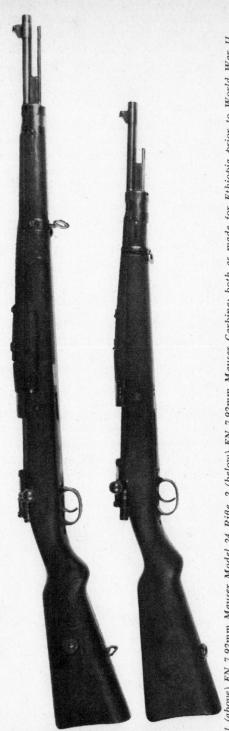

Belgian 7.65mm M1935 Service Rifle. This weapon has the 98 Mauser type bolt action.

1 (above) FN 7.92mm Mauser Model 24 Rifle, 2 (below) FN 7.92mm Mauser Carbine; both as made for Ethiopia prior to World War II.

Belgian 7.65mm M1936 Service Rifle. This weapon is a conversion of M1889 Rifles and Carbines. It has a 98 Mauser type bolt sleeve and firing pin mechanism.

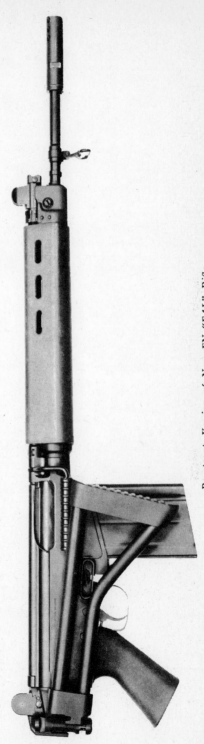

Paratroop Version of New FN "FAL" Rifle.

FN Semiautomatic Rifle Cal. .30-06

FN Semiauto Rifle With Scope and Cheekpiece

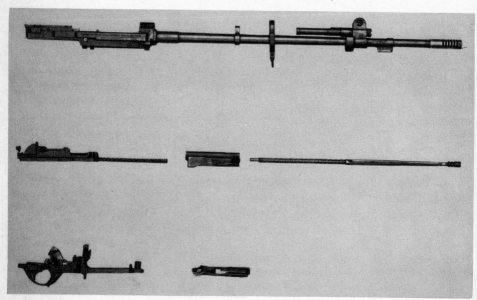

FN Semiautomatic Rifle Stripped

It passes through a gas port located on top of the barrel and issues into the gas tube located over the barrel, delivering a sharp blow to the tappet rod contained therein. In moving back, the rear of the tappet slides through a hole in the top of the receiver, striking the face of the bolt carrier situated over the bolthead. The bolt carrier now moves back, camming up the rear end of the bolt. In locked position, the rear of the bolt, which is tilted downward, bears against a

TABLE SHOWING VARIATIONS AMONG SOME FN LIGHT AUTOMATIC RIFLES PRODUCED AT FN

Country	Barrel	Flash Suppressor	Bayonet	Extractor in:	Butt stock	Butt plate	Handguard	Bipod	Loading
Austria	3	3	3	2	2	2	2	2	1
Belgium	1	1	1	2	2	1	3	1	2
Cambodia	2			2	2	1	3	1	1
Chile	1	2		2	2	2	3	1	1
Dominican Republic	2	2		2	1	2	1	1	1
Ecuador	2	3	2	2	2	1	3	1	1
Ireland	1			1	2	2	3	1	1
Israel				2	2	2	1	1	1
Kuwait	1			1	1	1	1	2	1
Luxembourg	3			2	2	1	3	1	
Lybia	1		2	2	2	2	2	1	1
Netherlands	3	3		2	1	1	1	1	1
Paraguay	1			2		2	3	1	1
Peru	1		2	2	1	2		2	1
Portugal				2	2	1	1	1	1
Qatar	1			1 & 2			3	1	1
San Domingo	1	1	1				1	1	1
South Africa							1		1
Syria	2		2	2	1	2	3	2	1
Venezuela	2	2	2				1		1
West Germany	1	2	2	2	2	2	2	2	2

Key to numbered options in each column:
- **Barrel:** 1. Smooth muzzle 2. Threaded muzzle 3. Threaded muzzle for combined grenade launcher/flash suppressor
- **Flash Suppressor:** 1. Without 2. With 3. Combined with grenade launcher
- **Bayonet:** 1. Flash suppressor type or normal 2. Tubular type 3. Without
- **Extractor in:** 1. One piece 2. Two pieces
- **Butt stock:** 1. Without front socket 2. With front socket
- **Butt plate:** 1. Without butt trap 2. With butt trap
- **Handguard:** 1. Wood 2. Metal 3. Moulded material
- **Bipod:** 1. Without 2. With
- **Loading:** 1. Without charger (stripper clip) 2. With charger

There are other variations as for example, the British produced L1A1 and the Canadian produced C1.

crosspiece in the receiver. The bolt return spring propels the bolt and carrier into their forward locked positions, stripping a round from the magazine and chambering it. Being independent of the bolt, the tappet rod can move in a straight line; it is not bent around the magazine as in the M₁ Garand.

Danger of fouling the gas system has been reduced by hard chrome-plating of the gas tube and tappet rod. Having delivered a blow against the tappet rod, the gases are permitted to escape out of two port holes diametrically opposite each other in the gas cylinder. The gas serves to flush the combustion residue resulting from the preceding explosion. Cleaning of the cylinder may be done with a rod after the gas plug and tappet rod have been removed.

This rugged and well-constructed rifle has an unusual feature. There is an indicator which protrudes beneath the trigger when the weapon is cocked; consequently only a touch is needed to tell whether the gun is ready for action.

Field stripping is not complicated. A latch at the rear of the receiver revolves. When it is upright, grasp firmly the receiver cover on which the rear sight is mounted and slide it as far as possible toward the muzzle. Lift up to withdraw both the receiver cover and bolt return spring. Pull back bolt handle until projections on the sides of the bolt carrier are in line with related openings above the receiver runways, then lift up. The bolt is contained within the carrier. To re-assemble the gun, reverse this procedure.

The sturdy rear aperture sight requires no special skill to manipulate. It is of tangent-type construction common with Mauser rifles, having protective wings on either side, and adjusts in 100-meter increments up to 1,000 meters. Windage is controlled by counter-locking screws.

The magazine contains ten cartridges. Loading can also be accomplished from above with 5-round, standard Mauser-type clips, or 10-round, horseshoe-shaped clips.

Caliber: .30-06, also made in 7.92mm and 7mm
Length overall: 43.7"
Barrel length: 23.2"

Weight unloaded: 9.1 lbs.
Magazine capacity: 10 rounds
Feed device: 10 round, staggered column, non-detachable box

FN "FAL" Rifle

This weapon is the most widely used postwar military rifle and undoubtedly is one of the best. Originally introduced in the German 7.92mm short cartridge (PP 43me) this weapon is currently used by more than thirty countries including Belgium, Great Britain, Canada, Australia, New Zealand, South Africa, Israel, Peru, Argentina, Venezuela, Cuba, Austria, Chile, the Netherlands, Ireland, Portugal, Syria, Luxembourg, and Ecuador.

The weapon is essentially a modification and improvement of the earlier FN semiautomatic rifle. It was tested in the United States as the Model T48; Harrington and Richardson made 500 for the United States government and a total of 3,303 were purchased from FN by the United States for field test. The weapon comes in a number of basic models and there are numerous differences regarding handguards, flash suppressors, etc. Although the rifle may be made capable of either automatic or semiautomatic fire, many countries use only a semiautomatic version as the basic individual weapon. A commercial version of the semiautomatic rifle is currently being sold in the United States by the Browning Arms Company. There are heavy barrel versions of the rifle fitted with bipods which

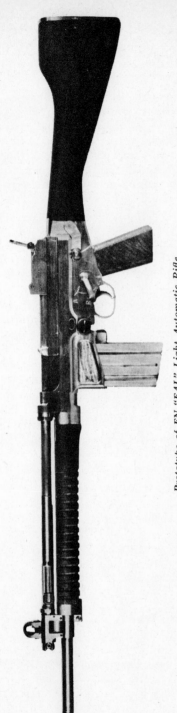

Prototype of FN "FAL" Light Automatic Rifle.

One of the Early FN 7.62mm NATO "FAL" Light Automatic Rifles.

are used as squad automatic weapons by Australia, Canada, South Africa, Israel, and Peru, among others.

Most FN "FAL" rifles have been chambered for the 7.62mm NATO cartridge, but the weapon has also been made for the experimental British .280 (7mm) cartridge.

When the weapon is fired, gas is tapped from the barrel near the muzzle. It passes through a gas port located on top of the barrel and issues into the gas tube located over the barrel, delivering a sharp blow to the tappet rod contained therein. In moving back, the rear of the tappet rod slides through a hole in the top of the receiver, striking the face of the bolt carrier situated over the bolthead. The bolt carrier now moves back, camming up the rear end of the bolt. The bolt and bolt carrier travel rearward in unison to extract the expended case, and to compress the bolt return spring housed in the butt stock. The compressed return spring drives the bolt and bolt carrier forward; during this movement, the bolt strips a cartridge from the top of the magazine and chambers it. Forward movement of the bolt is stopped when it contacts the rear face of the barrel. The inclined surfaces on the bolt carrier, acting on the shoulders of the bolt, force the rear end of the bolt down into its locked position against a crosspiece in the receiver. The weapon is now ready for re-firing.

A regulator controls the flow of gas within the system. By rotating the gas cylinder plug 180 degrees it is possible to shut off the flow of gas completely so that the gun can be used as a grenade launcher. Rotating the gas cylinder plug 90 degrees permits its removal for the purpose of cleaning the gas cylinder.

Field stripping is exceedingly simple. Remove magazine and cock rifle by pulling back operating handle. Release bolt by depressing bolt holding catch located at left rear of magazine port. Depress catch on left side of butt frame beneath the rear sight; the weapon can then be broken apart like a shotgun. Grasp bolt return spring rod, pulling it back and out of receiver, freeing the bolt carrier which contains the bolt. Receiver cover can also be removed by drawing it back and out of the receiver grooves. To further dismantle the rifle, the butt stock and trigger group can be unhinged from the receiver by unscrewing the crosspin. This procedure is reversed for reassembly.

Caliber: 7.62mm NATO

Length: 40" (w/o suppressor or grenade launcher)

Barrel length: 21"

Weight—
  w/o magazine and sling: 8.6 lbs.

Weight of magazine—
  unloaded: .5 lbs.
  loaded with 20 rounds: 1.57 lbs.
Number of grooves: 4
Rifling: Righthand twist, 1 turn in 20".
Sights—front: Protected post.
  rear: Aperture graduated to 600 meters.

Belgian Rifles In World War II

While the basic rifles and carbines were the 7.65mm M 1889 the following rifles were listed as being widely issued:

(1) *Model 1916*: Slight variant of the 7.65mm 1889. Barrel jacket.

(2) *Model 1898 Belgian*: Same as German Gew. 98, but in 7.65mm.

(3) *Model 1924 Series*: Calibers 7, 7.65 and 7.92mm. These were export Mauser System rifles, made by F. N.

(4) *Model 1935 Belgian*: Officially adopted for use in 7.65mm.

FN "FAL" Rifle as used by the Belgian Army.

FN 7.62mm NATO "FAL" of 1962 type.

(5) *Model 1936 Belgian*: The old projecting box magazine M1889 modified to take the German Gew. 98 style bolt sleeve and shortened, 7.65mm.

(6) *Model Enfield 1914:* Usually in 7.92mm German. Large quantities of these and of the U. S. Enfield 1917 rifles were reworked in Belgium for export in the 1920's, and some were in Belgian warehouses in 1939.

EARLIER OFFICIAL BREECHLOADERS: The first metallic cartridge breechloader *officially* used by the Belgian Army was the British-made Albini-Braendlin. The system was adopted as a means of converting muzzle loaders cheaply. Many early conversions are .60 R.F., but the official form is .43 R.F. (11mm). A slightly modified form, the Terssen, was used in limited numbers. The 1871 Comblain was used by the Civil Guard, but was not an Army rifle.

FN Sporting Weapons

FN currently is producing high-powered Mauser type sporting rifles for the world market. Those made for the U.S. market are stocked in American styles and made in American calibers. These rifles are very well made and come in a number of grades. The Olympian grade is a very finely finished weapon with beautiful engravings and hand checkering. Weights of these rifles run from 6.75 pounds in .243 Winchester to 8.25 pounds in .458 Winchester. Barrel lengths are from 22 to 24 inches. A sliding type safety mounted on the right of the receiver close to the bolt sleeve and a modified, more compact bolt stop is used on these rifles. The FN Mauser Sporter is now made in .243 Win, .264 Win, .270 Win, .30-06, .308 Win, .300 H&H, .338 Win, .375 H&H, and .458 Win, among other calibers.

FN also makes superposed (over and under), shotguns and two different types of automatic shotguns. These weapons are all sold under the Browning name and are world renowned for reliability and beauty of finish.

F. N. also manufactures under Browning patents, for sale outside the U. S., a hammerless .22 pump and a medium power autoloader which were the counterparts of those marketed in the U. S. under the Remington trademark. Other rifles made there are a Browning .22 autoloader and a series of standard low power turn-bolt plinking and pest rifles.

August Francotte & Cie., S. A. Sporting Rifles

Francotte is one of the world's finest custom gun builders. Their products embrace a wide range of arms and calibers almost unknown and seldom encountered in the United States.

The following list affords a comprehensive picture of their general rifle output. Since special specifications are the rule with this manufacturer, is is impracticable to attempt to give details of weights, lengths and stock styles.

MAUSER ACTIONS (F.N. AND GERMAN MAUSER): Specially barreled and stocked. Common calibers 7mm., 8mm. (7.9mm) 9mm. and 9.3mm.

DOUBLE BARREL RIFLES: Built to order on either Purdey or Greener bolting systems, usually with treble bolts. Common calibers: .22 H.P., 8x57mm, 8x60mm, 9x57mm, 9.3x74mm, 10.75x52mm, .405 Winchester, .35 Winchester. Also made in all American, Austrian, British and German high power and magnum calibers rim or rimless to order, as well as for elephant cartridges.

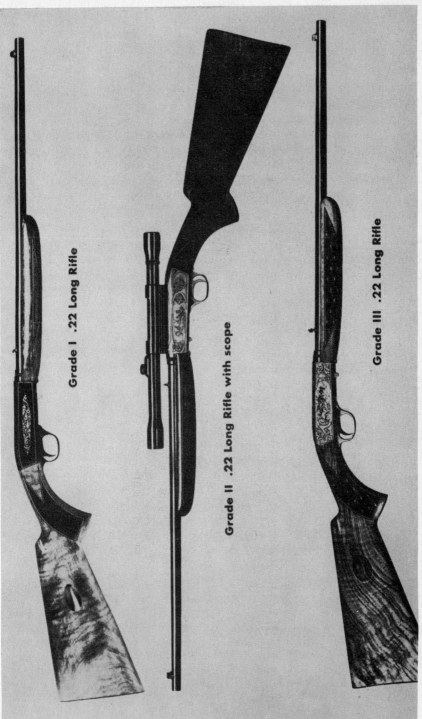

Grade I .22 Long Rifle

Grade II .22 Long Rifle with scope

Grade III .22 Long Rifle

Browning .22 Long Rifle Automatic as currently made by FN.

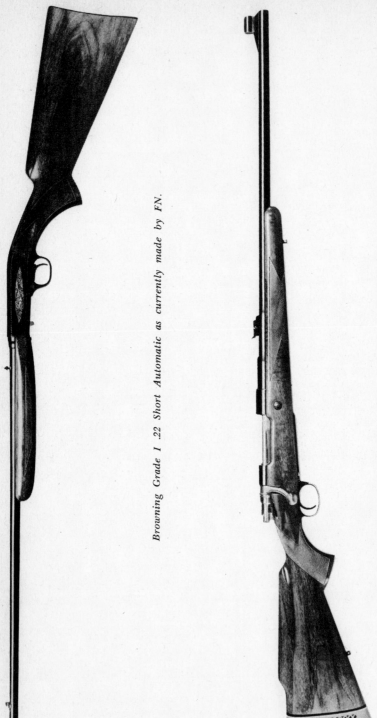

Browning Grade I .22 Short Automatic as currently made by FN.

FN 375 Magnum Sporter, Safari Grade. These weapons are handled in the U. S. by the Browning Arms Company.

COMBINATION RIFLE AND SHOTGUN DOUBLES: Any combination ordered. Also Paradox bored (the last few inches of shotgun barrels rifled to handle special slugs).

THREE BARRELED RIFLES: Anson & Deeley box locks with either Purdey or Greener treble bolt system.

FRANCOTTE-MARTINI RIFLES: Single shot falling block rifles on the Martini system with Francotte quick-removable lock system. Any caliber. Any conceivable type of stock and rest. Also bolt rifles built on F. N. actions to order.

MISCELLANEOUS: Warnant system lifting block, Flobert system, Leclerc system (tip-up barrel operated by right side thumb lever) and Remington rolling block small bore rifles and shot shell arms.

Belgian 7.65mm Mauser Cartridge

Other Names: 7.65mm Mauser
Type: Rimless, Necked, Centerfire
Overall Length: 3.06"
Average Wt.: 441 grs.
Type Powder: Nitrocellulose
Approximate Chg.: 42.5 gr.
Type Primer: Boxer and Berdan

BULLET

Type: Jacketed, Round Nose
Diameter: .310"
Weight: 215 grs.
Length: 1.205"

CARTRIDGE CASE

Length Overall: 2.09"
Length Head to Shoulder: 1.75"
Length of Shoulder .10"
Length of Neck .24"
Diameter at Rim: .474"
Diameter at Base: .470"
Diameter at Neck: .340"
Diameter at Shoulder: .425"

BALLISTICS (approximate)

Muzzle Velocity: 2034 f.s.
Pressure: About 42,000 lbs./sq. in.

Notes: 1. This cartridge was the basis for the Turkish 7.65mm Mauser cartridge and the 7.65mm Mauser cartridge used in South America.

2. Cartridge sold in U. S. under name "7.65mm Mauser" interchanges.

Belgian 11mm M1867 Cartridge

Other Names: Albini-Braendlin 11mm
Type: Rimmed, Beveled base, Necked, Centerfire
Overall Length: 2.59"
Average Wt.: 648 grs.
Type Powder: Black
Approximate Charge: 80 grs.
Type Primer: Berdan

BULLET

Type: Lead, Paper patched
Diameter: .433"
Weight: 386 grs.
Length: 1.10"

CARTRIDGE CASE

Length Overall: 2.08"
Length Head to Shoulder: 1.45"
Length of Shoulder: .280"
Length of Neck: .350"
Diameter at Rim: .678"
Diameter at Base: .577"
Diameter at Neck: .482"
Diameter at Shoulder: .534"

BALLISTICS (approximate)

Muzzle Velocity: 1440 f.s.

Belgian Model 1867 Albini-Braendlin Single Shot

Caliber: 11mm
Overall length, rifle without bayonet: 53.2"
Overall weight, rifle without bayonet: 9.87 lbs.
Type of action: Lifting Block
Barrel Length: 38.1"   *No. Grooves:* 4
Bore Diameter: .433"   *Groove Dia.:* .445"

With bayonet attached: 72.7"
With bayonet attached: 10.65 lbs.

Direction of Twist: Right
Rate of Twist: 21.6"

Belgian Model 1871 Comblain Single Shot

Caliber: 11mm
Overall length, rifle without bayonet: 49"
Overall weight, rifle without bayonet: 9.1 lbs.
Type of action: Lever—Falling Block

Barrel Length: 32.8"	*No. Grooves:* 4	*Direction of Twist:* Right
Bore Diameter: .433"	*Groove Dia.:* .445"	*Rate of Twist:* 21.65"

Notes:

1. This rifle was invented by a Belgian gunsmith.

2. While the Comblain was not an official Belgian Army rifle, it was used by the Civil Guards. Comblains were encountered by the Germans in World War II.

3. The Comblain was officially used in various parts of South America, notably in Chile.

Chapter 14

BOLIVIA

(Republica Boliviana)

GOVERNMENT PLANTS: None.

PRIVATE PLANTS: None.

PRINCIPAL MILITARY RIFLES: Model 1891 (Mauser) 7.65mm. This is the same as the Argentine M. 1891. Original rifles were made by L. Loewe & Co., Berlin, Germany. The F.N. 1924 and 1934/30 Mausers are also used. (See under *Belgium*.)

EARLIER OFFICIAL BREECHLOADER: Spanish Remington rolling block 11mm.

Chapter 15

BRAZIL

(Estados Unidos Do Brazil)

GOVERNMENT PLANTS: None currently.

PRIVATE PLANTS: None of consequence as yet.

PRINCIPAL MILITARY RIFLES: Cal. .30 FN M1949, some 7.62mm FN "FAL" rifles, Mauser Model 1908, 7mm. Some U.S. M1903 and M1 rifles and M1 carbines.

EARLY OFFICIAL BREECHLOADERS: Model 1894 Mauser, 7mm. Very slight modification of Spanish Model 1893 (See under *Spain*.)
Belgian Comblain single shot and Spanish Remington single shot, both 11mm. (.433.)

Brazilian Mauser Model 1908 Rifle

The description of the German Gew. and Kar. 98 series (see under *Germany*) covers all mechanical details of the Brazilian M. 1908, which differs only in caliber and non-essential externals. The cartridge is the same as that described under *Spain,* or the latest 7mm types as described under F.N. *(Belgium)*.

Recent manufacture for Brazil showed steel jacketed pointed bullets of 139-grains weight. Average velocity about 2950 f. s. This ammunition has also been supplied by U. S. manufacturers loaded to the same velocity with 139-grain gilding metal jacketed bullet.

Note

Brazil has imported large numbers of American hunting arms. The former German export house of Gustav Genschow of Baden also supplied large quantities of sporting arms and equipment.

Brazil's very large Japanese population purchased quantities of Arisaka rifles

131

Brazilian Mauser Model 1904 Carbine. Rifle is same except for bolt handle projection and barrel length, Caliber 7mm rimless.

Bulgarian Mannlicher Model 1895 Straight Pull Carbine, Caliber 8mm rim. This is the same as the Austrian Service arm.

before World War II from Japan direct and through the Japanese export house of Yamanaka in New York City. These rifles in caliber 6.5mm Japanese and also in caliber 7mm Mauser are found both in Brazil and in Mexico.

During World War II, Brazil was armed militarily with U.S. equipment. The common cartridge calibers therefore are the 7mm Spanish Mauser and the .30-06 U.S. service.

Chapter 16

BULGARIA

(Blgariya)

GOVERNMENT PLANTS: Soviet small arms are currently being made.

PRINCIPAL MILITARY RIFLES: Generally same as Austria until period of World War II. Weapons are Soviet 7.62mm SKS carbine and Soviet 7.62mm AK-47 assault rifle.

Soviet-Designed, Bulgarian-Made 7.62mm AK-47 Assault Rifle.

EARLIER OFFICIAL BREECHLOADERS: Earliest was Russian Berdan II. (See *U.S.S.R.*)

Chapter 17
CANADA

GOVERNMENT PLANTS, Long Branch, Ontario.

PRIVATE PLANTS: Ross (no longer in production). John Inglis, World War II.

Canadian Ross Rifles Cal. .303. From top to bottom: Mark III*, Mark II*, Mark II, and Mark III.

PRINCIPAL MILITARY RIFLES: (1). Rifle, 7.62mm FN C1. (2). The only rifle manufactured in Canada and issued during World War II was the Service Rifle, No. 4 Mark I and Mark I*.

The above Lee-Enfield pattern is discussed under *Great Britain*.

Rifle 7.62mm FN C1

Canada was among the first to adopt the FN "FAL" rifle and commenced manufacture of the rifle in a "semiautomatic fire only" version at the Canadian Government Arsenal, Long Branch, Ontario. C1 is basically the same in operation as the "FAL" but differs in some details such as the rear sight. Three different lengths of butt—long, normal, and short are available for the C1.

Rifle 7.62mm FN C1. The Canadian version of the FN "FAL" Rifle.

Caliber: 7.62mm NATO
System of operation: Gas, operated, semi-
   automatic
Overall length: (normal butt) 44.75"
Barrel length: 21"
Weight, loaded: 10.93 lbs.

Feed device: 20 rounds, detachable, staggered
   box magazine
Sights—front: Protected blade
   rear: Aperture, graduated from 200-600
   yds.
Muzzle velocity: 2750 f.p.s.

There is also a 7.62mm C1A1, the latest version of the C1. C1A1 differs from the C1 in having a plastic carrying handle rather than wood and in having a two-piece firing pin. The 7.62mm C2 is a heavy barreled FN rifle which is used as the squad automatic weapon.

Canadian Automatic Rifle 7.62mm FN C2. The heavy-barreled version of the "FAL," this rifle is capable of selective fire and is used as the squad automatic weapon. Many countries have adopted heavy barreled versions of the FN. Australia has adopted the Canadian version as Rifle L2A1.

EARLIER OFFICIAL BREECHLOADERS: Ross rifles.

The Ross straight pull rifle was invented by Sir Charles Ross. Various models were manufactured at his arms plant in Quebec, Canada. The Ross appeared in a wide variety of "Marks." Minor modifications included sight changes, while major modifications included types of magazines employed and construction of bolt locking lugs. All these rifles are now obsolete, but a brief description is given because many of the rifles are still in use or in the hands of collectors.

The Ross in caliber .303 Mark VII (British) was the Canadian Service Rifle at the outbreak of World War I. However, after a comparatively short service under actual battle conditions, it was found that the extracting power of the straight pull bolt design was inadequate for the type of trench warfare then being waged.

The Ross rifle in all its Marks was a failure from a military standpoint, partly because of the complicated design of the bolt assembly. This bolt should not be stripped or reassembled except by one thoroughly familiar with the procedure. The visual test to determine if the bolt is correctly assembled is the distance the bolt head protrudes from the bolt sleeve. The bolt should project forward from the bolt sleeve. If the bolt has been incorrectly assembled, the bolt head will protrude one-quarter of an inch or less from the sleeve. In this condition the rifle can sometimes be fired, but the breech will not be locked.

When the correctly assembled Ross bolt is pushed forward, the thrust must be quite stiff.

The locking lugs differ in various marks. There are solid Mauser type lugs in the Mark II, in the Mark III the lugs are cut with interrupted threads.

The original models of the Ross through the Canadian Service Mark II used the "Harris" magazine. In this design the action cannot be loaded with a clip. Instead, when the bolt is to the rear, a finger piece projecting from the rifle and attached to the magazine follower is thrust down. This lowers the follower and compresses the spring below it. Five cartridges may then be spilled into the action without pressure from above. One side of the follower is raised higher than the other as in Mauser design, and when pressure is released on the finger piece, the follower supports the cartridges in double column ready for feeding.

The Mark III Model uses a modified form of the Lee magazine and is loaded with standard British charger. This design also has a cutoff to hold the magazine in reserve.

Ross Rifle Mark II Cal. .303

In all Marks and Models, the Ross .303 is a straight pull action with two-piece bolt. The handle is integral with the hollow bolt cylinder into which the bolt head is inserted from the front. The bolt head carries dual opposed lugs at its forward end, and is hollowed out to receive the striker and the mainspring.

Outside ribs on either side of the bolt cylinder work in receiver guides to prevent any turning motion of the cylinder. Inside the cylinder there are screw threads which engage with corresponding threads on the exterior of the bolt head to provide the necessary rotation to engage and disengage the locking lugs in their seats in the receiver. The screw threads on the bolt head are cut in two spiral ribs.

The long spring extractor has a lug at its rear end. While the forward claw is drawing the cartridge back, this rear lug is engaged with the rear edge of the bolt head to take the pull. During extraction a cam surface is working against the extractor lug, forcing the claw to grip the case firmly.

The flat ejector works in a slot in the left side of the receiver, where it is held by a pin and is actuated by a spring which presses its point inwards towards the bolt.

The trigger is pivoted to a special frame which also carries the sear and a

Typical Canadian Ross Military Pattern Straight Pull. Locking lugs are solid in some variants. Methods of attaching the cocking piece also vary.

The magazine shown can be loaded from standard British clips.

Detail illustrates position of bolt assembly units, and method of straight pull operation.

special safety stop. The upper end of the trigger has two ribs which furnish the military double pull in the same manner as the British S.M.L.E.

The most common magazine is of a box type with an interesting type of follower construction clearly shown in the drawing. It may be loaded with the British charger-clip, cartridges being stripped in through the top of the open action.

The Mark I Ross was made in very limited quantities. The Mark II or 1905 was made in several variations. Early production has a tangent type rear sight and a cut-off which was operated by a lever just forward of the trigger. The Mark II** has a leaf-type rear sight. Some Mark II** rifles may be found with two rear sights—the standard leaf mounted ahead of the receiver and a target-type leaf mounted at the rear of the receiver. There is also a target version of the Mark II with target leaf rear sight mounted on the receiver and a 30.5-inch barrel, rather than the 28-inch barrel as on other variations of the Mark II.

Canadian Model Mark II Ross

Caliber: .303	*Type of magazine:* Staggered Box
Overall length, rifle: 47.81″	*Type of bolt:* 2 piece—rotating head, solid
Overall weight, rifle: 8.3 lbs.	lugs.
Type of action: Straight pull	*Capacity:* 5
Barrel length: 28″ *No. Grooves:* 4	*Direction of twist:* Right
Bore diameter .303″ *Groove Dia.:* .313″	*Rate of twist:* 10″

Canadian Mark III Ross

Caliber: .303	*Type of magazine:* 5-round staggered box,
Length, overall: 50.5″	charger loaded
Barrel length: 30.5″	*Type of action:* Straight pull
Weight: 9.75 lbs.	*Type of bolt:* 2 piece—rotating head with
	interrupted thread-type lugs.

Ross Rifle Model 10

This rifle, commonly encountered in caliber .280 Ross, is the Ross design best known in the U. S. It was widely sold in this country as a sporting rifle. It was also manufactured in calibers .303 British and to a limited extent in calibers .30-06 and .35 Winchester.

The mechanics of this rifle are the same as of the earlier design, except for minor refinements.

A gas escape vent is provided in the bolt head between the two locking lugs.

The magazine in the Model 10 is very much like the standard Mauser. The magazine cutoff on the left side of the receiver resembles the U. S. Springfield. Turning it down, limits the rearward length of the bolt travel to prevent a cartridge from rising from the magazine high enough to feed. Turning the cut-off up permits the bolt to move back far enough to enable the magazine follower, forced up by its spring, to bring a cartridge in line for the forward feeding stroke of the bolt. Placing the cutoff in the center position permits withdrawal of the bolt.

Ross .22 Caliber Rifles

Ross manufactured a line of straight pull .22 caliber rifles for a time.

Chapter 18
CHILE
(Republica De Chile)

GOVERNMENT PLANTS: None.

PRIVATE PLANTS: None for rifles. Excellent imitations of Colt and S&W revolvers are made in Chile, as well as semi-automatic pistols.

PRINCIPAL MILITARY RIFLES: FN 7.62mm light and heavy barrel, 7.62mm NATO SIG Model 510 rifles, cal. .30 M1 rifle and carbine, and 7mm Mauser M1904.

EARLIER OFFICIAL BREECHLOADERS: Belgian Comblain S.S. Model 1870, 11mm. Mauser Model 1895 (same as Spanish Model 1893) 7mm.

NOTE: Chile was among the first to recognize the value of magazine rifles. Large numbers of Winchester .44-40 M. 1873 were used in the border wars in the late '70's. The earliest Mannlichers were also used there.

AMMUNITION: See F.N. (Under *Belgium*). As manufactured in the United States for Chile in recent years, the Chilean 7mm cartridge was loaded with a pointed gilding metal jacketed bullet with a muzzle velocity of about 2950 f. s.

Chilean 7mm Model 1895 Mausers

There are three versions of this weapon, rifle, short rifle, and carbine. Quantities of all types have been on sale in the U.S. market for the past several years.

M1895 Rifle	*M1895 Carbine*
Caliber: 7mm	7mm
System of operation: Manually operated bolt action	Manually operated bolt action
Weight: 8.9 lbs.	Approx. 7.5 lbs.
Length overall: 48.5"	37"
Barrel length: 29.06"	18.25"
Feed device: 5 round, nondetachable staggered box magazine	5 round, nondetachable staggered box magazine
Sight—front: Barleycorn	Barleycorn
rear: leaf	leaf
Muzzle velocity: Approx. 2700 f.p.s.	Approx. 2600 f.p.s.

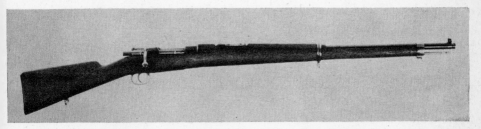

Chilean 7mm M1895 Rifle. Specimens with horizontal bolts also exist.

Chilean 7mm M1895 Carbine.

Chilean Mauser M1895 7mm Rifle, made in Germany. This rifle is essentially the 7mm Spanish M1893 Rimless.

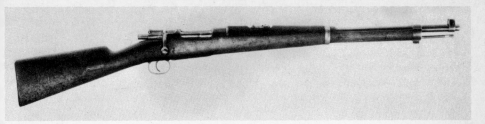

Chilean 7mm M1895 Short Rifle.

Chilean Model 1904 Mauser

Caliber: 7mm
Overall length, rifle without bayonet: 49.2"
Overall weight, rifle without bayonet: 8.8 lbs.
Type of action: Turnbolt
Type of Magazine: Integral Box—Staggered
  Column

Barrel Length: 29.2" *No. Grooves:* 4
Type of bolt: 1 piece—rotating head
Capacity: 5
  Direction of Twist: Right
  Rate of Twist: 8.66"

Notes:
  1. This rifle is the same as the Brazilian 1904 pattern.

Chapter 19

NATIONALIST CHINA

(Chung-Hua Min Kua)

GOVERNMENT PLANTS: There are facilities on Taiwan (Formosa) for the manufacture and repair of small arms.

PRINCIPAL MILITARY RIFLES: The basic equipment is the cal. .30 M1. However, during World War II U. S. Model 1903 and 1917 rifles (Springfields and Enfields) in Caliber .30-06 were supplied in quantity to the Chinese Government troops.

China began the purchase of German Mauser rifles with the very first commercial design, the Mauser 1871 single shot. As Paul Mauser developed his new rifles, China purchased quantities of the constantly improving types. The tube loading Model 71-84, and the official German Commission Model 1888 in caliber 7.92mm German service was ordered from Mauser's partner, Ludwig Loewe & Co. of Berlin.

China has used a large number of different types of rifles within the past thirty years. Most are no longer used by either Chinese Nationalist or Chinese Communist regular forces but some may still be found in the hands of Chinese Communist Militia. The Chinese manufactured a modified copy of the German 7.92mm 88 at Hanyang Arsenal which they call Type 88 Hanyang. This rifle has the same .318 bore as the German Model 88 and cannot be used with 7.92mm .323 IS (JS) ammunition. The Chinese also had quantities of 7.92mm Model 98 rifles, Kar 98 carbines, and Mauser "Standard" Model rifles, all of German man-

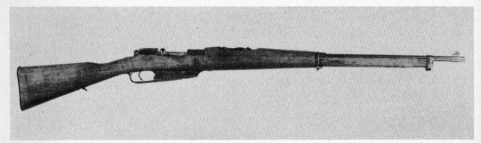

Chinese "Hanyang" Type Rifle. This 7.92mm rifle is a Chinese modified copy of the German M1888 Rifle, large quantities of which were bought by China. Also called Type 88 by the Chinese.

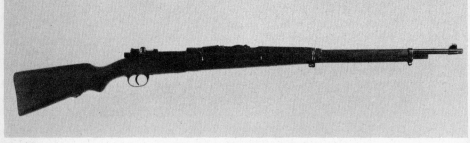

Chinese-made 7.92mm Mauser.

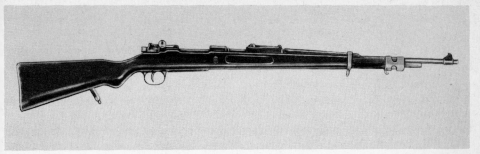

Chinese 7.92mm Model "Chiang Kai Shek" Mauser. This rifle is a copy of the Mauser "Standard Model."

ufacture. Copies of the "Standard" Model Mauser were made in China and were known as the "Chiang Kai Shek" Model. 7.92mm Belgian FN M1924 and 1930 rifles and Chinese-made copies were also used as were Czech-made Model 24 rifles and Chinese copies thereof. The Chinese also used quantities of captured Japanese 6.5mm Type 38 and 7.7mm Type 99 rifles. When the Japanese armament plants in Manchuria were captured in 1945 the Chinese continued manufacture of the weapons they made, which included 7.7mm Type 99 rifles. They also made a large number of Type 99 rifles barreled for the 7.92mm cartridge. A number of these rifles were used by Chinese Communist troops in Korea and as a result they may be found in American collections.

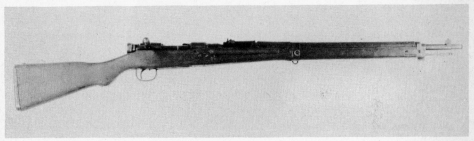

Type 99 Rifle of Japanese Design Chambered for the 7.92mm Cartridge. This rifle was made in the Japanese-founded Manchurian plants after they were seized by China at the end of World War II.

Chapter 20

COMMUNIST CHINA

The Chinese Communist Army entered the Korean War with a mixture of Chinese, Japanese, and U.S. rifles. During the course of that war they lost many of these weapons and were equipped with Soviet weapons. All common models of the Soviet 7.62mm Mosin Nagant rifle and carbine were used by the Chinese Communist Army in Korea. The Soviet 7.62mm M1944 Mosin Nagant rifle was produced by the Chinese Communists as the Type 53.

The Chinese Communists are currently arming their troops with the Soviet 7.62mm SKS semiautomatic rifle and the Soviet 7.62mm AK assault rifle. Both are being produced in Communist China as the Type 56.

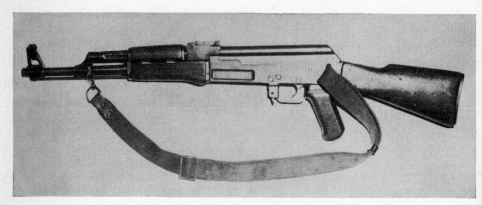

Chinese Communist 7.62mm Type 56 Assault Rifle, Copy of Soviet AK-47.

Chapter 21

COLOMBIA

(La Republica De Colombia)

GOVERNMENT PLANTS: None.

PRIVATE PLANTS: None.

PRINCIPAL MILITARY RIFLES: U.S. cal. .30 M1 rifle, cal. .30 M1 carbine, cal. .30 Dominican carbine, cal. .30 Mauser rifle.

EARLIER OFFICIAL BREECHLOADERS: M1891 7.65mm Mauser, Remington Rolling Block S.S. 11mm (.433) Spanish.

Chapter 22
COSTA RICA
(Republica De Costa Rica)

GOVERNMENT PLANTS: None.

PRIVATE PLANTS: None.

PRINCIPAL MILITARY RIFLES: F.N. Mausers. Commonly 7mm (See under *Belgium*).

EARLIER OFFICIAL BREECHLOADER: Remington R.B. Single Shot. 11mm (.433) Spanish.

Chapter 23
CUBA
(Republica De Cuba)

GOVERNMENT PLANTS: None.

PRIVATE PLANTS: None.

PRINCIPAL MILITARY RIFLES: Cuba was equipped with U.S. cal. .30 M1903 and M1 rifles prior to the seizure of power by Fidel Castro. A quantity of FN "FAL" light automatic rifles were delivered to Cuba before the Western powers established an embargo on arms shipments to that country. Cuba has within the past several years been receiving large shipments of weapons from the Soviet bloc. The Cubans at present have respectable quantities of Czech 7.62mm Model 52 rifles plus other Czech and Soviet small arms in their possession.

EARLIER BREECHLOADERS: Model 1869 Remington R.B. Single Shot, 11mm. Model 1893 Mauser, 7mm (Spanish).
The first production Mausers to use the double-line staggered flush box magazine were made in Germany in 1892 for shipment to Spanish troops in Cuba. This rifle also introduced the 7mm Mauser cartridge.

Chapter 24

CZECHOSLOVAKIA

(Československá Republika)

GOVERNMENT PLANTS: Ceska Zbrojovka (Brno) now under State control. This is one of the largest rifle plants in the world. Manufacture before 1939 was largely military Mausers for export. Currently some sporting Mausers are being manufactured, as well as some conventional .22 bolt actions. Considerable develment work has been done on gas-operated military semi- and full automatic rifles.

PRINCIPAL MILITARY RIFLES: The 7.62mm Model 58 Assault Rifle is now the principal military rifle. Quantities of the 7.62mm M52/57 and M52 rifle may also be on hand.

EARLIER MILITARY RIFLES: Short Rifles VZ-24, VZ-33 and Mauser system rifles in 7.9mm caliber, all of which are mechanically practically identical with the Kar. 98 k. (German). Manufacture was started in 1924. Receiver commonly thinner than the German.

Shorter and somewhat modified versions were introduced as the VZ 12/33 and 16/33, though mechanically there were no changes.

When the Germans took over Czechoslovakia they kept the arms factories going. They renamed the Czech arms Gew. 24 (t) and Gew. 33 (t) and instituted minor changes in slings and furniture to compare more closely to the German ideas of external design.

A modification of the VZ 16/33 was also issued as the Gew. 33-40 which has a 19.29 inch barrel. The overall length is 39.1". The bore diameter is .312". The groove diameter .323". The twist is right at a rate of 9.45". This design was used by the Germans for mountain, truck and similar service where a short weapon was desirable. Some were made with iron plates on the left side of the stock just ahead of the butt plate so that the weapon might be used as an aid in climbing steep hills.

Another form sometimes listed as the Gewehr 33-40 was provided with a folding butt hinged on the right and held in position by a catch on the right of the receiver. This design permitted the arm to be carried by paratroops.

The Gewehr 33-40 was extensively manufactured at Waffenwerke Brunn, A. G. (ZB) at Brno.

7.62mm M58 Assault Rifle

This weapon is chambered for the Soviet 7.62mm Model 43 "intermediate" sized cartridge. The weapon outwardly resembles the Soviet AK Assault Rifle, but is much lighter than the Soviet weapon. It is likely that this selective-fire rifle will in time replace the Model 52/57 rifle and the conventional submachine guns. The Model 58 comes in fixed wooden stock and folding metal stock versions.

Czechoslovakian VZ (Model) 1924, Caliber 7.9mm. This rifle was manufactured extensively for the Germans during World War II and may be encountered with various styles of stocks and slings, and with various markings.

Postwar 7.92mm Czech Mauser. Note enlarged, stamped trigger guard and stamped upper band. The hole in the butt plate is for dismounting the firing pin.

Czech 7.62mm Model 58 Assault Rifle with Wooden Stock.

Czech 7.62mm Model 58 Assault Rifle with Folding Stock, Stock Fixed.

Caliber: 7.62mm
System of operation: Gas, selective fire
Weight, loaded:
  with wooden stock: 8.75 lbs.
  with metal stock: 8.75 lbs.
Length overall:
  w/wooden stock: 33"
  w/fixed metal stock: 33"
  w/folded metal stock: 25"

Barrel length: 14"
Feed device: 30-round staggered column, detachable box magazine
Sights—front: Protected post
    rear: Tangent leaf, adjustable in 100 meter increments from 100 to 800 meters.
Cyclic rate: 700-800 R.P.M.
Muzzle velocity: 2,300 f.p.s.

The Model 58 Assault Rifle has a two-piece bolt consisting of the bolt body and the locking lugs. The locking lugs lock in recesses in the side of the receiver. The bolt carrier is thrust to the rear by a gas piston which is mounted above the barrel. The gases tapped from the gas port move the piston to the rear against the pressure of its spring and it strikes the top front of the bolt carrier and forces the carrier to the rear. The piston then is forced forward by its spring. The bolt carrier takes the bolt to the rear after the locking lugs are cammed upward out of their locking recesses in the receiver. This weapon uses a spring loaded striker-firing pin arrangement similar in concept to that of the average bolt action rifle.

Czech 7.62mm Model 58 Assault Rifle with Folding Stock, Stock Folded.

There is no rotating hammer in this weapon. The bolt and bolt carrier are buffed by the recoil spring and striker spring; at this point the sear nose slips into the sear notch of the striker. The bolt carrier and bolt return forward and the bolt strips another cartridge from the magazine and chambers it. The locking lugs are again cammed down into their recesses in the receiver. If the trigger is still being held to the rear with the selector set on automatic fire or if the trigger is pulled again the weapon will fire again and the process is repeated.

FIELD STRIPPING. To field strip Model 58, the following procedure is used. Remove magazine and clear weapon to insure it is not loaded. Pull trigger—do not attempt to strip the gun while it is cocked! Pull receiver cover assembly retaining pin to the right and remove the receiver cover. Draw bolt carrier assembly to the rear and lift it up and out of the receiver; rotate the striker—which projects from the rear of the bolt—1/8th of a turn counter-clockwise and withdraw it to the rear; the bolt, bolt locking lugs, and the bolt carrier will then be separated. Disengage the handguard retaining pin by pulling it to the right; tip the rear of the handguard up and withdraw it to the rear. Pull the piston to the rear and tip the piston head up, withdrawing it toward the muzzle. Reassembly is accomplished in reverse fashion.

7.62 Model 52 Cartridge

Other names: 7.62 x 45
Type: rimless, necked, center-fire
Overall length: 2.36"
Type powder: tubular, single base
Weight: 280 gr.
Propellent weight: 28 gr.

BULLET

Type: full jacketed, pointed boat tail, gilding metal clad steel jacket
Diameter: .311"
Length: 1.11"
Weight: 131 gr.

CARTRIDGE CASE

Length overall: 1.77"
Diameter at rim: .441"
Diameter at base: .442"
Diameter at neck: .334"

BALLISTICS

Muzzle velocity: 2440 f.p.s.

Czech 7.62mm Model 52 Rifle

Caliber: 7.62mm, Czechoslovak Model 52
System of operation: Gas, semi-automatic fire only
Weight, loaded: 9.8 lbs.
Length, overall: 39.37"
Barrel length: 20.66"
Note:
Model 52/57 has the same characteristics but is chambered for the Soviet 7.62mm M43 (7.62 x 39mm).

Feed mechanism: 10-round, double staggered-row, detachable box magazine (loaded with 5-round chargers)
Sights—front: Hooded blade (removable hood)
  rear: Notched tangent with curved ramp
Muzzle velocity: 2440 f.p.s.

Czech 7.62mm Model 52 Rifle with Bayonet Fixed.

Czech 7.62mm Model 52 Rifle with Bayonet Folded.

7.62mm Model 52 and Model 52/57 Rifles

This weapon is a combination of several foreign designs added to a few Czech ideas. The trigger mechanism is similar to that of the U.S. M1 rifle, the gas system is similar to that of the German MKb 42 (W) and several earlier Walther rifle designs. The bolt which is a tipping type with frontal locking lugs appears to be a native design. The Model 52 has a permanently attached bayonet fitted to its right side. The 7.62mm cartridge used by the Model 52 is an "intermediate" size but is not interchangeable with the Soviet 7.62mm "intermediate" sized cartridge. It is slightly larger and has a bit more power than the Soviet cartridge.

The Model 52/57 is basically the same as the Model 52 but is chambered for the Soviet 7.62mm M43 "intermediate" sized cartridge. The adoption of this cartridge by Czechoslovakia gave the Sino-Soviet bloc complete standardization of small arms ammunition.

The magazine of the Model 52 and 52/57 is loaded with two 5-round chargers (stripper clips). The operating handle is pulled slightly to the rear and released and the bolt carrier and bolt go forward chambering the cartridge. When the

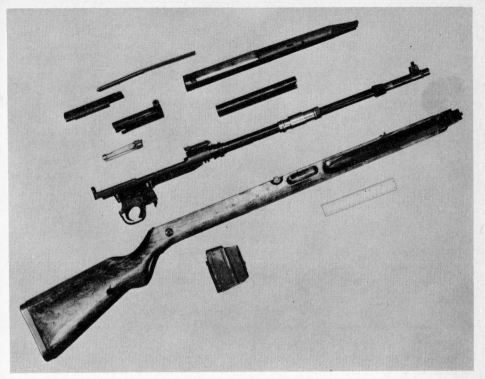

Czech 7.62mm Model 52 Field Stripped.

trigger is pulled the sear releases the hammer which pivoting forward strikes the firing pin, and the firing pin strikes the cartridge. After the bullet passes the gas port, gas enters the port, driving the sleeve to the rear. The sleeve transmits this blow to the sheet steel piston which in turn passes it on to spring-loaded tappets mounted under the rear sight base. These tappets strike the bolt carrier, which moves to the rear carrying the bolt out of its locked position. The bolt and bolt carrier continue to the rear, compressing the recoil spring and cocking the hammer. When the bolt and bolt carrier reach the rear of the receiver the kinetic energy developed in the recoil spring forces them to return to the battery position, picking up and chambering a cartridge as they travel forward. If the trigger is pulled again this cycle will be repeated.

The gas system of this weapon, as that of the Walthers on which it is patterned, is somewhat unusual. There is no gas tube to channel the gas rearward. A ring mounted forward of the gas port prevents the gas from escaping forward; the movable slide, also a ring encircling the barrel, is free to move to the rear under the pressure of the gas. The piston, a semi-circular piece of sheet steel, transmits the blow of the slide rearwards and engages the tappets. This is a rather complex system although it should be easy to clean and maintain, since all parts are exposed. A metal handguard is used; this handguard probably heats up considerably in sustained fire.

Other Mausers Made by ZB

Other Mausers manufactured by ZB in addition to the Models 24, 12/33,

16/33, and 33/40 were the 98/22 rifle, 98/29 carbine, 98/29 rifle, and a postwar modified Kar 98k. The 98/22 is similar to the German Model 98 rifle but has the new type tangent rear sight and its handguard extends to the front of the receiver. The 98/29 carbine and rifle were used by Iran and are described under that country. The Model 12/33 and 16/33 carbines differ mainly in barrel

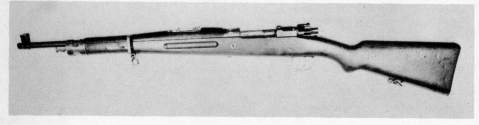

Czech 7.92mm Model 12/33 Carbine.

length; the 12/33 has a barrel length of 21.89 inches and the 16/33 has a barrel length of 19.29 inches. The 16/33, in addition to being used as the basis for the German 33/40, was used as a Czech service weapon under the designation Vz 33. Vz stands for "Vzor"—in English, "Model."

CHARACTERISTICS

	M98/22 Rifle	M24 Rifle	M12/33 Carbine	M16/33 Carbine
Caliber:	7.92mm*	7.92mm	7mm*	7.92mm
Overall length:	49.2"	43.3"	42"	39.2"
Barrel length:	29.13"	23.2"	21.89"	19.29"
Weight:	9.9 lbs.	9.2 lbs.	8.5 lbs.	7.7 lbs.
Sights—front:	barleycorn	barleycorn	barleycorn w/guards	barleycorn w/guards
rear:	.... Tangent			
Feed device:	.... 5-round, integral, staggered column, box magazine			

*These weapons may have been made in other calibers as well.

The last military Mauser made in Czechoslovakia was made after World War II. Some of these weapons bear the "Narodni Podnik" marking, indicating they were made in Czechoslovakia after 1948. A number of these weapons have been imported into the United States from the Middle East within recent years. The weapon is basically a modified Kar 98k. It has a large stamped trigger guard, fabricated upper band, additional gas relief ports in the bottom of the bolt, and the firing-pin dismounting hole in the bottom of the butt plate. The finish is rough as compared with the pre-war Czech Mausers and some components of wartime manufacture were probably used in the manufacture of these weapons.

Czech Prototype Semiautomatic Rifles

The Czechs developed several prototype semiautomatic weapons which were never mass produced. Two of these weapons appeared prior to or during World War II and are chambered for the 7.92mm cartridge.

The gas operated ZK 420S is a postwar product. It was offered by ZB as a commercial military rifle. The weapon has a resemblance to the U. S. M1, but with the exception of the trigger mechanism, the resemblance is mainly superficial. The

Czech Prototype 7.92mm Semiautomatic Rifle. This rifle has not been identified as to designation but has some external features that resemble the ZK 391.

Czech 7.92mm Model 38 Semiautomatic Rifle. This rifle was made only in prototype form.

bolt is moved by a bolt carrier, which is an integral part of the operating rod, and is quite similar in operation to the bolt of the Soviet AK Assault Rifle. The weapon has a detachable ten-round magazine and is loaded with five-round chargers. The rifle was a failure and very few were made.

A pre-war Czech semiautomatic rifle which gained some acceptance was the 7.92mm ZH-29. This rifle was among those submitted to the United States for test before the adoption of the M1. ZH-29 was exported in limited quanties, Ethiopia being among the buyers. ZH-29 is gas operated and fed by a detachable box magazine. It has an unusual aluminum radiator mounted around the barrel and gas cylinder tube just forward of the handguard. The weapon breaks for stripping in a fashion similar to the current FN "FAL" rifle. ZH-29 was among the first of the successful military semiautomatic rifles and is a design of Vaclav Holek, the famed Czech small-arms developer.

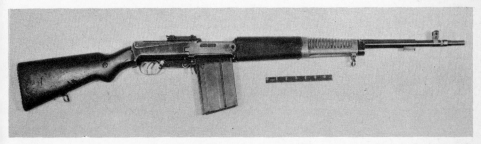

Czech 7.92mm ZH 29 Semiautomatic Rifle. A pre-World War II semiautomatic rifle, it was in limited use in a few countries before that war.

Czech 7.92mm ZK 420S Semiautomatic Rifle. This weapon was made in prototype form only and is of postwar design.

Sporting Rifles

A complete line of Mauser-type sporting rifles is manufactured by Zbrojovka Brno. The .22 rimfire magazine rifles Brno 1 and Brno 2 (also known as ZKM 452) are sold internationally, as is the .22 Hornet magazine rifle, ZKM 465. A semiautomatic .22 rifle, the ZKM 581, is also made. ZB has also made a .22 rimfire training rifle, the ZKM 454. This weapon is built to the same basic lines as the 7.92mm Czech Model 24 Mauser. It uses a 5-round box magazine. The current ZB high-powered rifle, called the ZG-47, is a Mauser-type weapon made in .270 Winchester, .30-06, and most popular European calibers.

Chapter 25

DENMARK

(Kongeriget Danmark)

GOVERNMENT PLANTS: Haerens Tojus and Gevaerfabriken, Copenhagen.

PRIVATE PLANTS: *Schultz & Larsen Gevaerfabrik, Otterup*. Target rifles of dropping block, triggerguard lever type, single shot .22 caliber bolt actions, the Model 65 bolt action high-powered rifle chambered for the 7x61mm Sharpe and Hart, and the .358 Norma Magnum.

Dansk Industri Syndicat (Madsen): This old arms firm has produced some Ljungman semi-automatic rifles since World War II. In addition, a shortened light-weight military rifle—the Model 47—was developed as was a 7.62mm NATO light automatic rifle. The automatic rifle is covered in detail later in this section.

PRINCIPAL MILITARY RIFLES: Denmark, at the conclusion of World War II, was temporarily supplied with Swedish 6.5mm Mausers, German 7.92mm Mausers, and some British weapons. Current weapons listed with their common and Danish nomenclature are as follows:

Common Nomenclature:	Danish Nomenclature:
.30 cal. Rifle M1	7.62mm G M/50
.30 cal. Rifle M1917	7.62mm G M/53 (17)

Early Military Rifles

Denmark adopted the Krag-Jorgensen rifle in 1889 and it continued to be the Danish service rifle until World War II. A number of variations of the weapon were designed during that period. Listed below are the varying types:

8mm Rifle M1889: Covered in detail later in the text.

8mm Infantry Carbine M1889: This is a shortened rifle M1889 having a horizontal bolt handle and a barrel jacket. A tangent-type rear sight is fitted to the barrel jacket. The letter "F" found before the serial number indicates that the weapon is an infantry carbine; this letter is also found on the stock.

8mm Artillery Carbine M1889: Basically the same as the infantry carbine, but has a turned-down bolt lever, a triangular front-sling swivel and a stud on the left side of the stock. The stud was used to carry the weapon by being fitted into a leather piece worn on the gunner's back. The lower sling swivel is fitted into the left side of the butt. The letter "A" before the serial number and on the stock indicates that the weapon is an artillery carbine.

8mm Cavalry Carbine M1889: This weapon also has a wooden handguard. The upper sling swivel is fitted to the lower band and the lower swivel is on the left side of the butt stock. A stud, similar to that of the artillery carbine, is fitted to the left side of the stock above the trigger guard and the bayonet lug is fastened to the forward end of the forearm. The letter "R" before the serial number and on the stock indicates that the weapon is a cavalry carbine.

8mm Engineer Carbine M1889: This weapon has no outer barrel jacket; instead it has a wooden handguard. The letter "I" found before the serial number and on the stock indicates that the weapon is an engineer carbine.

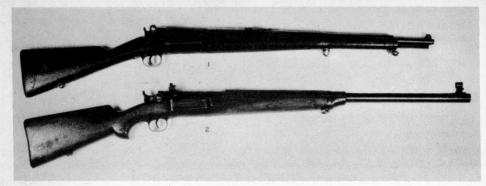

Top: Danish 8mm M1889 Engineer Carbine.
*Bottom: Danish 8mm M1928 Sniper Rifle. Most of these rifles have **bent bolt handles** rather than horizontal, as on the specimen shown here.*

8mm Sniper Rifle Model 1928: This weapon has a heavy barrel, sporting type stock with pistol grip, and a micrometer-type rear sight. The stock and action are marked "FSK" and the action is marked 1928. The bolt handle is bent.

Model 1889

DESCRIPTION OF DANISH KRAG-JORGENSEN: This is a turn-bolt rifle of a distinct type. The bolt is of one piece design with a recessed head. It has only one locking lug at the head of the bolt and turns downward to engage in the receiver locking recess. The guide rib also serves as a locking lug. The bolt handle also turns down into a recess in the receiver to provide a "safety locking lug" of sorts. Prominent feature of the bolt assembly is the long, flat spring extractor, fastened to the bolt sleeve at the rear and extending forward over the entire top of the bolt. Thus the extractor serves as a partial bolt cover.

Mechanically this rifle has changed very little since its adoption in 1889. Except for alteration of cocking piece and addition of a manual safety, later patterns vary only in sights, slings, stocks and the like.

The peculiar characteristics of the Danish Krag-Jorgensen are:

(1) The unusual box magazine. This is a fixed horizontal design with loading gate projecting from the right side of the receiver. The gate hinges forward to open for loading, and the feeding mechanism is mounted on the inner face of the gate.

(2) Barrel jacket for protection of both the barrel and the hands of the shooter when the barrel becomes heated from rapid fire. (The jacket is replaced by a heavy barrel in the M. 1928 version.)

(3) The Krag bolt with single forward locking lug.

The bolt is of one-piece design, being bored out from the rear to receive the striker assembly. The bolt face is recessed to accept the base of the cartridge and pierced for the firing pin to emerge. There is only one locking lug, at the head of the bolt, which locks into the bottom of the receiver ring.

When the bolt is closed, the guide rib bears against the forward right side of the split bridge of the receiver and serves as a locking lug.

The straight handle is at the rear end of the bolt cylinder. The rear of the bolt has a cam faced recess and a groove in which the point of the cocking stud

Danish Krag-Jorgensen, Model 1889, Caliber 8mm. Rifle. Numerous minor modifications exist. Some have half cock notch while others have special manual safeties. The Model 1889 Carbine has a barrel jacket as shown in the rifle above.

Danish Model 1889 Krag-Jorgensen

Caliber: 8mm
Overall length, rifle without bayonet: 52.28"
Overall weight, rifle without bayonet: 9.5 lbs.
Type of action: Turnbolt
Type of Magazine: Horizontal hinged box
Barrel Length: 32.78"
Bore Diameter: .315"

With bayonet attached: 63"
With bayonet attached: 10.3 lbs.
Type of bolt: 1 piece
Capacity: 5
No. Grooves: 6
Groove Dia.: .329"
Direction of Twist: Right
Rate of Twist: 11.8"

Notes:

1. As originally issued this rifle had no manual safety, but the cocking piece had a half-cock notch. Later models have rotating safeties which positively block the sear. Some of these do not have the half-cock notch. Safeties normally can be applied only when arm is cocked. Manual safety was adopted in 1910.

seats when the action is open. A flange partly around the rear end of the bolt retains the bolt sleeve in position. A gas escape safety vent is provided in the right side of the bolt cylinder.

A bolt sleeve fits into the rear section of the bolt, the striker passing through it. It provides a rearward compression point for the mainspring. The striker is a two-piece unit whose point forms the forward end of a hollow cylinder fitting over the rear section where it is secured by a joint. The mainspring takes a forward bearing against the end of the forward part of the striker unit.

The bolt sleeve is bored out to receive the cocking piece and is also provided with a slot in its lower surface in which the cocking stud travels. The top section of the sleeve extends over the bolt and travels in a slot cut in the receiver well. The mainspring is prevented from forcing the sleeve out of the bolt by a flange on the bolt which works in a groove in the rear section of the sleeve.

The rear section of the striker is screwed into the cocking piece. The cocking stud projects downward and rides in the groove cut for it in the tang. The forward face of this stud is cut to fit the cam recess in the bolt and has both a half and a full cock notch on early models. Late models dispense with the half-cock notch. A thumbpiece is provided at the end of the cocking piece to permit cocking without opening the action.

Instead of the customary bolt stop, rearward movement is halted by the locking lug striking the receiver bridge shoulder in the receiver. The extractor must be lifted clear of the receiver and the bolt handle turned to the left to bring the locking lug opposite the slot in the receiver bridge before the bolt can be withdrawn.

This rifle has no manual safety in the early patterns but the cocking piece can be set at half-cock.

The flat spring extractor is pivoted by a screw to the bolt sleeve. When the bolt handle is raised the extractor fits over the guide rib on the bolt. A secondary spring mortised into the extractor slips under a projection in the receiver to prevent the extractor from rising during primary extraction.

When the action is closed, the end of the extractor fits into a recess in the receiver. As the bolt handle is raised, a projection on the front of the guide rib bears against a projection on the extractor and holds it against the left wall of the receiver while the bolt is pulled to the rear.

In late patterns the manual safety usually encountered is in the form of a pivoting hook on the receiver to the rear of the bolt handle. When worked forward it blocks the sear and locks the bolt handle down. Some types have other safety modifications.

The ejector is a spring which is dovetailed into the bottom of the boltway. As the bolt is drawn back, the front end of the ejector presses upward and enters the groove in the head of the bolt to hit the base of the cartridge case.

The sear is pivoted underneath the receiver on a pin, and its nose passes up into the groove in the tang. It is operated by a flat spring.

The trigger is a bent lever. It is pivoted on a pin in a slot at the upper end of the sear. It has two ribs on its upper surface which bear in succession against the lower face of the tang to give the standard double military pull.

The magazine is a steel box which is fastened by two screws to the lower side of the receiver. It turns up on the left side opposite a guide cut in the receiver.

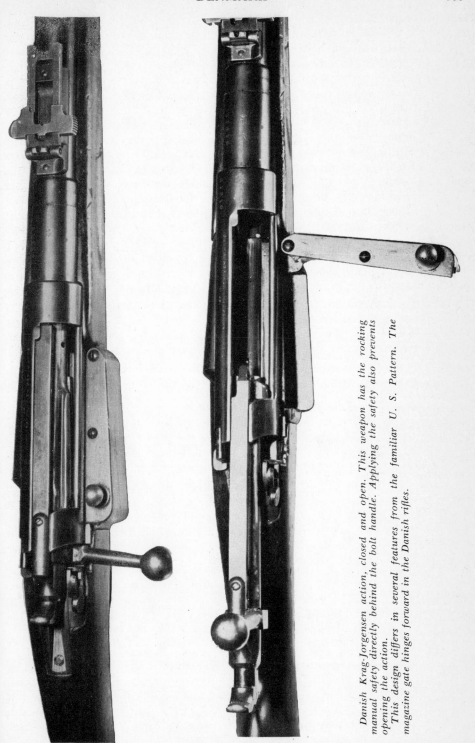

Danish Krag-Jorgensen action, closed and open. This weapon has the rocking manual safety directly behind the bolt handle. Applying the safety also prevents opening the action.

This design differs in several features from the familiar U. S. Pattern. The magazine gate hinges forward in the Danish rifles.

The loading door on its right side is hinged at the front. It is held closed at the rear by a spring catch and is operated by a thumb knob. The feeder is secured to the inside of this door. It consists of a lever operated by a flat spring and a follower which is hinged to the lever.

Note that in this design the loading door does not turn *down* on lower hinges as in the case of the American Krag-Jorgensen. Instead the Danish Model is hinged at the front and *pivots out* from the rear.

LOADING: When the loading door is opened, the rear arm of the lever is caught by a projection on the front of the magazine. This holds the follower and the lever back against the loading door. Cartridges are dropped into the open magazine. When the loading door is closed, the lever is released and the spring forces the follower against the last cartridge inserted. The cartridges are thrust across beneath the boltway, then upward and around through the loading cut in the side of the receiver. The rear end of this cut is too narrow to permit the base of a cartridge to pass through it. This prevents the cartridges from being forced out of the magazine if the gate is closed when the bolt is open.

As the bolt is thrust forward, its face hits the rim of the cartridge on the right side and pushes it ahead along an incline machined into the left side of the receiver until the head of the cartridge case reaches the enlarged section where it comes clear of the magazine for chambering.

The magazine cutoff is a split spring pin which works in a hole in the left side of the receiver parallel to the bolt. It is fitted with a thumb piece. When this thumb piece is turned up, the blade of the cutoff turns into the cartridge way to hold the cartridges back out of reach of the bolt.

OPENING THE BOLT: As the bolt handle is raised, a rear cam recess in the bolt pushes the cocking stud, which cannot rotate, back until it drops into the bolt groove. Primary extraction occurs during the lifting movement of the bolt handle when the handle hits the curved surface at the rear of the receiver bridge and starts the bolt assembly back slightly. During this motion, the extractor is thrust firmly down around the cartridge rim by the projection on the receiver.

When the bolt comes back, the point of the ejector rising into the groove in the bolt head hits the cartridge case head and ejects the case to the right. Rearward travel of the bolt is halted when the locking lug hits the bridge of the receiver.

CLOSING THE BOLT: The bolt is thrust forward until the guide rib has cleared the receiver bridge. As the bolt handle is then turned down camming surfaces on the rear of the guide rib and the forward edge of the receiver bridge co-operate with the camming surfaces on the locking lug and its seat in the receiver ring to force the bolt forward completing the compression of the mainspring and leaving the arm locked and cocked ready for firing.

DISASSEMBLY: A peculiar feature of this design is that there is no formal bolt stop—the locking lug is halted when it hits a special recess in the receiver.

To remove the bolt (1) Raise the handle and pull the bolt back as far as it will go. (2) Lift up the extractor where it catches the bolt rib until it clears the top of the receiver. (3) At this point the bolt can be further rotated to the left.

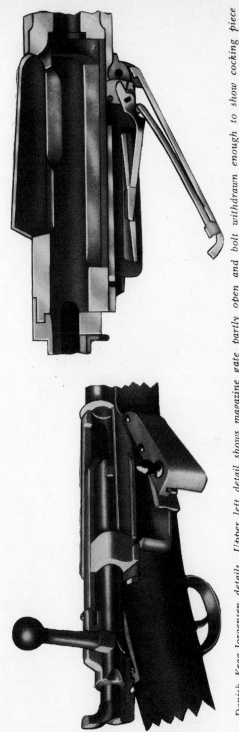

Danish Krag-Jorgensen details. Upper left detail shows magazine gate partly open and bolt withdrawn enough to show cocking piece design. This is the early pattern with half-cock notch and no manual safety.

Upper right is a top view showing construction of follower assembly and loading arrangement on left side of receiver.

(4) The locking lug is now in line with a slot in the receiver bridge and can be drawn back out of the receiver.

Dismount the bolt. (1) Remove bolt sleeve and rear section of striker. (2) Remove extractor screw from bolt sleeve and lift extractor off. (3) Remove cocking piece and unscrew rear striker section. (4) Remove mainspring and front striker section from bolt cylinder.

Further dismountings. Drive out sear pin and remove sear. Drive out trigger pin at rear of sear and remove trigger. Remove flat sear spring. Remove two magazine screws from below receiver and remove magazine. Remove follower, connecting lever and follower spring. Remove the third retaining screw (To rear of triggerguard) and remove triggerguard. Remove lower and upper bands and lift barrel and receiver units out of stock. Depress spring catch below reinforce at rear of barrel and unscrew barrel casing with front sight. Barrel is screwed into receiver.

Danish Model 1889 Krag-Jorgensen Infantry Carbine

Caliber: 8mm
Overall length, rifle without bayonet: 43.5″
Overall weight, rifle without bayonet: 8:75 lbs.
Type of action: Turnbolt
Type of Magazine: Hinged Horizontal Box
Barrel length: 24.02″

Bore diameter: .315″
No. Grooves : 4
Groove Dia.: .329″
Type of bolt: 1 piece
Capacity: 5
  Direction of twist: Right
  Rate of twist: 11.02″

· Danish Model 28 Krag-Jorgensen

Caliber: 8mm
Overall length, rifle without bayonet: 46.1″
Type of action: Turnbolt
Type of magazine: Hinged horizontal box
Barrel length: 23.1″
Bore diameter: .315″

No Grooves: 4
Groove Dia.: .329″
Type of bolt: 1 piece
Capacity: 5
  Direction of twist: Right
  Rate of twist: 11.02″

Notes:
  1. Has special receiver sight. This is a sniping rifle.

Danish 8mm M1889 Cartridge.

Other Names: 8mm Krag-Jorgensen
Type: Rimmed, Necked, Centerfire
Overall Length: 2.99″
Average Wt.: 470 gr.
Type Powder: Nitrocellulose
Approximate Chg.: 34 gr.
Type Primer: Berdan

BULLET
Type: Jacketed, Round Nose
Diameter: .325″
Weight: 237 Gr.
Length: 1.187″

CARTRIDGE CASE
Length Overall: 2.28″
Length Head to Shoulder: 1.64″
Length of Neck: .44″
Diameter at Rim: .575″
Diameter at Base: .550″
Diameter at Neck: .355″
Diameter at Shoulder: .457″

BALLISTICS (approximate)
Muzzle Velocity: 1986 f.p.s.
Pressure: About 44,000 lbs./sq. in.

Note: Bullet weights and ballistics vary with time and place of cartridge manufacture.

The Spitzer pointed M1908 cartridge differs from the 1889 cartridge as follows:

Propellent weight: 49 gr.
Bullet length: 1.2″
Bullet weight: 196 gr.

Complete round length: 3″
Muzzle velocity: 2360 f.p.s.

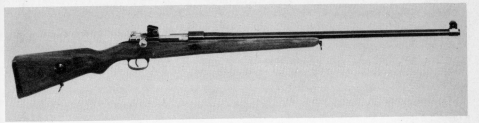

Danish NRA Rifle M52.

A shooting organization in Denmark called "De danske Skytte, Gymnastik-og Idraetsforeninger" (similar to one in Norway and which can best be compared with the National Rifle Association of The United States) was also in urgent need of weapons. The Danish government, which contributes such rifles free of charge, solved the problem by resorting to the large stock of captured German M98 Mausers which it had on hand. Most of these Mausers had been manufactured by Brno in Czechoslovakia and had the horizontal bolt handle. In order to alter the Mauser into the Danish NRA rifle called the M52, the members contract for the work through their organization with the Danish firm of Schultz & Larsen (well-known for their splendid target rifles). Total cost of converting a government-donated Mauser into a fine target rifle amounts to only $25.00 and, so far, over 15,000 rifles have been converted for Danish NRA shooters.

The M52 conversion consists of substituting a target-weight barrel in caliber .30-06 or 6.5 x 55mm as specified by the individual shooter. Where the .30-06 cartridge is to be used, the magazine is lengthened. The action is smoothened and polished, and the trigger is adjusted for a clean, crisp pull. The original military stock is shortened and new swivels fitted. The stock is then finely polished.

In the interest of national defense, by making the transition to use of the M1 Garand by civilian riflemen as effortless as possible, the sights of the M52 were designed to offer the same sight picture as that presented by the M1 Garand. Front sight of the M52 is identical with that of the M1, and the receiver sight is an adaptation of that on the M1 with click-adjustments for 200, 300, 400, and 500 meters. In Denmark, 200 meters is the normal range for target shooting. The rear sight of the M52 covers the clip-loading port in the receiver and prevents clip loading.

Another Danish NRA model is the M58 rifle which is the M52 fitted with

Danish NRA Rifle M58.

special aperture-type receiver and front sights to satisfy those shooters who prefer finer sighting equipment than is available on the M52.

SPECIFICATIONS OF THE M52 and M58

Total length of weapon: 47.6"
Total weight of weapon: 9.5 lbs.
Length of barrel: 27.6"

Front diameter of barrel: .76"
Rear diameter of barrel: 1.1"
Number of rifling grooves: 4

	Caliber 6.5 mm.	Caliber .30-06
Groove diameter:	.2657"	.308"
Bore diameter:	.256"	.30"
Groove width:	.118"	.177"
Rifling, righthand twist, 1 turn in:	8.27"	10.25"

Madsen Light Automatic Rifle

The Dansk Industri Syndicat has developed a new rifle which currently exists only in prototype form. This weapon makes extensive use of light weight material having an aluminum alloy receiver, receiver cover, trigger guard, rear sight, magazine, and bipod.

Caliber: 7.62mm NATO
System of operation: Gas, selective fire
Weight w/loaded magazine: 10.6 lbs.
Length overall: 42.3"
Barrel length: 21.1"
Feed device: 20-round detachable, staggered box magazine

Sights—front: Hooded blade
rear: Aperture, graduated from 100 to 600 meters
Rifling: 4 lands and grooves, right hand twist, 1 turn in 12 in.
Muzzle velocity: Approx. 2,650 f.p.s.
Cyclic rate: 550-600 r.p.m.

Madsen 7.62mm Assault Rifle, First Model.

Madsen 7.62mm NATO Assault Rifle. Current model with tubular steel stock. A wooden stock model is also made.

To load, insert a loaded magazine into the magazine port and push home until locked by the magazine catch. Cock the weapon by pulling the operating handle to the rear as far as it will go, then release. The weapon is now cocked and ready to fire.

This weapon has its return spring mounted above the barrel where it circles the piston rod. The piston rod has a ball-shaped end which fits into a cut-out area in the bolt carrier. The return spring thus pulls the bolt and bolt carrier into the battery position rather than pushing them as in most weapons. The bolt and bolt carrier operate in a manner similar to that of the Soviet AK-47 assault rifle. The bolt rotates to lock and has frontally-mounted locking lugs. It is rotated by means of a lug on the bolt operating a cam on the bolt carrier. The trigger mechanism is similar to that of the Soviet AK.

This weapon has a combination flash hider and grenade launcher. It has a bipod which can be easily fitted and it can also be fitted with a telescopic sight. The weapon can be made with a wooden stock or a fixed, plastic covered, metal-tube stock.

Chapter 26

DOMINICAN REPUBLIC

(Republica De Santo Domingo)

GOVERNMENT PLANTS: Facilities for the manufacture of rifles exist.

PRIVATE PLANTS: None.

PRINCIPAL MILITARY RIFLES: U.S. Springfield, Model 1903 30/06, 7.62mm FN "FAL," U.S. cal. .30 M1.

The Dominican Republic has developed respectable sized small arms design and production facilities since World War II. This has been done with the help of refugee Hungarian technicians and Italian tooling. The first native weapon to be built in quantity was the Cristobal Model 2 Carbine.

Caliber .30 Automatic Carbine Cristobal Model 2

Caliber: .30 (U.S. M1 carbine cartridge)
System of operation: Delayed blowback, selective fire
Weight w/o. magazines 7.75 lbs.
Length, overall: 37.2"
Barrel length: 16.1"

Feed device: 25 or 30-round, detachable, staggered-row box magazine
Sights—front: Hooded blade
      rear: Notch with elevator
Muzzle velocity: 1,875 f.p.s.
Cyclic rate: 580 r.p.m.

Although this weapon resembles the Beretta submachine guns externally and in its trigger mechanism, its operating mechanism resembles that of the Hungarian Model 39 and Model 43 submachine guns. The bolt is in two main parts: the bolt body, and a heavy section called the striker. These parts are joined by a two-armed inertia lever which is seated in the rear end of the bolt. The upper long arm of the movable inertia lever engages the striker, and the lower short arm of the lever projects down from the bolt. When the bolt is closed, the short arm of the inertia lever stands before a stationary shoulder which is firmly attached to the bottom of the receiver. When a round is fired, the gases thrust rearward on the cartridge case base, which pushes back against the face of the bolt. Before the bolt can open, its inertia must be overcome. When the bolt begins to move rearward, the lower arm of the inertia lever bears against the bottom shoulder of the receiver. The rearward movement of the bolt then causes rearward rotation of the inertia lever, swinging the bottom arm up and out of engagement with the receiver, and forcing the upper arm back against the striker. During the closing of the bolt, another lateral arm of the inertia lever slides on the receiver wall, and retains the inertia lever and the striker in a cocked position long enough for the bolt to run fully home. When the bolt is fully closed, the lateral arm of the inertia lever moves above a slot in the receiver wall, permitting forward rotation of the lever by the striker and the firing of the round. The inertia lever therefore prevents the weapon from firing before the bolt is fully closed.

To load the Cristobal Carbine: insert a loaded magazine in the magazine well. Pull the operating handle located on the right side of the receiver to the rear, then push it forward. If the forward trigger is pulled, the weapon will fire

Dominican Cal. .30 Carbine Cristobal Model 2.

single rounds; if the rear trigger is pulled the weapon will fire full automatic. To put the weapon on safe, pull the lever mounted on the left side of the receiver to the rear.

Caliber .30 M1962 Automatic Carbine

This weapon is a modification of the Cristobal Model 2. The main difference between the models is the use of a perforated metal barrel jacket in lieu of a wooden handguard and the production of the Model 1962 in a folding metal stock version as well as the wooden stock version. The Model 1962 also has a shorter barrel than the Cristobal Model 2 carbine.

Dominican Cal. .30 M1962 Carbine. This weapon uses the .30 carbine cartridge and is made with a folding steel stock or with a wooden stock.

Caliber: .30 (U.S. M1 carbine cartridge)
System of operation: Delayed blowback, selective fire
Weight, loaded:
  w/wooden stock—8.7 lbs.
  w/folding steel stock—8.2 lbs.
Length, overall:
  w/wooden stock—34.1"
  w/steel stock extended—37"
  w/steel stock folded—25.6"

Barrel length: 12.2"
Feed device: 30-round, detachable, staggered-row box magazine
Sights—front: Protected blade
  rear: "L" type
Muzzle velocity: 1875 f.p.s.
Cycle rate: 580 r.p.m.

7.62mm M1962 Automatic Rifle

This weapon is a native Dominican design which combines the gas system of the U.S. M14 rifle with the bolt mechanism of the FN light automatic rifle.

Caliber: 7.62mm NATO
System of operation: Gas, selective fire
Weight, loaded: 10.4 lbs.
Length overall: 42.5"

Barrel length: 21.3"
Feed device: 20-round, detachable, staggered row, box magazine
Muzzle velocity: 2700 f.p.s.

Dominican 7.62mm M1962 Rifle.

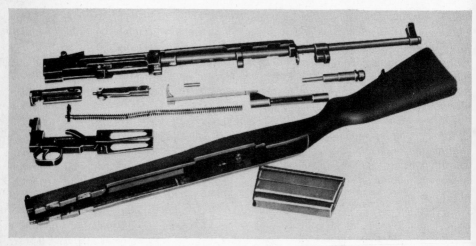

Dominican 7.62mm M1962 Rifle Field Stripped.

Chapter 27
ECUADOR
(Republica Del Ecuador)

GOVERNMENT PLANTS: None.

PRIVATE PLANTS: None.

PRINCIPAL MILITARY RIFLES: 7.62mm FN "FAL"; Mauser Model 1891, 7.65mm. Also later F.N. Mausers. (See under *Belgium*).

EARLIER OFFICIAL BREECHLOADING RIFLE: About 1873 adopted the Remington Single Shot 11mm (.433) Spanish.

Chapter 28
EGYPT (United Arab Republic)

GOVERNMENT PLANTS: Facilities exist for production of rifles and sub-machine guns.

PRIVATE PLANTS: None.

PRINCIPAL MILITARY RIFLES: Egypt was formerly equipped mainly with British .303 S.M.L.E. No. 1 rifles. Prior to the overthrow of the monarchy, Egypt purchased substantial quantities of the Model 1949 F.N. semi-automatic rifle in 7.92mm caliber. Production facilities were also set up for the production of the Swedish Model 42 Ljungman rifle in 7.92mm.

The Egyptian model of the Ljungman is a very faithful copy of the Swedish Ljungman AG42, differing only in caliber and other minor details. Unlike the Swedish Army pattern, the Egyptian Ljungman has eight gas adjustment settings to compensate for variations in ammunition. The last setting cuts off gas completely, permitting manual operation of the bolt if necessary. The final product is an excellently machined weapon. One sample placed ten shots within a three-inch circle at 100 yards—pretty good for a semi-automatic rifle. Its clean lines and simplicity of design also make it a fine infantry weapon. (Since the Egyptian and Swedish Ljungman models are basically the same, see also under Sweden.)

Egypt purchased quantities of Soviet 7.62mm SKS carbines and Czech 7.62mm Model 52 rifles from the Soviet bloc. Syria, while a member state of the United Arab Republic, was supplied with Soviet 7.62mm AK-47 assault rifles. All of these weapons are covered under their countries of origin.

EARLIER OFFICIAL BREECHLOADING RIFLES: Prior to World War I Egypt used various European rifles, none truly standard.

In 1870 Egypt, then a part of the Turkish Empire with semi-independent status, ordered 60,000 Remington Single Shot R.B. rifles to the following speci-

Egyptian Ljungman Semiautomatic Rifle.

Egyptian Ljungman Stripped.

fications:
Overall Length: 50.2"
Barrel: 35.2"
Weight: 9.25 lbs.
Caliber: 11mm (.43) Egyptian

The order was defaulted after being partly filled. One hundred and thirty thousand of these rifles were then delivered to France during 1870/71. In 1876 the Egyptian Government re-opened negotiations with Remington, and the order for the full 60,000 was completed.

Chapter 29

ETHIOPIA

(Abyssinia)

GOVERNMENT PLANTS: None.

PRIVATE PLANTS: None. However, crude gunsmithing is common.

PRINCIPAL MILITARY RIFLES: U.S. cal. .30 M1, .303 P-14 (Rifle No. 3 Mark I*) and .30 M1917 rifles. Every conceivable type and vintage of rifle from flintlock to modern semiautomatic was encountered in Ethiopia during World War II.

Col. G. B. Jarrett, on an intelligence and ordnance mission to the Near East early in World War II, catalogued hundreds of varieties and variations of rifles in Ethiopia. Despite unusually wide experience as a collector of military arms, he found it impossible to definitely classify all the arms encountered.

Chapter 30

FINLAND

(Suomi)

PRINCIPAL GOVERNMENT ARMS PLANTS: Valmet.

PRINCIPAL PRIVATE ARMS PLANTS: O.Y. Sako, A.B., Helsinki.

PRINCIPAL GOVERNMENT AMMUNITION PLANTS: Lapuan Patruunatehdas, formerly Valtion Patruunatehdas.

PRINCIPAL PRIVATE AMMUNITION PLANTS: None.

PRINCIPAL MILITARY RIFLES: 7.62mm Assault Rifle M60, Mosin-Nagant models M24, M28, M28/30, and M39—caliber 7.62 x 53mm.

Finland, a nation of less than four million people (about half the population of New York City) welcomed freedom from the Russian Czar late in 1917. But this new-found independence was not without its problems, not the least of which was equipping its armed forces. Not having a weapons industry capable of meeting the demand, nor the wherewithal to establish one, Finland solved its dilemma by appropriating from warehouses a variety of Russian-made materiel which included Mosin-Nagant M91 rifles. Naturally, they relied on the Russian 7.62mm cartridges, caliber of which has been retained by Finland to this day. It also proved practical during the Russian Invasion of Finland and World War II to make immediate use of Russian small arms, pistols, rifles, machine guns, etc. which fell into Finnish hands.

In creating their versions of the Mosin-Nagant rifle, the Finns have, without exception, used Russian-made M91 actions, although they have manufactured all other parts such as stocks, barrels, sights, bayonets, metal fittings, and a small quantity of bolts for these weapons.

All Finnish Mosin-Nagant models are recognized for their exceptional accuracy, but proper bedding is essential. Contact between wood and the barrel should be permitted only at the forward swivel band. Because of the location of the horizontal bolt on Mosin-Nagant rifles, manipulation of the bolt is not rapid compared with the U.S. Springfield or British Lee Enfield. Trigger design is inferior on Finnish and Russian Mosin-Nagants, resulting in poor trigger pull. The Finns set a minimum trigger pull of 4 lbs. 5 ozs. on their rifles. Nevertheless, these inherent drawbacks have been mastered by Finnish riflemen who have performed outstanding feats in marksmanship on target ranges and on the battlefield.

M91.

When the Finns desired greater accuracy from the M91 Russian rifles, they substituted a heavier, target-weight barrel—reputed to be the heaviest used in any military rifle. A new rear sight with U-shaped notch and streamlined post front sight were installed, and the resultant model was designated the M91.

M27.

By 1927, Finnish authorities concluded that the barrel of the M91 could be shortened 4½ inches without sacrificing accuracy. They decided also to employ a new front sight with protecting wings, which prompted them to nickname the M27, "Pystykorva" . . . translated freely into English, this means "Spitzear." This sobriquet carried over to the M28, M28/30, and M39 models which followed. Bolt handle of the M27 was turned down, and a new knife-type bayonet with a blade of 11⅞" was adopted in lieu of the Russian quadrangular blade.

M28.

Based on their experience with the M27, Finland restored the original horizontal bolt handle, but made further modifications in metal stock fittings. This model became the M28.

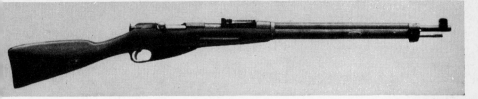

M28/30.

In 1930, a noticeable improvement was made in the M28 sights, this particular model being called the M28/30. The new front sight adjusts for windage by the use of opposing lateral locking screws. Around the periphery of the screw are calibrations, each constituting a movement equal to the width of one ring on a 300-meter target. Rear sight is better constructed, permitting adjustments from 200 to 2,000 meters. This is the gun with which Olavi Elo set a world's record of 530 points in the 1937 International Army Matches. It is, in the opinion of Finnish marksmen, the most accurate of all Finnish service rifles.

M39.

The year 1939 saw the adoption of the M39 rifle. Essentially, it is the same as its predecessor, the M28/30, except for the substitution of an ingeniously designed pistol-grip stock, consisting of two separate pieces of wood joined together. This innovation in the stock imparts greater rigidity to the forearm. To prevent warping, special wood is selected for the forearm. Fitting of the forearm to the stock, proper, is accomplished by a three-finger interlocking-type joint, demanding skilled woodworking ability . . . an example of the loving care and artistry Finns lavish upon their weapons.

Each time an M39 comes off the production line, it is test-fired. Unless it groups three shots within a diameter of 1.3″ at 100 meters, it is unacceptable. This exacting standard of performance Finland requires of its military rifles is a contributing factor to the high scores reached in international shooting competition.

Finnish riflemen have playfully bestowed on the M39 the pet name of "Ukko-Pekka"—which is "Old Man Pekka" in English—in honor of a beloved and avid shooter who was, incidentally, a former President of Finland.

7.62mm Cartridge

The official cartridge for the Finnish Mosin-Nagant rifles is the rimmed 7.62 x 53mm, which is interchangeable with the Russian cartridge of the same caliber and size. The decision to standardize Finnish small arms production with that of the Russians proved wise, in particular when the Russians invaded Finland in 1939. Finnish factories were unable to cope with the demand for war materiel. Resorting to the use of captured Russian arms and ammunition (which their foresight assured them was interchangeable with their own) placed in the Finn's grasp the means of exacting a frightful toll from the ranks of the hated invader.

In 1936, the 200-grain, boattail, D-166 bullet was selected. (Muzzle velocity at 25 meters—2,297 feet per second; maximum range—5,700 yards.) It has an un conventional slight step at the rear, where the boattail section begins. This step is purported to have the property of enabling the bullet to follow its trajectory better at longer ranges.

Primer is non-mercuric and non-corrosive, consisting of: Trisinate, Tetratsen Bariumnitrate, Lead peroxide, Sulphurantimony, and Calcium silicide.

Italian M38 Carbine—Swedish M96 Mauser

During the first winter of war with Russia, Finland procured from Sweden approximately 15,000 Swedish 6.5mm M96 Mausers and 6.5mm ammunition which Finland decided to manufacture for these weapons during World War II. Finland received, in addition, a supply of Italian M38 7.35mm carbines via Germany during World War II. Both weapons saw limited service as they were relegated to use by stationary troops, such as guards on bridges, airfields railways, waterworks, etc. Today, the greater portion of M38 carbines Finland received can be traced to the U. S. market as surplus war goods. (Description of the M38 carbine is given under *Italy*. The M96 Mauser is described under *Sweden*.)

7.62mm M60 Assault Rifle

This weapon is chambered for a Finnish copy of the Soviet 7.62mm M43 "intermediate sized" cartridge. Internally the M60 is a close copy of the Soviet AK-47 assault rifle. It is loaded, fired, and field stripped like the Soviet weapon Externally it is considerably different than the AK-47, having a fixed tubular metal stock, a handguard of composite material, and the rear sight mounted on the rear of the receiver. First production had a bar in front of the trigger to serve as a trigger guard, but later production has a conventional trigger guard.

Caliber: 7.62mm (7.62x39mm)
System of operation: Gas, selective fire
Weight loaded: 9 lbs.
Length overall: 36"
Barrel length: 16.5"

Feed device: 30-round detachable, staggered box magazine
Sights—front: Hooded post
    rear: Tangent w/aperture
Cyclic rate: 650 r.p.m.
Muzzle velocity: 2362 f.p.s

Finnish 7.62mm M60 Assault Rifle.

Finnish 7.62x39mm Cartridge

Although basically a copy of the Soviet M43 cartridge, the Finnish-made
round differs in a number of respects. The Soviet-made M43 cartridge has a
gilding metal clad steel case; the Finnish case is made of brass.

Sako

Sako has the unique distinction of being an arms factory owned outright by
the Red Cross of Finland. The Russians lost no time during the closing days of
World War II in appropriating any and all arms factories in occupied territory.
Desperate to prevent Sako from suffering the same fate, the Finns persuaded the
Finnish Red Cross to accept ownership of the firm—lock, stock, and barrel, which
it retains to this day. This may be the only instance in which the Red Cross is
known to be engaged in commercial enterprise.

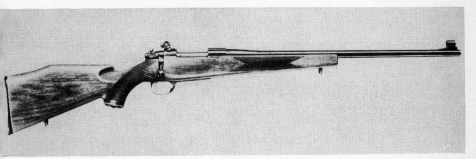

Sako Forester.

Sako suspended production of small arms ammunition at the conclusion of
World War II. In addition to manufacturing the M39 rifle, Sako is responsible
for the splendid Sako short-action L46 rifle. They recently introduced a medium-
length, bolt-action, sporting rifle called the Forester. The L46 and the Forester
are both modernizations by Sako of the Mauser bolt action. Rifles based on
Mauser actions made by Fabrique Nationale of Belgium are also produced by
Sako.

Valmet

In addition to manufacturing military arms, the government factory of Valmet
turns out shotguns and the noted .22 caliber Finnish Lion target rifle.

Lion .22 Rifle.

Characteristics of Finnish Rifles

	M24	M27	M28	M28/30	M39
Length of Weapon (in inches)......	51.18	46.73	46.73	46.73	46.73
Length of Weapon with Bayonet (in inches)......	67.72	58.43	58.43	58.43	58.43
Weight of Weapon (in lbs.)........	9.26	9.26	9.26	9.26	9.7
Length of Barrel (in inches)......	31.50	26.97	26.97	26.97	26.97
Diameter of Bore (in inches)...... Plus tolerance of .0014"	.2984	.2988	.2988	.2988	.2988
Groove Diameter (in inches)...... Plus tolerance of .0014"	.3094	.3083	.3083	.3083	.3102
Pitch of Rifling (in inches)...... 1 Turn In	9.449	9.449	9.449	10.236	9.449
Number of grooves	4	4	4	4	4
Bullet Weight (in grains)......	148.28	148.28 & 177.45	148.28 & 177.45	148.28 & 185.16	200.55
Velocity at 25 Meters .... (feet per second)......	2,887	2,789 & 2,428	2,789 & 2,428	2,789 & 2,411	2,297
Pressure (lbs. per sq. inch)......	39,852	39,852	39,852	39,852	41,276

Chapter 31

FRANCE

(La Republique Francaise)

GOVERNMENT PLANTS: Chatellerault, St. Etienne, Tulle.

PRIVATE PLANTS: Manufacture Francaise d'Armes et de Cycles de St. Etienne. This firm is the premier French rifle and shotgun manufacturer. (Other irms are relatively unimportant.)

St. Etienne in Loire is the French equivalent of Suhl, Germany. It is an area where scores of small plants and assembly factories turned out arms built on he various systems described in the historical chapters in this book. Quality an from poor to fine and calibers and specifications covered too great a range o warrant listing. Exports of French arms have been limited. No French small arms designs have been important enough to warrant other nations copying hem to any important degree.

PRINCIPAL MILITARY RIFLES: 7.5mm M1949/56 and 7.5mm M1949.

7.5mm M1949 and M1949/56 Rifles

The MAS M1949 evolved from an earlier design, the 7.5mm MAS 1944. The MAS 1949 was designed by the French government arsenal, Manufacture d'Armes de St. Etienne, better known as MAS. Basically, it uses the same simplified gas system found in the Swedish Ljungman AG42 semiautomatic rifle (see under Sweden) wherein no tappet rod is used but where gas issues through an orifice in the top of the barrel, entering the gas tube through a gas port. Gas coursing through the tube delivers a sharp blow against the bolt cover to unlock the bolt, causing it to ride back in unison with the bolt carrier.

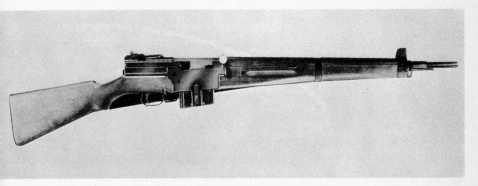

French 7.5mm MAS M1949 Semiautomatic Rifle.

The bolt system of the MAS 1949 is of the prop-down, rear-locking type, typical of FN, Ljungman, and SKS automatic rifles. In traveling to the rear, the bolt carrier cams up the rear end of the bolt to unlock it. The return motion of the bolt carrier cams the rear end of the bolt down into its locking abutment.

177

One-quarter inch of the forward end of the rectangular bolt is rounded and th
bolt face is recessed. The ejector is a short stud that slides through the left sid
of the bolt face at 30° angle and projects into a groove in the left side of th
receiver. Rearward movement of the bolt is halted when this projection hits
stud at the end of the receiver groove which also causes the ejector to slid
forward to strike the head of the expended cartridge case which pivots on th
claw extractor and is thereby ejected from the gun. The tip of the firing pi
has a sharply-tapered, wedge-shaped point.

The MAS 1949 is ruggedly built and performs soundly. It bears a stron
resemblance to the fine bolt action MAS M36 rifle. With each MAS 1949, fou
10-shot magazines are issued. A conveniently located catch arrangement facili
tates interchange of magazines. A lever-type catch on the right side of th
magazine engages a machined recess which is centrally located on the right sid
of the receiver when the magazine is fully seated. The rifle can also be loadec
from the top with conventional 5-shot stripper clips. The aperture-type rea
sight adjusts from 200 to 1200 meters in 100-meter increments. Adjustment fo
windage is by clicks with a knob situated on the right side of the sight. A blun
post front sight is an integral part of the barrel. The sight protecting wings plu
a stacking hook are integral with the front stock band, as in the MAS M3
bolt action rifle, except that this unit serves as part of the grenade-launchin
device. On the left side of this stock band is fitted a sighting device for launchin
grenades; it lies alongside the stock forearm and pivots up for use.

French 7.5mm MAS M1949/56 Semiautomatic Rifle.

Recently, the French have introduced a revised model of the MAS 1949 which
has been designated MAS 49/56. It is identical with the MAS 1949 except for
shorter forearm and handguard, exposing more of the barrel. Grenade-launchin
rings are machined on the barrel surface near the muzzle and grenade-launchin
sights are built into the weapon.

Field stripping of the MAS 1949 is accomplished as follows. Remove magazine
and cock weapon. Depress breech cover lock. By pushing forward and lifting
up, the breech cover, which contains the rear sight, can be removed as well a
the bolt return spring. Draw back bolt handle and lift bolt assembly up out o
the receiver. Then separate bolt from bolt carrier. Procedure is reversed to re
assemble the weapon. French Army regulations prohibit further disassembly o
the weapon by soldiers.

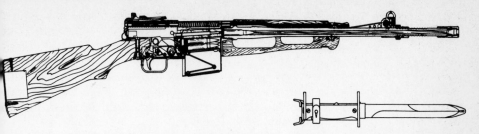

Section View of French 7.5mm MAS M1949/56 Semiautomatic Rifle.

M1949   M1949/56

	M1949	M1949/56
Caliber:	7.5mm French M/929 cartridge	
System of operation:	gas, semiautomatic fire only	
Weight, loaded:	10.4 lbs.	9.44 lbs.
Length, overall:	43.3"	40.2"
Barrel length:	22.8"	20.7"
Feed device:	10-round, detachable, staggered row box magazine	
Sights—front:	blade w/protecting ears	
rear:	ramp w/aperture	
Muzzle velocity	approx. 2700 f.p.s.	

EARLY FRENCH BREECHLOADERS: During the Franco-Prussian War of 1870/71, both armies were outfitted basically with needle fire rifles using the inefficient self-consuming ammunition. During the course of that War France turned frantically to every corner to obtain superior equipment. Many breech loaders were received from the U. S., including 130,000 Remington rolling block single shot rifles of .43 Egyptian caliber.

However, the first *official* French cartridge rifle of importance to use metallic cartridges was the M.1866 conversion of the needle fire Chassepot rifle.

It was continued in service until 1874. This changed the Chassepot rifle to a center fire metallic cartridge breech loader. A characteristic of the design was that the cocking could be accomplished by merely raising and lowering the bolt handle. Many of these conversions were made in England at the Kynoch Gun Factory. These arms were followed by the Gras of 1874 and 1878.

After considerable experimentation with repeaters, the French navy in 1879 adopted a bolt action, tubular magazine repeater, the Gras-Kropatschek. This arm, slightly modified in 1884, was known as the Marine Rifle. Arms of these types were seized by the Germans during their occupation of France in World War II.

Rifles encountered in quantity by the Germans during World War II:

(1) *M. 1874 (Gras) Rifle and Carbine:* Bolt action single shot, 11mm.

(2) *M. 1886 and 86/93 Rifles:* Bolt actions, tube under barrel, 8mm.

(3) *M. 1890 and 1892 Carbines:* Bolt actions, 3-shot Mannlicher clip type magazines, 8mm.

(4) *M. 1907 Rifles:* Bolt action, 3-shot Mannlicher clip type magazine, 8mm.

(5) *M. 1907/15 Rifles:* 3-shot Mannlicher clip type magazine, 8mm.

(6) M. *1916 Rifle and Carbine:* Bolt action, 5-shot Mannlicher clip type magazines, 8mm.

(7) *M. 1917 and 1918:* Gas operated semiauto rifles, 8mm.

FRENCH RIFLES AND CARBINES OF PRE-WORLD WAR II DESIGN.

Weapon	System of Operation	Overall Length	Barrel Length	Feed Device	Sights	Muzzle Velocity	Weight
Rifle: 8mm M1886 M93	Manually operated 2-piece bolt	51.3 in.	31.4 in.	8-rd tubular magazine	Front: Notched blade; Rear: leaf	2380 f.p.s.	9.35 lb.
Rifle: 8mm M1886 M93R35	Manually operated 2-piece bolt	37.64 in.	17.7 in.	3-rd tubular magazine	Front: Notched blade; Rear: leaf	2080 f.p.s.	7.84 lb.
Carbine: 8mm M1890	Manually operated 2-piece bolt	37.2 in.	17.7 in.	3-rd Mannlicher-type, integral, in-line magazine	Front: Blade; Rear: Leaf	2080 f.p.s.	6.83 lb.
Mousqueton 8mm M1892	Manually operated 2-piece bolt	37.2 in.	17.7 in.	3-rd Mannlicher-type, integral, in-line magazine	Front: Blade; Rear: Leaf	2080 f.p.s.	6.8 lb.
Rifle: 8mm M1902 "Indo-China Model"	Manually operated 2-piece bolt	38.6 in.	24.8 in.	3-rd Mannlicher-type, integral, in-line magazine	Front: Blade; Rear: Leaf	2180 f.p.s.	7.9 lb.
Rifle: 8mm M1907 "Colonial Model"	Manually operated 2-piece bolt	52 in.	31.4 in.	3-rd Mannlicher-type, integral, in-line magazine	Front: Blade; Rear: Leaf	2380 f.p.s.	8.6 lb.
Rifle: 8mm M1907/15	Manually operated 2-piece bolt	51.42 in.	31.4 in.	3-rd Mannlicher-type, integral, in-line magazine	Front Notched blade; Rear: Leaf	2380 f.p.s.	8.38 lb.
Rifle: 8-mm M1916	Manually operated 2-piece bolt	51.42 in.	31.4 in.	5-rd Mannlicher-type, integral, in-line magazine	Front Notched blade; Rear: Leaf	2380 f.p.s.	9.25 lb.
Carbine: 8mm M1916	Manually operated 2-piece bolt	37.2 in.	17.7 in.	5-rd Mannlicher-type, integral, in-line magazine	Front: Blade; Rear: Leaf	2080 f.p.s.	7.17 lb.
Rifle: 7.5mm M1907/15 M34	Manually operated 2-piece bolt	43.2 in.	22.8 in.	5-rd integral, staggered-row, box magazine	Front: Blade; Rear: Leaf	2700 f.p.s.	7.85 lb.
Rifle: 7.5mm M1932			Prototype of M1936, made in limited quantities				
Rifle: 7.5mm M1936	Manually operated 1-piece bolt	40.13 in.	22.6 in.	5-rd integral, staggered-row, box magazine	Front: Barley-corn w/guards; Rear: Ramp w/aperture	2700 f.p.s.	8.29 lb.
Rifle: 7.5mm M1936 CR39	Manually operated 1-piece bolt	Stock extended 34.9 in. Stock folded: 24.3 in.	22.6 in.	5-rd integral, staggered-row, box magazine	Front: Barley-corn w/guards; Rear: Ramp w/aperture	2700 f.p.s.	8 lb. (approx.)

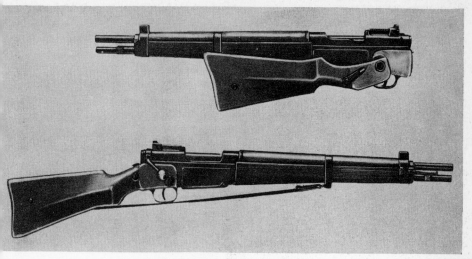

French 7.5mm M1936 CR39 Rifle.

(8) *M. 07/15/34:* The 07/15 action altered to take 7.5mm M. 1929 ammunition and with a 5-round Mauser type magazine.

(9) *M. 1886 M93R35:* The 1886 rifle modified to carbine 3-round magazine.

(10) *M. 1886 M27:* Carbine version of M1886 M93 modified to use a 7.5mm cartridge with a 5-round Mauser type magazine.

(11) *M. 1917-35,* M1918-35—Conversion of the M1917 and 1918 semi-automatic rifles into manually operated magazine rifles, 8mm.

Note: French Colonial Forces were equipped during the course of the War and later with U. S. Model 1903 and 1917 rifles as were the French troops trained in England to accompany U. S. Forces in Europe.

Description of M. 1936

The bolt is a one-piece design of unusually large diameter. It is bored out from the rear to receive the striker assembly. The two locking lugs are carried far back on the bolt cylinder locking high in the left wall and low in the right wall of the receiver bridge section. The handle is at the rear of the bolt cylinder.

The striker is a cylindrical one-piece type with a lower cocking stud; its mainspring being housed within the hollow striker as in Japanese practice.

The extractor is the conventional long flat spring with claw, dovetailed into the bolt. It rotates with the bolt.

The ejector is a forward prolongation of the bolt stop operating through a groove in the bolt cylinder. The bolt stop itself is a springloaded block which protrudes into the boltway from below. It is attached to the sear. Pressing the trigger while pulling back the bolt lowers the stop to permit bolt removal.

The magazine is of the staggered box type. Pressing a release catch frees the entire magazine assembly for removal.

No magazine cutoff is provided. The floor plate does not rise in front of the bolt to hold it open when the magazine is empty. The trigger has the standard military double pull. There is no manual safety. Mechanical safety is insured

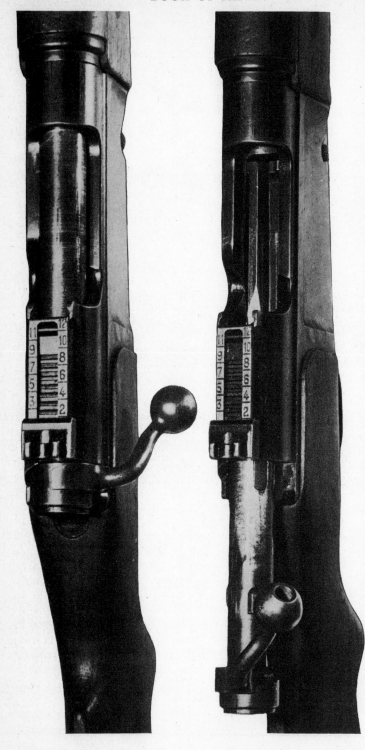

French Model 1936, action closed and open. Locking lugs are on rear of bolt cylinder near handle knob; they lock into receiver bridge to rear of magazine. Note cam shape of left face of receiver bridge which affords leverage for primary extraction cam on modified Mauser system. Rifle is loaded with Mauser-type charger clip. Note cuts in receiver for finger pressing cartridges into magazine. This is necessary because of large bolt diameter.

by the fact that the cocking piece moving forward will hit the cam cut in the rear of the bolt cylinder if the bolt handle is not all the way down. This will close the bolt and rotate it completely should it not be entirely closed and locked as the firing pin starts ahead. In such an event, a misfire will normally occur.

In opening the bolt, as the bolt handle is lifted it comes against the inclined plane machined at the rear of the receiver bridge. At the same time a cam face in the bolt cylinder pushes against a camming surface on the striker to force back the nose of the striker.

The stock is of two piece design, the separate fore-end being fitted ahead of the magazine.

The front sight is a fixed barleycorn. The rear sight has a radial aperture. Elevation is adjusted by a spring arm controlled by a slide on a fixed rod.

The one-piece striker is a cylinder which houses the mainspring as in Japanese rifles and carries the cocking nose at its rear.

The magazine floor plate with follower spring and follower is removable by pushing floor plate catch.

A special cruciform bayonet 13 inches long is carried in a tube in the fore-end. In the fixed bayonet position, its knurled projecting end locks into the tube opening.

DISMOUNTING: (1) Push bottom release and remove magazine units and cartridges. (2) Open action, hold trigger down and withdraw bolt. (3) Press down and turn plug at rear of bolt and remove from bolt cylinder. (4) Remove striker and mainspring. (5) Pry out extractor.

Note: The 7.5mm Model 1936 M51 is the 1936 with a grenade launcher built into the end of the barrel.

French Model 1886 M93 Lebel

The Lebel Rifle of 1886 was the most important rifle of its time, entirely because of the cartridge it used. It was the first mlitary cartridge designed for the then new smokeless rifle powder which had been developed in 1885 by M. Vielle, a chemist at the French Government powder factory.

General Boulanger, Minister of War, issued orders for the design of a "small bore" rifle. These orders stipulated that the design be ready within three months to take advantage of the new powder. The rifle developed was a bolt action design with a tubular magazine. The caliber was 8mm (.315 inch) with rim. This rifle was continued in service by the French through the period of both World Wars. It was supplemented by later designs, including box magazine modifications.

This is the first military rifle designed specifically for use with bottle necked smokeless cartridges. It has a turn-bolt action with a two piece bolt. The bolt handle is straight. There is a square block of steel forged integral with the bolt cylinder at its forward end and on the same plane as the bolt handle. It projects forward far enough to bear against a cam surface cut in the left side of the receiver ring when the bolt handle is lifted. This provides primary extraction. See top view of Model 1892. The dual opposed locking lugs are on the bolt head which is fastened to the bolt cylinder through the block above

French 7.5mm M1936 MAS Rifle. This rifle uses the French M1929 rimless cartridge. Pressing magazine floor plate release, seen at lower front of receiver, permits instant removal of plate, spring, and follower together with any cartridges in magazine. Spike bayonet is carried in tube in fore-end. Bayonet handle can be seen projecting under barrel.

French 8mm 1886 M93 Lebel Rifle. The turn bolt action is based on the 1874 (Gras). Tube magazine below barrel in forestock holds 8 cartridges. This is really the parent of all modern small-bore high-power rifles, in the sense that it introduced the smokeless powder charge with a comparatively small caliber bullet, at a time when black powder and large calibers were the rule.

mentioned with a machine screw—a crude form of bolt assembly by modern standards. The bolt head is recessed to take the head of the rimmed case. The bolt cylinder is bored out from the front to a sufficiently large diameter to accept the bolt head and the spiral striker spring which surrounds the striker. The rear portion of the bolt cylinder is bored just large enough to accommodate the striker passing through to the rear where the cocking piece is affixed. The square shoulder provided at the point where the inside diameter of the bolt cylinder is sharply reduced provides the bearing point for the rear of the striker spring. The forward end of the spring bears against a conventional collar turned on the striker. The rear end of the striker is flattened and T-shaped. It is fastened to the cocking piece by inserting this T through a slot in the cocking piece then giving the latter a half turn which engages the T in an annular ring cut inside the cocking piece behind the slot in conventional "quick detachable" form.

The major portion of the cocking motion takes place as the bolt handle is raised. The turning bolt exerts a camming effect on the cocking piece. Cocking is completed as the bolt is pushed fully forward and the sear engages the forward edge of the cocking piece.

The extractor is a short, flat spring, dovetailed into the bolt head. The ejector is a screw head projecting from the left side of the receiver. The bolt is grooved to clear this screw head as the bolt is operated.

The bolt stop is a square shoulder turned in the receiver. It operates against the rear surface of one of the locking lugs so that the bolt can only be withdrawn by unfastening the bolt head from the bolt cylinder.

The trigger pull is the double pull type. The sear is of rather crude design and is actuated by a flat spring rather sharply bent into almost a V shape, the top arm operating the sear and the bottom arm pinned into the receiver. The sear is pivoted on the elevator axis pin.

The magazine is the tubular type mounted in the fore-end. The magazine spring is the conventional coiled spring closed at the rear with a round plug which serves as the follower to press the cartridges backward into the elevator. The elevator is operated by camming and lever action exerted by the lower locking lug as the bolt is moved backward and forward. The bolt handle exerts pressure on the elevator to hold it down while the locking lugs are engaged in their recesses in the receiver. The forward section of the elevator is bent downward to form a finger which blocks the exit from the tubular magazine until the elevator has been depressed to the loading position. There is a magazine cut-off on the right side of the receiver just at the forward edge of the triggerguard. It is operated by pushing it forward to engage the elevator and hold it in its depressed position. Single cartridges may then be loaded directly into the chamber through the top of the receiver.

The bridge of the receiver is split to allow passage of the bolt handle. The handle locks down into a notch in the receiver wall ahead of the bridge.

The bottom of the receiver is closed with a floor plate on which the elevator and sear mechanisms are mounted.

The stock is of two piece pattern. There is no handguard.

An early .22 Trainer resembling the 1886 was noteworthy for a fully enclosed

Top, French 8mm M1886 Lebel Rifle; Bottom, French cal. .22 Training Rifle Modeled on the Lebel.

case head type bolt, forerunner of today's strong M 721 design. Externally the trainer resembles the Model 1886.

French Model 1878 Kropatchek (Marine Infantry)

Caliber: 11mm
Overall length, rifle without bayonet: 49"   *With bayonet attached:* 69"
Overall weight, rifle without bayonet: 10.3 lbs.   *With bayonet attached:* 11.5 lbs.
Type of action: Turnbolt   *Type of bolt:* 2 piece—Rotating head
Type of Magazine: Tubular   *Capacity:* 7
Barrel Length: 29.5"   *No. Grooves:* 4   *Direction of Twist:* Left
Bore Diameter: .433"   *Groove Dia.:* .4417"   *Rate of Twist:* 21.65"

Notes:

1. Original cartridge was modified for this arm which was the Model 1866 Gras converted to the tubular magazine.

French Model 1866 Gras (Chassepot Conversion) Single Shot

Caliber: 11mm
Overall length, rifle without bayonet: 51"   *With bayonet attached:* 74"
Overall weight, rifle without bayonet: 9.3 lbs.   *With bayonet attached:* 11.5 lbs.
Type of action: Turnbolt   *Type of bolt:* 2 piece—Rotating head
Barrel Length: 32.3"   *No. Grooves:* 4   *Direction of Twist:* Left
Bore Diameter: .433"   *Groove Dia:* .4448"   *Rate of Twist:* 21.2"

Notes:

1. Modified in 1874 and 1878.

2. The 1874 modification in both rifle and carbine forms is still a common rifle in the Balkans.

French Semiautomatic Rifle Model 1918

Caliber: 8mm   *Barrel Length:* 23.4" *No. grooves:* 4
Overall length, rifle without bayonet: 43.3"   *Bore Diameter:* .315" *groove dia.:* .326"
Overall weight, rifle without bayonet: 10.3 lbs.   *Type of bolt:* 2 piece—rotating head
Type of action: Gas operated semiautomatic   *Capacity:* 5
Type of magazine: Hinged box   *Direction of twist:* Left

Notes:

1. This rifle saw some use in both War I and War II in France. It was also used in the Balkans in War II. Manufacture was uniformly poor and exteriors crude. This is an obsolete design.

French 1886 M93. Right side detail showing action open, cartridge in elevator ready to be chambered, and hooked front of elevator preventing next cartridge in magazine tube from emerging.

The bolt is two piece. The dual lugs are carried on the bolt head. Primary extraction is effected by the rising projection at the front of the bolt cylinder proper working against a camming face on the receiver ring. The pivoted switch with thumb button at the forward end of the triggerguard is the magazine cut-off which locks the cartridge elevator down. Cartridges are fed in standard tubular magazine fashion by a coil spring and follower in the tube. When action is open, it is necessary to remove screw from bolt cylinder projection before rear bolt units can be pulled out of receiver. Bolt head is then lifted out of the boltway. This drawing also applies in general to the Model 86-RM-35 also.

French Model 1886-RM-35 (1886 M93 R35). This is the old M. 1886 M93 altered in 1935 to a carbine form. The 8mm caliber was retained, as was the tubular magazine form. Magazine holds 3 cartridges.

Model 1874 (Gras) Single Shot Rifle. Cal. 11 mm. The first French service rifle using metallic cartridge. Evolved from the Chassepot Needle Fire. Also made in Carbine form.

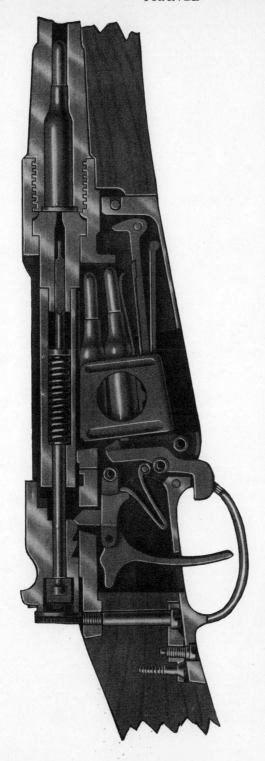

Model 1890. Right side detail drawing showing essential features of the modified French bolt popularly known as the "Berthier". Note that it varies somewhat from the older M. 1886 ("Lebel") design.

This is the first French form developed to use a 3-shot clip of Mannlicher type. Magazine follower is being forced up between clip side walls to feed cartridges. When action is open, pressing clip release in front end of triggerguard pivots upper end of clip out of contact with projection on back of clip and pressure of follower drives clip and cartridges up for removal.

Design has two-piece bolt with removable head which carries the two locking lugs.

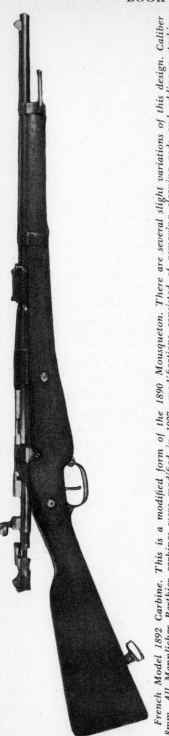

French Model 1892 Carbine. This is a modified form of the 1890 Mousqueton. There are several slight variations of this design. Caliber 8mm. All Mannlicher Berthier carbines were modified in 1927; modifications consisted of removing cleaning rods and adding a stacking hook.

French 8mm M1916 Rifle.

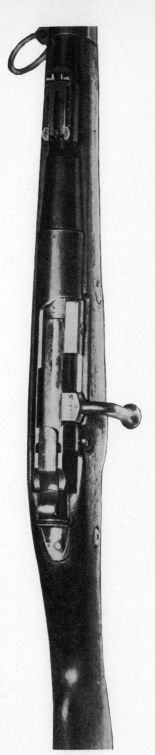
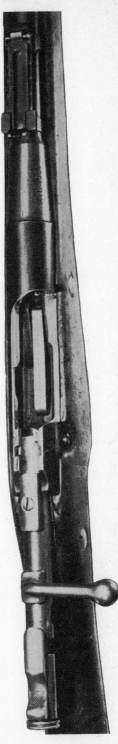

French M. 1892, action closed and open. Upper picture shows the bolt cylinder projection which works against a cam face at top of receiver ring to give primary extraction as the bolt handle is lifted.

Lower picture shows cocking piece partly withdrawn by standard cam action at rear of bolt cylinder. Note that primary extracting projection is part of the bolt cylinder forging. A screw passes through a hole in this lug to secure the bolt head. The head will not pass through the split receiver bridge, but must be lifted out of boltway after screw has been unfastened and bolt cylinder withdrawn to rear.

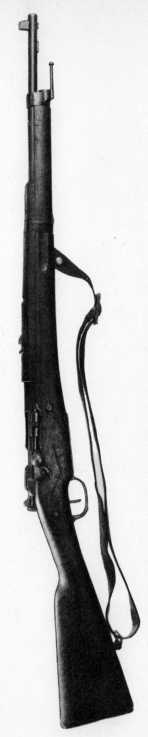

French Model 1907/15. Caliber 8mm. 3-shot Mannlicher type clip. This is a minor variant of the Model 1907. Both these models (and also the 5-shot Model 1916) derive directly from the M. 1890 and 1892 Carbines.

French 7.5mm Model 07/15M34 rimless. Modified 5-shot magazine to permit strip loading from standard Mauser-pattern clips.

French Model 1917 Semi-Auto Rifle, Caliber 8mm. The 1918 pattern is very similar but has a shorter barrel. These are popularly known as the "St. Etienne rifles." Magazine holds 5 cartridges. Operating rod works on outside of rifle. This is a turnbolt, locked breech operated by gas drawn off through barrel port.

French Model 1916 Mannlicher Berthier Carbine. 5-shot Mannlicher clip type magazine. Bolt design may be modified from either 07/15 or 1890 Model. Several minor variations exist in these types. The 1916 Rifle is similar except for barrel length, etc.

French 7.5mm M1929C Cartridge

Other Names: 7-5 Mas
Type: Rimless, Necked, Centerfire
Overall Length: 3.000"
Average Wt.: 376 gr.
Type Powder: Nitrocellulose
Type Primer: Berdan

CARTRIDGE CASE

Length Overall: 2.12"
Length Head to Shoulder: 1.69"
Length of Shoulder: .14"
Length of Neck: .287
Diameter at Rim: .488"
Diameter at Base: .481"
Diameter at Neck: .343"
Diameter at Shoulder: .450"

BULLET

Type: Jacketed, Pointed (Balle 1924 C)
Diameter: .307"
Weight: 139 gr.

BALLISTICS (approximate)

Muzzle Velocity: 2700 f.s.
Pressure: About 40,000 lbs./sq. in.

Notes: 1. This cartridge superseded the unsuccessful M1924 which had a longer case. The M1924 bullet was retained in the new 1929 cartridge. Cupro-Nickel and gliding metal jackets are both found on the bullets. Clips are generally made of aluminum.

2. The 1929 Balle D bullet for this cartridge weighs about 190 grains and is boattailed.

French 8mm M1886 Cartridge

Other Names: 8mm Lebel
Type: Rimmed, Necked, Centerfire
Overall Length: 2.95"
Average Wt.: 426 gr.
Type Powder: Nitrocellulose
Approximate Chg.: 46.3 gr.
Type Primer: Berdan

CARTRIDGE CASE

Length Overall: 1.98"
Length Head to Shoulder: 1.46"
Length of Shoulder: .16"
Length of Neck: .36"
Diameter at Rim: .634"
Diameter at Base: .535"
Diameter at Neck: .350"
Diameter at Shoulder: .456"

BULLET

Type: Solid Bronze, Pointed, Boattailed
(Balle D)
Diameter: .323"
Weight: 197.6 gr.
Length: 1.542"

BALLISTICS (approximate)

Muzzle Velocity: 2380 f.s.
Pressure: About 38,000 lbs./sq. in.

Notes: 1. The original M1886 cartridge was loaded with a 232 grain flat nosed bullet (Balle M).

French Semi-automatic Rifle Model 1917

Caliber: 8mm
Overall length, rifle without bayonet: 51"
Overall weight, rifle without bayonet: 10.8 lbs.
Type of action: Gas operated
Type of Magazine: Hinged box
Barrel length: 31.3"   *No. Grooves:* 4
Bore diameter: .315"   *Groove Dia.:* .326"

Type of bolt: 2 piece—Rotating head

Direction of twist: Left

French Sporting Rifles

The great Manufacture Francaise d'Armes et Cycles de St. Etienne manufactures an extensive line of sporting rifles and rifle-shotgun combinations.

The following list describes the production (prior to World War II):

BUFFALO-MITRAILLE: Turning bolt rifles having a single heavy barrel bored to receive three caliber .22 L.R. cartridges which are fired simultaneously by a single pull on the trigger. This arm is primarily intended for long range wing shooting.

SIMPLEX EXPRESS: This is a hinged frame, enclosed hammer (hammer-less), single barrel rifle. The triggerguard lever is pushed down to release the shotgun-type underbolt which locks the breech.

Standard calibers are 8mm Lebel (French Service), 9.5mm (.375 Magnum) and 10.3mm (.405 Winchester).

IDÉAL EXPRESS: Double barrel enclosed hammer (hammerless) rifle. Hinged frame, general shotgun design with two parallel barrels. Besides the shotgun type underbolts, the breech is supported by a peculiar form of "doll's head" top extension. This extension snaps down into the top of the standing breech, but it is hollowed out from below to position over an upright projection in the breech. The sides of the barrels are also held to the sides of the receiver by modified Purdy side clips. Operation is by triggerguard lever.

Standard calibers are 9.5mm (.375 Magnum), 10.3mm (.405 Winchester) and 11.5mm (.450 Express).

FUSIL-CARBINE: Double barrel over-under hammerless. Box locks. Under-lug bolts and short bite top extension breech lock. Top lever (thumb) release. Upper barrel is for shot, usually 12-gauge. Lower barrel is rifled. Standard rifle barrel is .32 Winchester Special (8mm).

EXPRESS-MIXTE: Three barrel hammerless. Box locks. Greener triple bolts, two under lug and one through circular hole in top extension. Top lever release. Parallel upper barrels are customarily 12-gauge or 16-gauge. Lower barrel centered between uppers. Standard rifle barrel caliber is 10mm (.40-82 rim). There is a separate trigger for each of the 3 barrels.

RIVAL: Mauser magnum actions barreled and stocked by MAS. Customary caliber is 10.75mm. Magazine capacity 5 cartridges. Rear sight is the common European type consisting of a number of separate leaves, 5 in this design. Set triggers are standard equipment. Hinged magazine bottom plate released by pushing catch at forward end of triggerguard.

BUFFALO-SLAVE: Turning bolt rifles, single shot, in calibers 8mm Armeé (French Service revolver caliber) and .32 W.C.F. Special MAS system bolt with turned down flat handle. Breech system eliminates receiver bridge.

POPULAIRE: Very simple turning bolt single shot arm with split receiver bridge and with bolt handle locking down into receiver ahead of bridge. Fires European 9mm Short and Long Rim Fire ball cartridges and 9mm Rim Fire Extra Long shot cartridge. Barrels are customarily smooth bored.

BUFFALO: Turning bolt single shot with special MAS breech system. Same ammunition as Populaire Model. The entire Buffalo series uses the same breech system. The receiver comprises also the triggerguard and upper and lower tangs and has a standard receiver ring at front for the barrel. There is no receiver bridge at the rear. In place of a bridge this system employes a rear cocking piece housing. The bolt handle unit bearing interior locking lugs is inserted into the front of this housing. When the bolt handle is turned down, the bolt head lugs engage in locking cuts in the rear of the barrel itself, not in the receiver. The mainspring is cocked on forward bolt thrust. Customary caliber is 9mm Rim Fire.

BUFFALO-EUREKA: This is the Buffalo breech system with firing pin and extractor adapted to a special barrel system. Two separate over and under bores are drilled in the single heavy barrel blank. The upper bore is for the 9mm R.F. shot and ball charges. The lower bore is rifled for the 6mm Bosquette R.F. cartridge.

ÉTOILE: Is a cane rifle for the 6mm Bosquette or the 9mm R.F. calibers. A skeleton shoulder stock of steel rod is provided for attachment to the cane to permit shoulder shooting.

POPULAIRE-SPORT AND JUNIOR: The Populaire turning bolt action in caliber 6mm Bosquette. The Sport has a half stock and the Junior has a three-quarters stock.

BUFFALO-SPORT: The Buffalo action with half-stock in either 6mm Bosquette or 5.5mm (.22 L.R.).

BUFFALO-JUNIOR: Same as the Sport except that stock is three-quarters and special sights are provided.

BUFFALO-STAND, CONCOURS, CHAMPION, SUPER CHAMPION, MATCH: Buffalo actions with special sights and stocks. Differences are in grades only.

Other French Sporting Rifles

All custom types of single shot, Mauser and Mannlicher actions were made by small shops in France. None are sufficiently distinctive to warrant discussion here. A number of .22 caliber weapons of French manufacture are currently being sold in the United States. Among these is the semiautomatic Unique X-51.

Chapter 32
GERMANY

GOVERNMENT PLANTS: None since 1918; pre-1918 plants were Spandau, Amberg, Danzig, and Erfurt.

PRIVATE PLANTS: Prior to May 8, 1945: Adamy Gebrüder (Suhl). (2) I. G. Anchütz (Zella Mehlis). (3) Astora (a trademark of BSW). (4) Berlin-Suhler Waffen- und Fahrzeugwerke (Berlin, Suhl and Weimar) BSW. (5) Bock-Drilling (a trade name used by S. Gunther in Suhl). (6) Bolte & Anschütz (Zella Mehlis). (7) Büscher-Gewehre (Zella Mehlis). (8) Burgsmuller & Söhne (Harz). (9) G. C. Dornheim A.-G. (Suhl). (10) Emil Eckoldt (Suhl). (11) Erma (Erfurt). (12) F. L. (trade name for Fr. Langenhan). (13) F & L (trade name for Franken & Lunenschlos makers of the Dreyse carbine). (14) Funk & Co. (Suhl). (15) Christoph Funk (Suhl). (16) Gecado (trade name for G. C. Dornheim). (17) Geco (trade name for Gustav Genschow & Co.). (18) Greifelt & Co. (Suhl). (19) Haenel C. G. (Suhl). (20) Helfricht & Fischer (Zella Mehlis). (21) Herold (a trade name for Franz Jäger). (22) Fr. Wilhelm Heym (Suhl). (23) Heym Gebrüder (Suhl). (24) Max Heym (Suhl). (25) H. W.-Z. (Hersteller Weihrauch, Zella Mehlis). (26) F. Jäger & Co. (Suhl). (27) E. Kerner & Co. (Suhl). (28) F. W. Kebler (Suhl). (29) Fritz Kies & Co. (Suhl). (30) Emil Langenhan (Zella Mehlis). (31) Max Lepper (Zella Mehlis). (32) August Lüneburg (Kiel). (33) Manteuffel & Co. (Z-M). (34) I. Meffert (Suhl). (35) B. Merkel (Suhl). (36) E. A. Merkel (Suhl). (37) Gebrüder Merkel (Suhl). (38) O. Merkel & Co. (Suhl). (39) F. Neuman (Suhl). (40) B. Paatz (Suhl). (41) Gebr. Rempt (Suhl). (42) Sauer & Söhn (Suhl). (43) A. Seeber (Suhl). (44) Sempert & Krieghoff. (45) Simson & Co. (Berlin-Suhl). (46) Albert Sühn (Suhl). (47) F. Schmidt (Suhl). (48) August Schüler (Suhl). (49) Stotz & Goessl (Suhl). (50) Strempel, F. (Suhl). (51) Venuswaffenwerk (Z-M). (52) E. Schmidt & Haberman (Suhl). (53) Carl Walther (Z-M). (54) O. Will (Z-M). (55) Zentrum (trade mark for F. Neuman-Suhl). (56) A. Ziegenhan (Suhl). (57) H. Burgsmuller & Söhne (Harz). (58) W. Brenneke (Leipzig). (59) G. Teschner & Co.

The foregoing lists cover only the major manufacturers. Thousands of small manufacturers did sub-contract, piece and custom work both before and during the War.

PRINCIPAL MILITARY RIFLES: The primary German rifle in World War II was the Kar. 98k (Karabiner 98 kurz—Carbine 98 short). This was the short rifle evolved from the M. 98 actions used in World War I. Caliber 7.9mm.

OTHER MILITARY RIFLES USED: (1) German Model 98 patterns of every type, including long rifles, true carbines and short rifles officially listed as "Karabiners." Caliber 7.9mm.

(2) German Model 1888 patterns and conversions using the early form of the 7.9mm cartridge. (Case dimensions are same as for M. 1898, but bullet diameter average is theoretically .3189" for round nosed bullet; while the pointed "S" bullet 7.9mm should measure .323" average.)

Note: Although most M. 98 type actions of early manufacture were con-

Gewehr (Rifle) 98. Originally issued to use the 7.9mm cartridge M. 1888. Most rifles made prior to 1905 were later altered to take the new cartridge with larger diameter bullet but same case, the M. 1898. All rifles made after 1905 were chambered for the new cartridge.

This is the direct parent of every modern Mauser pattern rifle wherever made. It was the standard Germany Infantry weapon in War I and was used in War II.

German Gew and Kar 98b Mauser

Caliber: 7.9mm
Overall length, rifle without bayonet: 49.2"
Overall weight, rifle without bayonet: 9 lbs.
Type of action: Turnbolt
Type of Magazine: Box—Staggered column
Barrel Length: 29.13"   No. Grooves: 4
Bore Diameter: .312"   Groove Dia.: .323"

With bayonet attached: 69.7"
With bayonet attached: 9.9 lbs.
Type of bolt: 1 piece—Rotating head
Capacity: 5
Direction of Twist: Right
Rate of Twist: 9.45"

Notes:

1. Cartridges for the M. 1898 and its later variations have been variously listed as 7.9, 7.91 and 7.92mm. Many German "98-40" rifles will be found stamped 7.87, 7.88 or 7.89mm. All use the Standard German cartridge.

2. The 98b differs from the Rifle 98 in having a bent-down bolt handle, side sling, and tangent type sight.

3. Rifle 98 was also made, after World War I, with a tangent-type sight.

verted when the pointed bullet "S" cartridge was adopted in 1903, some of these early arms are occasionally encountered for the original cartridge. These early types and the M. 1888 types are all potentially dangerous to use with recent German military 7.9mm ammunition. All M1898 rifles which were converted to use the .323 bullet are stamped with a large "S" on the barrel.

(3) German semiautomatic rifles in standard 7.9mm caliber. The 41-W, and 41-M were issued only in small numbers and were really experimental. The Gewehr (later Kar.) 43 appeared in fairly large numbers.

Note: The FG 42 (Fallschirmjaeger Gewehr 42—Paratrooper Rifle 42) in two types was a full and semiauto rifle issued in small numbers. It is an automatic weapon.

(4) Volkssturmgewehr 1 (Peoples Assault Rifle 1)—crudely made turn bolt 7.9mm rifles which used the 10-round magazine of the semiautomatic rifle Model 43 and b., Volkssturmkarabiner 98-Model 98 barreled actions cheaply stocked and finished. Some of these 7.9mm weapons were single shot and some used the Model 43 10-round magazine. All these weapons are suspect as far as safety is concerned.

(5) German Model 1871 and 71/84 patterns in caliber 11mm. These were not encountered in large numbers in Germany, but were used.

(6) Gewehr 33/40, a Czech-made short rifle in 7.9mm caliber. Also the Czech M. 24 and 33 in various modified forms. (See under *Czechoslovakia*).

(7) Gewehr 98/40, a Hungarian-made Mannlicher turn bolt modified with a Mauser type magazine. Caliber 7.9mm (See under *Hungary*).

(8) Belgian and Polish Mauser pattern rifles of various types. (See under *Belgium* and *Poland.*)

(9) Miscellaneous arms of all countries overrun by the German armies. Calibers various.

SPECIAL CARBINES: These arms used the 7.9mm kurz (short) cartridge, (pp 43 me) *not* the standard rifle 7.9mm. The earliest form was reported from the Russian front in 1942 as being an experimental machine carbine. Production types listed as MP (Machine Pistol) 43, 43/1 and 44 differed very little from each other and were all machine weapons. In 1944 the name was officially changed to StG 44 (Sturmgewehr 44—Assault Rifle 44).

A semiauto arm using the 7.99mm short cartridge was the Volkssturm Gewehr 1-5, an extremely crude arm intended for home defense.

Evolution of the German M98 System

Mechanically there has been no essential difference in any German service bolt action arm since the introduction of the Gewehr 98. There have been various modifications of the original Mauser design as required for mass production or for production in various plants; and there have been modifications of barrels, stocks, slings and sights.

Gewehr (Rifle) 98

This design was developed by Mauser. It was the first production Mauser to cock on the opening of the bolt. Other improvements were: larger diameter receiver ring, extra large gas escape holes in the bolt, shorter firing pin fall, larger gas escape holes in the under side of the bolt, bolt sleeve lock, and lock screws for the trigger guard screws. Improvements which had been introduced in earlier

Kar. 98a. This is the short rifle and officially adopted and designated "Kar. 98" in 1908. Designation Kar. 98a was adopted after appearance of other carbines. While mechanically the same as the original Kar. 98, it differs radically in length and exterior form. This was generally used by artillerymen and engineers (pioneers) in War I. It was also encountered in War II. Length overall: 43.3". Barrel length: 23.62". Weight: 8 lbs.

Kar. 98b. This is basically the same as Gew. 98. Sights and magazine follower are improved design. Sling is mounted on the side of the rifle.

Mausers such as: thumb cut in the left receiver wall, guide rib on the bolt, safety lug, shrouded bolt head, gas shield, and undercut extractor; were also incorporated in the Model 98 design. The magazine follower did not hold the bolt open when arm was empty. It was not until World War I that the Germans appreciated the wisdom of a device to hold the action open and warn the soldier that his rifle was empty. This rifle was adopted April 5, 1898 as the Gewehr 98. It used the same 7.9mm cartridge as its predecessor, the Gew. 1888. (Note: Most of these rifles were converted to take the new 7.9mm with larger diameter bullet about 1903-04.) Depending upon point of manufacture, barrels varied from 29.1″ to 30″ in length, a fact which permits a good deal of hair-splitting by anyone who wishes to carry detail to extremes. Overall length was 49.25 inches (more or less, dependent on actual barrel length). Slings were on underside. Stocks were walnut. Straight bolt handle. Weight about 9.5 pounds without bayonet.

Gewehr 98 Modified

This differs from the Gew. 98 only in having a flat tangent leaf rear sight.

Kar. (Karabiner-Carbine) 98

This was a true carbine for cavalry use. Like the Gewehr it was orginally issued for the M1888 cartridge and was generally altered about 1905-06 to take the new pointed bullet cartridge.

This arm had a bolt handle turned down against the stock, and was full stocked to the muzzle. Barrel length was 17″. It was equipped to take a bayonet.

The *original* "Kar. 98" is today an uncommon weapon. Practically all later German patterns called "Karabiner" are actually short rifles.

Kar. (Karabiner) 98a

When the United States adopted the Springfield in 1903, it established a new military rifle type—an arm of about the same overall length as a sporting rifle. It eliminated the excess length of older military rifles, retained enough overall length with bayonet attached to pacify the bayonet-minded, yet was short enough to be carried in a saddle scabbard, carbine-fashion.

The Germans set out to develop a similar weapon. In 1904 they introduced a new form with 24″ barrel, side sling and pierced buttstock. The bolt handle was turned down, the stock being recessed at the point where the knob rested. During World War I this weapon was primarily issued to artillery and pioneers (engineers) and to assault troops in the latter part of W.W. I.

Although the name clashed with that of the earlier true carbine form, the Germans originally called this new short rifle the "Kar. 98." It was officially adopted in 1908. After the introduction of new carbines, it was called Kar. 98a.

In 1917 finger grooves were provided below the rear sight area.

Gewehr 98/17 and Gewehr 18

During the course of World War I the Germans checked on certain undesirable features in their rifles. Compelled to substitute other woods for walnut in stocks, they found that the substitutes often warped, were heavier than desirable, and had wastage in manufacture. Lack of interchangeability in parts caused considerable trouble. Men in heat of battle were found working

German 7.92mm Kar. 98. This is the original Kar. 98 and is a rare weapon, since it apparently was never in general issue.

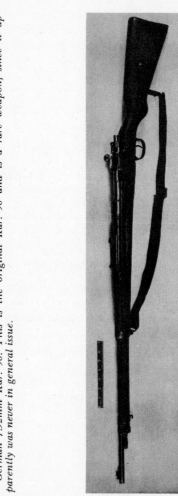

German 7.92mm Gewehr 98 modified. This rifle is the same as the Geweher 98, but uses a tangent type rear sight.

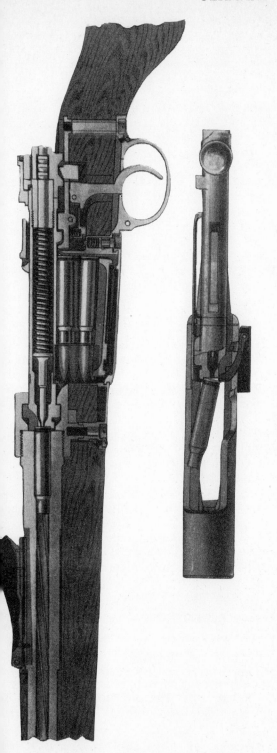
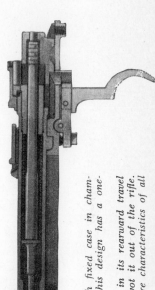

German Gew 98. Top drawing shows left side section of rifle with fixed case in chamber. Except for compressed magazine spring, all parts are at rest. This design has a one-piece striker.

Center drawing illustrates ejection system. Ejector operated by bolt in its rearward travel is being swung out to free empty case from grip of extractor and pivot it out of the rifle. Note guide rib on top of bolt cylinder and safety lug at rear; these are characteristics of all rifles based on the Mauser 98 system.

The bottom drawing shows chamber loaded and rifle ready to fire. Note that in this design the bolt sleeve screws into the rear of the bolt cylinder. This is considered the strongest form of bolt design.

their rifles after they were empty, as the magazine follower did not interfere with bolt closing when the arm was empty.

The necessity for maximum production would not permit changeover to new models at that time, but they evolved two major experimental models.

The 98/17 was developed to permit speeding up manufacture by reducing machine operations without interfering with the basic 98 design. A bolt cover was added to protect the bolt in trench warfare. It was soon discarded. The magazine follower was altered to hold the action open when empty. A tangent leaf sight with a 100-meter setting was provided for the short range fire demanded by fighting in the close quarters developed by trench warfare.

The Gew. 18 was a different approach entirely. It used the Gew. 98 bolt altered slightly for a new enclosed mainspring. A bolt cover was built in. The bolt stop was part of the trigger assembly. Magazines of 5, 10 and 25-round capacity were provided. These were detachable box types inserted from below. They could be clip loaded from above. The magazine could be removed only when the action was open.

It must be emphasized that these were experimental rifles. The Treaty of Versailles at the close of World War I prohibited the Germans from changing over, and these arms were not put into general production.

Kar. 98a and Kar. 98b

The Reichswehr, the 100,000 man Army permitted Germany after World War I, immediately turned attention to altering the Gew. and Kar. in line with the lessons learned during the War.

The Gewehr 98 was equipped with 100 meter sights having interchangeable ramps. These ramps permitted adjusting sights to handle either the older "S" bullet with pointed nose and flat base, or the new "SS" bullet with pointed nose and boat tail base. The magazine floor plate was altered to permit use as a dismounting tool when removing or replacing the firing pin. The magazine follower was designed to hold the action open when empty. The sling was still on underside of rifle.

At this time the older Kar. 98 was renamed "Kar. 98a." The "a" in this instance is a code designation to differentiate the pre-War from the post-War design.

The Gew. 98 as altered was fitted with side sling and the bolt handle was bent down. This slight modification was named the "Kar. 98b" and was issued to armored and cavalry units. (Note: These arms are often encountered stamped "Gew. 98" or "Mod. 98".)

Trainer Rifles

Service ammunition of 7.9mm caliber was restricted to 60 rounds per soldier per year. To permit practice and underground training, the Germans developed auxiliary barrels and magazines to permit the use of .22 R. F. ammunition in the standard Gew. and Kar. The next step was the development of a wide variety of .22 rifles closely resembling the Service arm. The ultimate form of these was the "German Sports Model 34" (DSM 34) and the "KKW Model"—"Small caliber service sport rifle."

Typical German Training Rifles. Upper photo shows J. G. Anschütz turn-bolt 4mm rifle. Lower view shows one variety of turnbolt spring operated air rifle.

The Kar. 98k

Tests conducted for accuracy, range and general handling convinced the Germans that shortening the barrel of their arm would greatly improve its effectiveness in the hands of the average soldier. Barrel length was therefore reduced from 29.1 inches to 23.6 inches. This was about 1924.

At this time, Belgium and Czechoslovakia both began commercial production of similar new design, making incidental changes in stocks, slings, sights and calibers as specified by South American and Asiatic customers. Poland, Spain and Yugoslavia manufactured similar designs.

In 1935 Germany was ready for mass production of the new form, and the short barreled arm was officially issued as standard to all service branches under the service designation "Kar. 98k." In this instance the "k" was a symbol for "kurz," meaning "short."

Kar. 98k Stocks

Early in 1930 the Germans experimented with and discarded metal stocks for the Kar. 98k. Next tested were laminated stocks usually of beech wood. This laminated stock proved superior in strength, resistance to weather and chemicals, and in ease of manufacture. Manufacturing wastage was under 2% as compared with 10% when using walnut.

The laminated beech stock was therefore generally adopted, though rifle specimens may be encountered stocked with any type of wood, and even with plastic. Plastic stocks were issued experimentally during World War II.

Description of Mauser Model 98 Series Rifles and Carbines

All Mauser model rifles wherever made from 1898 Model on are merely minor variants of the Gew. 98. The description of the mechanism as given in detail below covers all late Mausers with minor exceptions as noted under the individual arms. The Portuguese M. 1904 (Mauser-Vergueiro) is a modified, not a true Mauser, hence is not covered under the M. 98 series. The current Portuguese Mauser is the same as the Kar. 98k.

Military Mausers were made in the following countries besides Germany: Austria (Steyr); Belgium (F. N.) Models 24 and later; China; Czechoslovakia (Brno); Poland (Warsaw and Radom); Mexico (Mexico City); Spain (Madrid and Oviedo), Iran, and Argentina.

Sporting Mausers using similiar actions were sold throughout the world in short, standard and magnum sizes. These various actions were also sold throughout the world for special barreling by gunmakers and gunsmiths. These sporters vary from the military types generally only in stocks, sights, calibers, set triggers, special magazine floor plate release, and similar non-essentials.

These are turn-bolt arms. The bolt is of one piece design with dual opposed locking lugs at the head. The bolt cylinder is bored out from the rear to receive the striker assembly. The bolt handle was straight on the military model until after World War I when it was turned down on some models. The locking lugs lock into recesses in the receiver ring. On designs subsequent to 1904 a third, "safety," lug is provided which locks down into a square notch in the right side of the receiver just forward of the receiver bridge. A longitudinal rib on the bolt helps guide its travel by bearing in a slot on the underside of the receiver

Kar. 98k. This was the primary German service rifle in War II. Barrel length is 23.6".
This design was modified slightly in the interest of mass production as the war progressed. Various types of stock were used. The above is a photograph of a typical Kar. 98 k. but many minor variations may be encountered.

Model: German Kar 98k
Caliber: 7.9mm
Overall length, rifle without bayonet: 43.6"
Overall weight, rifle without bayonet: 9 lbs.
Type of action: Turnbolt—rotating head.
Type of Magazine: Box—Staggered column.
Barrel Length: 23.6"
Bore Diameter: .312"

Type of bolt: 1 piece—rotating head
Capacity: 5
Direction of Twist: Right
Rate of Twist: 9.25"

No. Grooves: 4
Groove Dia.: .323"

Notes:
The primary German service weapon during World War II.

bridge. This slot also provides clearance for the safety lug on models equipped with that feature.

Two gas vents, each 5 x 10mm, are placed in the bolt cylinder forward of the position where the mainspring bearing collar on the striker rests when the gun is fired. Thus the collar on the striker serves as a gas baffle in the case of a ruptured primer.

The face of the bolt is recessed for the head of the rimless cartridge.

On earlier models the bolt could be closed when the magazine was empty but on models and conversions made after World War I the magazine follower rises to prevent the closing of the bolt on an empty magazine; the follower must be depressed to close the bolt.

The striker is of one piece design. Suitable flat surfaces on the striker and on the inside of the bolt cylinder engage to prevent the striker turning independently of the bolt. The coiled mainspring surrounds the striker. Its forward bearing is against a collar turned on the striker rod. The rear bearing is against the bolt sleeve which screws into the rear of the bolt cylinder. The striker rod passes through the bolt sleeve and is engaged in the headless cocking piece with an interrupted thread. A cam surface on the upper side of the cocking piece engages a camming notch in the rear of the bolt cylinder when the striker assembly is in its forward position. As the bolt handle is lifted the camming action of the notch operating against the cocking piece cam forces the cocking piece to the rear and provides the greater part of the mainspring compression. The remainder of the cocking action takes place on the forward motion of the bolt. The nose of the cocking piece engages the sear and the camming of the bolt head lugs as they are cammed forward and downward into locking position completes the compression of the mainspring.

A spring loaded plunger on the bolt sleeve engages a notch in the rear of the bolt cylinder to prevent accidental unscrewing of the bolt sleeve assembly from the bolt when the action is partly or fully cocked.

The bolt stop is a spring loaded latch pivoted on the left side of the receiver bridge. It engages the rear face of the bottom (left hand) forward locking lug as the bolt is drawn to the rear.

The safety is of the rotary type. It consists of the conventional horizontal spindle inserted through the top of the bolt sleeve and actuated by a thumb lever. The lever serves as a "flag" giving a clear visual indicator as to whether the gun is "safe" or "ready." In the "ready" position the thumb lever is turned down on the left of the bolt sleeve. In this position all portions of the spindle are

German 7.92mm Kar. 98k with ZF4 Scope.

German VG 1 (VolkssturmGewehr 1–People's Assault Rifle). This is a crude short rifle manufactured with the intention if issuing it to civilians for home defense. Picture shows left side view with bolt partly retracted. The magazine is the ten shot detachable box used on the Kar. 43. The rifle itself is a turn-bolt design.

Models: German VG 1 (VolkssturmGewehr 1, People's Assault Rifle)
Caliber: 7.9mm
Overall length, rifle without bayonet: 43"
Overall weight, rifle without bayonet: 8.3 lbs.
Type of action: Turnbolt
Type of Magazine: Detachable Box—Staggered column
Barrel Length: 23.2"
Bore Diameter: .312"
No. Grooves: 4
Groove Dia.: .323"
Type of bolt: 1 piece—rotating head.
Capacity: 10
Direction of Twist: Right
Rate of Twist: 9.25"

Notes:

There are several versions of this rifle. The one pictured was made by Walther. Another version was made by Mauser and has the regular Mauser action and was called Volkssturm Karabiner 98. A weapon similar to the VG-1 made by Erma used the 7.92mm short cartridge and the MP44 30-round magazine. The stock and barrel are crude as in the case of the Walther. Haenel also made some.

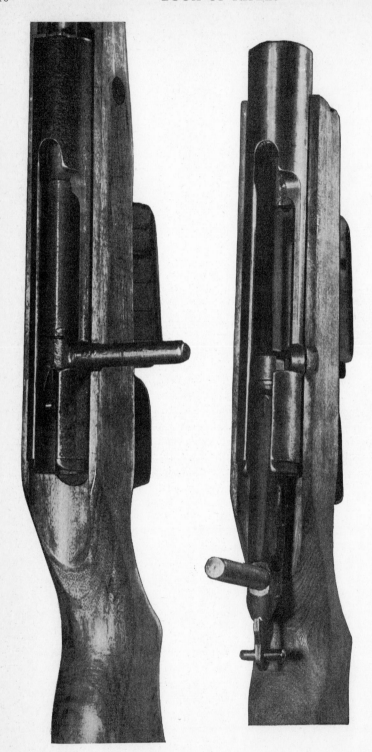

German VG 1, action closed and open.
This is a split bridge receiver action made with one piece bolt. Besides the dual locking lugs at the front end of the bolt cylinder, the handle locks down into its receiver seat forward of the bridge. The locking lugs are not cam cut to provide the customary primary extraction. Because of the crudity of manufacture and materials, this design cannot be recommended for American use.

clear of the bolt and cocking piece. Rotating the lever to the vertical position turns a flange on the spindle into a groove on the cocking piece, at the same time camming the striker slightly to the rear withdrawing the cocking piece nose from contact with the sear nose. Forward travel of the striker is thus effectively blocked. Further rotation of the thumb lever to a horizontal position on the right side of the bolt sleeve leaves the locking flange still in the notch on the striker and also turns a segment on the forward end of the spindle into a recess on the rear of the bolt cylinder firmly locking the bolt cylinder to the bolt sleeve. Because the underside of the bolt sleeve has square shoulders which ride on the flat upper surface of the tang of the receiver it is then impossible to lift the bolt handle and the bolt is firmly locked in the closed position and in the "safe" position.

The forward face of the bolt sleeve is a flat surface at least twice the diameter of the bolt. This serves as an excellent baffle to turn from the shooter's eye any primer or powder gases which may rush back through or around the bolt as a result of a punctured primer or split case.

The extractor is a long spring dovetailed to a split spring band fitted into and around the bolt cylinder. It is held clear of the bolt cylinder at a distance permitting the bottom (right hand) forward locking lug to turn up under the extractor spring and ride to the rear in that position when the bolt handle is lifted. When the bolt handle is turned down the longitudinal guide rib turns in under the extractor spring. The extractor does not rotate with bolt being held in place on the right side of the bolt by a groove in the receiver bridge. A projection from the extractor spring fits into a groove cut around the outside of the bolt cylinder, preventing the extractor from sliding backward or forward over the bolt.

The ejector is a sturdy piece of flat steel pinned into the bolt stop latch on the left side of the receiver bridge. As the bolt is retracted the ejector rides through a slot in the left hand bolt locking lug striking the rim of the cartridge case on the side opposite that held by the extractor claw knocking the cartridge out of the grip of the extractor and out over the right side of the receiver.

The sear bar is pivoted near its front end to the receiver. It is actuated by a spiral spring. The sear projects through a cut into a groove in the tang of the receiver to engage the nose of the cocking piece which rides in this groove. The trigger is pivoted in a slot in the sear bar. The let-off is of the double military type.

The magazine housing is inserted from the underside of the receiver. Its capacity is five cartridges. It is wide enough to permit stacking the cartridges in staggered fashion thus making it possible to keep the bottom of the magazine flush with the underside of the stock. Lips are formed at the top of the magazine to insure feeding only one cartridge at a time to the bolt face. A tang extends forward from the bottom of the magazine housing along the underside of the fore-end. A "guard screw" through this tang is fastened through the stock into a boss on the underside of the receiver ring which also serves as a recoil shoulder. Another tang extending to the rear houses the spring loaded magazine floorplate catch, carries the triggerguard (integral with the magazine housing forging) and provides a seat for the rear guard screw which extends through the stock into the tang of the receiver.

German Gewehr 33/40. This is a shorter modified form of the original Czech model 33. It was extensively used by the Germans and its manufacture was continued by them after seizure of Czechoslovakia. The system of operation is mechanically the same as the Kar. 98 k. Specimen shown has 19¼" barrel.

German Gewehr 98/40. This is the Hungarian Army rifle Model 1935 as modified in 1940 for use by German services. Caliber was changed from 8mm Hungarian to 7.9mm German. A generally similar rifle was used by the Hungarian Army as the Model 43. This is a Mannlicher turn-bolt rifle. Essentially it is the same system as the Roumanian Mannlicher. The cocking piece is modified along the lines of the Austrian M 95 to permit thumb cocking without opening the action. The bridge is split and the bolt handle turns down ahead of the receiver bridge. The two-piece stock is characteristic of this design. The magazine is a modified Mauser.

The magazine spring is the conventional Z-shaped flat spring with the magazine follower mounted at the top and the magazine floor plate mounted at the bottom. This sub-assembly is instantly removable by pressure with the point of a cartridge on the magazine floor plate catch just forward of the triggerguard.

The stock is of one piece design with a short handguard over the barrel extending only from the forward edge of the rear sight to the lower barrel band. It has a semi-pistol grip. The upper barrel band, about two inches wide, is cut away under the fore-end and over the barrel so that, at those points it is really two bands. It encircles and is pinned to the rear portion of the bayonet lug which also covers the fore-end for about two inches and then extends forward under the barrel for another two inches. This forward portion of the bayonet lug is deeply slotted on both sides to provide a secure fit for the bayonet.

The front sight is of the barleycorn type dovetailed into the conventional front sight stud which is integral with the front sight band. Rear sights are of the ramp type with open notch.

Note: For details on the Czech Mausers and the Belgian Mausers made in German military calibers, and for the adaptations made under German control, see *Czecho-Slovakia* and *Belgium*.

For details of the Hungarian conversion known as "the German 98-40" see *Hungary*.

German Semiautomatic Rifles

While Germany was among the first nations to do extensive experimental work in the field of semiautomatic rifles, her army failed grievously in evaluating the needs for such weapons for their infantry.

As early as 1901 Germany outfitted an entire regiment with Mauser semiautomatic recoil operated rifles for field tests. The experience gained indicated that while recoil operated rifles could be manufactured which would be satisfactory for sporting use, it was at that time impractical, if not impossible, to produce such an arm to meet rigid military requirements. Experience showed it possible to develop excellent light machine rifles or guns on the recoil principle, but their weight (23-27 pounds) made them special duty arms, not general infantry equipment.

The Germans used several semiautomatic rifles during World War I, but in very limited quantities. A recoil operated Mauser was used in aircraft for awhile. This weapon had a 25-round magazine and the stock was cut back at the fore-end in a fashion similar to a sporting rifle. It was chambered for the standard 7.9mm cartridge. A full stocked version of this weapon was issued in 1916, also in very limited quantity. The best known semiautomatic rifle used by the Germans in World War I was the Mexican-designed, Swiss-produced Mondragon. This 7mm weapon was gas-operated and was also used by the Germans in aircraft. It was called the Aircraft Self-loading Carbine Model 15 by the Germans. Between World Wars I and II, Mauser developed a 7.9mm semiautomatic rifle known as the Model 35; this rifle was never made in quantity.

When the United States introduced the first Garand rifle the German military were so thoroughly familiar with it that commercial publishing houses in Germany included photographs and descriptions of the Garand and its operation in popular books on firearms published in that year. Germany did experimental

German Model 41(M) Semi-Automatic Rifle. This is a Mauser design which did not prove practical in field use. Cocking handle must be turned up to engage bolt before being pulled straight back to retract the bolt.

Operation is by gas which expands in cap over muzzle. Operating rod is below barrel. Rod being driven back acts on rear section of two-piece bolt, causing it to start back. Rear section by cam action compels bolt head to turn out of locking engagement and then to travel straight back for ejection.

This design is essentially a collector's item. It was not successful in field use.

work on a blast cone system, utilizing a turning bolt for locking and unlocking, but the results were not considered satisfactory.

Both Russia and Germany—as well as Italy—supplied their latest arms developments to the Spaniards during the Civil War. Spain was the testing ground for many of the primary weapons of World War II.

It was not until the introduction of the Russian Tokarev rifles in quantity into the field that the Germans realized the need for a rifle of semiautomatic type for the infantryman, and the potentialities of the gas operated system. When they finally went into full scale operation, their experimentation was rapid.

However German rifle designers, quite unlike their other technicians, were bound too much to the past in their initial experiments. They tended toward re-trials of their own failures, rather than a branching out at once on new lines of research.

German 7.92mm Mauser M1916 Semiautomatic Rifle. This rifle was issued in limited quantities and is similar, except for its full stock, to the 7.92mm Mauser "Flieger Selbstladekarabiner"— "Aircraft Self-Loading Carbine."

Mauser had very early developed a muzzle booster, a form of muzzle cone to assist in the recoil of the barrel in his early rifle. This was merely a modification of the device used on machine guns. By combining this blast cone with an operating rod system, the Germans sought to develop a new rifle. A turning bolt lock had been their most successful rifle creation, therefore an attempt was made to use that locking principle in a semiautomatic just as they had done in their M.G. 34. The general design of the receiver and of operating springs were also patterned after early Mauser experiments. The result was a rifle which was a pretty complete failure, the 41 (M) described below.

Meanwhile, parallel experimentation conducted at other plants also depended on the blast cone for gas operation. The new design worked on a locking system which was a variant of one of Mauser's earliest designs. This breech locking design was finally perfected, but the muzzle cone system of gas operation again proved impractical. The new rifle was the 41 (W). These were built by Walther.

When finally in 1943 the Germans combined the gas operating system of the Russian rifle with a modified form of the locking system of the 41 (W) they produced a new and quite successful design. By that time their resources had sunk to the point where mass production was the determining factor rather than quality. As a result, these rifles were made as cheaply and as rapidly as possible. Manufacturing short cuts were taken wherever possible, resulting in the development of improved forms of cast receivers and special steel stamped parts. These arms however were weapons of opportunity intended to give terrific fire power to the infantry company and recognized the comparatively short life such rifles might have. The rifles as manufactured therefore never approached the value of the design itself.

A paratrooper's light machine rifle was also built. This arm, since it has the characteristics of a machine weapon, must be considered elsewhere.*

In the last gasp, German designers produced a number of remarkable designs whose potentialities might have been considerable had they been developed earlier.

The important German semiautomatic arms which were actually put into production are the following:

The 41 (M)

This was the only semiautomatic rifle introduced by the Germans utilizing the projecting bolt cocking handle externally resembling the standard Mauser rifle. It was a product of the engineering of the Mauser organization, experimental forms of it having been tested for years. The design had never proved entirely acceptable in tests, and its introduction to field use proved the impracticability of the design.

Characteristics: This is a semiautomatic rifle operated by trapping gases in a muzzle cone so that they thrust a piston and operating rod to the rear to actuate the breech mechanism.

Description and Operation: This arm differs from the other German semiautomatic rifles in that the operating rod is housed *below* the barrel. The gas system consists of a cylinder carrying the front sight mounting which is assembled over the muzzle of the barrel, and which encloses the tip of an operating rod positioned below the barrel and protected by the stock. A second unit, a blast or muzzle cone is screwed into the cylinder. The gas expansion in the muzzle cone pushes a piston back against the operating rod. The operating rod is thrust back, compressing the operating rod spring. The rear end of the rod connects with a yoke which passes through receiver cuts below the chamber.

The bolt in this arm is a two-unit assembly. Its forward end carries two locking lugs which are securely seated in cuts in the receiver when the arm is locked. The rear of the operating rod yoke is in contact with a projection on the bottom of the rear section of the bolt. As the rod is driven back, it thus compels the bolt to travel back in its guides in the receiver. When the rear section of the bolt goes back compressing the coil operating spring housed within it, cam faces operate to compel the front bolt head section to rotate out of locking engagement. As a result of this turning movement primary extraction is provided which frees the cartridge case in the chamber. When the lugs are completely unlocked, the entire bolt assembly continues to the rear to extract and eject. This is a striker fired arm, the striker being cammed back within the bolt during the opening motion and held cocked when the operating spring drives the bolt assembly ahead.

At the end of the rearward stroke, the standard box magazine feeds a cartridge into line. The recoil spring asserts itself and pushes the bolt forward chambering the cartridge.

---

* *Small Arms of the World*, by W. H. B. Smith and Joseph E. Smith, The Stackpole Company, Harrisburg, Pa.

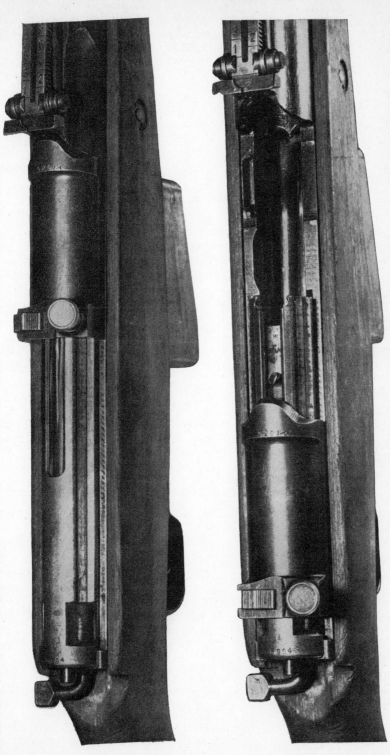

German 41(W) Semi-Automatic Rifle, action closed and open. Top picture shows detail of construction of bolt slide. Note its position at forward end where it rests on receiver. Operating rod on top of barrel passes through receiver and rests against the top of the bolt slide. The lever at the rear of the receiver is the manual safety which can be applied only when the action is cocked. Projecting rod above safety is recoil spring guide tip which is part of the takedown system.

Lower picture shows bolt slide fully retracted and locked manually as required before magazine can be loaded. This design had a fixed magazine loaded through the top of the open action. Later designs have detachable box magazines.

German Gew 41(W) sectional drawings showing details of construction and operation.

Top detail shows overall construction with chamber loaded and arm ready to fire. Note that while operating rod works along the top of the barrel and is fully enclosed by guards, its return spring is positioned below the barrel. Arms extend down on either side at the rear of the rod to compress the rod return spring. The two-piece bolt return spring is housed in receiver.

Center detail illustrates gas operation. Bullet has left barrel muzzle and is momentarily blocking the gas as it emerges. Expanding gas is deflected by the muzzle cone to the rear against the face of the cylindrical piston around the barrel. The rear face of the cylindrical piston hits the operating rod and drives it to the rear.

The bottom detail shows the unlocking operation. The operating rod driven back through a receiver cut above the line of the bolt starts the bolt slide (or carrier) to the rear. When pressure drops, a finger inside the bolt slide passing through a cut in the top of the bolt

When the bolt *head* is fully forward against the face of the barrel chamber, *the rear bolt section* can still move forward. As it does so, operating cams twist the bolt head so that the locking lugs engage in their seats.

The trigger must be deliberately pulled for each shot. A disconnector prevents "doubling" by making it necessary to fully release the trigger before it will again engage the sear.

Notes: The locking and unlocking system used in this arm is in many ways analogous to that of the Mannlicher Model 95 straight-pull rifle.

The top of the receiver from the rear of the bolt backward is covered with a hinged plate. Pressing the releases at the forward end permits the plate to be hinged up to the rear. The breech assembly can then be moved back and lifted up out of the top of the receiver.

The Semiautomatic Model 41(W)

This gas operated rifle must not be confused with the previously described Model 41 (M). The Model 41 (W) uses the muzzle cone plan for trapping gas to operate the breech mechanism but the operating rod in this model is on top of the barrel and the breech mechanism differs radically from that used in the 41 (M).

The breech mechanism of the Model 41 (W) is essentially the same as that employed in the later Kar. 43 or Gew. 43 described below.

There are several variants in the 41 (W). One variant is equipped with a bolt release on the left side of the receiver while on the other it is necessary to hold back the bolt with one hand while the magazine follower is depressed with the thumb of the other hand and the bolt then eased forward (as in the case of the Garand.)

The breech locking and firing mechanism of the Model 41 (W) proved quite satisfactory in service and very cheap to manufacture but the guns showed other defects. The fouling, carbonization and corrosion which has generally characterized attempts to use the muzzle cap system for trapping gases caused complaints. So did the weight of the rifles. These criticisms from the battle field resulted in the development of the Kar. 43 and the Gewehr 43.

Model: German G 41 (W)
Caliber: 7.9mm
Overall length, rifle without bayonet: 44.25″
Overall weight, rifle without bayonet: 8.75 lbs.
Type of action: Gas operated—Semiautomatic
Type of Magazine: Detachable box—Staggered column.

Barrel Length: 21.5″ *No. Grooves:* 4
Bore Diameter: .312″ *Groove Dia.:* .323″
Type of bolt: 2 piece—Wedge locked dual lugs.
Capacity: 10

Direction of Twist: Right
Rate of Twist: 9.45″

The Gewehr 43 or Kar. 43

This is a gas operated semiautomatic rifle. The action is of the straight-line (non-rotating) bolt type. The bolt remains open when the magazine is empty. It must then be pulled back to its rearmost position and locked open with a finger latch to permit recharging the magazine.

The breech action assembly (to coin a phrase) consists of the (1) gas valve and operating rod assembly (2) operating slide, called the "cover" by the Germans (3) bolt assembly (4) bolt housing, called the "lock case" by the Germans, and (5) the recoil or bolt return spring.

German 41(W) Semi-Automatic Rifle of Walther design.
Operation is by gas expanding in cap over muzzle. Operating rod works along top of barrel.
The breech locking design formed the basis for the German Gewehr and the Kar. 43 Models which were put into production with a different type of gas system.

German M 43 Semi-Automatic Rifle with ZF-4 telescope. This is the improved and greatly modified version of the M 41(W). It combines the essentials of the M 41(W) locking system with the Russian Tokarev gas operating system. The design is good, the manufacture fair to poor.

A gas port or vent is drilled through the top of the barrel about midway between the throat of the chamber and the muzzle. A barrel band carrying a housing is pinned in place over the vent. A round steel cylinder bored through from end to end is threaded into the rear of the housing so that it lies over the barrel and parallel to it with the open end of the cylinder to the rear. We will refer to this as the "gas-port cylinder" for lack of a better name. A bottle-necked steel sleeve, bored out from front and rear so as to leave a solid steel wall inside the cylinder at the bottle neck, is slipped over the gas-port cylinder to form a sleeve valve. The operating rod assembly consists of (1) a tappet rod, one end of which slips into the rear end of the bottle-necked sleeve valve (2) a coupling into which the tappet rod slips from the front while the main operating rod slips into the coupling from the rear (3) the main operating rod which extends rearward from the coupling through a tunnel drilled through the top of the receiver. The rear end of the main operating rod impinges on the forward nose of the operating slide. (4) The operating rod return spring is a coil spring surrounding the main operating rod. Its rear end is supported by a shoulder in the tunnel through the receiver and its forward end bears against the coupling which joins the main operating rod and the tappet rod.

As the bullet passes the gas port in the barrel some of the gas forces its way upward into the gasport housing and expands to the rear through the gasport cylinder. Emerging from the rear of the gas-port cylinder it is trapped inside the sleeve valve and forces the sleeve sharply to the rear. This movement of the sleeve valve is transmitted to the tappet rod and through it and the coupling to the main operating rod. After movement of about ⅝ of an inch a port in the sleeve valve is uncovered so that any remaining pressure in the valve is released and any further motion to the rear is only the result of momentum. The return spring, which has been compressed by the rearward motion of the operating rod then takes command and returns the sleeve valve and operating rod assembly to its forward position ready for the next shot.

In the meantime the energy from the expanding gas has been transmitted through the sleeve valve and operating rod assembly to the operating slide on the bolt. The operating slide then continues to the rear under its own momentum, unlocking the bolt and carrying it to the rear to extract the fired case.

The operating slide is a rugged steel casting or forging formed with a heavy nose on its upper forward end to take the impact of the operating rod. It carries the "bolt handle" on its upper left rear end projecting to the upper left at about a 45° angle from the perpendicular. It is permitted to slide straight forward and backward by grooves which engage longitudinal ribs on the bolt housing or "lock case." When the bolt is fully forward a groove in the operating slide also engages a flange on the left side of the receiver to lock the slide securely to the receiver before firing. A stud projects downward from the operating slide through a slot in the top of the bolt. This stud engages the "locking piece" which operates the locking lugs. The slide latch, called the "retainer" by the Germans, is located at the right rear of the operating slide. When the operating slide is drawn fully to the rear the latch may be manually engaged to hold the action open.

The bolt assembly consists of the conventional steel cylinder carrying on its under side a ramp which depresses the hammer and cocks the piece as the bolt

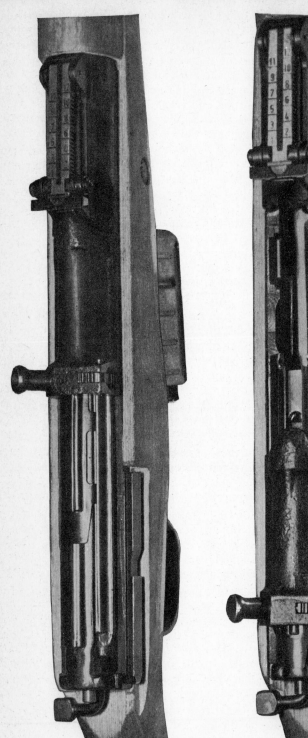

German M 43 (Gewehr or Kar,) system, action closed and open. The locking system resemblances to the earlier 41 W can be seen in these pictures. The exteriors are rough, but interior finish is usually good.

These models use detachable box magazines, normally of 10-shot capacity. These arms may be clip loaded through the top of the open action or may be loaded by insertion of loaded box magazines from below.

moves to the rear. The head of the bolt is deeply recessed to take the head of the rimless cartridge case. The recess is so deep that most of the cannelure on the cartridge case is also held inside the bolt head. The extractor is a sturdy steel claw, spring loaded, fitted into the upper right quadrant of the bolt head. Held by a flat headed screw, it is easily replaced. The forward face of the extractor lies in line with the forward rim of the bolt and does not project forward—a type of construction made possible by the deeply recessed bolt face. The lower left quadrant of the bolt is slotted to travel over the husky, spring loaded ejector mounted in the lower side of the receiver.

The locking lugs are not integral with the bolt. They are so designed that they fit, without hinge pins, into slots on either side of the bolt near the bolt head, one on the right and one on the left side, to provide dual opposed locking lugs supporting the head of the bolt. They engage in the receiver. The inner surface of each lug is provided with camming surfaces. The "locking piece" is slipped into the bolt from the rear. Its forward end is also provided with suitable camming surfaces to engage the inner surfaces of the locking lugs. With the locking piece in place the locking lugs are held in their slots in the sides of the bolt. As the locking piece is moved forward it cams the locking lugs outward through their slots into the locking recesses in the receiver. Moving the locking piece to the rear cams the locking lugs back into their slots where the outer surfaces of the locking lug lie flush with the perimeter of the bolt. Thus the bolt is unlocked from the receiver and is free to move straight to the rear. Because the action of the locking piece in forcing the lugs outward to engage in their locking recesses is a wedging action this type of bolt action is coming to be commonly referred to as the "wedge type" bolt action.

When the gun has been fired the operating slide is forced to the rear as previously described. The slide moves a short distance to give the bullet an opportunity to clear the muzzle and to let the residual pressure drop in the chamber so that the cartridge case will release its grip on the chamber walls. After this short motion of the slide the stud on the slide engages the locking piece and moves it to the rear. This motion cams the locking lugs out of engagement in the receiver. At this instant the stud on the operating slide also engages the bolt and the entire bolt assembly moves to the rear extracting and ejecting the fired case.

The striker assembly is a three piece unit which slips inside the locking piece. It consists of (1) a nail-shaped firing pin (2) a tappet, called the "firing piece" by the Germans and (3) a coupling into which the striker fits. A vertical pin on top of the tappet fits into a slot in the locking piece. This pin limits the forward travel of the tappet so that it merely strikes a sharp blow through the coupling against the firing pin which moves forward against the primer under its own momentum. All three units of the firing pin assembly are free floating. The three piece construction and the use of the tappet are apparently designed to keep down the weight of the firing pin so that it will not move forward with enough energy to discharge the primer as the bolt slams forward on a loaded round. The need for care in this case is indicated by the fact that, even with the three piece construction, the floating firing pin does generally make a slight impression in the primer when the bolt slams home. There are, however, no reports of accidental discharges with this design.

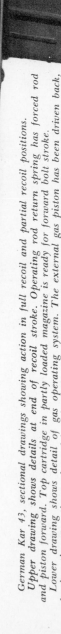

German Kar 43, sectional drawings showing action in full recoil and partial recoil positions.

Upper drawing shows details at end of recoil stroke. Operating rod return spring has forced rod and piston forward. Top cartridge in partly loaded magazine is ready for forward bolt stroke.

Lower drawing shows detail of gas operating system. The external gas piston has been driven back, forcing the operating rod to drive the bolt slide to the rear. The bolt slide operating the firing pin carrier has withdrawn the two wedge-type locking lugs and is carrying the bolt assembly to the rear. The cartridge case is being drawn back by the extractor. The operating rod spring is compressed and will return the rod to its forward position before the cartridge case has been ejected.

The bolt housing or "locking case" covers the entire receiver from the magazine well to the tang. It houses the action closing springs and the bolt assembly and carries on its outer surfaces the guide ribs which engage the operating slide. A "long" and a "short" coiled spring (so called by the Germans) provide the power to close the action after they have been compressed by the opening of the bolt. These springs are mounted around a guide rod over the forward end of which a guide tube fits. The forward end of the guide tube fits into the rear of the bolt. This assembly of guide rod and tube prevents the buckling of the coil springs under compression and provides for smooth, uniform delivery of the power of the compressed springs for the forward movement of the bolt and operating slide. Projecting from the rear of the bolt housing is a spring loaded plunger. This is the release catch which permits lifting the complete breech assembly, housing, slide and bolt, out of the receiver for disassembly.

The safety is mounted over the tang to the rear of the bolt housing. Turning it to the right locks the piece. The slide must be latched in its rearmost position and the safety turned to the right before the release plunger can be pressed in and the housing assembly lifted out of the rifle.

The hammer is of conventional design. It is provided with two hammer hooks one of which must be disengaged by allowing the trigger to move forward after a shot has been fired. The other is then disengaged by normal pressure on the trigger. This type of action, conventional in all semiautomatics, is to prevent "doubling" or full automatic fire.

The magazine is removable through the bottom of the action. The magazine catch is at the rear of the magazine well. The magazine is of the staggered box type holding ten cartridges. It is charged through the top of the receiver by use of the conventional Mauser 5-round charger clips. Although the bolt remains open after the last round is fired out of the magazine it is necessary to draw the slide fully to the rear and latch it in that position before the charger clip can be inserted in its guides in the top of the receiver.

The front sight is of the hooded ramp type mounted on a heavy barrel band and provided with a broad, flat topped post sight.

The rear sight is of the ramp leaf type with square notch.

On the right side of the receiver is a long, stout rib, dovetailed top and bottom to take a telescopic sight. Considerable numbers of this model were issued with such sights.

Stocks are of the modified pistol grip, one-piece type plus handguard which protects the gas valve and operating rod. Butt plates are provided with a trap covering a receptacle in the butt for oil, tools and a most clear, concise illustrated manual on the care and field servicing of the rifle.

Differences between the early and later models: The original hand guards on the 41 models were plastic. Magazines were fixed, projecting boxes. Receivers were forgings and were machined. The bolt slides were also forgings with the operating handle on the right and the release catch to the left. The trigger assembly differed from the later models in which the trigger worked off of a sear instead of directly off the hammer.

In the 43 and 44 models handguards were plastic or wood. Magazines were detachable steel stampings. Receivers were cast and were not finish machined. Gas systems differed as already described. Operating slides were cast. Bolt housings were stampings.

German Kar 43, section drawing showing rifle at instant of firing, and various other details.

Top drawing is sectioned and shortened to show bullet still in barrel and approaching the gas port. The bolt is locked to the receiver at this point. After the bullet passes the gas port, gas expanding in the hollow cylinder will drive the exterior piston and operating rod to the rear. Detail at lower left shows section of receiver with bolt slide manually locked back ready for loading.

Detail to right shows section of bolt slide manual lock.

Muzzle details show front sight and hood mounting and front muzzle view.

Lower bolt details show locked position with firing pin carrier inside the bolt cylinder forcing the dual locking lugs out into the receiver. The firing pin cannot emerge until the action is fully locked. The unlocked detail shows the cam system by means of which the firing pin carrier draws the two locking lugs back into the bolt cylinder to unlock the action. A finger on the underside of the bolt slide passes down into the hole shown in the top of the firing pin carrier to provide the motive power for locking and unlocking.

German Semiautomatic Volkssturm Gewehr 1-5

This arm was developed at Suhl by Gustloff in 1944-45. It was apparently not used until 1945. Designed to provide a very cheap semiautomatic weapon for home defense use, it was not considered primarily an army design. Crude in appearance, it is quite remarkable in design and has unusual factors of strength, reliability, and low cost and ease of manufacture. It is an original type of weapon firing from a closed breech by fall of a rotating hammer. It operates on a new form of retarded blowback principle.

Description and Operation: The receiver is a series of stampings riveted together. The barrel is rigidly assembled to the receiver. The wooden butt and forestock are also attached by rivets.

A cylindrical slide is fitted around the barrel in the general manner of the slide on the Colt Automatic Pistol. The firing mechanism is housed in a separate unit at the rear, so mounted that the rear of the slide can pass inside it during recoil.

A heavy steel muzzle sleeve about 4.75 inches long and a powerful recoil spring are carried in the forward end of the moving slide. The recoil spring is first mounted over the muzzle and around the barrel. The sliding member is then mounted about the barrel. The muzzle sleeve is inserted and turned until engagement lugs on it lock securely into the forward end of the slide. A magazine of standard arc box design is inserted from below in the receiver. The slide is then retracted by pulling on a projection provided near the ejection port. As it moves back, the slide compresses the recoil spring against the front end of the muzzle sleeve.

The breechblock of steel is inserted in the rear of the slide behind the ejection port opening and is riveted in place. It carries the extractor and firing pin. The hammer and trigger mechanism are housed in a standing mount in the receiver to the rear of the slide.

Pulling the slide back runs its rear surface *inside* the stamped hammer housing and cocks the hammer. Releasing the slide permits the recoil spring to pull it forward and chamber a cartridge.

Four holes are drilled in the barrel about 2.5 inches back from the muzzle, one on top and bottom and one on right and left. As the bullet starts down the barrel, the rearward thrust of the cartridge case against the breechblock tends to open the breech. Gas escaping from the four holes, however, expands in the strong steel sleeve within the slide and blows forward, tending to draw the sliding members *ahead*. This counters the rearward thrust to the cartridge case to a remarkable degree. The breech opening is effectively slowed down until dangerous pressure has dropped.

The gas rapidly exhausts from the sleeve through the slide. The slide is carried back by residual pressure as the cartridge case thrusts back against the face of the breechblock riveted in the rear of the slide.

As the slide moves to its full recoil position, it exposes the holes in the barrel momentarily.

The extractor resembles that of the Russian rifle. The firing pin is of floating type secured by an interrupted thread. Pushing the firing pin in and twisting it permits removal.

German People's Assault Rifle (Volkssturm Gewehr) caliber 7.9mm kurz (short). This is a semiautomatic arm using the shortened cartridge developed by the Germans for assault rifle use.

A slide around the rigid barrel is blown back to operate the action as in the standard blowback automatic pistol. However, holes drilled in the forward end of the barrel permit gas to escape forward into a sleeve which tends to hold the action closed until breech pressure from the powerful cartridge has dropped to safe limits.

The detachable magazine is the 32-shot form used in the German assault rifles. This is a mass production weapon designed for low cost and speedy manufacture, and intended primarily for home defense.

German Volkssturm Gewehr (People's Assault Rifle)

Caliber: 7.9mm
Overall length, rifle without bayonet: 34.87"
Overall weight, rifle without bayonet: 10.37 lbs.
Type of action: Semi-Auto. Delayed blowback.
Type of Magazine: Detachable box-double   Capacity: 30
        Column
Barrel length: 14.9"
Bore diameter: .312"

Direction of twist: Right
Groove diameter: .323"

Top to Bottom: Walther G A115 No. 1, G A115 No. 2, G A115 No. 3, Semiautomatic Rifles; and Walther MKb-42 (W) Assault Rifle. The rifles appeared in prototype form and their gas system was used on the MKb-42 (W) Assault Rifle and in modified form is currently being used on the Czech Model 52 Rifle.

German World War II Assault Rifles

Considerably before World War II, the Germans laid down a requirement for a selective fire rifle to replace the standard bolt action rifle, submachine gun, and the light machinegun and an "intermediate"-sized cartridge for this weapon. The requirement for the cartridge originated in 1934 and several types were produced for test by Gustav Genschow and the Rheinisch Westphalische Sprengstoff A.G. These rounds varied in case length from 37 to 46mm and used 140 to 150 grain bullets.

In 1938, Polte was given the contract which resulted in the development of of the 7.92mm short cartridge. By 1941 Polte had designed a 7.9mm cartridge with a case 33mm long and 24.6 grains of propellent. This cartridge was called the "7.9mm Infanterie Kurz Patrone." In the same year development contracts were given to Haenel for selective fire rifles for this cartridge. By 1940 Hugo Schmeisser of Haenel had produced a gas-operated design for the cartridge. By July, 1942, fifty specimens of the prototype were produced. Walther started to design a weapon to meet the Army requirement sometime in 1940; by July 4 specimens of a prototype had been produced. Walther adapted the design of an earlier semiautomatic rifle to produce their weapon. The weapons designed by Haenel and Walther were called Maschinen Karabiners (Machine Carbines) which was shortened to MKb.

After test of prototypes and changes, including fitting of a bayonet lug and threading of the muzzle for a grenade launcher, both the Haenel and Walther weapons were put into production. The Haenel was designated the MKb 42 (H) and the Walther the MKb 42 (W). Approximately 7,800 of both designs were produced. The Haenel design was reworked in the spring of 1943 by Schmeisser and became the MP 43. Walther dropped this type of weapon completely. First deliveries of MP 43 were made in July 1943 and by January 1944 the German Army had received more than 14,000 MP 43's. Production rose to about 5,000 per month in February 1944. MP 43/1 was identical to MP 43 but used a screw-on type grenade launcher rather than the clamp-on type used with the MP 43. In April 1944, the nomenclature was changed to MP 44 and to "Sturmgewehr 44" (StG 44)—assault rifle 44-late in 1944. There was no apparent reason for the

German 7.92mm MKb-42 (H) Assault Rifle.

German 7.92mm MP 43 Assault Rifle.

German 7.92mm MP 43 Assault Rifle Field Stripped.

change in nomenclature to MP 44; this weapon is identical to MP 43. Most specimens of the MP 43/1 have a V-type telescope mounting bracket on the right side. Some MP 44's have this bracket, no MP 43's have been found with the bracket. The change in nomenclature to StG 44 "assault rifle 44" was probably done mainly for propaganda purposes, but it also indicated the true nature of the weapon more correctly than the "MP—Machine Pistol" designation did. The MKb 42, MP 43, 44 series of weapons are not submachine guns in the conventional sense of that term. They were the first true assault rifles manufactured in quantity and as such are the ancestors of weapons like the Soviet AK-47 and the Czech Model 58.

During the last year of the war, several companies—Gustloffwerke, Haenel, Mauser, and possibly Erma, came out with prototypes of improved assault rifles. The Mauser prototype which is known as Gerät o6H or StG 45 (M) had considerable influence on later designs. This weapon operated on the delayed blowback system—an earlier Mauser prototype, Gerät o6 was a combination of gas operation with delayed blowback. The bolt of Gerät o6H is divided into two sections: the head section contains two vertically mounted roller bearings; the firing pin is inserted through the rear bolt section. This rear section has a thinned nose section which protrudes into the bolt head when the weapon is locked. Forward movement of the rear section of the bolt under the pressure of the recoil spring forces the nose of the rear bolt section into the head section. When the bolt closes, the nose section forces the two roller bearings into cut-out sections in the receiver. The firing pin is driven forward by the hammer functioning the cartridge. The pressure of the gas forces to the rear against the base of the case and thereby against the head of the bolt. This pressure forces the bolt head rearward which in turn pushes the nose of the rear bolt section back. This allows the roller bearings to be cammed back into their seats in the bolt

head and the bolt is unlocked. Since this type of action makes no provision for
slow initial extraction—a slight rearward or turning motion which loosens
up the case before it is completely extracted from the chamber—the chamber is

*Mauser Prototype Assault Rifle, the 7.92mm StG-45 (M). This weapon, sometimes called
Gerät 06 (H), has the delayed blowback locking mechanism currently used in the German G3,
and the Spanish CETME.*

The StG-45 (M) Field Stripped.

luted for about half its length to ease extraction. This fluting can cause extraction problems with brass cases unless they are sufficiently hard.

This locking system is currently used in the Spanish CETME assault rifle, the German G3 assault rifle, and the Swiss Model 57 assault rifle. A modification of this system is used on the French Model 52 machine gun. The CETME and G3 are direct descendents of the StG 45 (M).

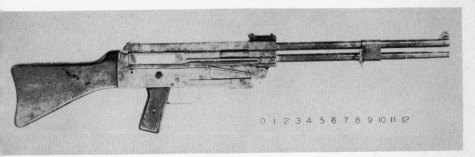

Haenel Prototype Assault Rifle Model 45 chambered for the 7.92mm Short Cartridge.

CHARACTERISTICS OF GERMAN ASSAULT RIFLES

	MKb 42 (W)	MKb 42 (H)	StG 44	StG 45 (M)
Caliber:	7.92mm	7.92mm	7.92mm	7.92mm
System of operation:	Gas, selective fire	Gas, selective fire	Gas, selective fire	Delayed blowback, selective fire
Weight—				
w/empty magazine:	9.75 lbs.	11.06 lbs.	11.5 lbs.	8.18 lbs.
Length, overall:	36.75″	37″	37″	35.15″
Barrel length:	16.1″	14.37″	16.5″	15.75″
Feed device:	.... 30-round, detachable staggered row, box magazine ....*			
Sights—				
front:	.... hooded barley corn			
rear:	.... tangent w/notch graduated from 100-800 meters			
Muzzle velocity:	2132 f.p.s.	about 2100 f.p.s.	2132 f.p.s.	about 2100 f.p.s.
Cyclic rate:	600 r.p.m.	500 r.p.m.	500 r.p.m.	350-450 r.p.m.

* A ten-round magazine was also designed for this weapon.

Model 1871 Bolt Action

The first was the Model 1871, first deliveries of which were actually made in 1872. Some of these rifles saw service in the World War II. Caliber 11mm.

German 11mm Mauser Cartridge M1871

Other Names: 11.15x60R
Type: Rimmed, Necked, Centerfire, Type A Base
Overall Length: 3.07″
Average Wt.: 660 gr.
Type Powder: Black
Approximate Chg.: 77.16 gr.
Type Primer: Berdan (Two Hole)

BULLET
Type: Lead, Paper Patched
Diameter: .448″ (With Patch); .440″ (Without)
Weight: 386 gr.
Length: 1.082″

CARTRIDGE CASE

Length Overall: 2.37"
Length Head to Shoulder: 1.46"
Length of Shoulder: .10"
Length of Neck: .81"
Diamete: at Rim: .582"

Diameter at Base: .513"
Diameter at Neck: .463"
Diameter at Shoulder: .508"

BALLISTICS (approximate)
Muzzle Velocity: 1443 f.s.

Notes: 1. Cartridge assembled with a beeswax wad between two card wads behind th bullet.

German Model 71/84

Caliber: 11mm
Overall length, rifle without bayonet: 50.9"
Overall weight, rifle without bayonet: 10.2 lbs.
Type of action: Turnbolt
Type of magazine: Tubular
Barrel length: 31.5"   *No. Grooves:* 4
Bore diameter: .433"   *Groove dia.:* .4409"
Notes:

Type of bolt: 2 piece—Rotating head

Capacity: 8

Direction of twist: Right
Rate of twist: 21.65"

1. This rifle was developed by Mauser and an Army Commission. It was merely the 1871 SS altered to a tube magazine repeater. A spring in the magazine tube forces cartridges back onte a "riser." Rearward movement of the bolt cams down the rear of the pivoted riser to bring a cartridge in line for the forward feeding stroke of the bolt.

Model 1888 Bolt Action

The German Army Commission in 1888 adopted a rifle of hybrid design built for a new cartridge, the 7.92mm rimless.

Except for the initial 11mm black powder Mausers, all German service Mausers have been built around the original 7.92mm cartridge which has only been modified by a change in bullet design and by improvements in powder and primers.

The M1888 utilizes a form of the Mannlicher loading system. The clip loaded with 5 rimless cartridges is inserted into the top of the magazine. The bolt is a modified early Mauser two piece design bored out from the front and having a removable bolt head. The locking lugs are on the bolt cylinder to the rear of the removable head. A jacket surrounds the light barrel. The German Gewehr 1888 was neither a Mauser nor a Mannlicher. Huge quantities were manufactured by Ludwig Loewe at Berlin, a firm which at that time owned controlling interest in the Mauser organization. The rifle was also manufactured in quantity at Steyr Armory in Austria, in a Belgian plant, by the German arsenals, Haenel, and by Schilling.

When the Model 1888 was discarded, hundreds of thousands of these rifles were remodeled into sporting designs. Very large numbers were imported into the U.S., some being sold "as is" at very low prices. Others were altered and some engraved and sold under the names of Haenel-Mannlichers, Schilling-Mannlichers, etc. after the names of the German manufactures who modified them.

Rifles of this pattern, while excellent target and sporting arms for the cartridge known in the U.S. as the 8mm Mauser are not intended for and are dangerous to use with any *modern* German military ammunition.

The Model 88 rifles and carbines *should not be used* with any 7.92mm (8mm Mauser) ammunition which uses .323 diameter bullets. European manu-

German Model 1871 Single Shot

Caliber: 11mm
Overall length, rifle without bayonet: 52.9"
Overall weight, rifle without bayonet: 10 lbs.
Type of action: Turnbolt
Barrel length: 33.5"   No. grooves: 4
Bore diameter: .433"   Groove dia.: .4487"

With bayonet attached: 72.6"
With bayonet attached: 11.8 lbs.
Type of bolt: 2 piece—Rotating head
    Direction of twist: Right
    Rate of twist: 21.65"

Notes:

1. This rifle was adopted in 1871 but first deliveries were made in 1872. Photo shows a short rifle version.

2. This was the first metallic cartridge breech loader officially adopted by Germany.

German Model 1888 Carbine. This carbine is mechanically the same as the M. 1888 rifle. This rifle and carbine were designed by a German military commission which combined a modified Mauser 1871 type (two-piece) bolt with a modified Mannlicher 1886 magazine. A jacket surrounds the barrel.

These were the first arms designed for the German 7.9mm caliber cartridge. The cartridge case is essentially the same as that of the modern German 7.9mm. However, the bullet diameter of the new cartridge is considerably greater than that of model 1888. Dangerously high breech pressures may be encountered when using the modern German military cartridge in the 1888 weapons.

Model 1888 actions may be encountered as sporters or with modified Mauser magazines. These designs differ from modern Mausers in their locking system in that they have two-piece bolts with removable bolt heads and split bridge receivers with bolt handle locking down forward of the bridge.

German Model 1888 Mauser & Commission

Caliber: 7.9mm
Overall length, rifle without bayonet: 48.91"
Overall weight, rifle without bayonet: 8.56 lbs.
Type of action: Turnbolt
Type of magazine: Mannlicher box—Vertical column
Barrel length: 29.1"   No. grooves: 4

Bore Diameter: .310"
Groove Dia.: .317"
Type of bolt: 2 piece—Rotating head
Capacity: 5
Direction of twist: Right
Rate of twist: 9.45"

Notes:

1. This design appears also in 2 carbine forms: (a) As shown above stocked to muzzle. Bent bolt handle. Barrel 17.62". (b) Same as (a) except that a stacking rod is incorporated—Model 91.

2. Barrels equipped with jackets.

3. Modern German Service ammunition is dangerous in these rifles, as actual bullet diameter is too large. U. S. made "8mm Mauser" ammunition is safe, since it uses a compromise bullet and relatively weak load safe for use in either 1888 or 1898 patterns.

German Model 1888 sectional drawing with action open ready for loading. The magazine feeding system varies from the Mannlicher. Note that barrel jacket is screwed in to receiver. Details of removable bolthead can be seen. Since this design bolt is bored out from the front there is no bolt sleeve. Instead the cocking piece is mounted over the rear of the projecting striker and held by a nut screwed into the threaded rear end of the striker.

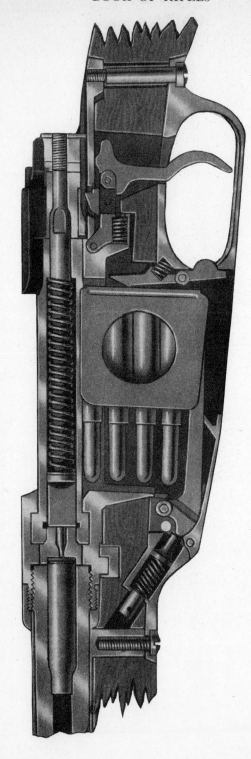

German Model 1888, sectional view with magazine loaded, one cartridge fired. In this construction the clip forms a part of the magazine. The magazine follower works between the side walls of the clip. When the last cartridge has been chambered, the clip drops out through the bottom of the magazine. This clip differs from the early Mannlicher forms in that it may be inserted in the action either side up.

actured 7.92mm ammunition with .323 diameter bullets is frequently called
7.9mm (or 7.92mm) "I.S.," "J.S.," "S," or "sS." The "I.S." means Infanterie
Spitzgeschoss (Infantry Pointed Bullet); this is the original German designation.
The "J.S." designation is actually an error; in German script the letter "I" is
frequently printed similar to a "J" and unfortunately it was understood to be a
"J" by non-German speaking people and printed as "J.S." in so many English
language publications that it is even referred to as "J.S." in English language
catalogs printed by some European firms who definitely know better! The "sS"
is actually the designation for the heavy ball bullet—"Schweres Spitzgeschoss."

Some of these 1888 actions have been modified to load in the Mauser fashion
instead of on the Mannlicher clip system. The one infallible rule, therefore, for
identifying this design, is the two piece bolt. If the bolt head is removable the
gun is not intended for modern military ammunition. Mauser rifles made for the
improved 7.92mm cartridge are all one-piece bolts. The dual locking lugs are
close to the head of the bolt.

8mm Mauser (7.92mm) Cartridge

Other Names: 8x57 Mauser, 7.92mm Mauser,
7.9mm
Type: Rimless, Necked, Centerfire
Overall Length: 2.765"
Average Wt.: 378 gr.
Type Powder: Nitrocellulose
Type Primer: Boxer (Large Rifle)

BULLET
Type: Soft Point (U. S. commercial load)
Diameter: .321"
Weight: 170 gr.
Length: .915"

CARTRIDGE CASE
Length Overall: 2.24"
Length Head to Shoulder: 1.81"
Length of Shoulder: .125"
Length of Neck: .305"
Diameter at Rim: .470"
Diameter at Base: .471"
Diameter at Neck: .351"
Diameter at Shoulder: .4314"

BALLISTICS (approximate)
Muzzle Velocity: 2530 f.s.
Pressure: 47,000 lbs./sq. in.

Notes: (1) Sporting type commercially manufactured in the United States to lower pressure
with smaller diameter bullet can be used in German 1888 types as well as 98.

2. This cartridge is made in Europe in armor piercing, tracer and incendiary types also.

German 7.92mm M1891 Rifle.

German Sporting Rifles

It is not practicable in a book of this nature to describe—or indeed even to
itemize—all the makes and calibers manufactured in Germany before World
War II.

Hundreds of small firms and individual gunsmiths made rifles of all types

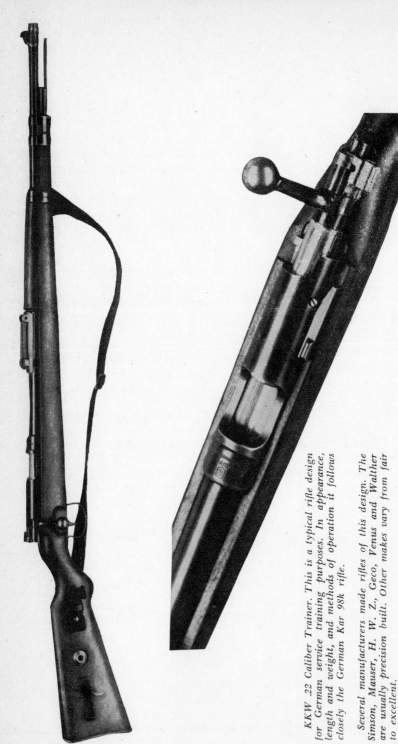

KKW .22 Caliber Trainer. This is a typical rifle design for German service training purposes. In appearance, length and weight, and methods of operation it follows closely the German Kar 98k rifle.

Several manufacturers made rifles of this design. The Simson, Mauser, H. W. Z., Geco, Venus and Walther are usually precision built. Other makes vary from fair to excellent.

Note that the bolt removal system and general bolt construction follows that of the German service pattern to a remarkably close degree. Breech lock is by bolt handle locking down into a receiver cut.

n small numbers. The Germans have deliberately cultivated this type of arms manufacture and experimentation for hundreds of years as an essential part of their armament development programs. Thus a vast body of technical and experimental knowledge developed by shooters and technicians in times of peace has been available in time of war.

Every important principle of firearm construction and operation is dealt with in this book. With just one exception, every type of breech lock used in Germany will be found herein. The lone exception is in the field of the single shot rifle lock—a type now practically extinct in the United States and a type which can hold no future value except to the wildcat enthusiast. My personal files include drawings of 68 varieties of single shot breech lock systems. None of these are in any way superior to the standard types already described. However, the existence of so many types indicates the tremendous scope of German experimentation.

For the purposes of this book we must confine ourselves to the German types exported in quantity, or manufactured in such quantity that a reasonably large number may have been brought back by our servicemen. We cannot give attention to the freaks, off-trail designs, or too specialized types.

Because scores of small German manufacturers purchased standard actions, did not use identifying names or trademarks on their rifles, and often provided specially trademarked guns to order for exporters, effective cataloging is possible only for the products of known firms.

The records of the firm of Gustav Genschow & Co. of Baden, exporters for all quality German arms, are the prime source for determining German large scale manufacture in sporting guns. This firm, together with the following firms have sold most of the good rifles exported from Germany in the last few decades.

Arms sold by this firm, together with arms reported through the Customs, are listed below:

Single Shot Rifles

Bolt Actions: In general these parallel the familiar American types. In quality they run from cheap plinking rifles to high grade target rifles in the .22 caliber series. Breech locks vary from those in which the bolt handle serves as the lock when turned down into a receiver cut to types with standard bolt lugs.

Prime large scale manufactures: BSW (Simson & Co.), Geco and Gecado (made by G. C. Dornheim for G. Genschow & Co.), Erma, Mauser and Walther.

Block Actions: Buschel vertical dropping block; Haenel-Aydt arc block; H.W.Z. Martini falling block and special vertical dropping block; and Neuman-Zentrum dropping block were the most common in large scale manufacture. In general these are precision rifles of a very good order. Calibers and specifications vary. Those listed were commonly made as .22 L.R. Target Rifles, but specimens may be encountered for any conceivable rim or rimless cartridge.

Hinge Frame Actions: While occasionally encountered in .22 caliber single shot, rifles with this action are more commonly precision rifles intended for German stag or boar hunting. Sauer & Söhn specialized in rifles of this type. The common varieties are hammerless shotgun types and may be operated either by top lever or under-triggerguard lever (The lever around the triggerguard was often used for cartridges which gave extraction trouble requiring greater leverage).

Warrant and Flobert actions were confined to small caliber generally cheap

German Aydt Action, closed and open. As made by Haenel this design often had the special tang sight mount shown here. The Aydt action is an original form of a falling block. The block is hinged below the barrel chamber. When the trigger guard lever is operated it draws the block down in an arc and automatically cocks the hammer. This design uses a flat mainspring. The firing pin is machined with the hammer.

Typical German Sporting Mauser Rifle. The actions were customarily made by Mauser, but special barreling and stocking was done to individual specifications by hundreds of small European gun makers. As a result, it is impossible to give set specifications for weapons of this type.

The rifle shown is built upon the standard 98 action which is identical with the military action. Shorter receivers of the same mechanical design were made for use with short cartridges. Magnum actions are the same except that they are larger. Magazine designs were frequently altered by custom builders to meet the needs of special cartridges.

German Schuler-Mauser Magnum, action closed. This rifle weighs in the vicinity of 11 lbs. Because of the size of the cartridge a special extension magazine with thumb lever release is normally used. The bolt and receiver design are identical with that of the German service rifle in all important aspects, except that they are of larger size. The basic large (Magnum) action was specially machined by Mauser at Oberndorf for cartridges of specified dimensions and power. The actual final Magnum measurements vary considerably with cartridge used and identity of custom gunmakers who built most of the special rifles.

German Cal. .22 DSM 34 (German Sport Model 34).

rifles, and to special "parlor" practice rifles in 4mm and 6mm calibers not mad in the U. S.

Zimmerstutzen (Parlor Rifles)

These are a special class of rifle. They are uniformly very heavy, and are ofter made to duplicate the measurements and weight of the Scheutzen forms o target rifles common in Bavaria, the Tyrol and Switzerland.

The common caliber is a special 4mm, which may be short or long. Normall these rifles fall into one of two classifications: (1) The common precision typ loads through a port in the underside of the barrel 8 inches or less back from the muzzle. This type is discharged by a long firing piston, spring driven from the breech end. (2) The second type usually loads into the breech directly int a 4mm barrel section. This barrel is rifled with shallow 12-groove rifling for ; distance of not over 9 inches. From that point on the long barrel is smootl bored to a customary caliber of 11mm. (.433).

The Zimmerstutzen was developed for indoor shooting in serious competition While the fulminate alone is the propellant, the cartridges have considerabl power; and accuracy up to 30 meters often approximates that of the .22 L.R cartridge.

These 4mm (.17) cartridges differ from the common rimless type used in pisto adapters. In general the rifle ammunition is of two classes: (1) 4mm short anc long (they may or may not be interchangeable) with rim. These were manufac tured as fixed ammunition, and were also sold separately as primed case anc bullet units. The cases are straight. The projectiles are balls, and come in sizes, .169, .171 and .173 inches. (2) The second class is a rimmed bottlenecl cartridge.

Any type of block or bolt action rifle common in Germany may be founc altered for Zimmerstutzen cartridges. It was a common European practice tc match up favorite sporting or service rifles with an altered specimen for thi indoor caliber. Such weapons, therefore, may have the markings of the maker o the original arm on them; and much confusion is possible in attempting tc classify them unless it is understood that these are individual gunmaker's con versions.

"Kleinkaliberbuchsen" (small caliber rifles) and "Sportmodell" (small calibe

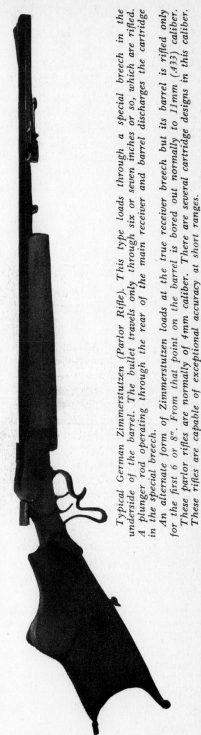

German Haenel Aydt, left side view. The two levers on the left side of the receiver are typical of the Aydt action and of its modification, the "Neumann-Original-Zentrum." The upper one is an external extractor. The lower one is a takedown lever.

Like the Aydt, N-O-Z has an internal hammer in the falling breechblock. However the mainspring and sear spring in this design are coil springs.

Typical German Zimmerstutzen (Parlor Rifle). This type loads through a special breech in the underside of the barrel. The bullet travels only through six or seven inches or so, which are rifled. A plunger rod operating through the rear of the main receiver and barrel discharges the cartridge in the special breech.

An alternate form of Zimmerstutzen loads at the true receiver breech but its barrel is rifled only for the first 6 or 8". From that point on the barrel is bored out normally to 11mm (.433) caliber. These parlor rifles are normally of 4mm caliber. There are several cartridge designs in this caliber. These rifles are capable of exceptional accuracy at short ranges.

rifles patterned after the Army design as trainers) are occasionally found con
verted to 4mm; but in the strict sense of the term are not Zimmerstutzen.

Double Barrel Rifles (and Combinations)

Double rifles and double arms with one rifle and one shotgun barrel wer
made in every conceivable combination and to all specifications to order.

Any type of parallel barrel or over-under firing lock and breech bolting systen
used on shotguns may be found on these rifles. They may be hammer, hammer
less (concealed hammer) or concealed striker fired.

The best known types were commonly built around hammerless hinge fram
actions, top lever operation, Anson & Deeley box locks, Greener treble o
quadruple bolts. Calibers usually started at .256 and ran to .600.

Astora (BSW product), Collath, Remo-Bock, Merkel Gebrüder, Sauer & Söh
and Simson & Co. are the best known names.

Unlocking may be top lever, under-triggerguard lever, or under-fore-end
turning lever. Bolts vary from one to as many as five.

Three Barrel Rifles (and Combinations)

Treble rifles and three barrel arms with any combination of rifle and shotgu
barrels were usually made-to-order arms.

Calibers (and gauges), positions of barrels, types of actions, breech locking
systems and general specifications varied with the whim of the maker or the
order of the purchaser.

The "Bock-Drilling" as made by S. Gunther in Suhl was reasonably popular
This arm mounted three barrels one above the other. The top barrel was com
monly .22 R.F., the center barrel was commonly a shotgun barrel, and the bot
tom barrel was a heavy caliber, usually in the 8mm type.

A second fairly popular arm of the three barrel type was the "Waldlaufer"
made by E. Schmidt & Habermann. The third barrel, usually of small caliber
was bored at top or bottom down a heavy rib which separated two paralle
barrels.

BSW, Genschow and Sauer & Söhn all manufactured three barrel arms of very
high quality in various caliber-and-gauge combinations. These were commonly
Anson & Deeley locks, Greener cross bolts, hammerless, top lever operated. Some
designs also used Purdy side clips. Firing was usually by two triggers, one of
which could be set by a thumb switch to fire the third barrel.

Four Barrel Rifles (and Combinations)

Four barrel rifles as such are uncommon. Most are combinations of rifle and
shotgun barrels. Again these are essentially made-to-order arms and the types
encountered are too numerous for description.

The common form is two parallel barrels, plus one on top of the normal rib
and one below the rib.

As made by H. Burgsmüller & Söhne, two parallel barrels have two small
barrels in over-under position centered below the rib of the parallel barrels.

Slide Action Repeating Rifles

Rifles of this type were made only in very limited quantity by the Rheinmetall
firm. They were imitations of the Browning (Remington) type, being based
on the Belgian F.N. manufacture directly.

Bolt Action Magazine Rifles

Mauser was the only large scale manufacturer. Mauser actions as specially
barreled and stocked by outside firms were often superior in finish to the
genuine Mausers, but these were not production rifles.

Genuine Mausers: Standard calibers were 6.5 x 51mm, 8 x 51mm, 7 x 57mm,
x 60mm, 9 x 57mm, 9.3 x 62mm, 10.75 x 68mm, .250-3000 Savage, .280 Ross,
30-06 U.S., .318 Westley-Richards and .404 Eley.

While the sporting half-stock was common, some models were stocked to the
muzzle (as in the Mannlicher-Schoenauer) and had flat bolt handles. Common
barrel lengths were 20 to 28 inches. Weights ranged from 7 to 11 pounds.

Mauser Conversions: Among the best known firms building rifles around
Mauser actions were the following: W. Brenneke, C. G. Haenel, V. Chr. Schilling,
E. Schmidt & Habermann, A. Rempt, Sempert & Krieghoff, August Schüler.

Calibers and specifications were to order as a rule. Schüler in particular was
famous for Magnum rifles in calibers for African and Asiatic big game shooting.
The Hof-Mann high velocity cartridges and the "Halger" cartridges were also
based on Mauser actions.

Mannlicher Conversions: Mannlicher actions, both the Schoenauer and the
Roumanian turning bolt patterns, were widely barreled and stocked by firms in
the Suhl area. The best known of these rifles is commonly called the Haenel-
Mannlicher, and is not to be confused with old Model 88 service rifles which
years ago were re-fitted by Haenel.

As built on modern genuine Mannlicher actions, Haenel produced standard
and magnum caliber rifles of quality to order.

Semiautomatic Sporting Rifles

The following were the only semiauto sporting rifles manufactured in any
quantity in Germany:

Krieghoff: Gas operated through barrel port. Piston and operating rod
below barrel. Block lock. Hammerless. Calibers issued: 6.5 x 57mm, 7 x 57mm,
8 x 57 J and 8 x 60 Magnum. Magazine capacity 4 or 5 depending on caliber.
Magazine in left side of receiver. Barrel length 23.4 inches. Overall length 41.2
inches. Weight about 7.25 lbs.

This rifle could be made in any standard high power caliber. The War halted
production before large scale manufacture could be started. This was designed
as a sporting rifle only.

Rhode: Blowback operated. Hammerless. Takedown. Detachable box magazines either 6 or 12 cartridges. Caliber .22 L.R.

This was a well made rifle of its type. It was never widely distributed outside
Germany, however.

Walther: Prototypes of 7.92mm gas operated rifles called Type A115 were
produced prior to World War II. Gas system and locking system similar to the
MKb 42 (W). Blowback operated. Hammerless. Detachable box magazines, 5 or 9
shot capacity. Caliber .22 L.R. This was an original design which introduced
the principle of a locking bolt which permitted the rifle to be used either
as a manually operated repeater or as a semiautomatic. Barrel length 24.5
inches. Overall length 43 inches. Weight about 7 lbs. Made in two models.

Note: Early in the century the Dreyse blowback carbine appeared in caliber

7.65mm Browning (.32 A.C.P.). Later imitations of the Winchester blowback rifles were attempted in Germany. None of these arms were successful.

About this same time Haenel manufactured several types of short and long recoil carbines and rifles for medium power cartridges. These operated on the system of a sliding barrel mounted in a rigid barrel jacket. They were not made in quantity, though since the end of the War several collectors have reported specimens.

"Halbe Automatische" (Half, or semiautomatic)

Occasional freak designs (Belgian as well as German) have been returned from Germany. A common form (though still very rare as numbers go) is the "Halbe Automatische."

This design is commonly in .22 caliber, and may be single shot or magazine type. The spring supported bolt is blown back by the discharge to eject the empty case, but in general the cocking piece must then be pulled back manually before the next shot can be fired. In some variants (single shot) the action must be closed after loading the chamber. In other types (magazine and single shot) the bolt is held back by the sear, and the arm is fired on the "slam" principle when the bolt goes forward.

While as a rule the European half-automatic (or semiautomatic) of this class is an auto *loader*, but not an auto *cocker*, the term at times is extended to cover other types.

German 7.92mm M1888, "S" Type and 7.92mm Short Cartridges

Other Names: 8x57, 7.9mm, 7.92mm
Type: Rimless necked, centerfire
Overall Length: 3.24" (M1888); 3.17"
("S" Type)
Type Powder: Flake smokeless
Type Primer: Berdan

BULLET

Type: round nose (M1888); Spitzer
("S" Type)
Diameter: .317" (M1888); .323" ("S" Type)
Weight: 226 gr (M1888); 154 gr
("S" Type)
Length: (M1888) 1.24" ("S" Type) 1.10"

CARTRIDGE CASE

Length Overall: 2.24" (57mm)
Length of Head to Shoulder: 1.82"
Length of shoulder: .10"
Diameter at rim: .473"
Diameter at Base: .470"
Diameter at Neck: .349"

BALLISTICS

Muzzle Velocity: 2099 f.s. (M1888); 2853
f.s. ("S" Type)
Pressure: 39,000 p.s.i. (M1888); 44,082
p.s.i. ("S" Type)

CARTRIDGE

Name: German 7.9mm Kurz, 7.92 mm Short
7.9mm pp 43 m.e.
Type: Rimless-Necked-Centerfire
Overall Length: 1.88"
Type Powder: Nitrocellulose, 24 grains
Type Primer: Berdan

BULLET

Type: Full Jacketed-Painted
Diameter: .323"
Weight: 122 gr.

CARTRIDGE CASE

Length Overall: 1.29"
Length of Shoulder: .16"
Diameter at Rim: .470"
Diameter at Neck: .354"
Length Head to Shoulder: .94"
Length of Neck: .19"
Diameter at Base: .470"
Diameter at Shoulder: .450"

BALLISTICS

Muzzle Velocity: Approx. 2132 f.p.s.

Chapter 33

EAST GERMANY

GOVERNMENT PLANTS: VEB Fahrzeug und Gerätewerk Simson, Suhl; Gebruder Merkel, Suhl; Fortuna Werke, Suhl; VEB Ernst Thaelmann, Suhl. All plants are government owned.

PRINCIPAL MILITARY RIFLES: The Soviet designed 7.62mm SKS carbine and AK-47 assault rifle are the principal military rifles. Older Soviet weapons such as the 7.62mm M1944 Mosin-Nagant carbine and German 7.92mm Kar 98k's may still be used by militia and Volks Polizei (VOPOS).

East German 7.62mm SKS Carbine.

The East Germans make both the SKS and the AK-47. The East German SKS differs from the Soviet in having its sling attached through the butt rather than having a butt swivel, and in not having a mounted cleaning rod. The East German made AK also does not carry a cleaning rod.

East German Sporting Rifles

A wide variety of East German sporting rifles are made, many of them for export. In addition Soviet produced target rifles in caliber .22 and 7.62mm are widely used.

.22 Caliber Training and Sporting Rifles

1. KKG Model 110—(KKG-Kleinkaliber Gewehr) training rifle with open sights, single shot bolt action.

2. KKG Model V—training rifle with open sights, bolt action with 5-shot magazine.

3. KKG Model I—target rifle for juveniles, drop block action, single shot with micrometer sight.

4. KKG Model IV—target rifle, single shot drop block with micrometer sight, heavier than KKG Model I.

5. KKG Model Olympia—match rifle, single shot bolt action with micrometer sight.

6. KKG Model KM (Krempel Meister)—bolt action match rifle, single shot with micrometer sight, palm, designed for women and young people.

7. KKG Model KW (Krempel Weltmeister)—bolt action match rifle, single shot with palm rest and micrometer sight—the best quality East German .22 rifle.

Over-and-under rifle-shotgun combinations are made by Simson and Gebrüder Merkel in Suhl, as are over-and-under rifles. Simson also makes drillings as does Fortuna. Drillings have two shotgun barrels over and a rifle barrel under.

Chapter 34

WEST GERMANY

GOVERNMENT PLANTS: None.

PRIVATE PLANTS: Rheinmettal Borsig, Dusseldorf; Heckler and Koch, Oberndorf A/M; J. G. Anschütz GmbH, Ulm/Donau; Carl Walther, GmbH, Ulm/Donau; H. Krieghoff K. G., Ulm/Donau; J. P. Sauer & Sohn A. G., Dusseldorf; and others.

PRINCIPAL MILITARY RIFLES: 7.62mm Rifle G3; quantities of 7.62mm G1 (FN "FAL") rifles are also on hand.

West German 7.62mm G3 Rifle

This weapon is the German version of the Spanish CETME assault rifle. The G3, which is covered in more detail under Spain, began as the StG 45 (M), a prototype weapon, developed in Germany at the end of World War II. Since this weapon is the same in functioning, firing, and field stripping as the Spanish CETME, these are described in the Spanish section. The principal difference between the Spanish CETME and the G3 is in the construction of the bolt head. The G3 bolt head is designed to function with full power NATO cartridges; the CETME bolt head is designed to function with reduced charge NATO cartridges. By change of bolt head, it could be used with the full power NATO cartridge. The G3 can be used with a bipod, a telescope, or an infra-red

West German 7.62mm G3 Rifle.

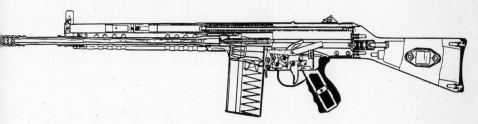

Section View of 7.62mm G3 Rifle.

251

West German 7.62mm G3 Rifle Field Stripped.

West German 7.62mm G3 Rifle with Bipod and Scope.

Folding Stock Version of G3 Rifle. Note that stock folds on top of rifle.

nooper scope. A combination flash hider and grenade launcher is built into he end of the barrel.

The G3 is made mainly of stampings; handguards may be made of plastic or wood. This weapon has been adopted by Portugal as the 7.62mm rifle M961.

Caliber: 7.62mm NATO
System of operation: Delayed blowback, selective fire
Weight:
  Loaded w/o bipod: 9.9 lbs.
Length, overall: 40.2"
Barrel length: 17.7"

Feed device: 20-round, detachable, staggered-row box magazine
Sights—
  front: Hooded post
  rear: L type
Muzzle velocity: 2,624 f.p.s.
Cyclic rate: 500-600 R.P.M.

West German 7.62mm G1 Rifle (the FN "FAL").

West German Sporting Rifles

West Germany produces a large number of sporting rifles of different types and generally excellent quality. J. G. Anschütz produces a complete line of sporting rifles ranging from simply made single shot .22 caliber rifles to fine .22 caliber match rifles and high powered Mauser type sporters. Like most European makers, Anschütz makes most of their weapons in popular American calibers as well as European calibers. Their high powered rifles are made in: .243, .270, .30-06, and .375 Magnum as well as 6.5x57mm, 7x57mm, 7x64mm, 8x57mm, and 9.3x62mm.

Probably the best known of the Anschütz rifles is the caliber .22 Model 54

Super Match Rifle. This rifle weighs 16 pounds, and has a 28-inch heavy barrel. The 50-inch long rifle has a detachable hook type butt plate, palm rest, and thumbhole type stock.

Anschütz Cal. .22 Model 54 Super Match Rifle.

Walther also produces a fine line of caliber .22 rifles, which includes their Model KKM match rifle. The Mauser type sporters produced by Walther are made in .22 L.R., .22 Hornet, .22 Magnum, .30-06, and .270 Winchester.

Krico makes bolt action rifles in .222 Remington, and .22 L.R. and a self loader in .22 long rifle. The .22 caliber drop-block rifle is being made by Weihrauch in both long rifle or Hornet. Drillings are currently being made by Krieghoff, Sauer, and Waffen Frankonia. Over-and-under rifles and over-and-under rifle shotgun combinations are made by Sauer, Krieghoff, and Waffen Frankonia.

Chapter 35

GREAT BRITAIN

(The United Kingdom)

GOVERNMENT PLANTS: Enfield Lock, Fazakerley, and Maltby.

PRIVATE PLANTS: B.S.A. Guns Ltd., Boss, Cogswell and Harrison, Gibbs, W. W. Greener, Holland & Holland, W. J. Jeffery, Parker Hale, Powell, Purdey, John Rigby, Vickers, Westley Richards, Woodward. Of these and scores of other gunmakers, only B.S.A. and Vickers have done real production work. The others are all custom makers.

PRINCIPAL MILITARY RIFLES: Rifle 7.62mm L1AI. *Former Military Rifles:* (1). Lee-Enfield series. (SMLE No. I Marks III and III* Rifles. (2). Rifle No. 3 Mark I* (modified Mauser). (3). Rifles No. 4 Mark I and I* (mass production Enfields), Rifle No. 5, Mark I*.

Note: Rifle No. 2 is a conversion to .22 caliber of Rifle No. 1.

Rifle 7.62mm L1A1

The United Kingdom adopted a slightly modified version of the FN "FAL" rifle in 1957, the L1A1. The L1A1 is built only for semiautomatic fire and has replaced the No. 4 as the basic British individual weapon. One of the modifications made by the British to the basic design has been the addition of cuts to the outside of the bolt carrier. These cuts serve as screening places for dirt which might otherwise get into the action through the ejection port. The cuts

British 7.62mm NATO FN L1A1 Rifle.

255

are deep enough to accumulate a good deal of foreign material and prevent i from impairing the functioning of the weapon. Functioning of the weapon i the same as that of the FN "FAL" which is covered in detail under Belgium

Caliber: 7.62mm NATO

System of operation: Gas, semiautomatic only

Weight, loaded: 10.48 lbs.

Length, overall: 44.5"

Barrel length: 21"

Feed device: 20-round, detachable staggere box magazine

Sights—front: Post w/protecting ears

rear: Aperture adjustable from 200 600 yards

Muzzle velocity: 2800 f.p.s.

L1A1 has been produced at B.S.A., Enfield Lock, and the Australian Govern ment arms factory at Lithgow, New South Wales. While in prototype form L1A1 was, at one time, called "Rifle 7.62mm FN, BR X 8E2, Type B." The L1A1 differs from the Canadian C2 and some of the other versions of the "FAL" in that it cannot be loaded with chargers while the magazine is in place on the rifle. The magazine must be removed for the weapon to be re loaded. Soldiers in the field will normally carry spare loaded magazines; the magazines are loaded with 5-round chargers by use of a charger guide placed over the magazine in a fashion similar to the loading of the U.S. Browning Automatic Rifle magazine. L1A1 was tested extensively in Malaya, Kenya, and the Middle East before being adopted. As a result of these tests, it was decided to manufacture the weapon in a semiautomatic version only rather than selective fire as the X 8E2.

British EM2

In 1945 British Defense Minister Shinwell appointed a panel of experts to determine the best automatic rifle and cartridge for Britain's armed forces to replace the Lee Enfield bolt action rifle with its rimmed .303 caliber cartridge. After intensive research, development work, and tests, the rimless .280 (7mm) round was designated as the ideal cartridge and various rifles designed around it.

Among the rifle designs in .280 caliber under consideration was the famous NATO rifle developed by Fabrique Nationale of Belgium (see *Belgium*), and prototypes by the Birmingham Small Arms Company as well as the Royal Small Arms Factory Enfield Lock. The BSA model was withdrawn from the tests but had a unique construction worth mentioning. While it was designed specifically as a full automatic, it had a very low cyclic rate of fire—300 rounds per minute. With a modicum of practice, squeezing off single shots could easily be mastered. This design was ultimately dropped.

At the conclusion of the trials, the domestic design of Enfield Lock, the EM2, was selected. One of the principal designers of the EM2 is Stefan Kenneth Janson, a naturalized citizen of Britain, who received the Order of the British Empire for his work on the weapon. Mr. Janson was formerly a native of Poland who, like so many others, fled to England when Hitler's troops overran Europe. He is currently Manager of the Arms Research & Development Department of Winchester.

The EM2, categorized as an experimental weapon, never having gone into full production, was, nevertheless, the standard infantry arm of Britain for a brief period after June 1951. The EM2 merits special attention inasmuch as it represents a milestone in advanced military weapons-design and because of its possible influence on future developments.

The EM2 is a radical departure from service weapons commonly encountered, resembling most closely what U. S. shooters know as Bull Pup rifles. The butt plate is in a straight line with the longitudinal axis of the barrel and is fitted to the end of the lengthy receiver housing, containing recoil spring and bolt mechanism. Consequently, when the gun is in offhand position, the side of the face rests above the area of the magazine instead of against the usual wooden stock. The 20-round magazine protrudes below and is centrally located between the butt plate and pistol grip which makes for fast, easy handling.

In lieu of ordinary metallic sights, the EM2 has an optic sight, sometimes referred to as a telescope, but without magnification. The weapon features full automatic or single fire, and is gas operated. The bolt is locked by two protruding levers diametrically opposite each other on the bolt. To protect the bolt mechanism from exposure to water, mud, dirt, etc. it is well covered by the receiver—open only on the right side for the ejection port.

The purpose of the non-magnifying optic sight is to permit faster and more precise aiming than can be expected with conventional metallic sights, where deliberation is necessary to align properly the rear with the front sight. The slightest degree of misalignment often results in a miss. With the optic sight, the shooter contends only with the post reticule. This is the first time in military history that an optic sight has been designed for general infantry use. It is well sealed against the effects of weather, etc. The sight is so protectively covered and ruggedly constructed that it makes an excellent carrying handle.

British EM2 Assault Rifle.

The reticule is a new concept, consisting of a post with tapered ends extending down to the center of the sight to avoid obscuring the target. In addition to the post, for easy reference there are alternately numbered range scales, 3, 5, 7, and 9, representing yards in hundreds. These horizontal range lines which are etched on the reticule glass are separated in the center beneath the post. The width of each central gap approximates the dimensions of a man with full equipment. By raising the post until the target conforms with one of the central gaps, the soldier has a reliable medium for judging distance. However, the tip of the post is lowered to the center of the target when firing up to 100 yards. When zeroed in, the post is permanently fixed for 100 yards. The optic sight is zeroed in by installing washers of predetermined thicknesses on windage and/or elevation mount-fixing screws.

In the first version of the EM2, the optic sight did not form a carrying handle, but it could be retracted into a protective housing when not in use. Adjustment of the sight was by a manually operated range drum on the side of the housing.

Whether fired full or semiautomatically, the EM2 is readily controlled in al. positions. It is considered effective up to 500 yards when operated semiauto matically, and up to 800 yards when fired as a light machine gun with bipod support. The gun can only be reloaded via magazine. A unique charger-loading device is incorporated within the magazine. It is flipped up to receive 5-shot stripper clips or the magazine can be loaded by hand.

The EM2 operates in the following manner. When fired, some of the gases following the bullet pass through a gas port centrally located in the barre. and enter the gas cylinder situated above the barrel. This forces the piston to the rear and compresses the return spring until the piston reaches the end of its stroke. As the piston is secured to the firing pin sleeve within the bolt, the initial movement of the piston withdraws the firing pin until the bent of the firing pin is engaged by the sear on the underside of the breechblock. At the same time, the faces on the firing pin cam the locking lugs out of engagement and thus release the bolt. The piston and bolt move to the rear. The piston having reached the end of its stroke, is forced forward by the return spring. A stud on the underside of the piston, engaging with a spring projection or top of the bolt, carries the breechblock with it. The face of the bolt meets the base of the first round in the magazine and forces it forward into the chamber As forward travel of the bolt is stopped at the chamber, the projection of the bolt is cammed out of engagement with the stop on the piston, and the piston continues its forward movement, carrying with it the firing pin sleeve. This last movement of the firing pin sleeve cams the locking lugs outward into locked position and they are retained there by the firing pin sleeve. The action is thus positively locked with the firing pin cocked.

To field strip the EM2, remove magazine and sling. Press butt retaining catch; swing butt to right until it disengages from the retaining stops. With draw butt, complete with return spring assembly. Pull cocking handle to rear and withdraw it from the piston. Pull out breechblock and piston from the rear of the gun, and detach piston from breechblock. Assembly is merely the reverse of this procedure.

Throughout the unrelenting advocacy by the United States of its 7.62mm NATO (or .30 caliber) cartridge, the British showed no sign of abandoning the EM2 design nor the .280 round. However, when Churchill returned to the office of Prime Minister, he was active in pleading the cause of standardization within the NATO sphere. After his talks with President Truman of the United States and high-level conferences with other NATO nations, the British capitulated and accepted the 7.62mm NATO cartridge. At this juncture, the British decided to re-evaluate the situation.

Despite the investment the highly regarded EM2 represented in caliber .280, the recent adoption of the 7.62mm NATO cartridge meant an additional expenditure of time and money to re-design and produce the EM2 in this new caliber. Because the British Army was in urgent need of an automatic rifle to achieve equal footing with other nations in that field, further delay was unthinkable. In considering the FN NATO Assault Rifle, it was presented as a tested, efficient automatic rifle—less expensive than the EM2 to manufacture —and, most important of all, ready for early delivery in quantity by the FN factory in Belgium. In January 1957 England announced the adoption of the FN Rifle in caliber 7.62mm NATO.

SPECIFICATIONS OF THE EM2

Total weight of weapon: 7 lbs. 8½ oz.
Weight of magazine loaded with 20 rounds:
  1 lb. 7 oz.
Total length of weapon: 35.0".

Length of barrel: 24.5".
Weight of barrel: 1 lb. 14½ oz.
Cyclic rate of fire: 600-650 r.p.m.
Type of sight: Optic non-magnifying.
Muzzle velocity: 2530 f.p.s.

General Description of Lee Enfield Designs

These are turn-bolt magazine rifles. The bolt handles are turned down instead of projecting straight out to the side as in most European practice. The bolt is of the two-piece type, the bolt cylinder being bored out from the front. The system is based on the original American Lee bolt.

The separate bolt head is inserted into the front of the cylinder and is held in place with a screwed tenon. A lug-like projection on the upper right quadrant of the bolt is undercutt so that it engages over a rib which runs along the top right side of the receiver and prevents the bolthead from turning as the bolt cylinder is turned. The bolt head is vented to permit the escape of gas in case of a ruptured primer or split case.

The bolt cylinder carries dual opposed locking lugs, one of the conventional type and one in the form of a long solid rib extending from the front of the cylinder backward to a point where it comes down solidly against the forward edge of the receiver bridge when the bolt handle is turned down. This locking lug or rib bears against the high left side of the receiver when the bolt handle is lifted and slides snugly through the split bridge of the receiver as the bolt is retracted. The combined bearing in the receiver bridge and against the left side of the receiver provides a rigid guide for the smooth backward and forward motion of the bolt. The conventional locking lug is also positioned near the rear of the bolt cylinder so that it engages in a locking recess in the rear of the receiver just forward of the bridge. The rear faces of both lugs are cut with cam surfaces. The forward face of the conventional locking lug is also cut with a cam surface to provide primary extraction as the bolt handle is lifted.

The striker and mainspring are inserted from the front of the bolt cylinder. The inside rear face of the cylinder serves as the bearing point for the rear end of the mainspring. The rear end of the striker passes back through a hole bored in the back end of the bolt cylinder. The cocking piece is fastened to the projecting end of the striker. The rear of the bolt cylinder carries a cut into which the cocking piece stud slides forward when the striker moves forward. This cut is provided with a camming surface so that as the bolt handle is lifted the cocking piece is cammed slightly to the rear, withdrawing the firing pin and providing a slight initial compression of the mainspring. Cocking is on the forward motion of the bolt.

The cocking piece is provided with a half-cock notch.

The safety engages the cocking piece from the left side.

The striker is of one-piece design with a collar to provide the forward bearing

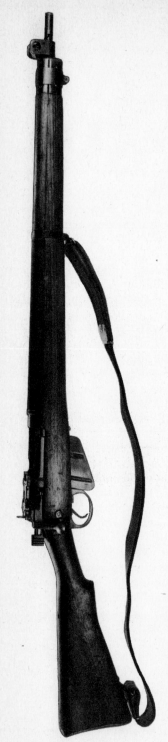

British Rifle No. 4, Mark 1.
The Rifle No. 4 series represents an attempt to apply mass production methods to manufacture of the old S.M.L.E. rifle system. Modifications are those required to modernize the rifle insofar as is possible, and to cut manufacturing steps.
No. 4 Rifles were made in the United States and Canada as well as in England. Differences in construction occur in relation to place of manufacture. Caliber 303.

British Rifle No. 5, Mark 1* (Jungle Carbine), Cal. 303.
This is essentially the production Rifle No. 4 shortened into carbine form. Since this carbine uses the standard rifle cartridge the muzzle flash may prove frequently undesirable—hence the flash-hider.

British Rifle #1, Mark III*. Sectional view showing details at moment of ejection. There are no locking lug seats in the receiver ring as in Mauser practice. Magazine is detachable, though it may be loaded through the top of the open action by stripping cartridges from a charger clip, or by inserting single cartridges.

Bolt detail shows general construction of locking and firing assembly. Note that this is a two-piece bolt, bored out from the front. The bolt head is screwed into the front of the bolt head cylinder. Lower left figure shows left side view of bolt as handle is being raised.

The lower right detail shows the form of the cam slots in the rear of the underside of the bolt cylinder. When the rifle is fired the cocking nose rests in the long cut. As the bolt handle is raised, the cam cut forces the cocking nose back to withdraw the firing pin. When the nose slips into the shorter cut it is held there. Cocking is done on forward stroke when the sear nose catches and holds the cocking piece and striker assembly, while the rest of the bolt assembly is thrust forward.

for the mainspring. The forward face of this collar seats against the rear of the bolt head tenon forward, thereby limiting the protrusion of the striker through the face of the bolt head.

The early designs and Mark III have a circular projection on the cocking piece cut away at the left and roughened. On the Mark III* the cocking piece is flat with vertical grooves on each side. These cocking pieces are interchangeable and are accordingly not an infallible guide in indicating the pattern of the rifle.

The extractor is mounted in the projecting lug on the upper right quadrant of the bolt head. It is a small but sturdy piece of steel with a comparatively narrow claw, spring loaded with a V-spring.

The ejector is a small screw in the left side of the receiver which projects into the boltway.

The trigger pull is the standard military double pull. The sear is a bell crank lever pivoted below the receiver on a screw which also holds the bolt stop. The sear works in a groove in the tang and is operated by a U-shaped spring which also operates the magazine catch. The long sear arm passes through a slot in the receiver into the groove where the cocking piece travels. Its short arm projects downward and is in contact with the trigger by a knuckle joint. The trigger works in a slot in the triggerguard where it is pivoted on a pin.

The magazine is a projecting, detachable steel box type holding ten cartridges in staggered columns. It is loaded from charger clips through the top of the action. The bolt can be closed over an empty magazine. The magazine catch is inside the triggerguard, forward of the trigger. Other designs which have magazine cut-offs have thumb-pieces for operating the cut-off.

The stocks are mainly of two-piece design plus handguards. They have a semi-pistol grip.

British Military Bolt Action Rifles

Large scale sales by the United Kingdom, Canada, and Eire have resulted in large quantities of British military bolt action rifles being sold commercially in the United States. These rifles are being sold at very low prices (considerably lower than they can be purchased in the U.K.) and some are in very good condition. For this reason coverage on the British bolt action rifles is being expanded.

The .303 Rifles and Carbines

Rifle, Magazine, Lee Metford Mark I: Adopted December 1888. The first British production Lee adopted as "Magazine Rifle Mark I" was first used with the .303 black powder cartridge Mark I which had a muzzle velocity of 1850 f.p.s. with a 215 grain bullet. This rifle has a 8-round magazine with a cut-off and also has a safety mounted on the left side of the receiver.

Rifle, Magazine, Lee Metford Mark I:* Adopted January 1892—differs from Mark I in having a re-graduated rear sight and a barleycorn front sight, rather than the notched front sight of the Mark I. The safety catch was removed; a smokeless powder cartridge—the .303 Cordite Mark I—was introduced shortly before this weapon appeared.

Rifle, Magazine, Lee Metford Mark II: Adopted 1892—differs from the Mark I* in: (1) having a 10-round magazine; (2) a lighter barrel; (3) a modified bolt; (4) a modified receiver; (5) the bolt cover was made of spring steel and held

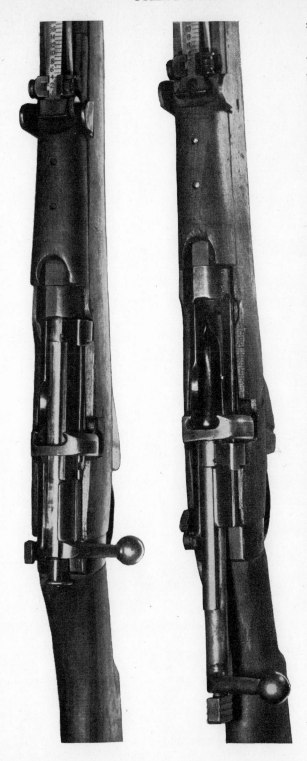

Rifle No. 1, Mark III* patterns, actions closed and open. These were the most widely used British patterns in World War I. The long rib on top of the bolt cylinder seen in the lower picture is the guide rib and also serves as a locking lug. Its rear surface locks down against the forward edge of the split receiver bridge. A smaller lug on the opposite side of the bolt cylinder engages a seat cut in the left side of the receiver and by its camming action provides primary extraction during opening movement. The rear sight of the upper rifle is adjustable for windage and is of the pattern originally used on the No. 1 Mark III. The rear sight of the lower rifle is not adjustable for windage and is of the pattern used on the No. 1 Mark III*.

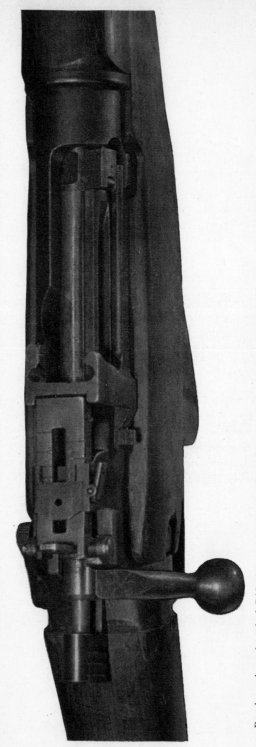

Receiver view of typical Rifle No. 4 Mark I. While the Lee two-piece bolt design is retained, its construction is greatly modified from the S.M.L.E. A smaller bolt head and a widened, lightened guide rib are used in addition to a new type breech bolt catch. Note placement of sight at rear of receiver. The sight shown is the Mark III which is made of stampings.

on by clipping in place rather than being screwed on as with early models; (6) the cut-off was altered, being made thinner and having a small stud to hold it in place when in the "off" position; (7) the rear sight was again modified; (8) the fore-end was made fuller and the finger grooves were omitted; (9) the upper band was combined with the nose cap and bayonet lug; (10) the rear

British .303 Lee Metford Mark II Rifle.

swivel was moved from the front of the trigger guard to the butt; (11) the cleaning rod was shortened; and (12) an indentation in the right side of the stock under the cut-off was omitted.

Rifle, Magazine, Lee Metford Mark II*: Adopted in 1895—had a safety catch added to the cocking piece; this required alteration of the firing pin and bolt in addition to the cocking piece.

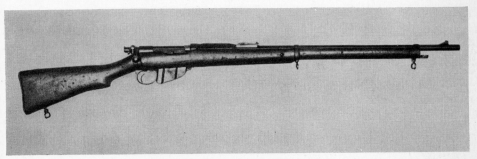

British .303 Lee Metford Mark II* Rifle.

Carbine, Magazine, Lee Metford, Mark I: Adopted in September 1894. This weapon is shorter than the rifles, has a 6-round magazine, the bolt handle is bent so that it lies close to the receiver, and the knob of the bolt handle is flattened on top. It has a safety similar to the Mark II* and differs in stock and sight details from the rifles.

Rifle, Magazine, Lee Enfield, Mark I: Adopted in November 1895—same as Mark II* Lee Metford except that deeper rifling—Enfield type—was used rather than the shallow Metford rifling, and the front sight is fixed further to the left.

Rifle, Magazine, Lee Enfield Mark I*: Adopted May 1899—same as Mark I Lee Enfield except that cleaning rod was eliminated.

Carbine, Magazine, Lee Enfield, Mark I: Adopted August 1896—differed from

Lee Metford Mark I carbine in type of rifling, position and height of front sight, and graduations on rear sight. The sling attachments were omitted and a leather cover issued for the rear sight. Used a six round magazine as the Lee Metford Carbine.

British .303 Carbine Lee Metford Mark I.

Carbine, Magazine, Lee Enfield, Mark I*: Adopted May 1899—same as Lee Enfield Mark I carbine except that cleaning rod was removed. Another pattern of Lee Enfield Carbine introduced in 1900 could be used with a bayonet and had a different type fore-end and handguard than the earlier carbines.

Rifle, No. 1, Short Magazine, Lee Enfield Mark I: Adopted Dec. 1902—first of the Short Magazine Lee Enfields (S.M.L.E.), and first British rifle adapted to charger (stripper clip) loading. The right charger guide is mounted on the bolt head; left charger guide is machined into the receiver. This rifle is stocked to the muzzle with handguards covering the barrel except at rear sight. A heavy nose cap which has the front sight guards, bayonet mounting stud, and stacking swivel is mounted at the muzzle. It has a tangent type rear sight with V notch which is adjustable for windage and also has a barleycorn (inverted "V")

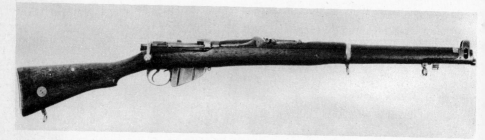

British .303 S.M.L.E. Rifle No. 1 Mark I.

front sight. In 1926 when British rifles received a numerical designation in addition to Mark designation it became S.M.L.E. No. 1, Mark I. All .303 S.M.L.E. rifles are designated No. 1. This rifle was originally made without cut-off, but in 1906 S.M.L.E.'s made or converted prior to that date were required to have them fitted.

Rifle, No. 1, Short Magazine, Lee Enfield (Converted) Mark II: Adopted 1903. Conversion of Lee Metford rifles Marks II and II* and Lee Enfield Rifles Marks I and I* into S.M.L.E.'s similar to the S.M.L.E. No. 1 Mark I.

Rifle, No. 1, Short Magazine, Lee Enfield Mark I*: Adopted July 1906. Slight modification of the No. 1 Mark I S.M.L.E. Modification concerned butt plate, butt stock, magazine body, swivel screws, and the striker keeper screw.

Rifle No. 1, Short Magazine, Lee Enfield (Converted) Mark II*: Adopted July 1906—conversion of earlier Long Lee Metford and Lee Enfield rifles to the No. 1 Mark I*.

Rifle No. 1, Short Magazine, Lee Enfield Mark III: Adopted January 1907. The basic British rifle of World War I and used to some extent in World War II. The Royal Small Arms Factory at Enfield Lock made over two million

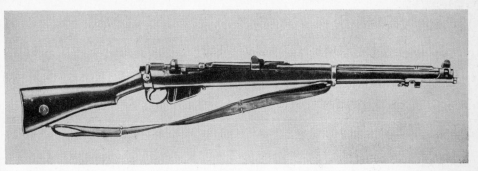

British .303 S.M.L.E. Rifle No. 1 Mark III.

S.M.L.E. Mark III and Mark III*'s during World War I; B.S.A. made 1,601,608 in the same period. This rifle has a bridge type charger guide on the receiver. The rear sight has a fine adjustment worm screw for elevation and is adjustable for windage—this sight used a "U" notch rather than the "V" notch used on earlier models. The front sight has a blade rather than a barleycorn and a different nose cap with altered sight guards was fitted. Other changes were made in the cut-off, handguards, butt plate, and fore-end.

British No. 1 Mark III* Short Lee Enfield (S.M.L.E.)

Caliber: .303

Overall length, rifle without bayonet: 44.5"   *With bayonet attached:* 61.7"
Overall weight, rifle without bayonet: 8.6 lbs.   *With bayonet attached:* 9.8 lbs.
Type of action: Turnbolt   *Type of bolt:* 2 piece—non-Rotating Head
Type of Magazine: Detachable Box—Staggered   *Capacity:* 10
Column
Barrel Length: 25.2"   *No. Grooves:* 5   *Direction of Twist:* Left
Bore Diameter: .303"   *Groove Dia.:* .312"   *Rate of Twist:* 10"

Rifle, Charger Loading, Lee Enfield Mark I*: Adopted in July, 1907. This rifle is a conversion of the Long Lee Enfield Marks I and Mark I* to charger loading. New front and rear sights were also fitted; the rear sight is adjustable for windage. The Long Lee Metford Marks II and II* were also converted to charger loading at this time and were first called Charger Loading Lee Metford; in 1909 their designation was changed to Rifle, Charger Loading Lee Enfield Mark I*.

Rifle No. 1, Short Magazine Lee Enfield (converted) Mark IV: Adopted in 1907. Conversion of Long Lee Enfields and Long Lee Metfords to the same general design as the No. 1, Mark III S.M.L.E.

Rifle No. 1, Short Magazine Lee Enfield Mark I**: Adopted in 1908. This

British .303 Charger Loading Long Lee Enfield Mark I*.

conversion of the No. 1 Mark I S.M.L.E. was done by the Royal Navy. The Mark III front sight was fitted and a new sight bar with a "U" notch was fitted to the rear sight. A number of other minor changes were also made. In 1912 these rifles were fitted with the bridge type charger guide.

Rifle No. 1, Short Magazine Lee Enfield Mark II**: Adopted in 1908. This conversion of Rifle No. 1, Mark II S.M.L.E. was also done by the Navy. All the remarks under Rifle No. 1 Mark I** S.M.L.E. apply to this rifle.

Rifle No. 1, Short Magazine Lee Enfield Mark II***: Adopted in 1908. Another Naval conversion—this time of Rifle No. 1 Mark II*. All the remarks under Rifle No. 1, Mark I** S.M.L.E. apply to this rifle. At this point the reader should be developing some pity for the poor British Ordnance Supply Officer of this period! Many of these weapons which are already conversions of conversions were again converted in 1915!

Rifle No. 1, Short Magazine Lee Enfield Mark III*: Adopted in January 1916. Same as Rifle No. 1, S.M.L.E. Mark III except: (1) long-range side sights omitted; (2) cut-off and cut-off slot omitted; (3) wind-gage on rear sight omitted; (4) lug on firing pin collar omitted; (5) sling swivel mounting on front of trigger guard replaced by wire loop; and (6) later—butt marking disc omitted and grooved cocking piece rather than rounded cocking piece fitted.

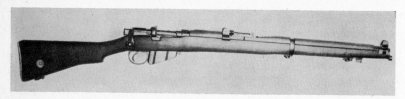

British .303 S.M.L.E. Rifle No. 1 Mark III.*

This rifle in conjunction with the No. 1 S.M.L.E. Mark III was the most extensively produced of the No. 1 rifles. It has even been produced since the introduction of Rifle No. 4—415,580 were made at Lithgow, New South Wales, Australia from 1939 to 1955, and a large quantity were made at Ishapore in India during the war. B.S.A. made 150,000 Mark III*'s from 1936 to August 1940 and after a shutdown of three months caused by bomb damage, production increased to 1,250 a week by November 1941. This production rate was continued until December 1943 when the last Mark III* was made in the United Kingdom.

Rifle No. 1, Short Magazine Lee Enfield Mark V: Never officially adopted—made in limited quantity in 1922. The Mark V has its rear sight on the receiver bridge, an additional upper band, a one-piece rear handguard, and has a cut-off.

British .303 S.M.L.E. Rifle No. 1 Mark V.

Rifle No. 1, Short Magazine Lee Enfield Mark VI: Made in limited numbers from 1923 to 1926. The predecessor of the No. 4, having a smaller bolt head, a heavier barrel, and a lighter nose cap than the earlier No. 1 rifles. It also has its rear sight mounted on the receiver bridge and is fitted for the spike type bayonet. The rifle differs in many other details from the earlier No. 1 types.

British .303 S.M.L.E. Rifle No. 1 Mark VI.

Rifle No. 4, Mark I: Adopted in November 1939. This rifle was the main British service rifle in World War II. Simplified for manufacture, the No. 4 has the heavy barrel, smaller bolt head, rear sight mounted on receiver bridge, lightened nose cap, projecting barrel with lugs for spike type bayonet, and front sight mounted on heavy band with protecting ears, similar to the Mark VI. The receiver is stronger and heavier than that of the No. 1's. The No. 4 Mark 1 has been made with four different patterns of rear sights varying from finely machined adjustable leaf to "L" types and six patterns of bayonets are usable on the weapon. This rifle was made by B.S.A., Maltby, and Fazakerly. B.S.A. production of this rifle and the No. 4 Mark 1 (T) was over 1,000,000 from 1940 to 1945. The No. 4 Mark 1 was also made for awhile at the Stevens Arms branch of Savage Arms Corp. at Chicopee Falls, Massachusetts, and Long Branch before production of the No. 4 Mark 1* was begun at those plants.

Rifle No. 4, Mark I:* Although not adopted officially by the United Kingdom

British .303 Rifle No. 4 Mark I. Early type with cut-off.

until November 1946, the No. 4 Mark I* was in production at the Canadian Arsenal at Long Branch, Ontario, and at Stevens Arms from 1942 to 1945. The Mark I* differs from the No. 4 principally in not having a bolt head catch. The bolt is removed by lining up the bolt head with a cut-out on the bolt head rib-way. Other differences were the fitting of a modified bridge piece, replacement of the magazine catch screw with a pin, and increase in length of the sear pin. Many No. 4 Mark I and Mark I*'s were made with two groove barrels, and Stevens made some with six groove barrels. Long Branch made almost one million No. 4's including sniper equipments and Stevens made over one million No. 4's. The No. 4 with its various modifications is still in wide use among some member nations of the British Commonwealth.

Rifle No. 4, Mark I* (lightweight): Developed by the Canadians at Long Branch, this weapon was never put into production. It has a one-piece stock and its trigger is pinned to the receiver. This weapon weighs about 6.75 pounds

British .303 Rifle No. 4 Mark I*.

and is 42.5 inches long with a barrel 23 inches long. The receiver and stock are lightened and the stock is fitted with a rubber recoil pad.

Rifle No. 4 Mark I (T): Adopted in February 1942. The Sniper version of No. 4 Mark I, it is fitted with a No. 32 telescope and a wooden cheek rest which is screwed on the top of the butt stock.

British .303 Rifle No. 4 Mark I (T).

.303 Rifle No. 4 Mark I (T) with Telescope C No. 67 Mark I. This is a Canadian issue item.

Rifle No. 4 Mark 1* (T): Sniping conversion of No. 4 Mark 1*, similar to No. 4 Mark 1 (T).

Canadian .303 Rifle No. 4 Mark 1* (lightweight).

Rifle No. 5 Mark 1: Adopted in September 1944. Light weight version of the No. 4 frequently called the "Jungle Carbine," the No. 5 has a shortened barrel and stock. Some stocks have the fore-end rounded like a sporting rifle, others have a metal cap on the fore-end. The barrel has lightening cuts around the reinforce and a flash hider mounted on the muzzle. The weapon is fitted with a knife-type bayonet which is not usable on the No. 4 rifles. A No. 5 Mark 1* version also exists.

British .303 Rifle No. 5 Mark 1. The type shown has metal nose cap; this rifle is also found with rounded fore-end without metal cap.

Rifle No. 4 Mark 2: Adopted in March 1949. Basically this is the same as the No. 4 Mark 1, but the trigger is pinned to a block on the under side of the receiver rather than being attached to the trigger guard. The fore-end also had to be modified.

British .303 Rifle No. 4 Mark 2.

Rifle No. 4 Mark 1/2: Conversion of the No. 4 Mark 1 to the pattern of the Mark 2.

Rifle No. 4 Mark 1/3: Conversion of the No. 4 Mark 1* to the pattern of the Mark 2.

Rifle No. 4 Mark 1/2 (T): Conversion of the No. 4 Mark 1 (T) to the pattern of the Mark 2.

Rifle No. 6 Mark 1 (Aust): Made as a prototype in 1944. Shortened, lightened version of the No. 1. A similar rifle was produced in prototype form at Enfield Lock.

The Mauser Pattern Bolt Action Rifles

Pattern 1913 (P-13): Made in prototype form using a modified Mauser type action of Enfield design and an integral five-round magazine. This rifle was designed for a high-velocity .276 cartridge which was remarkably similar to the

British .276 Pattern 1913 Rifle.

.280 Ross cartridge. This rifle, of which 1,000 were made for field trials, was the fore-runner of the P-14.

Pattern 1914 (P-14): This rifle was made in the United States by Winchester, Remington, and Eddystone during World War I. It is basically the same as the P-13 except that it is chambered for the .303 cartridge. The weapon was classed as limited standard in the British Army and except in sniping versions was not too widely used. When the United States entered World War I, production of the rifle in U.S. caliber .30 was continued and the rifle was called U.S. Rifle caliber .30 M1917; it was known commonly in the United States as the Enfield. In 1926 the United Kingdom changed the nomenclature of the P-14 to Rifle No. 3 Mark I*.

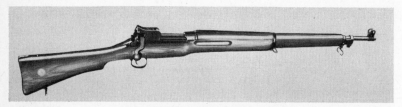

British .303 Rifle No. 3 Mark I (P-14).*

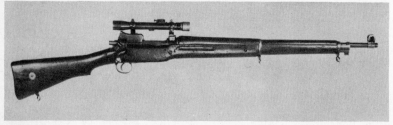

British .303 Enfield No. 3 Mark I (T), originally known as the Pattern 1914 (T), (P-14 (T)). This rifle has the Model 1918 Telescope.*

Pattern 1914 (F) (P-14 (F)): P-14 rifles fitted with a fine adjustment rear sight and issued in World War I for sniping purposes before the introduction of the telescope equipped P-14's. Nomenclature changed in 1926 to Rifle No. 3 Mark I* (F).

Pattern 1914 (T) (P-14 (T)): P-14 rifle fitted with Pattern 1918 telescope. This telescope has adjustments for range and windage. Nomenclature changed in 1926 to Rifle No. 3 Mark I* (T).

Pattern 1914 (T) A (P-14 (T) A): P-14 rifle fitted with Aldis telescope. This telescope is adjustable only for range. Nomenclature changed in 1926 to Rifle No. 3 Mark I* (T) A.

British .303 Rifle No. 3 Mark I (P-14 (T) A). This weapon uses the Aldis telescope.*

The Caliber .22 Rifles

.22 Cal. R.F. Short Rifle Mark I: Adopted in 1907. Conversion of Lee Metford Mark I* rifle, the rifle is approximately the same length overall as the S.M.L.E. Sights are adjustable blade front sight and tangent-type rear sight with windage adjustment.

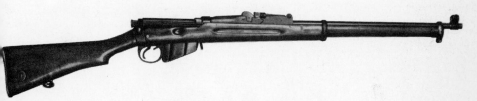

British .22 Cal. R.F. Short Rifle Mark I.

.22 Cal. R.F. Long Rifle Mark II: Adopted in 1911—conversion of Long Lee Enfield to .22 rimfire. The Mark I pattern of .22 Long Rifles was converted from Long Lee Metfords.

British .22 Cal. R.F. Short Rifle Mark II.

.22 Cal. R.F. Short Rifle Mark I:* Conversion to .22 rimfire in shortened version of Lee Metford Mark I*. Mark II of this pattern was converted from Lee Metford Mark II.

.22 Cal. R.F. Short Rifle, Mark III: Adopted in 1912—conversion of S.M.L.E. Marks II and II* to .22 rimfire. A five-cartridge magazine was fitted later.

During World War I a number of different patterns of Lee rifles were converted to caliber .22. Many of these were converted by boring out the .303 barrels and inserting .22 liners. One model—the .22 R.F. Pattern 1914—fed from the .303 magazine through the use of conveyors which were chambered and bored for the .22 caliber in a manner similar to the auxiliary cartridges which were popular on the American commercial market some years ago.

.22 Cal. R.F. Short Rifle, Mark IV: Adopted in 1921—Conversion from S.M.L.E. Marks III and III* using new .22 caliber barrels. This is a single-shot weapon. When rifle nomenclature changed in 1926 this rifle became Rifle No. 2 Mark IV*.

Rifle No. 7 Mark I: Developed at Long Branch during World War II. As made in Canada, it is a single-shot version of Rifle No. 4 Mark 1* and is called "Rifle C No. 7 Mark I." After the war B.S.A. made a small quantity of No. 7 rifles; the British-made rifles have a five-round .22 caliber magazine housed within the .303 magazine.

Rifle No. 8 Mark I: Adopted in 1950. A single-shot target-type weapon, its sights are similar to those of the No. 4 rifle. The trigger mechanism is adjustable for either single or double stage (military) pull.

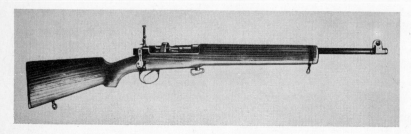

British .22 Rifle No. 8 Mark I.

Rifle No. 9: Adopted since 1950 by the Royal Navy, this rifle is a conversion of No. 4 made by insertion of a .22 caliber "Parker Rifled" liner in a bored out .303 barrel.

VERY EARLY BRITISH DESIGNS IN LARGE CALIBER
British Model 1853-66 Snider Single Shot

Caliber: .557
Overall length, rifle without bayonet: 55"
Overall weight, rifle without bayonet: 9.06 lbs.
Type of action: Side hinged block
Barrel Length: 39"
No. Grooves: 3
Notes:

Bore Diameter: .577"
Groove Dia.: .589"
With bayonet attached: 72.5"
With bayonet attached: 10 lbs.
Direction of Twist: Right
Rate of Twist: 78"

1. Sniders were converted muzzle loading Enfields.

British .577 M1853-1866 Cartridge

Other Names: .577 Snider
Type: Rimmed, Necked, Centerfire
Overall Length: 2.45"
Type Powder: Black
Average Wt.: 715 grs.
Approximate Chg.: 73 grs.
Type Primer: Boxer

BULLET

Type: Lead
Diameter: .570"
Weight: 480 grs.
Length: 1.04"

CARTRIDGE CASE

Length Overall: 1.63"
Length Head to Shoulder: 1.15"
Length of Shoulder: .07"
Length of Neck: .41"
Diameter at Rim: .746"
Diameter at Base: .660"
Diameter at Neck: .597"
Diameter at Shoulder: .625"

BALLISTICS (approximate)
Muzzle Velocity: 1240 f.s.

Notes: 1. The original .577 Snider was made with a heavy foil case body set in a brass base.

British .303 Mark VII Cartridge

Other Names: .303 British Service
Type: Rimmed, Necked, Centerfire
Overall Length: 3.037"
Average Wt.: 384 gr.
Type Powder: Cordite
Approximate Chg.: 37.5 gr.
Type Primer: Berdan

BULLET

Type: Jacketed, Pointed
Diameter: .312"
Weight: 174 gr.
Length: 1.28"

CARTRIDGE CASE

Length Overall: 2.21"
Length Head to Shoulder: 1.726"
Length of Shoulder: .1"
Length of Neck: .33"
Diameter at Rim: .54"
Diameter at Base: .460"
Diameter at Neck: .340"
Diameter at Shoulder: .401"

BALLISTICS (approximate)
Muzzle Velocity: 2440 f.s.
Pressure: About 44,500 lbs./sq. in.

Notes: 1. The ball bullet for this cartridge has an aluminum, plastic, or fiber filler in the nose of the jacket.

British Model 1871 Martini-Henry Single Shot

Caliber: .45
Overall length, rifle without bayonet: 49.5"
Overall weight, rifle without bayonet: 9 lbs.
Type of action: Falling Block
Barrel Length: 33.2" *No. Grooves:* 7
Bore Diameter: .450" *Groove Dia.:* .459"
Notes:

With bayonet attached: 71.5"
With bayonet attached: 9.75 lbs.

Direction of Twist: Right
Rate of Twist: 22"

1. Some Martini-Henry rifles were later modified to take the standard British .303 cartridge.

British Cal. .45 M1871 Cartridge

Other Names: 11.43 Martini-Henry; .45-
.577/450 Martini-Henry
Type: Rimmed, Necked, Centerfire
Overall Length: 3.2"
Type Powder: Black
Approximate Charge: 85 grs.
Type Primer: Boxer (Shotgun type)

BULLET

Type: Lead (Paper Patched)
Diameter: .45"
Weight: 480 grs.
Length: 1.27"

CARTRIDGE CASE

Length Overall: 2.31"
Length Head to Shoulder: 1.33"
Length of Shoulder: .27"
Length of Neck: .75"
Diameter at Rim: .765"
Diameter at Base: .66"
Diameter at Neck: .475"
Diameter at Shoulder: .615"

BALLISTICS (approximate)
Muzzle Velocity: 1350 f.s.

Notes: This cartridge was originally made with a coiled brass or iron case but was later made, including manufacture in this country with a solid brass case and regular Boxer type primer.

Pre-World War II British Sporting Rifles

There was little real mass production of sporting rifle manufacture in Great Britain. Quantity production methods have been used by B.S.A. and Vickers for small bore rifles, and by export firms at Birmingham producing cheap arms, but the general rule has been to follow custom production methods.

Lack of game animals except on rigidly controlled private hunting preserves plus the official discouragement of firearms ownership by the ordinary British citizen has prevented the development of mass production small arms techniques and has cost Britain dearly in her last two wars.

The following list of types and makes is representative of the best in British rifle making.

SINGLE SHOT RIFLES: (a) These when in small bore calibers are usually built on the Martini falling block action. B.S.A. and Vickers are the prime manufacturers of the advanced types using modified Martini-Francotte actions which permit removal of the entire firing and breech locking system without tools.

These are high priced precision rifles for the .22 L.R. cartridge.

(b) Any of the major gunmakers will produce single shot rifles to order in larger calibers. The best of these are generally built around the Farquharson dropping block action, though Greener and Westley Richards have at times built their own. Calibers, breech locking systems and specifications are to the order of the purchaser.

Double Barrel Rifles

These are made in every type of breech locking and firing lock design found in the various high grade British shotguns. In effect they are the respective maker's double barrel shotguns modified and strengthened to safely handle the appropriate rifle cartridges. They may be ordered in hammer or hammerless designs, though in recent years the hammer types have seldom been made.

The following list is representative, but is not complete:

Bland: Standard pattern doubles in Express calibers.

Boss: Standard pattern doubles in Express calibers.

Evans: Standard pattern doubles in Express calibers.

Gibbs: Standard pattern doubles in Express calibers. Popular Indian calibers in this make are .450-500 High Velocity and .470 Nitro Express.

Grant: Standard double hammerless with side locks. All calibers from .256 to .600.

Greener: Hammer and hammerless with the famous Greener multiple-bolt breech locking systems. Parallel barrels are the rule, but Greener has made some over-under rifles. All large calibers.

Holland & Holland: Parallel barrel hammerless with the well-known H&H detachable side plate locks. Customary calibers are: .240 Flanged, .300 Magnum, Holland's .375 Magnum and Holland's .465 India. All are rim cartridges.

Jeffery: Side lock and box lock models. Top lever or under-lever operation. Customary calibers: .333, .375 Magnum, .400, .470 and .475. The under lever action is customarily built in caliber .600, but to order is made in other sizes.

Purdey: Special side lock system with Purdey original side clips. Any large caliber to order.

Powell: Standard types with box locks. Made in any caliber.

Lang: Now combined with Grant. Originated the .470 HV.

British Farquaharson Dropping Block Rifle. This is one of the strongest single shot actions ever developed. This lock design may be encountered in any caliber, since these actions were barreled up to custom order. The special lever under the triggerguard provides greater extracting power.

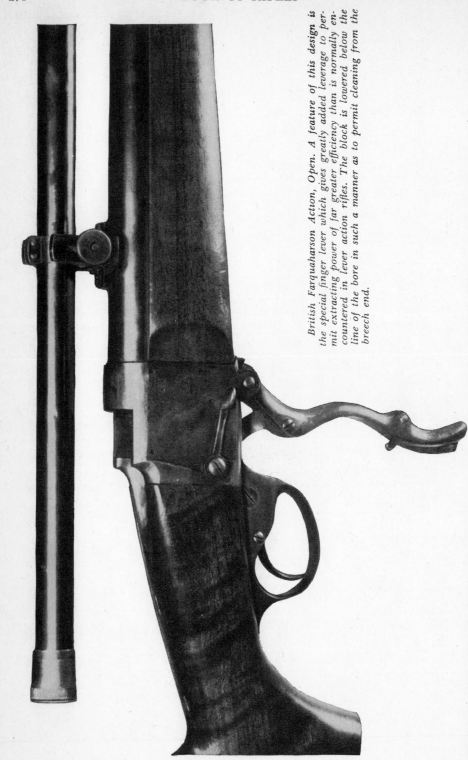

British Farquaharson Action, Open. A feature of this design is the special finger lever which gives greatly added leverage to permit extracting power of far greater efficiency than is normally encountered in lever action rifles. The block is lowered below the line of the bore in such a manner as to permit cleaning from the breech end.

Pre-war Westley Richards 315 Accelerated Express Rifle. This is a special W-R caliber rifle built on a standard Mauser action.

Pre-war British Westley Richards .425 Express Rifle. This is a typical custom built express rifle using a Mauser Magnum receiver. Stocks, sights, barrel lengths and similar details vary with individual specimens as ordered. The protruding box magazine is necessary because of the large size of the special cartridges used.

British Westley Richards .425 Express, showing details of construction. Bolt is removed to show details of construction. Note that except for shape of handle and increased size, it is the same as the Kar. 98k.

The leaf sights shown are common on British sporting rifles.

The box magazine is hinged at its forward end and is locked by a turning lever. This system is common also on European modifications of the general Mauser pattern.

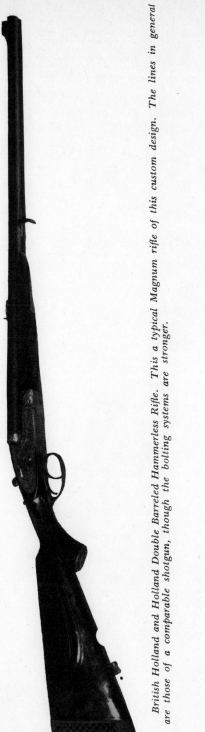

British Holland and Holland Double Barreled Hammerless Rifle. This a typical Magnum rifle of this custom design. The lines in general are those of a comparable shotgun, though the bolting systems are stronger.

Typical British Custom Made Box Lock Double Barreled Rifle. These are custom built to any caliber and to customer's specifications. Externally and internally they closely follow the shotgun design of the individual manufacturer.

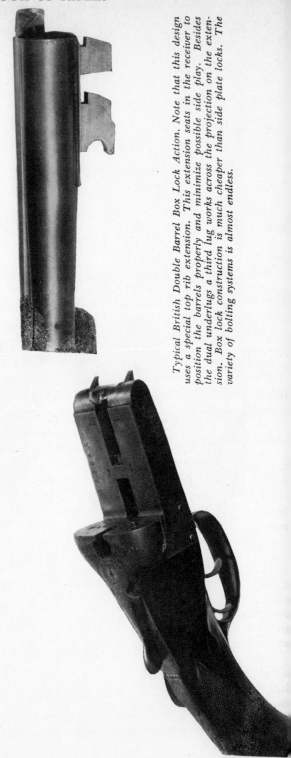

Typical British Double Barrel Box Lock Action. Note that this design uses a special top rib extension. This extension seats in the receiver to position the barrels properly and minimize possible side play. Besides the dual underlugs a third lug works across the projection on the extension. Box lock construction is much cheaper than side plate locks. The variety of bolting systems is almost endless.

Rigby: Both side plate and box lock actions. Customary calibers: .275 Magnum, .350 and .470. Made in other calibers to order.

Westley Richards: Standard W-R actions with simple firing mechanism consisting of only 7 pieces. Made as a "miniature" weighing 7.25 pounds in Caliber .300 Sherwood for small game; and in standard models weighing about 10.75 lbs. A common caliber is the .450-400 Magnum.

Woodward: Standard pattern with side plate locks. Made in any caliber from .303 up. Under lever operation.

Pre-World War II Bolt Action Magazine Rifles

These are all based on Enfield, Mauser, Mannlicher or Ross actions. The following are typical models:

B.S.A.: Sporting rifles on Enfield actions, usually in .303 or .315 calibers.

Gibbs: Mauser actions. The Calibers .30-06 U.S. and .505 Gibbs are best known.

Greener: Mauser actions. Calibers .30-06 U. S. and .318 Nitro Express are best known.

Jeffery: Mauser actions. Calibers are customarily: .333 Jeffery, .375 Magnum, .404 Jeffery and .500 Jeffery. Modified magazine. Note: Jeffery has also built rifles on Mannlicher actions.

Holland & Holland: Mauser actions. Calibers: .240 Apex, .300 Magnum and .375 Magnum.

Rigby: Mauser actions. Calibers: .275, .350 and .416.

Westley Richards: Mauser actions, modified magazines. (a) Flush magazine in caliber .242 Vickers Super Express and .318 (b) Projecting magazine in caliber .425 Magnum Express.

Semiauto and Slide Actions

B. S. A. manufactured an ingenious but expensive .22 semiauto "Ralock" rifle. This B.S.A. "Ralock" derives its name from the fact that the bolt moves radially and does not reciprocate. The design is fully enclosed. This is a "slam fire" design, the rifle firing as the bolt turns up against the breech face. Empty cases are held in a well inside the rifle instead of being expelled from the breech as fired. When the triggerguard is pulled down, it spills out any empties and cocks the action. Magazine tube is in butt.

Current British Sporting Rifles

After the close of World War II, it took the British small-arms manufacturers a long time to get into production on high-powered rifles. Until the '50's the only high-powered magazine rifles available were those converted from P-14 and Model 1917 Enfield rifles. B.S.A., Cogswell and Harrison, and Parker-Hale made up a number of .303 and .30 caliber rifles using these actions. Using the same action, Jeffery made .333, .375, and .404 rifles.

In the early '50's Jeffery and Cogswell and Harrison began importing Mauser actions and making up rifles on these actions. At about the same time B.S.A. began making their "Hunter" rifle. This rifle used the first British-made modified Mauser action and was made originally in .222 Remington and .22 Hornet calibers. Currently B.S.A. is making a series of bolt action rifles using short, long, and medium modified Mauser actions of their manufacture. The

B.S.A. 30-06 Majestic Sporting Rifle.

B.S.A. DeLuxe Majestic rifle is made in .222 Remington, .243 Winchester, and .308 Winchester in the medium-length action and .270, .30-06, and the .458 Winchester in the long action. Weights run from 6.25 pounds in the lighter calibers to 8.75 pounds in .458 Winchester. This rifle has a built-in muzzle brake called a BESA recoil reducer. The standard weight B.S.A. bolt action rifles are made in .22 Hornet and 7x57mm in addition to the calibers given above. Mauser actioned rifles are also currently made by Parker-Hale, Cogswell and Harrison, and Jeffery.

In .22 caliber rifles B.S.A. is the only current maker. The Supersport Five made by that firm is a conventional box magazine fed bolt action. The Martini International Mark III Match rifle is B.S.A.'s finest .22. This 14.25 pound rifle has a 6-pound, 29-inch barrel. It uses a Martini action, which has been a long-time favorite in British .22 caliber match rifles.

B.S.A. Supersport Five .22 Bolt-action Sporting Rifle.

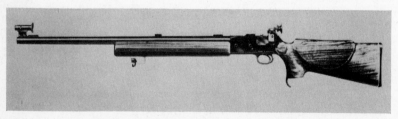

B.S.A. Martini International Mark III .22 Match Rifle.

Chapter 36
GREECE
(Hellas)

GOVERNMENT PLANTS: None of consequence.
PRIVATE PLANTS: None.
PRINCIPAL MILITARY RIFLES: U.S. cal. .30 M1, British .303 Rifle No. 4, and Rifle No. 1.
FORMER MILITARY RIFLES: Model 1903 (Mannlicher-Schoenauer) 6.5mm. F.N. (Belgian) Mausers are also found with Greek property markings.

Model 1903 (Mannlicher-Schoenauer) Rifle, Cal. 6.5mm

This is a standard Mannlicher turn-bolt design. The bolt cylinder is bored out from the front to accept the removable bolt head. The bolt head has tenons fitting into the end of the bolt cylinder which work in circular grooves on the inside to lock the head. The bolt head can be withdrawn only when the studs are turned so they are opposite their clearances. There are tenons and slots for the flats on the forward end of the striker provided within the hollow bolt cylinder.

This design has two locking lugs on opposing sides near the front of the bolt cylinder, but due to the removable bolt head they are placed farther back along the cylinder than in Mauser practice.

The bolt handle projects about ⅓ of the distance from the rear of the cylinder and has a large knob which is bored out to make it lighter. This handle turns down into a cut in the right side of the receiver. A strengthening rib is provided in line with the bolt handle; it is milled out to make a lighter bolt. There is a cam shaped recess provided at the rear of the cylinder to receive the stud on the cocking piece as the arm is fired. The lower side of the top rib of the cocking piece itself is cut out on the right side to clear a stop stud on the bolt. The striker hole is bored with interrupted rings by which the cocking piece is fastened to the striker. When the bolt handle is drawn back, the cocking piece stud rests in a shallow groove in the rear of the bolt cylinder.

Also at the rear end of the bolt is a recess to engage the end of the spindle of the manual safety. An escape hole is bored in the bolt cylinder to allow escape of any gas which might blow back due to a defective primer or cartridge head.

The spring extractor fits into a groove in the side of the bolt head, while a stud on the ejector lies in an undercut groove in the head.

The striker head has interrupted rings to permit attaching it to the striker. The front end of the mainspring bears against the striker collar. The flat on the striker working in the slot in the bolt head, prevents the cocking piece from turning as the bolt is turned up and drawn to the rear.

The cocking piece secured to the rear of the striker is prevented from turning by the end of its lock screw bearing on the flat on the striker. Its stud travels in the groove in the receiver tang where it engages with the sear nose. A rib on the cocking piece is bored out from the rear to receive the spindle of the manual safety bolt.

285

Greek Mannlicher-Schoenauer Model 03/14 Carbine, caliber 6.5mm. This model and its earlier variant the M 1903 are military versions of the common M-S sporting 6.5mm (or 6.7mm). This is a turn-bolt design with Mannlicher two-piece bolt. The bolt head is removable. The receiver bridge is split and the bolt handle locks down forward of the bridge. The magazine is the rotary Schoenauer type.

Greek Mannlicher-Schoenauer, action open ready for loading. Note that unlike other Mannlichers (except the Hungarian-made M 98/40 series) this rifle may be loaded from a charger clip. Guides are machined into the front faces of the receiver bridge. The corrugated button on the right receiver side wall is a magazine release. When pressed it permits the magazine spring to turn the rotary follower and expel any cartridges which may be in the magazine.

The pivoted lever at the left side of the receiver is the bolt release. Pushing its rear end in permits withdrawal of the bolt. Details of the cocking piece, safety and cocking piece nut construction may be seen.

This safety bolt is operated by a customary thumb piece. When the striker is cocked, the thumb piece is pointing to the left. The spindle of the safety bolt can be turned forward over the bolt, as a part of it is cut away underneath adjoining the bolt.

Turning the thumb piece to the right causes a small cam on the end of the safety bolt to engage the front of the recess in the cocking piece. This forces the safety bolt and the cocking piece back and disengages the cocking piece stud from the sear nose. In this position, the safety and the cocking piece cannot move on trigger pressure. This constitutes a positive safety.

While the head of the extractor fits in a groove in the bolt head, its shoulder rests against an opposing shoulder in the bolt head to absorb the strain during extraction.

The ejector is similar to the Dutch pattern Mannlicher. It slides backward and forward in the undercut groove in the bolt head. A screw working in the groove limits its travel. As the bolt is drawn to the rear, the back of the ejector hits the bolt stop, sliding the ejector forward. The front ejector edge is beveled off to allow the base of the cartridge being chambered to thrust the ejector back as the bolt is pushed fully forward. This leaves it ready for the next ejecting stroke.

The trigger operates in a fork in the rear end of the sear. It is pivoted on a pin. Its top end has two ribs bearing alternately against the underside of the receiver to give the standard Mannlicher double pull.

The sear itself is pivoted beneath the receiver on a pin positioned behind the magazineway. The nose projects through a slot into a groove in the receiver tang and is thrust upwards by a spiral spring bearing against a projection below.

The receiver is screwed to the barrel. The customary longitudinal grooves are provided at either side of the boltway to receive and guide the locking lugs as the bolt is drawn back and thrust forward over the magazine.

Cam shaped grooves at the forward ends of the longitudinal grooves lead to the locking recesses above and below the firing chamber. The lugs take their bearing against the rear faces of these recesses when the arm is locked.

The right hand groove is partly cut away to permit ejection and to facilitate magazine loading.

Clip guides are formed at the rear of the opening behind the magazineway in the receiver. The forward faces of these guides are sloped up to permit ejection of the empty clip as the bolt is thrust forward. (This rifle is loaded from a Mauser-type strip-in clip.) The receiver ahead is continued downward and shaped to form the upper section of the magazine. The receiver bridge behind the magazineway is cut through at top to permit the passage of the bolt handle, while the rear part of the receiver forms the tang in which the customary groove is provided for the cocking piece stud. The sear nose rises through an opening at the forward end of this groove, ready to catch and hold the cocking piece stud during the forward cocking stroke of the bolt.

The exterior of the barrel has a straight taper starting about 3-inches from the forward section of the receiver and extending to the muzzle. The diameter increases to the rear of the taper to form a shoulder against which a sleeve rear sight bed is fixed. The front sight is attached by a sleeve at the muzzle end.

The magazine is the spool or rotary type. A rectangular box which forms the lower part of the magazine is fitted into the bottom of the receiver where it is held in position by a fixing plate pivoted in the center of the box. When the follower is being revolved, each end of this plate enters a radial locking groove in the front and rear of the downward extensions of the receiver which form the upper sections of the magazine. A spring entering a recess in the plate retains the fixing plate in position.

A rotary follower is fitted into the rectangular box which forms the lower half of the magazine. Front and rear axis studs are provided in this follower and are attached to a spiral spring; the studs are formed to receive two retaining pins which prevent them from turning. This follower has five grooves to receive individual cartridges.

Operation

Opening the Bolt: As the bolt handle is turned up, the cocking piece stud engaged in the groove in the tang prevents the cocking piece from rotating with the bolt. Instead, a cam action is induced as the cut in the bolt cylinder acts against the stud, causing it to move back along the bolt cam face until it enters its groove. This cam action draws the striker back inside the bolt cylinder and hence partly compresses the mainspring which is positioned around the striker.

As the cocking piece stud passes over the bevelled sear nose, it depresses the sear; but the sear spring reacts to push the nose back up so its rear holding face will stop and hold the cocking piece stud when the bolt again goes ahead.

During the motion of turning the bolt handle up, the locking lugs pass along the cam shaped grooves from their seatings, effecting a cam withdrawal of the entire bolt assembly and thereby furnishing primary extraction to start the cartridge case from the chamber.

At the end of the bolt handle lifting movement, the lugs are opposite their longitudinal grooves in the sides of the receiver walls, and the bolt handle is opposite the opening in the receiver bridge. The bolt is now drawn straight back to the rear. The rear of the ejector hits against the bolt stop and is pushed forward until its forward travel is stopped by the left bolt lug. The ejector face hitting the cartridge case ejects it through the action.

The magazine: When cartridges are loaded into the magazine the follower rotates and its spiral spring is coiled. This spring is always under some tension, but the additional tension provides the motive power for feeding. A thumb piece on the cartridge stop projects through a slot in the top of the right side of the receiver, and is pivoted there. As the magazine is loaded, this stop is depressed by the cartridges. When the action is open, pushing the thumb piece pivots the stop out of engagement and permits the magazine follower to rotate and expel all the cartridges from the magazine without the necessity of working them through the action.

During the loading operation, the magazine follower rotates enough to bring a cartridge in line for feeding.

Closing the bolt: When the bolt is pushed forward, its lower face hits the base of the cartridge, pushing the bullet up the guide slope at the front of the magazine into the firing chamber. The head of the cartridge case rides up the face of the bolt head as the cartridge chambers and the extractor hook engages around the head of the case.

When the lugs reach the end of their longitudinal grooves, the stud on the cocking piece engages the sear nose. Thus as the cartridge is forced home and the bolt locked by turning down the bolt handle, the mainspring is completely compressed. (As in the German Mauser, this weapon can be cocked by raising and lowering the bolt handle; however this unlocks the action and is dangerous in case of a hang fire.)

This rifle cannot be fired until the bolt is locked. The stud on the cocking piece hits against the cam face of the recess on the bolt in the event the bolt handle is not forced fully home as the trigger is pulled. This will turn and close the bolt, but may result in a misfire as the striker pin may not retain enough drive from the mainspring to complete the firing action.

The stock in this design is a single piece with a modified pistol grip. Two grooves are cut in the bottom of the stock barrel groove to further lighten the weapon. It has a full length handguard.

The front sight is of the blade type mounted in a stud on the front sight band. The rear sight is of the ramp type with open notch.

Greek Model 1903 Mannlicher-Schoenauer

Caliber: 6.5mm
Overall length, rifle without bayonet: 48.3"
Overall weight, rifle without bayonet: 8.58 lbs.
Type of action: Turnbolt
Type of Magazine: Revolving box
Barrel Length: 28.5"

Bore Diameter: .256"
No. grooves: 4
Groove dia.: .267"
Type of bolt: 2 piece—Rotating Head
Capacity: 5
Direction of Twist: Right
Rate of Twist: 7.87"

Notes:

1. This arm, except for calibers, weights and measurements and stock is the same as the line of Mannlicher Schoenauer sporting rifles.

2. A thumbpiece on the right side of the receiver can be pushed to release the magazine follower when the action is open, thereby expelling all cartridges from the magazine.

Greek 6.5mm M1903 Mannlicher Schoenauer Rifle.

Greek 6.5mm M1903 Cartridge

Other Names: 6.5x53, 6.5mm Mannlicher-Schoenauer
Type: Rimless, Necked, Centerfire

Overall Length: 3.05"
Average Wt.: 348 gr.
Type Powder: Nitrocellulose

Approximate Chg.: 36 gr.

Type Primer: Berdan

BULLET

Type: Jacketed, Round Nose

Diameter: .263″

Weight: 159 gr.

Length: 1.24″

CARTRIDGE CASE

Length Overall: 2.12″

Length Head to Shoulder: 1.65″

Length of Shoulder: .16″

Length of Neck: .31″

Diameter at Rim: .450″

Diameter at Base: .447″

Diameter at Neck: .295″

Diameter at Shoulder: .425″

BALLISTICS (approximate)

Muzzle Velocity: 2225 f.s.

Pressure: About 44,000 lbs./sq. in.

Notes: 6.5mm in M-S sporting ammunition will interchange.

EARLIER OFFICIAL BREECHLOADERS: In the 1870's and '80's Greece was equipped with the French Gras conversions and Gras-Kropatschek rifles described under *France*.

The only rifle of Greek design to receive any attention was the Mylonas manufactured for a few years in the early '70's. This was a dropping block single shot rifle operated by triggerguard lever.

Other Rifles in Greek Service in World War II

(1) French Gras Model 74, 11mm carbine and rifle.

(2) French Model 1907, 8mm turn-bolt rifle with 3-shot Mannlicher type magazine.

(3) French Model 1892, 8mm turn-bolt carbine with 3-shot Mannlicher type magazine.

(4) Austrian Model 1895, 8mm Austrian. Straight pull rifle and carbine.

(5) Greek Mannlicher 95/24. This is a Model 95 Austrian receiver with magazine altered and barrel changed to take the standard German 7.9mm cartridge. The mechanical operating system except for the magazine alteration is the same as for the Austrian.

This conversion may be recognized by the fact that the bottom of the magazine does not have the customary Mannlicher cut to permit a clip to drop through. Cartridges are loaded through the top of the action and their heads are guided by a clip which is built into the magazine well.

(6) French Model 86/93, 8mm tubular repeater.

(7) French Model 07/15, 8mm turnbolt with three shot Mannlicher type magazine.

(8) Greek Model 1930 Mauser. This is a 7.9mm Mauser rifle on the German Kar. 98k system. It was made in Belgium by F-N. (See *Belgium*.)

(9) All types of captured Italian equipment.

Chapter 37
HUNGARY
(Magyar Orszag)

GOVERNMENT PLANTS: Budapest; all former private plants are now government owned.

PRINCIPAL MILITARY RIFLES: the Soviet designed 7.62mm AK-47 Assault Rifle and SKS carbine are the current Hungarian service rifles.

FORMER MILITARY RIFLES: (1) Model 1935 Mannlicher. (2) Model 1895 Austro-Hungarian Mannlicher straight pull. (Note: The modified and converted M1935 used by the Germans and designated "Gew. 98/40" was used in Hungary as the Model 1943. The Hungarian Model 1943 used Hungarian type fittings and bayonet lug.)

Model 1935

This rifle was adopted in 1935. It is a composite of several Mannlicher designs. The action is the Mannlicher turning bolt design with two-piece bolt, the bolt head being removable to permit striker and mainspring insertion from the front end. The cocking piece is the type used on the M. 95, which permits cocking without opening the action. The magazine projects below the bottom of the stock. It loads with a typical Mannlicher clip. Stock is two piece.

Model 1895
See *Austria*.

Modified Mannlicher M 95

Straight pull for 8x56R Hungarian M31 cartridge. These found in both rifle and carbine. Hungary used the Model 95 Mannlicher for the 8x52R Austrian cartridge until 1931 when they adopted the 8x56R cartridge. This case had the same head diameter, less belly, and a long tapering shoulder similar to the .300 H&H. Rifles and carbines were rebarreled for this, using the same length barrel throated for the pointed bullet. Only change was a larger rear sight graduated for the new ammunition, plus clamp-on front sight protector. These are identified with a large "H" 5/16" high on barrel over chamber. Barrels were numbered but do not agree with receiver numbers. Many were in service—we captured thousands of them.

Captured technical prisoners reported that extraction was poor, causing redesign of the action to Turning Bolt Mannlicher—this new model being called the 35M.

Hungarian caliber is common. Thousands were captured, marked Budapest.

Hungarian Model 1935M

Caliber: 8mm M31, 8x56mm	*Barrel Length:* 23.6"
Overall length, rifle without bayonet: 43.7"	*Bore Diameter:* .315"
Overall weight, rifle without bayonet: 8.9 lbs.	*No. Grooves:* 4
Type of action: Turnbolt	*Type of bolt:* 2-piece
Type of Magazine: Vertical Box (Straight line feed)	*Capacity:* 5
	Direction of Twist: Right

Hungarian Model 1935, Caliber 8mm M31 Hungarian. The bolt and receiver are modified from the earlier Roumanian Mannlicher. The design is a two-piece turn bolt. The receiver bridge is split and the bolt handle locks down forward of the bridge. The magazine is Mannlicher construction. The cartridge is rimmed. It is interchangeable with the Austrian 8mm Model 30.

7.92 Model 98/40. This is a development of the 1935 Hungarian design. Its name derives from the fact that it was developed in 1940 to use the German Model 98 (7.9mm) cartridge and charger clip. (Note: This basic design is referred to in Hungary as Model 43, indicating date of introduction.) The magazine is a modified Mauser.

Model 98/40, Action Closed and Open. Note that forward extension of the cocking piece travels through the cut in the receiver bridge and serves to guide the cocking piece. A bolt guide rib extends forward on the cylinder from the bolt handle root. It is grooved to lighten it. The bolt handle itself serves as a safety lug when the action is closed. The dual locking lugs are on the bolt cylinder to the rear of the removable bolt head.

Notes:

1. Bolt handle projects almost at right angles. Cocking piece is Mannlicher Model 189₉
type, permitting cocking without opening action. Magazine projects below stock. Caliber is
special rim type bottleneck 8x56mm. Point of manufacture: Budapest Arsenal.

2. This rifle as modified in 1940 was listed by the Germans as the "Gewehr 98/40"—indicatin
a modification made in 1940 for the standard German rimless 7:92mm cartridge used in th
Kar. 98. The modification replaced the original projecting single line box magazine with ι
Mauser type flush double line box.

3. In 1943 the 98/40, with slight modifications, was adopted by the Hungarians as the Mode
1943. The modifications consisted of using Hungarian type fittings—sling swivels, and bayone
lug rather than German type as on the 98/40.

Hungarian 7.92mm M43 Rifle.

Hungarian M1943

Caliber: 7.92mm
Overall length: 43.0"
Weight, loaded: 8.6 lbs.
Type of action: Turnbolt

Type of bolt: 2 piece
Type of magazine: Integral staggered rov
box; Capacity—5
Barrel length: 23.8"

8mm Cartridge M31

CARTRIDGE
Name: Hungarian M31, 8x56R, Austrian M30
Type: Rimmed, Nerked, Centerfire.
Type Powder: Square flake
Approximate Chg.: 55 gr.
Type Primer: Berdan
Length, overall: 3.02"
Weight: 441 gr.

BULLET
Diameter: .328
Weight: 208 gr.
Length: 1.35"

CARTRIDGE CASE
Length Overall: 2.21"
Diameter at Rim: .554"
Weight of Case: 180 gr.
Muzzle Velocity: 2395 f.p.s.

Hungarian Sporting Arms

Hungary, like most of the other European satellites, uses Soviet produced
sporting rifles extensively. In addition, Hungary produces several caliber .22
rifles which are also exported by Ferunion, Budapest. The "Béke" is a medium
weight, single shot, bolt action target rifle. Its only unusual feature is the
mounting of a peep rear sight on the barrel ahead of the receiver. The peep can
be removed and the sight is then usable as an open sight making it usable in
Soviet bloc pre-military training. The "Gyözelem" is a match type, single shot,
bolt action .22 rifle. It has a palm rest, thumbhole type stock and adjustable hook
butt plate. The trigger is made of heavy steel wire and can be curved to the
shooter's desire; it is adjustable for weight of pull. Target type front and rear
sights are used on this weapon.

Chapter 38

IRAN
(Persia)

GOVERNMENT PLANTS: Government rifle factory.

PRIVATE PLANTS: None.

PRINCIPAL MILITARY RIFLES: U.S. Rifle caliber .30 M1.

FORMER MILITARY RIFLES: Czech ZB and Iranian produced Model 98/29 rifles and carbines. The model designation 98/29 is the Czech commercial designation for the weapons. There is also a post World War II Iranian produced modification of the 98/29 carbine called the Model 49—Christian calendar designation—by the Iranians. Differences between the 98/29 and 49 carbines are confined to sling swivels and minor fittings. All of these weapons are similar in operation and functioning to the German Model 98 Mauser and modifications thereof.

	1938 Rifle	1930 Carbine
Caliber:	.... 7.92mm	
System of operation:	............Manually operated turning bolt action	
Weight:	9.1 lbs.	8.4 lbs.
Length, overall:	49.2″	38″
Barrel length:	29.13″	17.91″
Feed device:	5-round, staggered-row non-detachable box magazine........	
Sights—front:	.... protected barley corn	
rear:	Tangent w/V notch, graduated from 100-2000 meters	
Muzzle velocity:	Approx. 2800 f.p.s.	Approx. 2600 f.p.s.

Iranian 7.92mm Model 1938 Rifle, Czech designation 98/29.

Iranian 7.92mm Model 1930 Carbine, Czech designation 98/29.

Iranian 7.92mm Model 49 Carbine.

Chapter 39
ISRAEL

GOVERNMENT PLANTS: Facilities are available for the manufacture of small arms.

PRIVATE PLANTS: None.

PRINCIPAL MILITARY RIFLES: 7.62mm FN "FAL" light automatic rifle, Kar 98k Mauser rifle—some in 7.92mm; some have been converted to 7.62mm NATO.

After achieving status as an independent nation, Israel accepted the bolt action German Kar 98k Mauser as standard. Immediately thereafter, machinery to manufacture the complete rifle was acquired from Switzerland at a cost of nearly $2,000,000. However, before production began in earnest, the Israelis decided to adopt the FN NATO "FAL" Rifle in caliber 7.62mm NATO. (See BELGIUM.) Although Israel was not a member of NATO, they recognized the advantages of standardization among the nations outside the Iron Curtain.

The factory which the Israelis had equipped to produce the Mausers was subsequently assigned the task of turning out replacement parts for the Mausers which they had procured earlier in large numbers from Europe, particularly Czechoslovakia and Sweden. These Mausers are being rebarreled to use the new 7.62mm NATO cartridge.

Their ammunition factory, which had been manufacturing the 7.92mm Mauser cartridge, is now turning out the new 7.62mm NATO ammunition.

The stature of Israel's arms industry has increased considerably through the production of the Uzi submachine gun in 9mm Parabellum, recognized by many experts as being the best in its class today. It is the creation of the adept Israeli Army designer, Major Uziel Gal. It is not unreasonable to expect further strides to be made in automatic arms development from this quarter.

Chapter 40

ITALY

(Republica D'Italia)

GOVERNMENT PLANTS: Turin. Brescia. Gardone. Terni.

PRIVATE PLANTS: Fiat (Turin) was the largest. There were hundreds of small gunsmiths in Italy before World War II producing crude-to-fine rifles. Very few were exported except some fine specimens by P. Beretta.

Some custom built rifles from Italy rate with the best produced anywhere, but these are exceptions. The firms of Vincenzo Bernadelli and Luigi Franchi produce custom arms second to none in the world from the standpoint of manufacture and finish, though production is limited.

PRINCIPAL MILITARY RIFLES: 7.62mm BM 59 (Beretta conversion of M1), cal. .30 M1.

The firm of Pietro Beretta with plants at Gardone V.T. and Rome has developed a series of modifications of the U.S. Cal. .30 M1 rifle. These modifications consist of rebarreling the rifle to 7.62mm NATO and, in most models, making the weapon capable of automatic as well as semi-automatic fire. Beretta began making the M1 rifle, as did Breda, for the Italian Army. Beretta continued to manufacture the rifle, making quantities for Denmark and Indonesia. Characteristics of some of the M1 conversions are as follows:

	BM 59	BM 59 D	BM 59 GL
Caliber:	.... 7.62mm NATO		
Length, overall:	37.2"	37.2"	43"
Barrel length:	17.7"	17.7"	21"
Weight:	8.15 lbs.	9 lbs.	9 lbs.
Muzzle velocity:	2620 f.p.s.	2620 f.p.s.	2730 f.p.s.
Cyclic rate:	750 RPM	750 RPM	750 RPM
Feed device:	.........20-round, detachable, staggered row box magazine		

BM 59 is the simplest of the selective fire modifications. It has a short 7.62mm barrel, a selective fire trigger mechanism, and a detachable box magazine. The magazine can be loaded by 5-round chargers (stripper clips) while in the weapon.

BM 59 D is a selective fire modification with a new stock and pistol grip, a combination flash suppressor, muzzle brake, and compensator and can be fitted with a bipod.

BM 59 GL is a selective fire conversion with grenade launcher built into the end of the barrel and grenade launcher sight attached. The grenade launcher sight has a cam device which cuts off gas from the gas cylinder piston when it is fixed in the firing position.

Other Beretta M1 modifications are the M1 SL, BM 58, BM 59 R, BM 60 CB, BM 59 Mark I, BM 59 Mark II, BM 59 Mark III, and BM Mark IV.

Beretta has also developed a selective fire, gas operated carbine for the U.S. caliber .30 carbine cartridge. This weapon has the two trigger—one for semi-automatic fire, the other for automatic fire—mechanism characteristic of the Beretta Model 38 submachine gun. The weapon has a cyclic rate of 500 rounds per minute. Beretta also makes two caliber .22 semi-automatic sporting rifles.

297

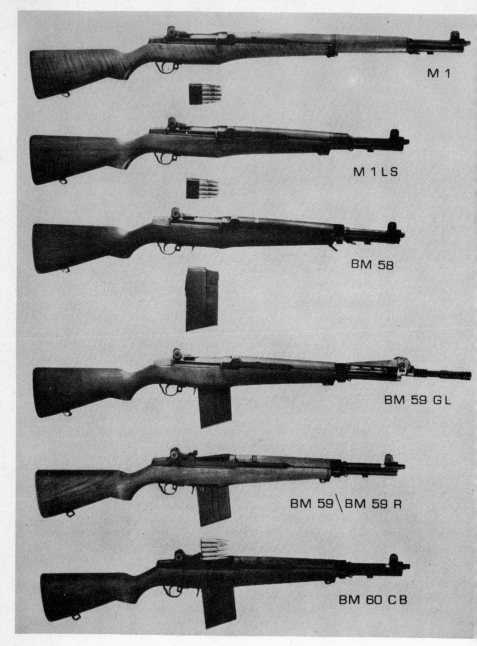

Caliber .30 M1 and Early Beretta Modifications of this Rifle.

FORMER MILITARY RIFLES: The rifle officially adopted for the Regular
Army was the 6.5mm Model 1891 and its many later modifications. None of
these modified types differ essentially from the first model except in sights,
lengths and furniture.

Beretta 7.62mm BM 59 Mark I.

Beretta 7.62mm BM 59 Mark II.

Beretta 7.62mm BM 59 Mark III.

Beretta 7.62mm BM 59 Mark IV.

Italian Mannlicher Carcano Bolt Action Rifles and Carbines

	Rifle M1891	Carbine M1891	Carbine M1891 TS	Carbine M1891/24
Caliber:	6.5mm	6.5mm	6.5mm	6.5mm
Overall length:	50.8"	36.2"	36.2"	36.2"
Barrel length:	30.7"	17.7"	17.7"	17.7"
Feed device:	6-round in line non-detachable box magazine	6-round in line non-detachable box magazine	6-round in line non-detachable box magazine	6-round in line non-detachable box magazine
Sights—front:	Barleycorn	Barleycorn	Barleycorn	Barleycorn
rear:	Tangent w/V notch graduated from 500-2000 M; leaf turned over for battle sight	Tangent w/V notch graduated from 500-1500 M; leaf turned over for battle sight	Tangent w/V notch graduated from 500-1500 M; leaf turned over for battle sight	Tangent w/V notch graduated from 500-1500 M; leaf turned over for battle sight
Weight:	8.6 lbs.	6.6 lbs.	6.9 lbs.	6.9 lbs.
Muzzle velocity:	2395 f.p.s.	2297 f.p.s.	2297 f.p.s.	2297 f.p.s.
Remarks:	Basic rifle, straight bolt handle, uses knife type bayonet	Bayonet permanently attached, bolt handle bent	Uses knife-type bayonet, bolt handle bent	Uses knife-type bayonet, bolt handle bent, except for lower band the same as M1891 TS carbine

	Rifle M1938	Carbine M1938	Carbine M1938 TS	Rifle M1941
Caliber:	7.35mm	7.35mm	7.35mm	6.5mm
Overall length:	40.2"	36.2"	36.2"	46.1"
Barrel length:	20.9"	17.7"	17.7"	27.2"
Feed device:	6-round in line non-detachable box magazine	6-round in line non-detachable box magazine	6-round in line non-detachable box magazine	6-round in line non-detachable box magazine
Sights—front:	Barleycorn	Barleycorn	Barleycorn	Barleycorn
rear:	Fixed	Fixed	Fixed	Tangent w/V notch graduated from 300-1000 M: leaf

Muzzle velocity:	2482 f.p.s.	Approx. 2400 f.p.s.	Approx. 2400 f.p.s.	Approx. 2360 f.p.s.
Remarks:	First of Italian rifles chambered for 7.35mm cartridge, bolt handle bent. Some have knife-type folding bayonet which can be carried folded on rifle or removed	7.35mm version of M1891 carbine, has permanently attached folding bayonet, bolt handle bent	7.35mm version of M1891/24 carbine, uses knife-type bayonet, bolt handle bent	Basically the same as the Rifle M1891 except for length and rear sight

	Rifle M1938	*Carbine M1938*	*Carbine M1938 TS*
Caliber:	6.5mm	6.5mm	6.5mm
Overall length:	40.2"	36.2"	36.2"
Barrel length:	20.9"	17.7"	17.7"
Feed device:	6-round in line non-detachable box magazine	6-round in line non-detachable box magazine	6-round in line non-detachable box magazine
Sights—front:	Barleycorn	Barleycorn	Barleycorn
rear:	Fixed	Fixed	Fixed
Weight:	7.6 lbs.	6.6 lbs.	6.9 lbs.
Muzzle velocity:	2320 f.p.s.	2297 f.p.s.	2297 f.p.s.
Remarks:	6.5mm version of 7.35mm Rifle M1938, made after beginning of World War II	6.5mm version of 7.35mm Carbine M1938, made after beginning of World War II	6.5mm version of 7.35mm Carbine M1938 TS, made after beginning of World War II

Notes: 1. All the pre-World War II 6.5mm weapons have right-hand gain twist (progressive) 19.25 to 8.25; 7.35mm weapons have constant right-hand 10-inch twist. 2. All weapons use 6-round Mannlicher type clips. 3. Some of the Model 1938 weapons were made in 7.92x57mm Mauser for the Germans during World War II. 4. Caliber is marked on sight base of all 1938 series weapons.

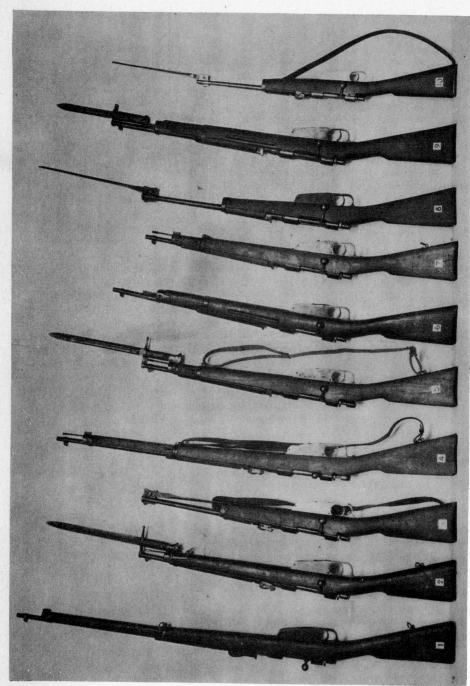

(1) 6.5mm M1891 Rifle. (2) 6.5mm M1891 TS Carbine. (3) 6.5mm M1891 Carbine. (4) 6.5mm 1941 Rifle.
(5) 6.5mm M1891/24 Carbine. (6) 7.35mm 1938 Rifle. (7) 7.35mm M1938 TS Carbine. (8) 7.35mm M1938 Carbine.
(9) 6.5mm M1938 Rifle. (10) Balilla (Youth) Rifle, this is not exactly a rifle; it is a .22.

The Model 38 is basically the Model 1891 designed for a new cartridge and modified accordingly. After Italy entered World War II (1940), supply problems caused a switchback to the 6.5mm cartridge. Therefore many of the M38 weapons were made in 6.5mm.

Model 1891 Series (Including Model 38)

This is a turn-bolt, modified Mauser design with Mannlicher type magazine. The modifications were designed by M. Carcano of the government arsenal at Turin (Torino).

The bolt is of one-piece design with dual opposed locking lugs at the bolt head. The lugs seat in the receiver ring. The bolt head is recessed, cut away on the underside to permit the cartridges to be fed upward from the magazine and under the extractor claw which grips the head of the rimless cartridge as the bolt thrusts forward. A gas vent is drilled through the bolt cylinder about $\frac{1}{2}$ inch behind the bolt face. When the bolt is locked the vent is on the right side of the piece. The bolt handle is straight. The bolt stop operates in the bolt-way in the right side of the receiver bridge.

The striker is of one-piece design with a forward collar to limit forward travel of the firing pin and to serve as the forward compression point for the mainspring. It extends to the rear out of the bolt cylinder. The striker assembly consists of (1) the striker, (2) the mainspring, (3) the safety sleeve, (4) the cocking piece, (5) the cocking piece nut retaining plunger and spring and (6) the cocking piece nut which has a knurled head.

The safety sleeve fits around the striker and inside the bolt cylinder. It has a small stud on the outside which travels in a suitably shaped slot cut near the rear of the bolt cylinder. At the rear of the sleeve a sturdy steel "flag" projects at right-angles to the sleeve to provide the means for operating the safety and to serve as an indicator as to whether the safety is "on" or "off." The rear surface of this "flag" is deeply checkered. The forward edge of the safety sleeve, inside the bolt cylinder, serves as the rear compression point for the mainspring.

The cocking piece slips on the striker behind the safety sleeve. The round striker rod has a flat place on it at this point so that it cannot turn inside the cocking piece. The conventional lug or "nose" on the cocking piece extends, on this rifle, about $2\frac{1}{2}$ inches forward. For about half its length its thickness is reduced so that it can extend forward over the bolt cylinder. It fits into a groove cut into the inside left wall of the receiver bridge to form a guide rib which thus prevents the cocking piece and striker from turning throughout the length of the bolt travel. The conventional cocking nose is a camming surface on the thicker portion of the lug (or guide rib, if you prefer) just at the rear of the bolt cylinder. At the rear end of the rib is inlet the spring loaded plunger which locks the cocking piece nut when the latter has been screwed into place on the threaded end of the striker to complete the assembly.

The rear end of the bolt cylinder has the conventional cut into which the cocking nose moves when the cocking piece and firing pin go forward to fire the piece. The right side of this cut is on an angle corresponding to the angle of the camming surface on the cocking nose. Hence, as the bolt handle is lifted, turning the bolt cylinder to the left, the camming surface on the bolt cylinder engages the camming surface on the cocking nose forcing the cocking piece to

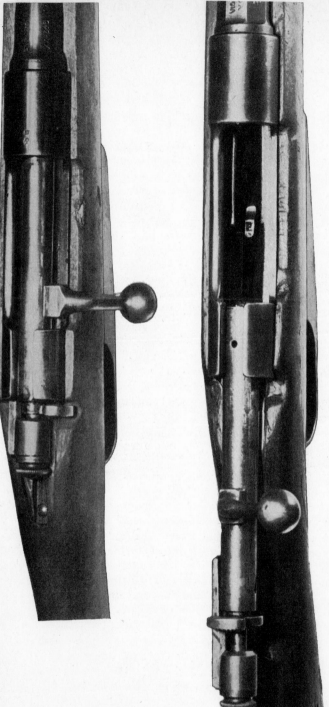

Italian Model 1891. Action Closed and Open. Gas escape port may be seen at forward end of bolt cylinder.

:he rear. As the bolt handle is fully lifted the nose of the cocking piece rides
out of the cocking notch onto the rear, flat face of the bolt cylinder, holding the
striker back with the mainspring about half compressed.

The cocking stud is on the bottom of the cocking piece and moves in a
groove in the tang. As the bolt is pulled fully to the rear the cocking stud is
engaged by the sear rising through the groove in the tang. As the bolt is thrust
forward and turned down, the bolt head locking lugs are cammed forward and
down into the locking recesses in the receiver ring. The forward motion of the
locking lugs as they cam into place completes the compression of the mainspring.

The extractor is a flat spring mounted in the outside of the upper right
quadrant of the bolt cylinder, flush with the outside of the cylinder. L-shaped,
the long shank extends about 2 inches backward from the bolt face along the
upper side of the right-hand locking lug. The short shank then passes to the
right, ahead of the locking lug and forms the extracting claw which grasps
about one quarter of the rim of the case. Obviously much of the strain of extraction must be taken by that portion of the claw which lies at the end of the
long shank—not a particularly rugged type of extractor when a "sticky" case
is encountered.

The ejector is mounted in front of the sear and is activated by the sear spring.
Its upper end passes through a slot in the lower left quadrant of the receiver
at the rear edge of the magazine well. The forward portion of the bolt is
slotted to permit the ejector to emerge through the bolt face and strike the
base of the cartridge. The bottom of this slot forms a ramp toward the rear so
that as the bolt is pushed forward the ejector is pressed downward until it is
riding on the smooth round surface of the bolt cylinder at the time the bolt
handle is turned down to lock the piece.

The trigger pivots on a pin and works in a slot in the sear. It provides the
standard military type double pull. An arm on the right side of the trigger
extends upward and is linked to the bolt stop. Pulling the trigger thus operates
the bolt stop and sear simultaneously. The sear is pivoted to the receiver. The
nose of the sear, which engages the cocking piece, is a separate piece pinned
to the rear of the sear. The forward end of the sear is drilled to receive the
sear spring and the rear tip of the ejector.

The magazine is the projecting Mannlicher type, formed by a continuation
forward of the triggerguard. The elevator bears directly on the bottom cartridge in the clip and does not carry a follower. This is possible because the
Italian cartridge is of the rimless type permitting the use of a straight clip,
eliminating the mechanical complications involved in handling rimmed cartridges requiring the use of a curved clip. Clip capacity is six cartridges.

The stock is of standard one-piece design plus a short handguard. It is
without a pistol grip.

The receiver is of the split-bridge type. The bolt handle turns down well
forward of the bridge and does not bear on it.

Austrian Mannlicher Rifles Used by Italy in World War II

At the close of World War I, Italy received large stores of Austrian supplies.
These included Model 1888 and Model 1895 rifles and carbines in caliber 8mm
Austrian. Many of these arms were used by Italian troops during World War II.

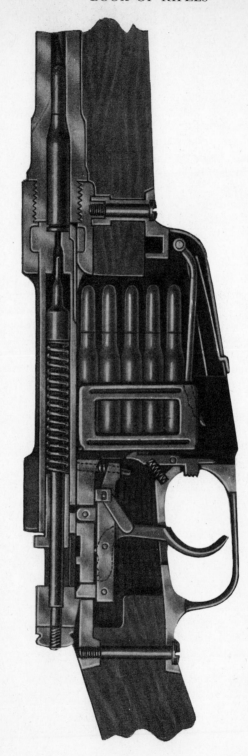

Italian M 91, Sectional Drawing Showing Action Closed and Ready to Fire. Note while clip is of Mannlicher pattern, the bolt head is solid Mauser type.

Italian M 91, Sectional Drawing Showing Action Open and Magazine loaded ready for forward bolt stroke.

Semiautomatic Rifles

While Italy was intensively engaged in experimental work on semiautomatic rifles very early in the present century, no *practical* semiautomatic rifle was ever issued for general troop use. The Cei-Rigotti gas operated conversion of the Model 91, the Austrian Freddi, recoil operated, and the Italian Terni, are seldom encountered and are classifiable as collectors' freaks rather than as standard weapons. The Breda Model P.G. is an early—1935—selective fire weapon. It is an interesting weapon but was not very successful. Limited quantities were used by the Italian Army in 6.5mm and Costa Rico in 7mm Mauser. The Model P.G. is gas operated, 44 inches long, with a barrel 18 inches long and weighs 11.5 pounds empty. An unusual feature of the rifle is that it does not have feed lips on the magazine; they are machined into the receiver. The Cei-Rigotti is of passing interest because it introduced in 1911 a gas operating system similar to that now used in the Russian Tokarev rifles. Limited numbers of Scotti 6.5mm semi-automatic rifles were issued during World War II.

Breda 6.5mm Model G.P. 1935 Semiautomatic Rifle.

Scotti Brescia 6.5mm Model X (10) Semiautomatic Rifle.

Earlier Official Breechloaders. In 1871 Italy adopted a modified Vetterli single shot rifle. This was a Swiss invention. The Italians adapted the rifle to handle a center fire cartridge.

In 1887 this rifle was modified and fitted with a special box magazine.

Rifles of these patterns variously modified were pressed into Italian service in both World Wars I and II.

Italian Model 1871 Vetterli Single Shot

Caliber: 10.4mm
Overall length, rifle without bayonet: 53.5"   *With bayonet attached:* 74"
Overall weight, rifle without bayonet: 9.56 lbs.   *With bayonet attached:* 10.5 lbs.
Type of action: Turnbolt   *Type of bolt:* Lugs at rear.
Barrell Length: 34"   *No. Grooves:* 4   *Direction of Twist:* Right
Bore Diameter: .409"   *Groove Dia.:* .427"   *Rate of Twist:* 26"
Notes:

1. This is the rifle designed by the Swiss Engineer F. Vetterli, but altered to shoot a Center Fire cartridge instead of the Swiss Rim Fire type. The locking lugs are on the rear of the bolt.

ITALY

Italian Model 1871-87 Vetterli-Vitali

Caliber: 10.4mm
Overall length, rifle without bayonet: 54"
Overall weight, rifle without bayonet: 9.9 lbs.
Type of action: Turnbolt
Type of Magazine: Box—Vertical column
Barrel Length: 34"   *No. Grooves:* 4

Bore Diameter: .4095"
      Groove Dia.: .4184"
With bayonet attached: 73"
With bayonet attached. 11.1 lbs.
Capacity: 4
Direction of Twist: Right

Notes:
1. This is the M1871 Single Shot rifle modified to receive the Vitali single column box magazine. This magazine was a modification of the American Lee, differing in form of follower and spring. Spring is a coil centered in the box.
2. There were several minor modifications of this model.

Italian 10.45mm M1871 Cartridge

Other Names: 10.35mm Vetterli, 10.2mm Vet-
  terli
Type: Rimmed, Necked, Centerfire
Overall Length: 2.59"
Average Wt.: 540 gr.
Type Powder: Black
Approximate Chg.: 61.7 gr.
Type Primer: Box

BULLET
Type: Lead (Heel Type)
Diameter: .411"
Weight: 313 gr.
Length: .996"

CARTRIDGE CASE
Length Overall: 1.84"
Length Head to Shoulder: 1.35"
Length of Shoulder: .25"
Length of Neck: .24"
Diameter at Rim: .626"
Diameter at Base: .537"
Diameter at Neck: .437"
Diameter at Shoulder: .517"

BALLISTICS (approximate)
Muzzle Velocity: 1430 f.s.

Notes: Cartridge has not been made in recent years.

Italian 6.5mm M1891 Cartridge

Other Names: 6.5mm Mannlicher Carcano,
  6.5mm Paravicino Carcano
Type: Rimless, Necked, Centerfire
Overall Length: 3.000"
Average Wt.: 350 gr.
Type Powder: Nitrocellulose
Approximate Chg.: 34.6 gr.
Type Primer: Berdan

BULLET
Type: Jacketed, Round Nose
Diameter: .2655"
Weight: 162 gr.
Length: 1.182"

CARTRIDGE CASE
Length Overall: 2.06"
Length Head to Shoulder: 1.64"
Length of Shoulder: .12"
Length of Neck: .30"
Diameter at Rim: .446"
Diameter at Base: .446"
Diameter at Neck: .286"
Diameter at Shoulder: .425"

BALLISTICS (approximate)
Muzzle Velocity: 2395 f.s.
Pressure: About 37,000 lbs./sq. in.

Notes: 1. Only minor ballistic changes were made in this cartridge over the years. It was the basic Italian cartridge in both World Wars.

Italian 7.35mm Cartridge

Name: 7.35mm Italian, 7.35mmx51mm
Type: Rimless-Necked
Overall Length: 2.89"
Type Powder: Smokeless
Type Primer: 2 hole Berdan

BULLET
Type: Metal Cased Pointed Nose
Diameter: .301"
Weight: 128 grs.

CARTRIDGE CASE
Length Overall: 2.021"
Diameter at Rim: .448"
Diameter at Neck: .325"
Diameter at Base: .446"

BALLISTICS
Muzzle velocity: 2482 f.p.s.
Pressure: 30,380 p.s.i.

Italian .22 caliber Trainer. This is a turn-bolt rifle based on the old Italian Vetterli system.

Chapter 41

JAPAN

(Dai Nippon)

GOVERNMENT PLANTS: World War II—Tokyo, Nagoya, Kokura; Jinsen (Inchon), Korea.

PRIVATE PLANTS: World War II—Chuo Kogyo Kabushiki.

PRINCIPAL MILITARY RIFLES: The Japanese Self-Defense Forces are currently equipped with U.S. caliber .30 M1 rifle. According to Japanese journals and papers, development is being conducted at present on a 7.62mm NATO caliber selective fire rifle. There are no producing government arsenals in Japan at present; all production is done in private plants.

FORMER MILITARY RIFLES: M1905 (Type 38) 6.5mm, and M1939 (Type 99) 7.7mm.
The Type 38 (Arisaka) is the basic design. All later models are merely modifications.
M1937 (Type 97) 6.5mm Rifle is generally the same as the Type 38. Somewhat better finished, it has a turned down bolt handle. Issued as a sniper rifle it was equipped with a telescope sight mounted on the left side of the receiver and

Japanese 6.5mm Type 97 Sniper Rifle.

with a steel wire monopod pivoted to the lower band so as to swing forward and upward under the fore-end when not in use.
(In Japanese nomenclature the character "Shiki" is used to indicate model designations. This character means "Type"; it is not therefore technically correct to call Japanese pre-war or World War II weapons "Model." The character for Model is "Kata" and it is possible in some weapons—especially naval weapons—to find the designation Type and Model used together, i.e., Type 2 Model 9.)

Model 1905 (Type 38) 6.5mm

This is a turn bolt rifle of modified Mauser design. It employs the one-piece bolt. The bolt handle is straight.
The Japanese modifications of the standard Mauser were worked out by unknown designers but the Imperial Commission which tested and approved the design was headed by a Colonel Arisaka whose name has ever since been popularly applied to the rifle. Officially it is designated the Type 38 having been adopted in the 38th year of the reign of the Emperor Meiji.
The bolt cylinder carries dual opposed locking lugs near the head of the bolt which lock into recesses in the receiver ring. The face of the bolt is re-

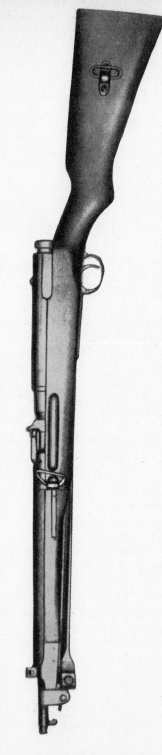

Japanese Type 38 (1905) Caliber 6.5mm Rifle. This is popularly called the Arisaka. The breech locking system and the magazine are modified Mauser pattern. The firing mechanism is a Japanese design of great simplicity.

This arm was made in three standard barrel lengths. Originally these rifles were fitted with sliding bolt covers to keep out dirt. In action they proved noisy and were often removed.

Japanese Type 44 (1911). This is a special cavalry carbine with permanently attached folding bayonet. Mechanically it is the same as the Type 38.

essed for the head of the semi-rim cartridge. The rim extends all around the recess, not being cut away to permit the rim of the cartridge to slip under the xtractor claw as the cartridge feeds upward from the magazine. When the ast cartridge is ejected the magazine follower rises to block the forward motion f the bolt.

A large gas escape vent is provided near the head of the bolt (on the left ide when the bolt is closed) and a vent is also drilled through the top of the eceiver ring. When the bolt is locked this vent is directly over the ejector roove which is cut backward from the face of the bolt and so provides an scape passage out through the top of the receiver ring for gas from a ruptured ase.

A secondary lug positioned about an inch behind the left-hand locking lug erves in a dual capacity. The lip of the receiver, over the magazine well on he left side, is cut away for about an inch to prevent interference with the humb of the right hand when the cartridges are stripped into the magazine rom the charger clip. At this point there is, accordingly, no top surface on the aceway which guides the bolt locking lug in its forward and backward travel. The secondary lug passes this opening and re-engages in the raceway to the ear before the locking lug reaches the opening. A continuous guide for the bolt s thus provided. The other function of the secondary lug is to engage the bolt top which is positioned in an extension of the receiver bridge on the left side.

The bolt stop latch lies along the left side of the receiver bridge and is held y a hinge pin to the rearward extension of the receiver bridge. On the inner urface of the latch is a projection which extends through a slot in the side f the bridge into the bolt lug raceway to act as the bolt stop. Swinging the atch outward withdraws the bolt stop from the raceway.

The striker design represents a major departure from common Mauser ractice. The striker assembly consists of (1) the striker, (2) the mainspring nd (3) the safety spindle. The forward part of the striker is turned down to orm the firing pin. Its after section is of large diameter forming a sliding fit nside the bolt cylinder. This after section is bored out from the rear to take he mainspring and the spindle of the safety. The mainspring forward bearing s against the forward end of its tunnel within the striker. Its rear bearing is igainst the safety spindle. On the rear end of the safety spindle is a short sleeve which extends forward over the rear end of the bolt cylinder. Mortises cut in he inner surface of this sleeve engage tenons on the outer circumference of he rear end of the bolt cylinder when the safety spindle is pressed forward igainst the pressure of the mainspring and given a quarter turn. This com-pletes the bolt assembly.

At the back of the sleeve is a still larger, heavily knurled piece, generally circular but with a lump on its perimeter which serves as a "flag" to indicate the position of the safety while it also provides an excellent pressure point for the thumb in rotating the safety.

The cocking stud is in the usual position on the underside of the striker. There is the customary notch with a camming surface into which the cocking stud moves as the firing pin goes forward and which cams back the cocking stud and striker into the half-cock notch as the bolt handle is lifted. On the

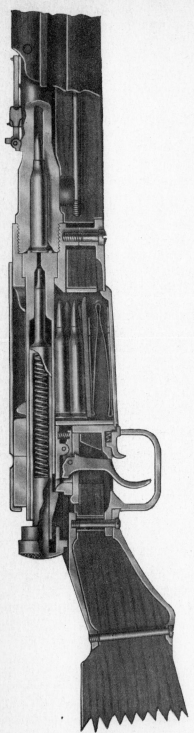

Japanese Service Rifle, sectional drawing showing details of mechanism with rifle ready to fire. Note that mainspring is positioned inside the hollow striker section.

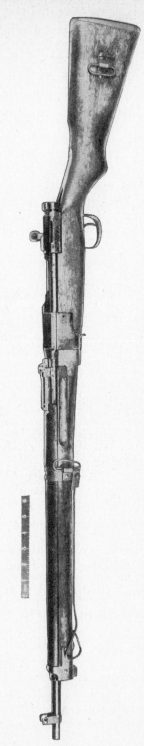

Japanese 7.7mm Type 99 takedown rifle for paratrooper use. Note that it has the folding wire bipod mount originally designed for the Type 99.

forward motion of the bolt the cocking stud is engaged by the sear in the usual manner and is held in the full-cock position.

Forward of the sear the cocking stud travels in the customary groove in the bottom of the receiver. BUT there is no groove to guide the cocking stud to the *rear* of the sear. There is a small stud on the forward end of the safety sleeve spindle. This slips into a longitudinal groove in the striker so that the striker with its cocking stud cannot rotate unless the safety spindle also rotates. When the bolt is fully closed, leaving the cocking stud without any visible means of lateral support, a small stud on the underside of the rim of the large knurled safety engages a groove in the tang. This holds the safety in a vertical position. The striker is unable to turn unless the safety spindle turns, so the cocking stud is held securely in line with the sear nose.

The groove in the tang, in which the stud on the rim of the safety engages, is fish-hook shaped with the "shank" extending forward and the "hook" curving to the left. As the safety is pressed forward against the pressure of the mainspring the safety stud moves forward in its groove. As the safety stud reaches the "hook" the safety is turned clockwise about an eighth turn and the safety stud travels around the curved part of the groove coming to rest at the end of the "hook" where it is held securely by the pressure of the mainspring.

A square notch is cut in the underside of the safety sleeve just to the rear of the cocking stud. As the safety is pressed forward this notch slips over the rear of the cocking stud gripping it on both sides. As the safety is turned clockwise the cocking stud is rotated to the left until it completely clears the sear nose and abuts a shoulder at the rear of the receiver. In this position the striker cannot possibly move forward. It cannot be jarred off and pressing the trigger has no effect because the cocking stud is not in contact with the sear nose.

The extractor is the conventional long, stout, flat spring riding on the outside of the bolt cylinder and extending from the bolt head along the right side of the bolt backward under the receiver bridge which is grooved to permit the longitudinal travel of the extractor as the bolt is operated. Sliding in this groove the extractor is prevented from rotating as the bolt is turned. The extractor is held to the bolt cylinder by a dovetail fitting into a flat spring-steel split ring which encircles the bolt, flush with the surface of the cylinder. The bottom (or right hand) locking lug turns up under the extractor when the bolt handle is lifted in conventional Mauser fashion. The extractor claw grasps about one-fourth of the diameter of the rim of the cartridge. A projection on the underside of the extractor rides in a cannelure cut around the bolt cylinder immediately forward of the locking lugs. This arrangement holds the extractor in place longitudinally.

The rear face of the receiver bridge is formed so that as the bolt handle is lifted it bears against a camming surface forcing it backward and providing primary extraction.

The ejector is a sturdy piece of flat steel mounted under the bolt stop latch and held in place by the same hinge pin. On its forward end a husky finger projects into the bolt raceway just at the rear of the magazine well through a slot in the receiver bridge. The flat steel spring which holds the bolt stop latch also bears on the ejector. As the bolt is pulled fully to the rear the ejector rides

Japanese Type 38 (1905) stock cut down and with a LMG magazine.

Japanese Type 99 (1939) Short Rifle, caliber 7.7mm. This is essentially the same as the earlier models except as modified to receive some mass production parts, and a change of caliber. The cartridge is a .303 rimless which is not interchangeable with others of its caliber.

through slots cut in the secondary and main locking lug, emerging through the head of the bolt to eject the cartridge case.

A bolt cover of thin sheet steel covers the top of the bolt and receiver. It is slotted to permit the lifting of the bolt handle. The cover slides backward and forward with the movement of the bolt. Probably designed to keep the action clear of mud, vegetation and the torrential downpours encountered in jungle fighting, this cover actually proved a noisy nuisance in jungle warfare and was generally discarded by the troops.

The trigger pull is of the standard double pull type. The sear is so pivoted that pulling the trigger raises the forward end of the sear bar and depresses the rearward end, withdrawing the sear nose downward out of contact with the cocking stud. On the forward end of the sear bar is a smaller nose which projects upward through a slot in the bottom of the receiver. When the bolt is fully turned down and the locking lugs are fully engaged, a small groove in the cylinder lies directly over the forward nose of the sear permitting the nose to rise. Until the bolt handle is completely turned down the forward nose of the sear bears against the outer face of the bolt cylinder which holds it depressed into its slot in the bottom of the receiver. In this position the front end of the sear bar cannot rise, so the rear end (the sear nose holding the cocking stud) cannot be depressed. Hence the trigger cannot actuate the sear until the locking lugs are fully engaged.

The magazine is of conventional Mauser design with a removable floor plate held in place by a spring loaded catch operating inside the triggerguard forward of the trigger. The conventional zig-zag ribbon-steel follower spring is mounted on the floor plate and the follower is mounted on top the follower spring. The magazine well is formed by a sheet steel box, open at top and bottom, which fits into grooves in the floor plate. The magazine holds five cartridges and is loaded through the top from a charger clip. Suitable vertical grooves in the receiver bridge are provided to accept the clip and hold it as the cartridges are stripped into the magazine. There is no magazine cut-off. The bolt is held open by the follower when the last cartridge case has been ejected.

The stock is a two-piece design with modified semi grip plus a long handguard extending from the rear sight base forward almost to the muzzle. The stock and handguard are held by conventional upper and lower bands, the upper band carrying the bayonet lug. The lower half of the stock is a separate piece from the remainder of the stock.

An upper tang extends rearward from the receiver over the grip. The triggerguard extends rearward to form a lower tang the full length of the modified pistol grip. In addition to the usual guard screws a third bolt goes through the stock at the rear of the grip to bind together the ends of the upper and lower tangs.

The barleycorn type front sight is fixed in a steel block protected by small wings integral with the front sight barrel band.

The rear sight is a folding leaf generally similar to the Springfield rear sight. When folded down an aperture "battle sight" is in position; early manufacture Type 38s have a "V" notch. A sliding aperture sight is used when the leaf is raised to the vertical. Notches on the outside of the leaf are gripped by spring-loaded catches to hold the sight at the desired range elevation.

Japanese World War II Bolt Action Rifles

Japanese forces were equipped with the 6.5mm Type 38 rifle, Type 38 car-bine, and Type 44 carbine for a long time prior to World War II and large quantities of these weapons were used throughout the war. The older 6.5mm Type 30 rifle and carbine were also frequently encountered during the war. After their experiences in China and Manchuria the Japanese decided they needed a heavier caliber rifle. They had adopted a 7.7mm semi-rimmed cartridge for use in a heavy machine gun—Type 92—in 1932 and wished to standardize ammunition. In April 1938, a formal requirement was laid down for a 7.7mm rifle. Four trial rifles were submitted including one each from Nagoya and Kokura arsenals. Two of the models were carbines modeled on the Type 38 and Type 44 carbines. Proving ground tests at Futsu Proving Ground

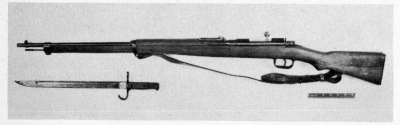

Japanese 6.5mm Type I Rifle. This weapon uses a Mannlicher Carcano type action. The reasons for Japanese use of this rifle have still not been explained.

proved that the recoil of the carbines with 7.7mm cartridges was too great for the average Japanese soldier and all further development of 7.7mm carbines was stopped. A decision was made to make a long and short 7.7mm rifle; the short rifle to be issued to cavalry and special troops. The 7.7mm cartridge used with these weapons was rimless rather than the semi-rimmed 7.7.mm used with the Type 92 machine gun. The 7.7mm rimless cartridge is usable in the machine gun; however the 7.7mm semi-rimless is not usable in the rifles.

Japanese 7.7mm Type 99 Long Rifle.

In 1939 the second test was made at Futsu and it was decided to adopt the Nagoya design "Rifle Plan No. 1" which was generally similar to the design of the 6.5mm Type 38 rifle. Accuracy problems, however, postponed adoption for awhile. In May 1939 the third series of tests was run with the long and short rifles and improved ammunition and satisfactory results were obtained. Service

ests were run at the Infantry and Cavalry school and the rifle was approved
and adopted. In 1941, a Type 99 rifle with 4-power scope was developed for
sniping—this weapon was officially adopted in June 1942.

In 1943 it was decided to develop a substitute Type 99 made of lower grade
materials and simplified for production. The rifle was made without sling
swivels and bolt cover, and inferior steel was used. The chrome plating in the
bore also was dispensed with. The sight scale is graduated only to 300 meters.
The rifle is called the substitute Type 99 and it can be dangerous to the user.

The Japanese had experienced problems with rifles in airborne operations
and in June 1941 a study was started on development of a paratroop rifle. In
October, 1942 the first prototype was completed and tested at Futsu Proving
Ground. This prototype was similar to the Type 99 but was of take-down type.

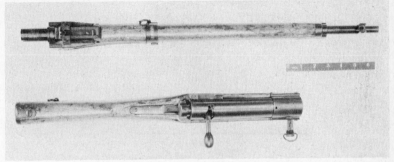

Japanese 7.7mm Type 2 Rifle Taken Down.

After further modification and testing, the weapon was adopted in May 1943
as the Type 2 Paratroop Rifle. In addition a number of Type 38 carbines were
modified for Paratroop use by having folding type stocks fitted. There is also

Japanese 6.5mm Type 38 Carbine, Converted to a Paratrooper Model by Hinging the Stock.

another modification of Type 99 for paratroop use. The two take-down weapons
can be distinguished by the presence of a locking key on the receiver of the
Type 2. This key is not on the modified Type 99.

Japanese Semiautomatic Rifles

Japan experimented with a number of semiautomatic rifles prior to World
War II. Among these was the U.S. designed Pedersen with a rotary magazine
which was experimented with by the Japanese soon after it was developed in
the United States. Original Japanese experiments in this field started in 1931,
but development of prototypes was discontinued in 1937. In March 1941 a new

program for development of a semiautomatic rifle was begun. Kokura Arsenal
developed several types of gas and recoil operated rifles, but none was completely successful. By March 1944 the demand for a semiautomatic by field
forces was insistent. This was undoubtedly due to the effect of the firepower
of the U.S. M1 rifle on Japanese forces. The Navy took the initiative to meet

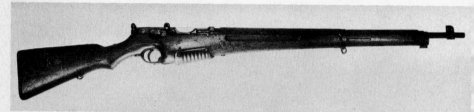

Japanese Copy of Pedersen Semiautomatic Rifle. This weapon has a rotary type magazine.

this demand, and developed a modified copy of the U.S. M1 rifle in 7.7mm
caliber. In April 1945 prototypes were completed and tested. Tests were not
completely satisfactory, being marked by a large amount of parts breakage—

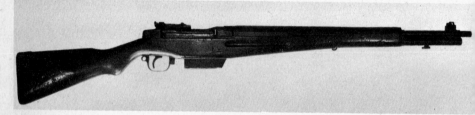

Japanese 7.7mm Type 5 Semiautomatic Rifle. This is the Japanese Navy copy of the M1.

Japanese ordnance metallurgy was at its low point at this time—and by loading and feeding problems. Disregarding these problems, the Japanese adopted
the rifle as the "Type 5 automatic rifle." It was never put into mass production
and only about 20 of these weapons were built.

Japanese 7.7mm Type 5 Rifle

Caliber: 7.7mm
Overall weight: 9.12 lbs.
Overall length: 43.25"
Type of action: Gas operated, semiautomatic
Type of bolt: 1 piece, rotating head

Type of magazine: Integral, box, staggered
  column; Capacity: 10
Barrel length: 43.25"
No. grooves: 5

Japanese "Simple" Rifles

As invasion loomed on the horizon in 1945, the Japanese, as the Germans,
started to develop the cheapest, most simple materiel they could to arm their
failing armies and civilians. The Japanese even developed cross-bows and long-
bows to be used with explosive arrows! Three emergency rifles were designed
and prototypes were produced. A 7.7mm bolt action single shot which could
be produced on a lathe was the first of these weapons. It was intended to issue
these weapons to front-line defense troops. The 7.7mm cartridge proved to be
too powerful for this weapon and it was redesigned for the 8mm pistol cartridge.

Comparison of Japanese Type 99 with action open and closed. Note that the royal chrysanthemum has been filed off the top of the receiver. The Japanese so mutilated their rifles before surrendering them, feeling it a disgrace to turn them in with the Imperial insignia. When used with proper ammunition, this is a very rugged military rifle. For strength, simplicity of design and for general use it is one of the simplest and most efficient of all the Mauser rifle variants.

Tests of this prototype were successful. The last type was made similar to a percussion rifle from an ordinary piece of pipe 13mm in diameter. It was loaded with black powder and the projectile was made from steel stock cut in 15mm lengths. A percussion type hammer and nipple type firing mechanism was used.

Earlier Official Breechloaders

The first Japanese service rifle, the Type 13 single shot Murata in 11mm caliber was modified in 1887 to convert it to a tube repeater. In 1897, a new rifle was adopted to use a new 8mm rim cartridge—the Type 20. This arm was the major infantry rifle of the Japanese in their war with China in 1894.

The next rifle was the Type 30, a rifle which resembles the Type 38 externally and in caliber.

Notes on Type 30 (Original Arisaka)

As a result of deficiencies found in field service during the war with China, the Japanese proceeded to develop a new design in a smaller caliber. The result was the first rifle credited to Colonel Arisaka (head of the Rifle Commission), the Type 30. This rifle was listed officially as the Rifle Meiji (also spelled "Meidje", when transliterated) indicating that it was adopted in the 30th year of the reign of the Emperor of that name. This was the rifle used in the war with Russia.

This rifle followed most of the Mauser design. It is a turning bolt action loaded with a Mauser type clip.

The rear end of the bolt, however, differs radically from that of any other rifle. A broad flange comprises its extreme rear and protects the guide grooves in the receiver, while it also serves as a gas shield in the event of a blown head or primer. An opening is milled just ahead of this flange and extends about 1" forward in the side of the bolt cylinder. Its front face has a curved cut which provides the rearward camming movement for primary extraction as the bolt handle is lifted. At the end of this cut is the safety notch.

The extractor has a heavy projecting claw resembling the Spanish Mauser. It is recessed in the head of the bolt. It is supported between the head and the bolt proper.

The bolt assembly consists of the striker and mainspring inserted in the front of the bolt cylinder. The rear of the striker has two wide grooves. A rear bushing slips over the striker.

Two semi-cylindrical units form a striker nut. The safety sleeve is a final unit inside the bolt itself.

The receiver bridge is solid as in standard Mauser practice. It extends to the rear and provides an L-shaped slot in which the bolt handle turns. When the bolt handle is lifted, the firing pin is cammed back into the bolt cylinder in Mauser fashion and the mainspring is partly compressed. The complete compression however occurs when the sear nose catches the cocking stud and holds completely locked. The magazine is also very close to the Spanish Mauser in design. The zigzag spring within it however is of round wire construction. it as the bolt is thrust forward during the closing motion. The trigger mechanism follows that of the Spanish Mauser to prevent firing before the arm is

:ompletely locked. The magazine is also very close to the Spanish Mauser in
lesign. The zigzag spring within it, however, is round wire construction.

The ejector and bolt stop are the same as in the Roumanian Mannlicher.

The rifle has a long two-piece stock with semi pistol grip. As in later Japanese
lesigns, the butt is of built-up construction. Its lower half is a separate piece
of wood stretching to the beginning of the grip section and is dovetailed, pinned
and glued to the stock proper.

The caliber is 6.5mm (.256 inch). The bottle necked cartridge case is of semi-
rim construction. (Note: The cartridge used by the Japanese at the beginning
of World War II was only an improved version of this cartridge.)

Japanese 11mm Type 13 Murata Rifle.

Japanese Type 13 (Model 1887) Murata

Caliber: 11mm
Overall length, rifle without bayonet: 50.25"
Overall weight, rifle without bayonet: 9 lbs.

Type of action: Turnbolt
Barrel Length: Approx. 32"
Type of bolt: 2 piece—Rotating head

Japanese 8mm Murata Type 20 (M1887) Cartridge

Type: Rimmed, Necked, Centerfire
Overall Length: 2.90"
Average Wt.: 468 grs.
Type Powder: Nitrocellulose
Approximate Chg.: 36 grs.
Type Primer: Berdan

BULLET
Type: Jacketed, Flat Nose
Diameter: .315"
Weight: 238 grs.
Length: 1.18"
CARTRIDGE CASE
Diameter at Base: .492"
BALLISTICS (approximate)
Muzzle Velocity: 1850 f.s.

Notes: Cartridge virtually unknown. Collector's item only.

Japanese Type 20 (1887) Rifle

Caliber: 8mm
Overall length: 47.5"
Overall weight: 8.68 lbs.
Type of action: Turnbolt

Type of magazine: Tubular; Capacity 8
Barrel length: 29.5"
Type of bolt: 2 piece, rotating head

Japanese 8mm Type 20 Rifle. This was the first Japanese small-bore magazine rifle

Japanese 8mm Type 27 Carbine.

Japanese Type 30 (1897) Arisaka

Caliber: 6.5mm
Overall length, rifle without bayonet: 50.2″
Overall weight, rifle without bayonet: 8.5 lbs.
Type of action: Turnbolt
Type of Magazine: Box—Staggered column
Barrel Length: 31.25″　　*No. Grooves:* 6

Bore Diameter: .256″　　*Groove Dia.:* .269′
Type of bolt: 1 piece—Rotating head
Capacity: 5
　Direction of Twist: Right
　Rate of Twist: 7.88″

Japanese 6.5mm Type 30 Carbine.

Japanese Type 38 (1905) Arisaka

Caliber: 6.5mm
Overall length, rifle without bayonet: 50.2″
Overall weight, rifle without bayonet: 9.25 lbs.
Type of action: Turnbolt
Type of magazine: Box—Staggered column
Barrel length: 31.4″　　*No. Grooves:* 4 or 6
Bore diameter: .256″　　*Groove dia.:* .262″

With bayonet attached: 65″
With bayonet attached: 10.4 lbs.
Type of bolt: 1 piece—Rotating head
Capacity: 5
　Direction of Twist: Right
　Rate of Twist: 7.88″ (Early Mfg.)
　　　9″ (Late Mfg.)

Notes:

1. Groove depths, rates of twist and sight equipment have varied considerably with time and place of manufacture.

2. Dust cover sliding with bolt was standard equipment, but since the cover is readily removed, rifles will often be found without cover.

3. Rifles with 25 inch barrels, overall length 44.25 inches, weight without bayonet 8.6 pounds were also issued.

4. From the standpoint of design simplicity and strength this is one of the best bolt actions ever made when in good condition.

Japanese 6.5mm Type 38 Cartridge

CARTRIDGE

Name: 6.5mm Japanese (Type 38)
Type: Semi-rimless-Necked-Centerfire
Overall Length: 3.00″
Type Powder: Nitrocellulose
Approximate Chg.: 33 grs.
Type Primer: Berdan

BULLET

Type: Full Jacketed-Pointed Bullet
Diameter: .262″
Weight: 139 gr.
Length: 1.28″

CARTRIDGE CASE

Length Overall: 2.00″
Length of Shoulder: 1.53″
Diameter at Rim: .4761″
Diameter at Neck: .291″
Length Head to Shoulder: .20″
Length of Neck: .27″
Diameter at Base: .449″
Diameter at Shoulder: .414″

BALLISTICS (approximate)

Muzzle Velocity: 2500 f.p.s.
Pressure: 38,000 p.s.i.

Japanese Type 38 (1905) Carbine

Caliber: 6.5mm
Overall length, rifle without bayonet: 34.2"
Overall weight, rifle without bayonet: 7.3 lbs.
Type of action: Turnbolt
Type of Magazine: Box, staggered column
Barrel Length: 19.2"   *No. Grooves:* 4
Bore Diameter: .256"   *Groove Dia.:* .262"

With bayonet attached: 52"
With bayonet attached: 8.5 lbs.
Type of bolt: 1 piece—Rotating head
Capacity: 5
Direction of Twist: Right
Rate of Twist: 9"

Notes:

1. This is merely the Pattern 38 Rifle cut down to Carbine size. Sling attachment is on side of Carbine.

Japanese Type 44 (1911) Cavalry Carbine

Caliber: 6.5mm
Overall length, rifle without bayonet: 38.5"
Overall weight, rifle without bayonet: 8.37 lbs.
Type of action: Turnbolt
Type of Magazine: Box—Staggered column

Barrel Length: 19.9"   *No. Grooves:* 4
Bore Diameter: .256"   *Groove Dia.:* .262"
Type of bolt: 1 piece—Rotating head
Capacity: 5
Direction of Twist: Right

Notes:

1. This is a modified Carbine version of the M. 1905.
2. It is fitted with a special folding skewer type bayonet. A special locking standard is provided on the muzzle cap to hinge the bayonet so it can be folded back when not in use. This Carbine was issued to mounted troops.
3. Carbines of this pattern are generally better made and finished than later Japanese rifles.

Japanese Type 99 (1939) Short Rifle

Caliber: 7.7mm
Overall weight, rifle without bayonet: 8.8 lbs.
Type of action: Turnbolt
Type of Magazine: Box—Staggered column
Barrel Length: 25.75"   *No. Grooves:* 4
Bore Diameter: .303"   *Groove Dia.:* .315"

Overall length, rifle without bayonet: 44"
With bayonet attached: 9.8 lbs.
Type of bolt: 1 piece—Rotating head
Capacity: 5
Direction of Twist: Right
Rate of Twist: 9.75"

Notes:

1. This is a modified form of the M. 38.
2. Late models with cast steel receivers are dangerous.

CARTRIDGE

Name: 7.7mm Japanese (Type 99)
Type: Rimless, Necked, Centerfire.
Overall Length: 3.15"
Average Wt.: 415 grs.
Type Powder: Nitrocellulose
Type Primer: Berdan

BULLET

Type: Full Jacketed-Flat based-Pointed
 bullet
Diameter: .310"
Weight: 184 grs.
Length: 1.225"

CARTRIDGE CASE

Length Overall: 2.27"
Length of Shoulder: .14"
Diameter at rim: .476"
Diameter at Neck: .337"
Length Head to Shoulder: 1.84"
Length of Neck: .29"
Diameter at Base: .473"
Diameter at Shoulder: .431"

BALLISTICS (approximate)

Muzzle Velocity: 2390 f.p.s.

Chapter 42
KOREA, NORTH

GOVERNMENT PLANTS: Rifle production facilities exist.

PRIVATE PLANTS: None.

PRINCIPAL MILITARY RIFLES: Soviet-designed 7.62mm AK-47 rifle and 7.62mm SKS carbine.

During the Korean War the North Korean Army was equipped with the Soviet 7.62mm M1891 Mosin Nagant rifle and its later variants—the M1891/30 rifle and the M1938 and M1944 carbines. Quantities of Japanese World War II 7.7mm type 99 rifles were also encountered, principally in the hands of Communist guerrillas. North Korea made 7.62mm PPSh M1941 submachine guns during the Korean War and is now making the AK-47 assault rifle.

North Korean Copy of Soviet 7.62mm AK-47 Assault Rifle.

Chapter 43

MEXICO

(Republica Mexicana)

GOVERNMENT PLANTS: Mexico City Arsenal.

PRIVATE PLANTS: None of consequence.

PRINCIPAL MILITARY RIFLES: Cal. .30 M1, cal. .30 M1954.

FORMER MILITARY RIFLES: Various Mauser patterns, 7mm. Chiefly 1895, 1902, 1912, and 1936. Current manufacture is Mexican, but Spanish and German makes are also in use.

Mexican Mausers

In 1895 Mexico officially adopted for military service a 7mm Mauser rifle, practically identical with the Spanish Model 1893.

The photographs, drawings and description of the Spanish Model 1893 (see *Spain*) effectively covers the Mexican Model 1895.

The 7mm M1902 Mexican Mauser was quite similar to the M1895. The principal difference is that a 98-type bolt is used on the M1902, as opposed to the 93 type bolt used on the M1895. Both of these rifles have straight stocks, leaf-type rear sights, and bayonet lugs on the bottom of their upper bands. The 7mm Model 1912 Mauser is similar to the German Gewehr 98; the principal

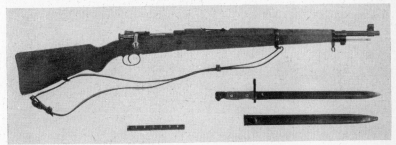

Mexican 7mm M1936 Mauser Rifle.

differences are the use of a tangent-type rear sight and longer handguard on the Mexican weapon. The 7mm M1936 is also a Mauser but in outward details it is patterned on the U.S. M1903 Springfield. It has a Springfield-type cocking piece, bands, and stacking swivel. This rifle has the "short" Mauser action and is of very good manufacture. A considerable quantity of these rifles was sold in this country several years ago. Since World War II, Mexico has adopted the U.S. .30-06 cartridge. In 1954 Mexico introduced a new Mauser chambered for that cartridge; this weapon is similar to the M1936 but has an aperture-type rear sight, similar to that of the U.S. M1903A3, mounted on the receiver bridge.

Mexico in the past has purchased comparatively small quantities of rifles from many different sources. This was particularly true during the time of the Mexican revolution, which with attendant troubles ran from 1911 through

327

World War I. As an example, Mexico purchased a quantity of Japanese Type 38 rifles chambered for the 7mm cartridge. These rifles have the Mexican escutcheon stamped on the receiver; they make a good collector's piece since they are quite rare. Mexico has also developed a number of shoulder weapons

Mexican Caliber .30-06 M1954 Rifle.

which have been made in limited quantities. There is, for example, a .30-06 bolt action carbine of postwar design and construction.

	M1936 Rifle	*M1954 Rifle*
Caliber:	7mm	.30-06
System of operation:	.... manually operated bolt action	
Length, overall:	42.9"	Approx. 48"
Barrel length:	19.29"	24"
Weight:	8.3 lbs.	9.7 lbs.
Feed device:	.... 5-round, staggered-row, integral box magazine	
Sights—front:	.... Hooded barleycorn	
rear:	Tangent w/V notch	Ramp-type aperture
Muzzle velocity:	Approx. 2650 f.p.s.	Approx. 2800 f.p.s.

Semiautomatic Rifles

The Mondragon semiautomatic gas operated rifle invented in Mexico, and used to some extent by the Germans in World War I, has been discussed in Part I. It is purely a collection piece today.

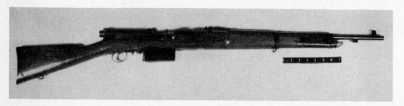

Mexican 7mm M1908 Mondragon. One of the earliest successful semiautomatic rifles.

A new 7mm semiautomatic rifle of gas operated type was manufactured to a very limited extent in Mexico in recent years. It is a product of the engineering genius of Rafael Mendoza, a designer of remarkable ability.

Aside from the Government Arms Factory, there is no rifle production in Mexico. Arms are imported from the United States and from the Continent.

EARLIER OFFICIAL BREECHLOADERS: 11mm Spanish Remington (see *Spain*).

The 1873 Winchester .44-40 was extensively used by revolutionaries.

Mexican M. 1902 Rifle. This is essentially the earlier M. 1895 Mexican pattern except that it uses the 3-lug German Gew. 98 pattern bolt. The M. 1895 uses the Spanish Mauser 1893 type bolt with 2 lugs. These rifles were made by D W M and Steyr.

Mexican Mendoza 7mm Carbine.

Chapter 44

NETHERLANDS

(Koningkrijk Der Nederlanden)

GOVERNMENT PLANTS: Hembrug Armory.

PRIVATE PLANTS: Nederlandsche Wapenen Munitiefabriek N. V. "De Kruithoorn" (NWM), S'Hertogenbosch, Holland.

PRINCIPAL MILITARY RIFLES: 7.62mm NATO "FAL" Light Automatic Rifle.
Rifle Cal. .30M1 and British rifles were also in service.

FORMER RIFLES: 6.5mm M1895 Rifle and carbines.

FN 7.62mm NATO Light Automatic Rifle. This version was made for the Netherlands. Attention is called to the bipod and the metal handguards.

Description of the Model 1895 Netherlands (Mannlicher) Caliber 6.5mm

This is a turn bolt rifle with Mannlicher type magazine. It very closely resembles the Roumanian Mannlicher for which sectional views are shown under *Roumania*.

The bolt is of two-piece design, the removable bolt head being inserted into the front of the bolt cylinder and held in place by tenons. Dual opposed locking lugs are carried on the forward end of the bolt cylinder where they turn into locking recesses in the receiver ring. The bolt handle is straight. A rib extends forward from the bolt handle on the outside of the bolt cylinder to serve as a guide as the bolt is drawn back through the split bridge of the receiver.

The striker is of one-piece design with a collar on the forward end which serves as the forward bearing for the mainspring and also serves to limit the forward travel of the striker. A flat place on the collar bears on a similar flat in the non-rotating bolt-head to prevent the striker assembly from turning as the bolt handle is lifted. The rear of the mainspring bears against the rear of the bolt cylinder. The threaded rear end of the striker projects through a hole in the rear of the bolt cylinder for the attachment of the cocking piece. The cocking piece is of conventional design with a knurled rim but is difficult to get hold of because the safety covers part of it. A stud on the underside of the cocking piece works in standard fashion in a groove in the tang of the receiver. The stud engages the sear as the bolt is thrust forward, cocking the piece. The safety,

urning from left to right to the "safe" position, is mounted on the cocking
piece. The safety acts by camming the cocking piece slightly to the rear out of
ngagement with the sear. The safety can only be applied when the gun is
ocked.

The extractor is a spring loaded steel claw fitted into the bolt head.

The ejector is mounted to slide in the bolt head. A stud on the ejector fits
n an undercut groove in the bolt head while a projection on the ejector
moves in a groove in the left side of the receiver to prevent the bolthead from
urning. As the bolt is drawn to the rear the ejector hits the bolt stop, pushing
he ejector smartly forward against the base of the fired cartridge case. The nose
of the ejector is beveled so that, as the next cartridge is forced upward from
he magazine, the head of the cartridge forces the ejector back into its slot in
he bolt head.

The bolt stop lug in this design is a separate unit pivoted on a vertical pin
n the left side of the receiver. It has a point which projects into the groove in
he receiver in which the left-hand bolt locking lug travels. Pressing the thumb
piece which projects from the rear end of the receiver on the left side withdraws the bolt stop from the path of the locking lug and permits withdrawal
o the rear, out of the receiver, of the bolt assembly.

The sear nose projects through the customary slot into the groove in the
ang in line with the cocking piece stud. The sear is pivoted on a pin to the
rear of the magazine and on the under face of the receiver. The sear spring
s a spiral spring. The trigger operates in a fork in the back end of the sear.
It is pivoted on a separate trigger pin. Two ribs on its upper end bear alternately
against the lower side of the receiver to furnish the standard military double
pull.

The receiver is of the split bridge type, the bolt handle locking down against
he forward edge of the receiver bridge. A guideway is milled into the receiver
at the forward edge of the magazine well to guide the cartridge into the chamber.

The triggerguard extends forward to form the protruding magazine well. A
coil-spring loaded catch in the rear wall of the magazine well projects to catch
above a projection on the back of the cartridge clip. It thus holds the loaded
clip down against the upward pressure of the elevator as long as any cartridges
remain in the clip. When the last cartridge has been stripped from the clip
nto the chamber there is no longer any upward pressure and the clip falls
through the bottom of the magazine well. The lower portion of the clip catch
protrudes through a slot in the forward circle of the triggerguard to form the
clip release latch. Pressure on this latch releases the loaded or partly loaded clip
which is pressed out through the top of the magazine by the elevator.

Because the bottom of the magazine well must be open to permit the empty
clip to drop out of the rifle, an "elevator" instead of the Mauser-type "follower"
is employed to raise the cartridges into place to be chambered by the bolt. The
"elevator" assembly consists of (1) the flat elevator spring, pivoted to the forward, lower corner of the magazine well and (2) the steel "elevator" bar which
is also pivoted to the forward, lower corner of the magazine well. The upper
end of the elevator is finished on an arc so as to bear properly on the bottom
cartridge throughout its upward travel. The rimmed cartridge requires a curved
cartridge clip. The top cartridge, ready to be chambered must always be held in

Netherlands (Dutch) Model 1895 Rifle. This is a turn-bolt Mannlicher design. The bolt has a removable head. Magazine must be loaded with a Mannlicher clip which holds 5 cartridges of 6.5 mm caliber. Otherwise all Dutch rifles and carbines of this type are mechanically the same. Ejector forms may vary in rifles manufactured at different periods.

Netherlands Model 1895 Mannlicher

Caliber: 6.5mm
Overall length, rifle without bayonet: 51"
Overall weight, rifle without bayonet: 9.3 lbs.
Type of action: Turnbolt
Type of Magazine: Box—Vertical column
Barrel Length: 31.1"   No. Grooves: 4
Bore Diameter: .256"   Groove Dia.: .269"

With bayonet attached: 61"
With bayonet attached: 9.9 lbs.
Type of bolt: 1 piece—Rotating Head
Capacity: 5
Direction of Twist: Right
Rate of Twist: 7.87"

ı horizontal position. Hence the angle at which the bottom cartridge in the clip lies changes steadily as it works its way to the top, under pressure from the elevator. The elevator, swinging from its hinge-pin at the lower forward corner of the magazine well, smoothly follows the curving upward trip of the cartridge. The straight upward thrust of the Mauser type follower, used so successfully with rimless cases, would cause jamming difficulties with the rimmed cases and curving clip.

The stock on the Netherlands Model 1895 is of one piece design, plus hand-guard. The grip is straight with no pistol grip attempted.

The front sight is of the ramp and barleycorn type, the ramp (front sight stud) being fixed on the barrel without barrel band. The sight is removable, being laterally dovetailed into the ramp.

The rear sight is of the tangent leaf type with open notch.

Quantities of these rifles were put to use by the Germans in World War II, and many were brought back as souvenirs. Many of these bear the name 'Hembrug" and a date on the receiver.

Other Dutch Weapons

The rifle just described is also encountered in two common carbine forms in Holland—the standard carbine and the Gendarmerie carbine. The latter is fitted with a permanently attached rod-type bayonet which pivots backward on a hinge-pin on the upper band near the muzzle so as to lie under the barrel in a recess in the stock. The Gendarmerie carbine was developed primarily for

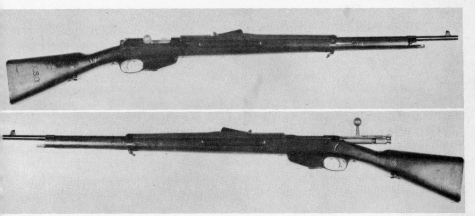

Dutch 7.92mm M1917 Mannlicher Rifle. This rifle is chambered for the 7.92mm rimmed cartridge.

colonial use. Carbines having the left side of the magazine protected by wood stock were so designed for mounted use, the stock protecting the magazine and preventing it from catching when the carbine was jerked out of the leather saddle bucket.

The Dutch used the 7.92mm rimmed cartridge (7.9x57R) in Schwarzlose and Lewis machine guns. During World War I they developed a version of the M1895 rifle for this cartridge; this weapon is the 7.92mm M1917 rifle and was apparently made in small quantities.

Model 1895 Variants in World War II

(1) Karabijn No. 1 O. M. This is the M 1895 system with 17.68″ barrel 37.5″ overall length. Sling swivel on left side of forearm and butt. Left side of magazine is entirely covered with wood. Short forestock without upper guards

(2) Karabijn No. 1. This is the same as the No. 1 O. M. above except that the stock is slightly shorter (overall length 37.0″). The fore-end is rounded like a sporting rifle.

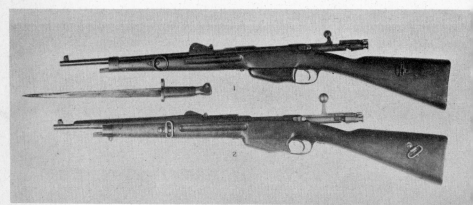

Top Dutch 6.5mm No. 1 O.M. Mannlicher Carbine. Bottom: Dutch 6.5mm No. 3 Carbine

(3) Karabijn No. 3 and No. 3. O. M. These forms have underslings and upper handguards. The upper guard extends farther forward than the forestock Mechanically they are the M1895 design.

(4) Karabijn No. 4 and 4. O. M. These variants have side slings, wood covered magazine on left side, and upper handguard approximately the same length as the forestock.

Note: Under the name of "Geweer tot kamerschietoefeningen," the Dutch used a practice rifle of 5.5mm caliber. In exterior appearance and method of operation it is the same as the standard M95 rifle. Barrel length and overall length are the same. Weight is 10.42 lbs. The rifling rate of twist is 8″ to the right. The special magazine is loaded with 5 cartridges on a clip.

Johnson Semiautomatic Rifle

In 1940 a quantity of Johnson semiautomatic rifles were ordered for the Netherlands-Indies armies. Another lot was purchased in the following year for the Netherlands Royal Navy. These were first manufactured in 1941 at Providence, Rhode Island. The model is listed as the 1941.

These rifles were manufactured for the Netherlands in caliber .30-06 U. S. Since the same model was manufactured in the same caliber for use by U. S. Marine groups, the rifle is thoroughly discussed under United States.

EARLIER OFFICIAL BREECHLOADERS: In 1871 the Beaumont single shot bolt action rifle was adopted in caliber .433 Beaumont. This was superseded in 1888 by a modification which combined the Beaumont bolt and the Italian Vitali magazine.

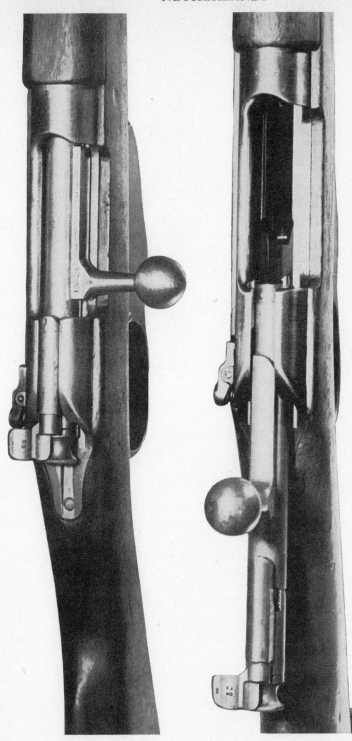

Netherlands Model 1895 Rifle, action open. This is a split bridge receiver design, with bolt handle locking down forward of receiver bridge. Dual lugs on the bolt to the rear of the bolt head lock into recesses in the receiver ring.

Except for minor details, this rifle is the same as the Roumanian Mannlicher Model 1893. Ejectors differ. The major apparent difference is in the strengthening rib seen on the bolt cylinder forward from the handle. The Roumanian does not normally have this rib.

War I rifles usually have the name HEMBRUG on receiver.

Model 1871 (Beaumont) Cal. 11mm (.43)

The Beaumont is a turning bolt action rifle with an unusual mainspring design. Instead of the standard coil mainspring, the mainspring in the Beaumont is a V-spring mounted inside a hollow two-piece bolt handle. While this design made for simplicity, and was a feature of several later rifles such as the Belgian Marga repeating rifle, in actual practice it was not a successful form. The locking lugs are carried far back on the bolt cylinder. The bolt handle is at the extreme rear of the cylinder. The rear section of the handle screws to the front section along its length, thereby permitting insertion of the mainspring before the two halves of the bolt handle are fastened with the screw. The striker pin traveling through the bolt had its head resting against a long arm of the mainspring. Thus when the trigger is pulled, pressure from the forward end of the long V-leaf can drive the striker ahead through the center of the bolt cylinder, which is hollowed out only sufficiently to permit insertion of the very light weight striker. While beautifully simple, the design is not rugged.

Netherlands Model 1871 Beaumont Single Shot

Caliber: 11mm
Overall length, rifle without bayonet: 52"
Overall weight, rifle without bayonet: 9.6 lbs.
Type of action: Turnbolt
Barrel Length: 32.8"   *No. Grooves:* 4
Bore Diameter: .433"   *Groove Dia.:* .457"
Notes:

With bayonet attached: 72"
With bayonet attached: 10.4 lbs.
Type of bolt: 2 piece—Rotating Head
    Direction of Twist: Right
    Rate of Twist: 29.5"

1. This rifle was invented by the Dutch engineer Beaumont in 1870.
2. Mainspring is inside the 2-piece bolt handle.

Netherlands 11mm M1871-1888

Other Names: 11mm Dutch Beaumont
Type: Rimmed, Necked, Centerfire
Overall Length: 2.537"
Average Wt.: .664 gr.
Type Powder: Black
Approximate Chg.: 77.1 gr.
Type Primer: Berdan (two hole)

BULLET

Type: Lead (heel type), paper patch on heel
Diameter: .456" (less patch)
Weight: 345 gr.
Length: .950"

CARTRIDGE CASE

Length Overall: 2.01"
Length Head to Shoulder 1.36"
Length of Shoulder: .13"
Length of Neck: .52"
Diameter at Rim: .664"
Diameter at Base: .576"
Diameter at Neck: .484"
Diameter at Shoulder: .525"

BALLISTICS (approximate)

Muzzle Velocity: 1476 f.s

Notes: Cartridge has not been made in recent years.

Beaumont-Vitali Repeating Rifle

In 1888 Holland modified the Beaumont single shot rifle to accommodate the Italian Vitali box magazine inserted in the action from below. This magazine is a modified form of the American Lee single column vertical type. It differs in the form of the magazine spring, which is a coil mounted in the center of the box and projecting well below the line of maximum follower compression.

The cartridge used and the ballistics are practically the same as for the single shot, although it must be noted that minor modifications ballistically

vere made in later times. None show any wide diversion, however, or are of
any particular importance.

Except that the rifle weighs 6 ounces more and is modified as required to ac-
ept and feed from the 4 shot box magazine, the repeater does not differ me-
hanically from the single shot.

Netherlands 6.5mm Mannlicher

CARTRIDGE

Name: Netherlands 6.5mm Mannlicher
Other Names: 6.5X53R Mannlicher
Type: Rimmed, Necked, Centerfire
Overall Length: 3.05"
Average Wt.: 338 grs.
Type powder: Nitrocellulose
Approximate Chg.: 35.2 grs.

BULLET

Type: Jacketed, Round Nose
Diameter: .263"
Weight: 162 grs.
Length: 1.22"

CARTRIDGE CASE

Length Overall: 2.11"
Length Head to Shoulder: 1.65"
Length of Shoulder: .14"
Length of Neck: .32"
Diameter at Rim: .527"
Diameter at Base: .450"
Diameter at Neck: .294"
Diameter at Shoulder: .421"

BALLISTICS (approximate)

Muzzle Velocity: 2400 f.s.
Pressure: 47,000 p.s.i.

Note: 1. This cartridge is interchangable with the Roumanian 6.5mm Mannlicher cartridge.

Chapter 45

NORWAY

(Norge)

GOVERNMENT PLANTS: Kongsberg Vapenfabrikk.

PRIVATE PLANTS: H. Larsen (Drammen). No large scale manufacturing o small arms. Imports usually from Denmark, Finland, Sweden, Germany.

PRINCIPAL MILITARY RIFLES: U.S. Rifle Cal. .30 M1; various other rifle such as British No. 4s, German Kar 98k's, etc., are held in reserve.

FORMER MILITARY RIFLES: 6.5mm Krag Jorgensen M1894 and it variants.

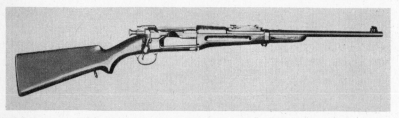

Norwegian 6.5mm M1895 Krag Jorgensen Carbine.

The Norwegian Army realized at the end of World War II that thei weapons situation was chaotic. While a number of Norwegian Krag service rifles and German M98 Mausers were extricated from the hands of the depart ing Nazis, their combined quantities were, nevertheless, insufficient to satisf Norway's needs. Hence, Norway obtained #4 Lee Enfields in caliber .303 from England, as well as Swedish Mauser rifles in caliber 6.5 x 55mm and AG42 Ljungman semiautomatic rifles from their neighbor, Sweden.

The M98 Mausers which the Norwegians seized from the Germans were pre dominantly of Czech-Brno origin having the horizontal bolt handle. These particular weapons were immediately designated standard issue for the Norwe gian Home Guard, a position they still hold, although the M1 Garand ha become the present standard of the Norwegian Army.

When converting M98 German Mausers to the new standard .30-06 caliber for Home Guard use, they are fitted with new .30 caliber barrels. The origina Mauser rear sight is retained, but the front sight is adjusted in order to give the same points of impact for the new cartridge. The box magazine is opened to accommodate the longer .30-06 cartridge and a U-notch is milled in the face of the receiver ring to permit clip loading. No further alterations are made by the Kongsberg Arsenal of Norway.

For a brief period after the war, the Kongsberg Arsenal manufactured the Krag rifle in caliber 6.5mm—a total of about 1,000—for Norway's quasi-official shooting association similar to the one in Denmark and comparable with the National Rifle Association of the United States. Since the Krag had ceased to be the official rifle of Norway, its limited production made the cost of over $90.00 prohibitive to the average Norwegian shooter. Under the circumstances, manufacture of the Krag ceased, but not the deep affection the Norwegian NRA members had for the accurate, light-recoiling, smooth-operating Krags. This attachment became a major obstacle in enforcing the association's rule stating that for defense purposes members must use the military-approved rifle and standard army cartridge. Even an offer to permit use of Home Guard Mauser rifles in caliber .30-06 was rejected by the membership. In effecting a successful compromise, the highly-regarded ammunition firm of Norma in Oslo proffered five prototypes, identical only in that each employed the German Mauser action.

The final pattern which evolved has a heavy .30 caliber target-weight barrel and bears the designation M59. The following alterations in the German M98 Mausers made by the Kongsberg Arsenal constitute the new NRA M59. The bolt handle is bent down, swept back, and polished as in U. S. National Match Springfields. Rear of the receiver is opened up by milling a U-notch to permit clip loading of the longer .30-06 cartridge. The magazine is also opened up for this reason. The trigger is adjusted for a clean, crisp 4½-pound pull and sandblasted to prevent slippage. A new target-type stock, including upper handguard, is made of French walnut. Special aperture rear sight, along the lines of an idea submitted by Norma, was developed at Kongsberg. It does not prevent clip loading and can be adjusted, by clicks, up to 600 meters. A conventional hood-type front sight permits interchange of post or aperture inserts. There is an upper handguard—unusual in match rifles.

Currently, a considerable amount of experimenting is being conducted by the Norwegian Army to develop a telescopic-sighted sniper rifle based on the NRA M59 utilizing German M98 Mauser actions.

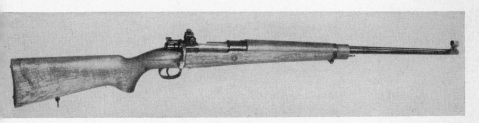

Norwegian NRA Cal. .30-06 Rifle.

SPECIFICATIONS OF THE NORWEGIAN NRA M59 RIFLE

Total length of weapon: 48.4".
Total weight of weapon: 9.9 lbs.
Length of barrel: 27.6".
Bore diameter: .2996" plus .002" tolerance.

Groove diameter: .308" plus .002" tolerance.
Land width: .167".
Rifling, righthand twist, 1 turn in: 10".

The Norwegian Krags

The Norwegian Krag is mechanically similar to the U.S. Krag. It has a Mauser type safety mounted on the bolt sleeve and its loading gate is hinged to open downward, rather than outward as does the loading gate of the Danish Krag.

(1) *Rifle Model 1894.* This was the original form designed to use the first cartridge with round nosed bullet. Barrel length 27.9", overall length 49.25". Weight 9.38 lbs. Carry sling on underside of rifle.

Norwegian Model 1894 (Krag Jorgensen System) caliber 6.5mm. The cocking piece and safety were evolved from the Mauser. This is one of the common rifle variants of this system as used in Norway. While there are various modifications, all are essentially the same mechanically.

Norwegian Model 1894 Krag-Jorgensen

Caliber: 6.5mm
Overall length, rifle without bayonet: 49.9"
Overall weight, rifle without bayonet: 9.38 lbs.
Type of action: Turnbolt
Type of Magazine: Horizontal Box
Barrel Length: 29.9"   *No. Grooves:* 4
Bore Diameter: .256"   *Groove Dia.:*

Type of bolt: 1 piece—Rotating Head
Capacity: 5
Direction of Twist: Left
Rate of Twist: 7.87"

Notes:

1. Mechanically this rifle follows very closely the original Danish Model 1889 designed by Superintendent Ole Krag of the Kongsberg Armory and Jorgensen.

(2) *Model 1894*. Sniper's rifle. Barrel 29.9", overall 49.9" and weight 9.9 lbs. This form has telescope as well as standard sights.

(3) *Rifle Model 1930*. This design has a sporting style half stock. Special receiver sights are adjustable from 100 to 1000 meters. Barrel 29.5", overall 49.9" and weight 11 lbs. (Note: This model was also sold as a commercial sporting rifle.)

(4) *Model 1895 Carbine* fitted with half stock. This weapon weighs 7.5 lbs. and is 40" long with a barrel 20.5" long.

(5) *Model 1897 Mountain Artillery and Engineer Carbine*. This is the same as Model 1895 Carbine except that the rear swivel is in a different position.

(6) *Model 1904 Engineer Carbine*. This weapon is stocked almost to the muzzle and has a full length handguard. The sling is attached to the lower band and trigger guard. The weapon weighs 8.4 lbs., is 40" long and has a 20.5-inch barrel.

(7) *Model 1907 Artillery Carbine*. The same as the M1904 carbine except that the swivels are positioned on the butt and left side of the lower band.

(8) *Model 1912 Carbine*. Full stocked with full length handguard, this weapon had a reinforcing band added to the upper band in 1916. The bolt handle is

Norwegian 6.5mm Model 1912 Krag Jorgensen Carbine.

knurled and flattened. The M1912 weighs 8.8 lbs. and is 43.6" long with a 24-inch barrel.

(9) *Model 1925 Sniper Rifle*. Generally similar to the M1894 rifle but has heavier barrel, micrometer-type rear sight, and checkered pistol grip. An earlier

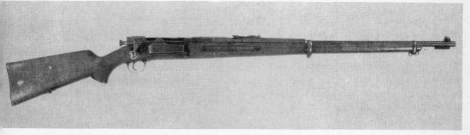

Norwegian 6.5mm Model 1925 Krag Jorgensen Sniper Rifle. This weapon is usually fitted with a micrometer-type rear sight.

model—the Model 1923—was dropped. The Model 1925 weighs 9.9 lbs. and is 49.7" overall with a 30-inch barrel.

Earlier Rifles Still in Use in World War II

Model 1887 (Jarman) 10.15mm. This is a turn bolt rifle with 8 shot tubula⟨
magazine below barrel. While it and its cartridge have long been obsolete, i⟨
was encountered in service in World War II.

Lund carbine, 8mm Danish. This is a single shot weapon built on the ol⟨
Remington rolling block action. Weapons of this type are common in Scand.
navia. Normal barrel length is 24.18″ and overall length 36.8″.

EARLIER OFFICIAL BREECHLOADERS: In 1881 the single shot Jarma⟨
(Norwegian) bolt action was adopted in caliber 10.15mm, replacing the ol⟨
1867 American Remington 11mm.

In 1887 the Jarman was modified and altered to make a tube repeate⟨

Note on Commercial Production. Rifles and Carbines on the Krag-Jorgense⟨
system are made in limited numbers by Kongsberg Vapenfabrikk, governmen⟨
plant, most in caliber 6.5mm Norwegian.

This firm makes a line of cheap .22 rifles on the old rolling block single sho⟨
system, as well as a very fine target match quality bolt .22. Because of high cos⟨
of importation, these rifles are seldom seen in America.

Norwegian Model 1887 Jarman

Caliber: 10.15mm
Overall length, rifle without bayonet: 53″   *With bayonet attached:* 71″
Overall weight, rifle without bayonet: 9.8 lbs.   *With bayonet attached:* 10.6 lbs.
Type of action: Rotating Bolt
Type of Magazine: Tubular   *Capacity:* 8
Barrel Length: 32.3″   *No. Grooves:* 4   *Direction of Twist:* Left
Bore Diameter: .40″   *Groove Dia.:* .413″   *Rate of Twist:* 22.4″
Notes:

1. This rifle is a modification of the Jarman 1881, the first bolt action adopted by Norwa⟨
The repeating mechanism is adapted from the original Austrian Fruwirth system. A scoo⟨
type elevator is operated by rearward action of the bolt to raise a cartridge in line fo⟨
chambering; and is depressed to receive a cartridge from the spring fed tube as the bolt i⟨
thrust forward. Most European repeaters of the period, notably the French Lebel 188⟨
used this system.

Norwegian 6.5mm Cartridge

Other Names: 6.5x55, 6.5mm Krag-Jorgensen   CARTRIDGE CASE
Type: Rimless, Necked, Centerfire
Overall Length: 3.07″   Length Overall: 2.16″
Average Wt.: 366 gr.   Length Head to Shoulder: 1.70″
Type Powder: Nitrocellulose   Length of Shoulder: .16″
Approximate Chg.: 40 grs.   Length of Neck: .30″
Type Primer: Berdan   Diameter at Rim: .478″
                                                   Diameter at Base: .476″
BULLET   Diameter at Neck: .281″
                                                   Diameter at Shoulder: .430″
Type: Jacketed, Pointed
Diameter: .263″   BALLISTICS (approximate)
Weight: 139 grs.   Muzzle Velocity: 2600 f.s.
Length: 1.3″   Pressure: 43,500 lbs./sq. in.

Notes: 1. This cartridge is interchangeable with tne Swedish 6.5mm Mauser.

Chapter 46
PARAGUAY
(Republica Del Paraguay)

GOVERNMENT PLANTS: None.

PRIVATE PLANTS: None of consequence.

PRINCIPAL MILITARY RIFLES: FN 7.62mm "FAL" Rifle, Mauser 1895, caliber 7mm (Slightly modified Spanish 1893). Some F. N. (Belgian made) Mausers, also 7mm, M1907 Mauser.

OTHER BREECHLOADERS: From 1870 until 1938 Paraguay and Bolivia fought bloody intermittent border wars. As a result modern weapons of all types circulate in both countries in considerable numbers.

Chapter 47
PERU
(Republica Del Peru)

GOVERNMENT PLANTS: None.

PRIVATE PLANTS: None of consequence.

PRINCIPAL MILITARY RIFLES: F. N. 7.62mm "FAL" Rifle, Cal. 30 M1. Mauser M. 1909. Also later F. N. M1935s some in caliber .30-06. The 7.65mm M1891 Mauser was formerly used.

EARLIER BREECHLOADERS: In 1870 the Belgian Comblain single shot 11mm was adopted (See under *Belgium* and *Brazil*).

During the "80's" Winchester '73 rifles in caliber .44-40 were imported in some quantity for army use.

Peruvian Model 1907 (Mauser) caliber 7.65mm. Except for caliber this is practically identical with the German Gewehr 98. It was made in Germany. Later patterns based on the improved Kar. 98k are also used in Peru, most being Belgian F. N. manufacture.

Polish Karabinek 1898, caliber 7.9mm. Except for minor details such as the shape of the stacking swivel and sling on underside this is the German Kar. 98.

Polish Karabin 29, caliber 7.9mm. This is the improved model designed on the Czech M24 specification.

Chapter 48

POLAND

(Rzeczpospolita Polska)

GOVERNMENT PLANTS: Warsaw and Radom.

PRIVATE PLANTS: None of consequence.

PRINCIPAL MILITARY RIFLES: Soviet designed 7.62mm AK-47 Assault Rifle and 7.62mm SKS Carbine.

Former Polish Rifles

Soon after the organization of the Polish nation at the conclusion of World War I, Poland obtained machinery for the manufacture of both the German Gewehr 98 and the German Karabiner 98.

Polish 7.92mm M91/98/25 Rifle. Note the German style upper band.

Except for minor details of manufacture, the Polish rifles are identical with the German. Early models were manufactured at Warsaw Arsenal. The Polish "Karabin 98a" is the late model German Gewehr 98.

The Polish Karabinek 1898 is the same as the German Kar. 98a except for minor details.

In 1929 the Poles began manufacture at Radom of the "Karabiner 29." This is a minor variant of the Czech Model 24. The sling is on the underside of the rifle and the front sight design differs. Sights are ranged from 300 to 2000 meters.

In 1918 the Poles obtained large quantities of Russian M 91 rifles. These were altered to take the German 7.9mm cartridge. They were then issued as "Karabinek 91/98/25." These weapons have the following characteristics: Barrel length 23.6", overall length 43.3", weight 8.16 lbs. Rifling 4 to the right. Magazine capacity 5 cartridges. Sights 400 to 3200 meters. German type bands are used.

Note: Polish manufactured Mauser system rifles were sold in some quantity to the Balkans before World War II. Pre-War Polish rifles customarily have the name of the manufacturing arsenal on the receiver ring, and the date of manufacture; not the model year. After World War II, Poland used Soviet 7.62mm M1891/30 Mosin Nagant rifles and Mosin Nagant M1938 and M1944 carbines.

Chapter 49
PORTUGAL
(Republica Portuguesa)

GOVERNMENT PLANTS: Lisbon.

PRIVATE PLANTS: None of consequence.

PRINCIPAL MILITARY RIFLES: 7.62mm M/961, is the German G-3 assault rifle; 7.62mm FN "FAL" rifle; 7.92mm M/937 Mauser, is the German Kar. 98k; .303 M/917, is the Lee Enfield rifle No. 1, Mark III and Mark III*. The earlier Portuguese Model 1904 Mauser Vergueiro is no longer a standard weapon.

Mauser-Vergueiro Model 1904

In this design, while the rifle somewhat resembles the standard long Mauser and has a one-piece stock with pistol grip, the receiver differs considerably.

The bolt is a solid Mauser design with dual locking lugs at the forward end, and with the cylinder bored out from the rear to receive the striker and cocking piece assembly.

However, the receiver bridge is the split type. As the bolt handle is turned up, it works up against the forward face of the receiver bridge instead of on a cam incline at the rear as in standard Mauser practice.

Primary extraction is produced as in Mannlicher design, by the camming action of the bolt lugs when the bolt handle is lifted. When the locking lugs are disengaged the bolt handle is lined up with the cut in the receiver bridge and is drawn straight back through the bridge as in Mannlicher Dutch and Roumanian practice.

Portugal Model 1937

In 1937 Portugal officially adopted the standard German Kar. 98k rifle as the Rifle 7.92mm M/937.

Portuguese 7.92mm M937 Mauser. This is the Kar. 98k made at Mauser for the Portuguese.

The second lot ordered (Rifle 7.9mm M/937-A) had a special front sight adjustable by a diagonal groove in the base, front sight guard, longer handguard, and provision for a sling on bottom of stock like the original Gew. 98.

EARLIER OFFICIAL BREECHLOADERS: (1) 1867 Westley Richards "monkey-tail" conversions of muzzle loaders. This was a lifting breechblock action. (2) 1871 Remington single shot 11mm. (3) The Austrian Guedes single shot. The Guedes was made at Steyr, Austria, and it was not used by any other Power.

EARLY OFFICIAL REPEATERS AND MAGAZINE RIFLES: The bolt action 8mm Austrian Kropatschek with tube magazine was used by Marine contingents for a few years.

When Von Mannlicher introduced his turning bolt rifle with revolving magazine in 1900, Portugal purchased 400, and an Army Commission recommended adoption. The recommendation was not acted upon, however, the Mauser-Vergueiro being developed instead.

SPORTING RIFLES: None of consequence are manufactured in Portugal.

Portuguese Model 1885 Guedes Single Shot

Caliber: 8mm
Overall length, rifle without bayonet: 48"
Overall weight, rifle without bayonet: 9 lbs.
Type of action: Falling Block

Barrel Length: 38.3" *No. Grooves:* 4
Bore Diameter: .315" *Groove Dia.:* .321"
Direction of Twist: Right
Rate of Twist: 11.4"

Notes:
1. This rifle was manufactured in Austria at Steyr. The finger lever extends to form a bottom for the frame recess, the extra long leverage being necessary for the special bottle necked cartridge employed.
2. The adoption of this rifle represented a forward step ballistically, as major Powers were using 11mm black powder cartridges at that period. It did not keep pace mechanically, however, as other Nations were then arming with repeaters of bolt action type.

Portuguese 6.5mm Cartridge

Other Names: 6.5x58mm Mauser-Vergueiro
Type: Rimless, Necked, Centerfire
Overall Length: 3.26"
Average Wt.: 372 gr.
Type Powder: Nitrocellulose
Approximate Chg.: 38 gr.
Type Primer: Center hole Berdan

BULLET

Type: Jacketed, Round Nose
Diameter: .263"
Weight: 155.3 gr.
Length: 1.25"

CARTRIDGE CASE

Length Overall: 2.28"
Length Head to Shoulder: 1.68"
Length of Shoulder: .26"
Length of Neck: .34"
Diameter at Rim: .466"
Diameter at Base: .467"
Diameter at Neck: .290"
Diameter at Shoulder: .426"

BALLISTICS (approximate)

Muzzle Velocity: 2350 f.s.
Pressure: About 41,000 lbs./sq. in.

Notes: Currently loaded in England for sporting use to slightly lower pressure.

Portuguese 8mm M1885 Cartridge

Other Names: 8mm Guedes
Type: Rimmed, Necked, Centerfire
Overall Length: 3.24"

Type Powder: Black
Approximate Chg.: 71 gr.
Type Primer: Berdan

BULLET

Type: Jacketed (Foil Patched), Round Nose
(Lead Exposure)
Diameter: .320"

Weight: 247 gr.
Length: 1.29"

CARTRIDGE CASE

Length Overall: 2.34"
Length Head to Shoulder: 1.49"
Length of Shoulder: .24"
Length of Neck: .61"
Diameter at Rim: .620"
Diameter at Base: .542"
Diameter at Neck: .354"
Diameter at Shoulder: .489"

Notes: Collector's cartridge. Very few originally made, as design was almost immediately replaced by smokeless.

Mauser Verguiero, M. 1904, 6.5mm. Note that this design differs from other modern Mausers in having a split bridge receiver with the bolt locking down forward of the receiver bridge. While Mauser did most of the engineering on this design, the Portuguese incorporated changes. This was replaced by 7.92mm Short Rifle identical with the German Kar. 98k.

Portuguese Model 1904 Mauser-Verguiero

Caliber: 6.5mm
Overall length, rifle without bayonet: 48"
Overall weight, rifle without bayonet: 8.4 lbs.
Type of action: Turnbolt
Type of Magazine: Box—Staggered Column
Barrel Length: 29.1"   No. Grooves: 4
Bore Diameter: .256"   Groove Dia.: .267"

With bayonet attached: 59.2"
With bayonet attached: 9.6 lbs.
Type of bolt: 1 piece—Rotating Head
Capacity: 5
Direction of Twist: Right
Rate of Twist: 7.87"

Notes:

1. This is not a standard Mauser design. The bolt handle locks down in front of a split receiver bridge, as in the Mannlicher turn bolt system.

Chapter 50

Roumania
(Romania)

GOVERNMENT PLANTS: Copsa Mica at Cugir, built in the 1930's by Zbrojovka of Czechoslovakia. No private plants.

PRINCIPAL MILITARY RIFLES: Soviet 7.62mm AK-47 Assault Rifle and 7.62mm SKS carbine.

PRIVATE PLANTS: None of consequence.

FORMER MILITARY RIFLES: Czech ZB Model 24 Mauser rifle in 7.9mm and the obsolete Model 1893 (Mannlicher turning bolt) 6.5mm. Also 1924 and later Mauser patterns made in Belgium 7.9mm. Steyr 8mm M1895, French 8mm M1907 Mannlicher Berthier, Soviet 7.62mm M1891 series, and Mosin Nagant rifles were also used. Later Model Mosin Nagant carbines may still be found.

Model 1893 6.5mm Roumanian Mannlicher

This is a turn-bolt Mannlicher generally similar to the Netherlands Model 1895. It is obsolete in Roumania.

The ejector on the Roumanian model differs from the Netherlands model. In the Roumanian Model 1893 the ejector is pivoted in the receiver at the rear of the magazine well. The bolt is grooved to permit the nose of the ejector to strike the base of the cartridge case as the bolt is drawn to the rear.

The Roumanian bolt does not have the guide rib which is prominent on the Netherlands model.

The thumb safety of the Roumanian can be turned all the way to the right to lock the bolt when the striker is fully forward. The Netherlands safety can only be applied when the striker is cocked.

In the magazine a "follower" is mounted on top of the elevator so as to cradle the cartridge instead of merely depending upon the upward thrust of the upper end of the elevator bar.

The handguard on the Roumanian extends about five inches farther forward than on the Netherlands model.

The Roumanian bayonet is carried on the right side of the barrel.

There is also a 6.5mm Model 1892 Roumanian Mannlicher rifle. There is no significant difference between this rifle and the Model 1893. The sight graduations are different and the ejector of the Model 1892 is mounted on the bolt while that of the Model 1893 is mounted in the receiver and the M1893 is somewhat heavier. The M1893 has a stacking rod on the left side of the upper band which is not present on the M1892. Model designations are stamped on the receiver.

Earlier Official Breechloaders

The early American Peabody falling block single shot rifle was used in Roumania. It was superseded by the Peabody-Martini, caliber .45 Turkish.

The Peabody, as we have seen, was the original successful falling block rifle operated by a lever to the rear of the triggerguard. The breechblock, hinged high at the rear, is lowered at the front when the lever is pushed down. This exposes the chamber for loading, and extracts the cartridge case from the firing chamber. However, it does not cock the hammer in the early model. The hammer in the original Peabody is a large exposed unit resembling that used in the American single shot Springfield, and must be thumbcocked. The firing pin is in the breechblock.

Roumanian 6.5mm Model 1892 Mannlicher Rifle.

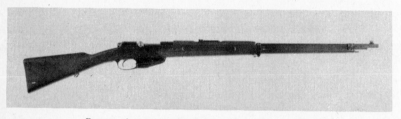

Roumanian 6.5mm Model 1893 Mannlicher Rifle.

The general history and description of various American and foreign examples of the Peabody will be found in the historical section of this book.

Roumanian Model 1893 Mannlicher

Caliber: 6.5mm
Overall length, rifle without bayonet: 48.3"
Overall weight, rifle without bayonet: 9 lbs.
Type of action: Turnbolt
Type of Magazine: Box—Vertical column
Barrel Length: 28.5"   *No. Grooves:* 4
Bore Diameter: .256"   *Groove Dia.:* .268"

With bayonet attached: 58.2"
With bayonet attached: 9.6 lbs.
Type of bolt: 2 piece—non-rotating head
Capacity: 5
   Direction of Twist: Right
   Rate of Twist: 7.87"

Notes:

1. The carbine is merely a shortened form of the rifle. It was also adopted in 1893. The bolt handle is turned down, no provision is made for bayonet mounting. A butt swivel on the left side of the stock and a front band ring also on the left receive the sling.

Model 1874-78 (Peabody-Martini) Rifle

This is the original American Peabody single shot falling block rifle as modified in Switzerland by von Martini. The improvement consists of the change in the firing lockwork.

Instead of the exposed hammer of the early Peabody, this model has a concealed hammer mechanism within the breechblock itself. The lever on the underside of the rifle to the rear of the triggerguard is pushed down and ahead. This withdraws the locking support from the front undersurface of the breechblock. The breechblock, which is hinged high at the rear, is then lowered at the front to expose the firing chamber. This motion also acts through leverage to cock the concealed hammer and extract the case from the firing chamber.

A cocking indicator is provided on the right side of the receiver to show when the concealed hammer is up. This design was also made as a carbine. Note that unlike many later models of single shot action, the lever employed here is to the rear of the triggerguard and is *not* the triggerguard itself.

Roumanian Model 1874-78 Peabody Martini Single Shot

Caliber: .45
Overall length, rifle without bayonet: 49″   *With bayonet attached:* 69″
Overall weight, rifle without bayonet: 9.62 lbs.   *With bayonet attached:* 10.5 lbs.
Type of action: Falling Block
Barrel Length: 33.2″   *No. Grooves:* 5   *Direction of Twist:* Right
Bore Diameter: 45″   *Groove Dia.:* 466″   *Rate of Twist:* 22″

Notes:

1. This is the original American Peabody lock as modified in Switzerland by Von Martini. The rifle was manufactured in Rhode Island. The original rifles were .45 Turkish Center Fire caliber. The design was also made for the .45 British Martini-Henry Service cartridge, which was larger than the Turkish.

2. These rifles were also official Turkish Service weapons.

Roumanian 6.5mm Mannlicher M1893

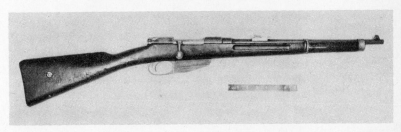

Roumanian 6.5mm Model 1893 Carbine.

Other Names: 6.5x53R Mannlicher
Type: Rimmed, Necked, Centerfire
Overall Length: 3.05″
Average Wt.: 350 grs.
Type Powder: Nitrocellulose
Approximate Chg.: 37.5 grs.
Type Primer: Berdan

BULLET

Type: Jacketed, Round Nose
Diameter: .263″
Weight: 162 grs.
Length: 1.22″

CARTRIDGE CASE

Length Overall: 2.11″
Length Head to Shoulder: 1.65″
Length of Shoulder .14″
Length of Neck: .32″
Diameter at Rim: .527″
Diameter at Base: .448″
Diameter at Neck: .294″
Diameter at Shoulder: .421″

BALLISTICS (approximate)

Muzzle Velocity: 2400 f.s.
Pressure: About 40,000 lbs./sq. in.

Notes: 1. The cartridge case for this cartridge is the same as the Netherlands 6.5mm Mannlicher.

Roumanian Model 1893 Mannlicher, sectional drawing showing magazine loaded and action ready for the forward loading stroke. Note that this magazine system utilizes the clip as part of its mechanism. This design has the Mannlicher two-piece bolt with separate head. All Mann-licher turnbolt rifles produced in quantity follow the general pattern of this design except for magazine systems.

ON OPPOSITE PAGE

Roumanian Model 1893 Details

Top line shows detail of safety and spring, bolt which is bored out from the front, and special nut which screws on to end of striker and holds cocking piece in place

Next line shows side view of cocking piece, early pattern Roumanian extractor, striker and mainspring. Note that in later models the extractor may be the same as the Dutch pattern, a type which is also found in the Mannlicher Schoenauer and Hungarian Mannlicher patterns.

Next line shows details of loaded clip, and two views of detachable bolt head.

The bolt detail itself shows the assembly in position for the forward bolt stroke.

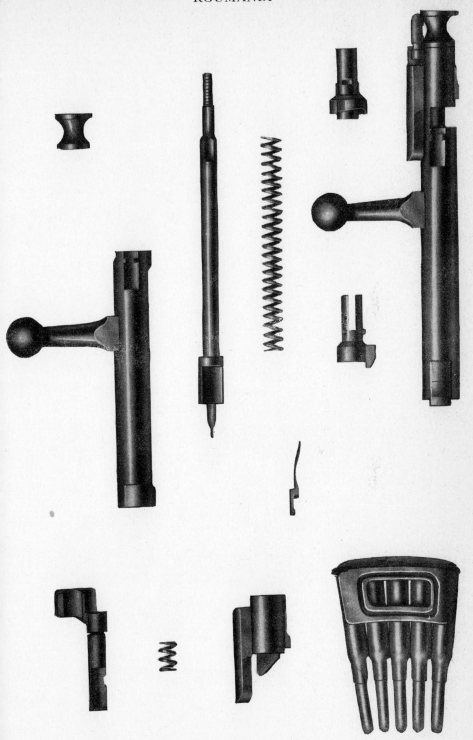

Roumanian Caliber .45 M1874-78 Cartridge

Other Names: Roumanian 11.43mm.
Type: Rimmed, Necked, Centerfire
Overall Length: 3.3"
Average Wt.: 802 gr.
Type Powder: Black
Approximate Charge: 85 gr.
Type Primer: Berdan

BULLET

Type: Lead (Paper Patched)
Diameter: .457"
Weight: 480 grs.
Length: 1.27"

CARTRIDGE CASE

Length Overall: 2.316"
Length Head to Shoulder: 1.425"
Length of Shoulder: .125"
Length of Neck: .766"
Diameter at Rim: .660"
Diameter at Base: .578"
Diameter at Neck: .482"
Diameter at Shoulder .541"

BALLISTICS (approximate)

Muzzle Velocity: 1380 f.s.

Notes: 1. This cartridge was commonly known as the ".45 Turkish."
2. Shoulder slightly longer on Turkish and Turkish much shorter overall Berdan type primer.

Chapter 51

SPAIN

(Espana)

GOVERNMENT PLANTS: Madrid. Oviedo.

PRIVATE PLANTS: There are literally hundreds of small arms manufacturers in Spain. Barcelona, Eibar, Madrid and Placencia are the headquarters of most of the larger ones. Comparatively few manufacture rifles, however. Pistols, revolvers, machine guns and submachine guns are the common manufacture, plus some shotgun production.

PRINCIPAL MILITARY RIFLES: 7.62mm NATO CETME Assault Rifle Model 58, 7.92mm Model 1943, some 7mm M1893 rifles, and some 7mm M1916 short rifles have been converted to 7.62mm NATO.

7.62mm NATO CETME Assault Rifle M58

This weapon was developed from the German 7.92mm short StG 45 (M) assault rifle. This weapon is covered in detail under "Germany." The development in Spain was done at the Centro de Estudios Tecnicos de Materiales Especiales, "CETME," a Spanish government establishment, by a group headed by L. Vorgrimmler, a former member of the Mauser design staff. Vorgrimmler had gone to France at the end of World War II and had worked for the French on development of a prototype delayed blowback carbine for a short 7.65mm cartridge; he then went on to Spain to work for CETME. In Germany much of the work was done on the StG 45 (M) by Dr. Karl Meier and Altenburger at Mauser.

Spanish 7.62mm NATO CETME Model 58 Assault Rifle.

The "CETME" has the roller bearing retarding lock of the StG 45 (M) and its method of operation is basically the same as that weapon with the following exception: the StG 45 (M) bolt rear section is of generally rectangular section with the exception of its nose section; the rear section of the W. German G3 and CETME 58 rifles is made in the form of a cylinder built as the underside of a long cylindrical piece which acts as a bolt carrier. The forward portion of

355

this "bolt carrier" rides in a tube over the barrel. The operating handle is mounted on the left side of this tube where it contacts the bolt carrier.

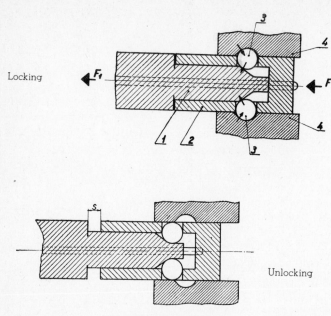

CETME Locking System.

The CETME and the West German G3 are loaded and fired in the same manner:

1. A loaded magazine is inserted in the magazine well.

2. Set selector lever, located on the right side above the pistol grip on whatever type of fire is desired. On the Spanish weapon the setting marked "T" is for semiautomatic fire, that marked "R" is for automatic fire, and that marked "S" is the safety. On the West German G3 the markings are "D" for automatic fire, "E" for semiautomatic fire, and "S" for safety. The selector lever on the G3 is on the left side.

3. Pull operating handle to the rear; if the safety selector is set on automatic fire, the bolt will remain to the rear when cocked. If the selector has been set on semiautomatic fire the bolt will close when the operating handle is released, chambering a cartridge. This weapon fires from an open bolt in automatic fire and from a closed bolt in semiautomatic fire. This helps to prevent "cook offs" at the conclusion of burst firing and gives the barrel a better chance to cool between bursts.

The CETME 58 and the West German G3 rifles are very simple to field strip. The two spring loaded receiver retaining pins mounted behind the pistol grip are easily driven out; at that point the stock can be drawn off to the rear and removed. The bolt carrier and bolt can then be removed and the trigger group can be hinged down for inspection and cleaning. No further disassembly is recommended.

Prototype 7.92mm CETME Assault Rifle shown with grenade launcher, 32-round magazine, and 20-round magazine.

As originally built, around 1953, the CETME assault rifle was chambered for a special 7.92mm short cartridge. This cartridge was longer than the German World War II 7.92mm short (PP 43 m.e.) and loaded with an unusual bullet. The bullet was extremely long and spire pointed, was made of aluminum, and had a short strip of gilding metal from ogive to rear to take the rifling. At a later date a similar cartridge in caliber 7.62mm was developed for the CETME. This used the same case as the 7.92mm CETME short necked down to 7.62mm. The Spanish service issue CETME is chambered for the 7.62mm NATO. The cartridge used by the Spanish Army in the CETME is physically interchangeable with the 7.62mm NATO cartridge as used in the United States, the United Kingdom, West Germany, etc., but is not as powerful. It has a lower muzzle energy because of its lighter load. The weapon can be made suitable for the higher powered NATO cartridge by fitting a different bolt head. Spain also makes another 7.62mm. This cartridge has a long spire pointed bullet similar in design to that of the early 7.62mm and 7.92mm CETME short cartridges. This cartridge is used in various Spanish machineguns and can also be used in the 7.62mm conversions of the Spanish Mausers. The CETME Model 58 has a built-in rifle grenade launcher/muzzle brake at the end of the barrel.

7.62mm CETME Model 58

Overall length: 39.37"
Overall weight: (loaded w/bipod): 11.3 lbs.
Type of action: Delayed blow-back
Type of bolt: 2 piece
Type of magazine: Detachable, staggered row box
Capacity: 20-rounds

Barrel length: 17.72"   *No. Grooves:* 4
Direction of twist: Right
Cyclic rate: 600 R.P.M.
Muzzle velocity: 2493 f.p.s.
Sights—front: Hooded blade
   rear: Tangent with W notch

Spanish Mauser Rifles

Spain has been using Mauser rifles since 1891. In that year a few 7.65mm M1891 rifles were purchased by Spain from Mauser. This rifle was similar to the Turkish M1890 having an "in line" magazine which protruded below the stock. Although few of the rifles were made, considerable quantities of carbines were manufactured; numbers of these were captured in Cuba in the Spanish American War by American troops and were brought back to this country; therefore the 7.65mm M1891 carbine is not too rare. The next Mauser rifle and carbine to be purchased in quantity by Spain was the 7mm Model 1892; this weapon introduced the 7mm cartridge and used an "in line" magazine similar to the M1891.

The 7mm M1893 Mauser is one of the best known of the Mausers and represents an advance in the development of the Mauser rifle. The M1893 introduced the staggered row, integral box magazine that is flush with the stock. The Model

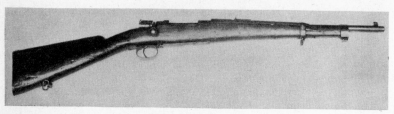

Spanish 7mm Model 1893 Short Rifle.

1893 also had a simplified safety lock and an improved bolt stop. The carbine version of the M1893 rifle is the Model 1895. This weapon is stocked to the muzzle as was the Model 1891 carbine. The M1893 also comes in a short rifle version. The Model 1893 rifles, carbines, and short rifles have been made by Mauser, Ludwig Loewe, Oviedo, and Industrias de Guerra de Cataluna.

The 7mm Model 1916 is a short rifle. It is called a "Mosqueton" by the Spanish. A large number of these rifles have been brought into this country in recent years, and many of these weapons do not have the manufacturers' marks. They usually have a floor plate release on the trigger guard and all have tangent type rear sights. The latest Spanish Mauser is the 7.92mm M1943. This weapon is similar to the German Kar 98k but has a straight bolt handle.

Spanish 7mm M1916 Rifle.

Description of the M1893 Spanish Mauser

Aside from the matter of caliber, the early Spanish M1893 Mauser differs from the German type already described only in the following essentials:

The receiver has an additional cut to the rear of the magazine well to permit the front end of the sear to project. When the trigger is pressed, this forward section of the sear rises and, if the locking lugs are fully engaged, enters a cut in the underside of the bolt cylinder. (This is the mechanical safety device found in the U.S. Model 1917-Enfield.) If the bolt is not turned as the lugs are fully engaged, the sear projection bears against the bolt cylinder so that the sear nose cannot be withdrawn from the striker, and the rifle cannot be fired.

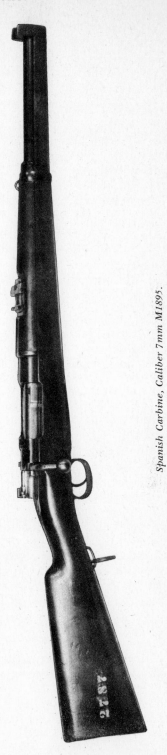

Spanish 7mm Mauser Model 1893. The rifle is shown cocked.

Spanish Carbine, Caliber 7mm M1895.

The bolt has only the dual front locking lugs (except on some very late patterns of Oviedo manufacture). The rear safety lug and guide rib of the German pattern 1898 (and later) does not appear on the 1893 Models.

The forward end of a stud on the cocking piece rests in a small grove to the rear of the bolt and prevents the bolt sleeve from rotating accidently as the bolt is pulled back.

The sear is the same as the German type except that it carries a projection at its forward end which engages in the underside in the cut in the bolt at the instant of firing as already mentioned.

On forward thrust of the bolt for loading, the cocking piece stud is caught and held by the sear while there is still about one inch of travel left. Thus, the cocking piece and the striker are held to the rear while the bolt cylinder and the bolt sleeve move forward to compress the mainspring. Locking takes place as the bolt handle is turned down, thereby turning the forward bolt locking lugs into their recesses in the receiver. (In the German design, the cocking stud does not come in contact with the sear until the lower part of the bolt handle reaches the receiver bridge. Downward pressure on the bolt handle in this design actually produces final mainspring compression for cocking.)

The Spanish Mauser design does not have a magazine cutoff.

The handguard on the Spanish type reaches from the receiver forward to the lower band. (The German patterns usually reach only from the rear sight to the lower band.) A sword bayonet attachment is provided in the Spanish design, below the upper band.

The Spanish rear sight is fitted with a thin metal tube which encircles the barrel and is screwed and soldered to it. It differs from the German design.

The M-R Semiautomatic Rifle

In 1932 the National Arsenal at Oviedo manufactured in limited quantity a 7mm gas operated semiautomatic rifle known as the "M.R." The initials represent the name of the designer, Arsenal Commandant Marinas y Ramirez Arellano. This 10-shot rifle loads through the open action with Mauser type clips. It fires the standard 7mm Spanish cartridge. It has not been production manufactured. It may be considered an experimental form. This rifle is unlikely to be encountered outside Spain except in the hands of a collector. It is of general interest only in that it represents an attempt at producing a semiautomatic military design.

EARLIER OFFICIAL BREECHLOADERS: In 1869 Spain purchased 10,000 Remington single shot rifles in caliber 11mm (.433) for her troops in Cuba. This arm was also supplied as a carbine.

In 1871 the Remington rifle and carbine were officially adopted by Spain for home use.

Model 1871 (Remington) 11mm

This is one of the simplest and strongest actions ever developed. Its principal defect is its comparatively low extracting power. When the external hammer is thumb cocked, the rolling breechblock (which carries the firing pin and is mounted on a cross pin) may be rolled back and down by pulling on its projecting handle. This action operates the extractor. When a cartridge is inserted, the breechblock is rolled up and ahead against the face of the breech. At this

)oint a flat spring in the action below supports the breechblock firmly. The
ower surface of the hammer below its pivot pin is shaped to permit it *to slide
under* a curved face on the lower side of the breechblock as the hammer falls.
Thus, when the hammer hits the firing pin in the breechblock, the lower steel
hammer surface is engaged firmly behind the breechblock to positively prevent
the action from opening.

Spanish Sporting Arms

While by no means in a class with the tremendous production of pistols
and revolvers, the manufacture of export rifles in the Eibar region has developed
considerably and consistently since 1920. None of these Spanish designs, however,
is in any way original; nor are any of them of outstanding quality. In this
connection note that Spanish pistols as made by Astra, Star, and Liama and
Spanish custom-built shotguns, are as fine as any produced anywhere in the
world today.

The common export rifle (found usually in South America) is the "Tigre"
(Tiger) Model of 1923. This is a .44-40 rifle which is a direct imitation of the
lever action Winchester Model 1892. The magazine tube holds 12 cartridges.
This rifle was manufactured at Eibar by Garate Anitua y Cia.

The Carbine "Destroyer" Model 1921 also made at Eibar is a bolt action
design commonly shooting the 9mm Bayard pistol cartridge which is standard in
Spain and in some parts of South America. The magazine holds 7 or 10
cartridges. These rifles are ordinary turn bolt types with detachable box magazine; but they appear with several designs of fore-ends and stocks. They were
commonly used as police weapons.

Extensive machine manufacture in Spain has been concentrated on light and
heavy machine guns, submachine guns and pistols and revolvers for military and sporting export. Comparatively little attention has been given to the
production of rifles and shotguns, and the only arms in these classes which are
of good quality are those manufactured by the occasional master gunmakers who
build custom weapons.

There has been a steady and marked improvement in general arms design
and manufacture in Spain which may eventually result in production of some
quality rifles. Rifle barrel steel from Spain is currently being shipped to countries like Sweden, whose knowledge of steel technology is an assurance of the
high quality of the Spanish product.

Experimental rifle designs are under development by some Spanish arms
makers whose other weapon production is top quality.

Spanish Model 1871 Remington Single Shot

Caliber: 11mm
Overall length, rifle without bayonet: 50.3"   *With bayonet attached:* 73"
Overall weight, rifle without bayonet: 9.3 lbs.   *With bayonet attached:* 10.9 lbs.
Type of action: Rolling Block
Barrel Length: 35.2"   *No. Grooves:* 6   *Direction of Twist:* Right
Bore Diameter: .433"   *Groove Dia.:* .449"   *Rate of Twist:* 20"

Notes:
The carbine versions of this arm are merely shorter and lighter because of barrel and
stock dimensions.
Another variant built in Sweden has an original cocking piece and safety.

Spanish 11mm M1871

Other Names: 11mm Remington
Type: Rimmed, Necked, Centerfire
Overall Length: 2.99"
Average Wt.: 640 gr.
Type Powder: Black
Approximate Chg.: 77.16 gr.
Type Primer: Berdan

BULLET

Type: Lead
Diameter: .437"
Weight: 387 gr.
Length: 1.1"

CARTRIDGE CASE

Length Overall: 2.25"
Length Head to Shoulder: 1.55"
Length of Shoulder: .13"
Length of Neck: .57"
Diameter at Rim: .627"
Diameter at Base: .524"
Diameter at Neck: .462"
Diameter at Shoulder: .510"

BALLISTICS (approximate)

Muzzle Velocity: 1340 f.s.

Notes: 1. This cartridge was also used by Denmark, Sweden and Norway.

Spanish Model 1893 Mauser

Caliber: 7mm
Overall length, rifle without bayonet: 48.6"
Overall weight, rifle without bayonet: 8.8 lbs.
Type of action: Turnbolt
Type of Magazine: Box (Staggered)
Barrel Length: 29.1"   *No. Grooves:* 4
Bore Diameter: .276"   *Groove Dia.:* .284"

With bayonet attached: 59"
With bayonet attached: 9.9 lbs.
Type of bolt: 1 piece—rotating head
Capacity: 5
Direction of Twist: Right
Rate of Twist: 8.6"

Notes:

1. The carbine version of this arm is the M1895, which is fitted with a turned down bolt handle. The stock commonly extends to the muzzle. Barrel projects slightly through a nose cap which is fitted with wings to protect the front sight. No provision is made for bayonet mounting. Sling is attached to sling swivels on the lower band and on the underside of the small of the stock.

Spanish 7mm Mauser M1893 Cartridge

Other Names: 7mm Mauser. 7x57 Mauser
Type: Rimless, Necked, Centerfire
Overall Length: 3.06"
Average Wt.: 384.8 gr.
Type Powder: Nitrocellulose
Approximate Chg.: 37.8 gr.
Type Primer: Berdan

BULLET

Type: Jacketed, Round Nose
Diameter: .284"
Weight: 173 gr.
Length: 1.21"

CARTRIDGE CASE

Length Overall: 2.24"
Length Head to Shoulder: 1.71"
Length of Shoulder: .18"
Length of Neck: .35"
Diameter at Rim: .474"
Diameter at Base: .470"
Diameter at Neck: .320"
Diameter at Shoulder: .420"

BALLISTICS (approximate)

Muzzle Velocity: 2300 f.s.
Pressure: 45,000 lbs./sq. in.

Notes: 1. See Cal. 7mm Mauser under F. N. (Belgium) for other data on this cartridge.
2. This cartridge is interchangeable with the Serbian 7mm Mauser cartridge.
3. Rifles chambered for this cartridge will chamber the 7mm sporting ammunition manufactured commercially in the United States, except the Remington 7mm Magnum.

Chapter 52

SWEDEN

(Sverige)

PRINCIPAL GOVERNMENT PLANTS: Carl Gustafs Stads Gevarsfaktori.

PRINCIPAL PRIVATE ARMS PLANTS: Husqvarna Vapenfabriks A. B.

PRINCIPAL GOVERNMENT AMMUNITION FACTORIES: Karlsborg.

PRINCIPAL PRIVATE AMMUNITION FACTORIES: Norma and Swedish Metalworks.

PRINCIPAL MILITARY RIFLES: Mauser Patterns: M96 rifle, M94 carbine, M38 rifle, M41 sniper rifle, and M40 rifle. Semiautomatic rifles: AG42 Ljungman and AG42B Ljungman.

Swedish 6.5 Mauser M94 Cartridge

Other Names: 6.5x55
Type: Rimless, Necked, Centerfire
Overall Length: 3.150"
Average Wt.: 362.6 gr.
Type Powder: Nitrocellulose
Approximate Chg.: 36.3 grs.
Type Primer: Berdan

BULLET

Type: Jacketed, Round Nose
Diameter: .263"
Weight: 155.8 grs.
Length: 1.25"

CARTRIDGE CASE

Length Overall: 2.16"
Length Head to Shoulder: 1.70"
Length of Shoulder: .16"
Length of Neck: .30"
Diameter at Rim: .478"
Diameter at Base: .476"
Diameter at Neck: .297"
Diameter at Shoulder: .430"

BALLISTICS (approximate)

Muzzle Velocity: 2400 f.s.
Pressure: About 41,000 lbs./sq. in.

Notes: 1. This cartridge is interchangeable with the Norwegian 6.5mm.

The invention of smokeless powder in 1885 by M. Vieille, a French chemist, triggered the development of high-velocity, small bore repeating rifles. Smokeless powders attain higher velocities at lower pressures, depositing very little residue in the barrel. The tactical advantage of not betraying a soldier's position by a cloud of smoke after firing could not be overrated.

There was a scramble among the European military to apply Vieille's invention which had doomed single shot, heavy-bore rifles using black powder cartridges, usually in .43 caliber.

M96

Sweden had been armed with the single shot, Remington, rolling-block rifle since 1867. It had been rebarreled in 1889 from 12.17mm rimfire cartridge to 8mm Danish Krag cartridge. However, Sweden was anxious to acquire a small bore repeating rifle. After testing the Mannlicher, Krag, etc., Sweden settled upon the Mauser rifle in caliber 6.5 x 55mm, officially designated M96 to commemorate the year of its adoption, although its origination at the German Mauser works at Oberndorf in collaboration with Swedish small arms experts dated back to 1890.

363

Swedish Mauser, Caliber 6.5mm. This rifle is the Model 1896. However, in its bolt form it is essentially a modified Spanish 1893. Some were made in Germany, but most Swedish Mausers were made in Sweden. Many of these rifles were modified into short rifles in 1938.

Swedish 6.5mm M1896 Mauser

Caliber: 6.5mm
Overall length, rifle without bayonet: 49.6"
Overall weight, rifle without bayonet: 8.8 lbs.
Type of action: Turnbolt
Type of Magazine: Box—Staggered Column
Barrel Length: 29.1"   *No. Grooves:* 4
Bore Diameter: .256"   *Groove Dia.:* .266"

With bayonet attached: 58"
With bayonet attached: 9.5 lbs.
Type of bolt: 1 piece—rotating head
Capacity: 5
Direction of Twist: Right
Rate of Twist: 7.9"

The Swedish M96 resembles closely the Spanish M93 Mauser which saw ervice during the Spanish-American war. The M96 was the first Mauser to use a bolt guide-rib to prevent cramping, and a thumb cut-out on the left receiver vall to facilitate clip loading. A small gas escape hole is located on the body of he bolt, just forward of the extractor collar. Cocking takes place upon closing he bolt. The handle of the bolt, itself, is horizontal. An odd arrangement for easy disassembly of the bolt, not found on Mausers of other nations, is a right-angle, upward projection on the cocking piece. The stock is straight, without pistol grip. The fine heavy barrel, 29.1″, is permitted to vibrate freely, unencumbered by straight-jacket devices, such as barrel bands, fore-end bayonet pands, and upper handguards. Its accuracy is superlative. Bayonet for the M96 was originally designed in 1896. The short knife-type blade measures 8 5/16″. The bayonet is well-balanced, finely constructed, and fits the weapon snugly.

The M96 has only two locking lugs at the head of the bolt. A third rear safety lug, found in later M98 German Mauser patterns, was never judged necessary for added strength. As a matter of fact, the original Mauser performed so reliably over a period of fifty years that, other than shortening the barrel to carbine length, Swedish ordnance authorities considered it unnecessary to change the design materially or alter its metallurgical specifications. Oddly enough, the disconcerting habit of stamping the year of manufacture on receivers has often been misinterpreted to denote model numbers which, contrary to fact, would indicate constant fluctuation in the design of the Swedish Mauser.

Swedish 6.5mm M94 Carbine.

In 1894, the M94 carbine (also developed at Oberndorf) was accepted by Sweden. First issues of the M94 carbine and M96 rifle emanated from the Mauser factory, but subsequent production was undertaken by the Swedish factories of Husqvarna and Carl Gustaf Stads Gevarsfaktori until discontinuance of both models in 1944 in favor of a semiautomatic rifle, the AG42 Ljungman.

The carbine utilizes the same action as the M96 rifle but the weapon differs in the following particulars: the bolt handle is bent down for cavalry use, and barrel length is 17.7″. The original M94 carbine was not used in conjunction with a bayonet; however, in 1917, provisions were made for the fitting on of a special bayonet, not interchangeable with Swedish rifles.

The excessive length of the M96 proved clumsy in the field, so in the 30's a decision was reached to modernize the M96 rifle. The ultimate model, M38, would also serve to eliminate the need for a carbine. The barrel of the M96 was shortened to 23.6″, thereby reducing the overall length from 49.6″ to

Swedish 6.5mm M38 Rifle.

44.1″. The horizontal bolt of the M96 was retained for the infantry, but the bolt handle was turned down for cavalry issue.

For sniping purposes, highly accurate M96 rifles are selected. The bolt handle is then bent down. A telescope is fitted on by a detachable German-type side mount with single locking lever. The telescope may be any of three different

Swedish 6.5 M41 Sniper Rifle.

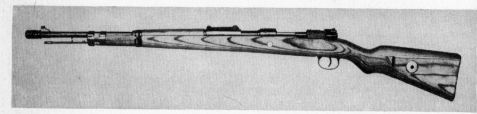

Swedish 8mm M40 Rifle.

models: German Ajack 4 x 90mm, or Swedish Aga 3 x 65mm M42 or M44. Reticules in all three scopes are typically German, featuring the three-bar sniping pattern. Each Swedish infantry company is issued six M41 sniper rifles.

In the year 1939, Sweden purchased 2,500 German Army Kar 98k Mauser rifles in caliber 7.92 x 57mm from Germany. In an effort to achieve uniformity in ammunition, Sweden rechambered these rifles for the Swedish 8mm M32 cartridge, universally regarded as the most powerful of infantry cartridges. The M32 cartridge had been adopted by Sweden in the late 30's for use in Browning light and heavy infantry machine guns.

Conversion of the German Kar 98k rifles consisted of opening the magazines at the rear to accommodate the Swedish 8 x 63mm cartridge. The altered magazine of the M40 holds only four M32 rounds because of their larger case diameter. The clip holds only four rounds. A muzzle brake was fitted on the end of the barrel to lessen recoil, but it prevents use of the bayonet.

The M40 rifles were issued to machine gun troops. However, since World War II indicated the 6.5mm cartridge to be fully adequate for infantry weapons, the 8mm cartridge was discontinued for military service. Sweden sold the M40 Mausers to Israel after this decision.

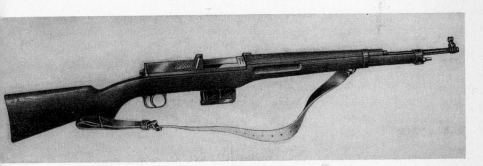

Swedish 6.5mm AG42 Ljungman Semiautomatic Rifle.

In 1942 Sweden deemed it essential to incorporate a semiautomatic military rifle among its standard arms and adopted the design of one of the country's foremost engineers, Eric Eklund. Mr. Eklund accomplished one of the most astounding feats in the annals of gun history. He conceived the idea of the AG42 Ljungman, transferred it to the drafting board, witnessed the prototype pass a thorough testing, and saw production of the gun begin—all within the space of one short year.

The well-made Ljungman rifle draws upon gas as its means of operation, as does the M1 Garand rifle. But the Ljungman is unique in that it has achieved the epitome in simplicity. In the conventional gas system, typified by the Garand, gas is tapped from the barrel near the muzzle and is transmitted through a tube located beneath the barrel, where the piston rod and return spring are contained. As a cartridge is fired, the expanding gases race through a gas port in the barrel, forcing the piston rod rearward. This action unlocks the bolt, impelling it rearward, simultaneously ejecting the fired case and cocking the firing mechanism. The return spring then re-positions the bolt for the firing of the next round.

The Ljungman gas system eliminates the expensive and complex piston rod mechanism. It consists solely of a gas tube and gas port. It is so designed that only a portion of the expanded gases released upon firing escapes through an orifice in the top of the barrel, located about one-third the length of the barrel back from the muzzle. Gas, speeding through the tube, delivers a hammer-like blow against the bolt cover to unlock the bolt and, together, they move backward. The bolt cover face and end of the gas tube are fitted together in cup-like form. The Ljungman gas system has since been copied by the French MAS 49 and U. S. Armalite rifles.

The Ljungman uses the same bolt system common with SAFN and "FAL" NATO rifles of Fabrique Nationale of Belgium, as well as the Russian Tokarev rifle. The rear end of the bolt tilts downward when locked in firing position, and bears against a crosspiece in the receiver. When a round is fired, gas strikes the bolt carrier, thrusting it rearward which cams up the rear end of the bolt and, together, they travel back to extract the fired case. The bolt return spring returns the carrier and bolt to their forward locked position. This action results in the removal of a loaded round from the magazine and insertion of the round in the chamber. Behind the rear sight there is a built-in muzzle brake.

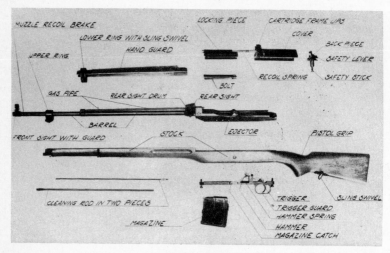

AG42 Stripped.

To disassemble the AG42, the safety arm is swung to midway or neutral position; then the safety is raised up and away from the receiver body. The cover, bolt carrier, and bolt are removed from the receiver by sliding them back and out of the receiver grooves. To assemble, reverse procedure.

A limited number of AG42 rifles were converted to test modifications of the gas system. The modified system consists of an adjustable gas port and an enlarged chamber in the center of the gas tube. The purpose of this chamber is to delay opening of the bolt until gas pressure within the barrel is at its lowest ebb in order to facilitate extraction of the fired case. However, since the quality of Swedish 6.5mm ammunition proved consistently high, it was unnecessary to adopt the new gas tube and regulator.

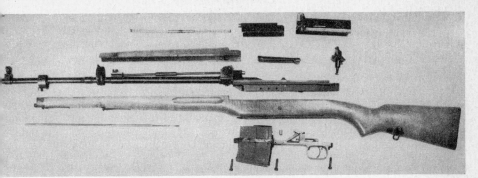

Swedish 6.5mm AG42 Second Revision Ljungman Semiautomatic Rifle.

By 1953, after ten years of use by troops, the AG42 was improved by revising the design of the trigger mechanism and extractor; the front sight and magazine were strengthened and, to lessen fouling, stainless steel was used in the construction of the gas tube. Because fired 6.5mm cartridge cases are reloaded, precaution is taken to prevent possible damage to the fired cases through automatic ejection. A rubber roller is fitted on the right forward side of the cover, serving as a buffer for the ejected cases.

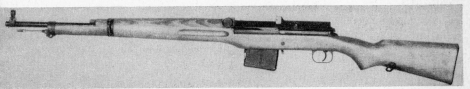

Swedish 6.5mm AG42B Ljungman Semiautomatic Rifle.

Sporting Rifles

Husqvarna manufactures shotguns and double rifles (utilizing the Greener and the Anson & Deeley systems), a Mauser-type sporting rifle of their own design, and various single shot, bolt action, sporting-type rifles in .22 caliber. They no longer produce the Swedish Army Mauser.

The Husqvarna Mauser type rifles are sold on the American market. The Mauser action has been modified in the Husqvarna so that a slide-type safety is used, the left bolt lug is not slotted for the ejector, firing pin fall has been shortened. The Husqvarna series of high-powered sporters is as follows:

Series 1740—chambered for the .270 Winchester, .30-06, 7.92x57mm, and 9.3x62mm cartridges; barrel length—23.75," average weight—6.8 lbs.

Swedish Husqvarna 3000 Series High-Powered Sporter. Note the Monte Carlo type stock and U.S. elevator type rear sight. These rifles are tapped and drilled for the better-known U.S. micrometer sights.

Series 3000 and 3100—chambered for .270 Win., 30-06, .308 Win., and .243 Win.; barrel length—23.75," average weight—7 lbs.

Series 4000 and 4100—chambered for .270 Win., 30-06, .308 Win., and .243 Win.; barrel length—20.75," average weight—6.6 lbs.

There are also a bolt action clip loading .22, the 1622; a .358 Magnum DeLuxe; and full length (Mannlicher type) stocked rifles—the 456 and 458. All Husqvarna high-powered rifles are tapped and drilled for American micrometer type rear sights and American scope mounts. The 3000, 3100, and 358 Magnum DeLuxe rifles have American type Monte Carlo stocks with ebonite fore-end tips. Other high-powered rifles with exception of the 456-458 series have full pistol grip stocks with European "Schnabel" type fore-ends.

While Carl Gustafs Stads Gevarsfaktori is government-owned, it manufactures sporting rifles employing M96 Swedish Army Mauser rifle actions. These weapons vie with those of Husqvarna on the market. While this might not seem too charitable an arrangement, government arsenals are entirely free in Sweden to compete with private enterprise in the manufacture and sale of arms and ammunition, regardless of whether the market exists at home or abroad.

All Swedish Mausers are proof-tested with loads developing 62,000 pounds per square inch, whereas Swedish service ammunition delivers 47,000 pounds per square inch.

Choice of the 6.5 x 55mm cartridge for the Swedish Mausers has for over a period of sixty years proved sound. Recoil is moderate, hastening marksmanship training of recruits. Light weight is another advantage, since 30% more cartridges can be carried than their corresponding weight in 8mm rounds. Trajectory is flat and stopping-power more than adequate.

WARNING. Large quantities of surplus Danish ammunition in caliber 6.5 x 55mm with 156 grain round-nose bullets have been offered to U. S. shooters. When these cartridges are erroneously identified as of Swedish manufacture, the results can be disastrous. Danish bullet jackets are of soft-rolled copper, causing excessive fouling of the barrel. When standard steel-jacketed Swedish cartridges or reloads with gilding-metal bullets are fired through a weapon from which fouling caused by Danish ammunition has not been scrupulously removed, there is danger of blowing up the rifle. Such incidents occurred frequently on Danish rifle ranges. As a precaution, be sure barrel is meticulously

The Pelo Semiautomatic Rifle. This rifle was developed by a Finnish Captain. The prototypes were manufactured in Sweden in 6.5mm and 7.92mm and the weapon was tested by the Swedish and British governments after World War II. The Pelo has a ten-round magazine and is 43.3 inches overall. It weighs 9.25 pounds and is an interesting example of a post-war prototype rifle.

clean; use genuine Swedish military cartridges or the superb, commercially-made Norma ammunition. Avoid use of Danish ammunition carrying the following notations on the base: V146 (Number of drawing), △ (Brass reworked to correct anvil), 48 (Year of manufacture), and HA (Haerens Army ammunition factory of Denmark).

Note: Danish cases are mercuric-primed and cannot be reloaded.

Characteristics of Swedish Service Rifles

Model	Carbine M94	Rifle M96	Rifle M38	Rifle M40	Sniper M41	Semiauto M42
Type	Mauser	Mauser	Mauser	Mauser 98	Mauser	Ljungman
System	Bolt-action	Bolt-action	Bolt-action	Bolt-action	Bolt-action	Gas operation
Caliber	6.5x55mm	6.5x55mm	6.5x55mm	8x63mm	6.5x55mm	6.5x55mm
Length of Barrel (in inches)	17.7	29.1	23.6	29.1 with muzzle brake	29.1	25.1
Length of Weapon (in inches)	37.4	49.6	44.1	49.2	49.6	47.9
Number of Cartridges in Magazine	5	5	5	4	5	10
Weight of Weapon, excluding bayonet or cartridges (in lbs.)	7.5	8.8	8.4	8.8	11.0 with telescope	9.7
Graduated Rear Sight (in meters)	300-1600	300-2000	100-600	100-2000	4X Ajack or 3X AGA scope	100-700
Velocity at 25 meters from Muzzle (in ft. per sec.)	2,313	2,542	2,460	2,428	2,542	2,460

Characteristics of Swedish Service Rifle Cartridges

Cartridge	Shape of Bullet	Bullet Weight (in grains)	Powder Weight (in grains)	Overall Length of Cartridge (in inches)	Velocity (in ft. per sec.)
6.5mm M94	Round-nose	155.8	36.3	3.15	2,295
6.5mm M41	Boattail spitzer	138.8	37.03	3.07	2,625
8mm M32	Boattail spitzer	219.1	55.5	3.34	2,491
8mm M39 tracer	Spitzer	169.7	55.5	3.11	2,557
8mm M39 A.P.	Spitzer	182.0	55.5	3.11	2,690

Swedish 6.5x55mm ammunition is interchangeable with the Norwegian 6.5x55mm ammunition.

Chapter 53

SWITZERLAND

(Schweiz-Suisse-Svizzera)

PRINCIPAL GOVERNMENT PLANTS: Federal Arms Factory, Bern (Waffenfabrik, Bern.)

PRINCIPAL PRIVATE PLANTS: Schweizerische Industrie-A.G., SIG (Neuhausen and Hämmerli of Lensburg). Except for the Swiss service rifle, manufacture is confined almost entirely to single shot rifles of the falling or dropping block types. The most common are those on the Martini-falling block action. Rifles of this type are sold in world export by the great Swiss gun house of W. Glaser of Zürich, and often bear that name instead of a maker's name.

PRINCIPAL MILITARY RIFLES: 7.5mm Assault Rifle Model 57, and 7.5mm Model K31.

Prototype Swiss Federal Arms Factory, Bern, 7.5mm Assault Rifle.

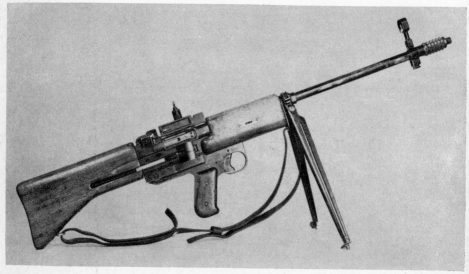

Prototype, Swiss Federal Arms Factory, Bern, 7.5mm Short Assault Rifle, right side view.

Prototype, Swiss Federal Arms Factory, Bern, 7.5mm Short Assault Rifle, left side view.

The Swiss have been searching for a suitable replacement for the Schmidt Rubin bolt action rifles for some time. In 1944 a prototype 7.5mm gas-operated rifle was made in limited quantities. In the early 1950's the Swiss Federal Arsenal at Bern developed several selective fire rifles including one for a 7.5mm short cartridge and another for a 7.65mm short cartridge. The weapon chambered for the 7.5mm short cartridge was similar in concept to the German FG 42 paratroop rifle. After extensive testing the Arsenal designs were dropped and a rifle for the 7.5mm M11 cartridge designed by SIG was adopted.

A careful appraisal of World War II developments led to the adoption by the Swiss of a new weapons system which would serve their particular tactical requirements. While various medium-range cartridges were rigorously tested, the Swiss concluded that their high-powered 7.5mm cartridge still suited them best.

The Swiss Industrial Company, popularly known as SIG, under the guidance of its capable designer-director, Rudolf Amsler, developed three experimental weapons in caliber 7.5mm, the first being the semiautomatic rifle called the

Swiss 7.5mm SIG SK46 Semiautomatic Rifle.

SK46. Outwardly, it resembles the Swiss K31 bolt action rifle. The SK46 features a remarkably short gas system and up-tilting bolt.

The second weapon to be tested was an assault rifle using a novel breech and blow-forward gas system—AK 53.

The third and only design to be adopted officially was the SIG automatic rifle, identified by the army as StGw 57. (The same weapon offered commercially by SIG was known as the AM55 and now is the SG 510.)

In addition to delivering flat firepower, the SIG rifle has a grenade launcher as an integral part of the barrel, permitting discharge of antitank, antipersonnel, or smoke grenades as required. Use of the rifle is intended to lessen dependency upon such supporting weapons as machine guns, mortars, etc. The versatility of the SIG weapon permits greater flexibility of operation. The individual soldier will, as a consequence, be equipped to contend with a greater variety of situations and be capable of defending a larger perimeter than heretofore expected of him or his weapon.

The delayed blowback or semirigid system of locking is used. The bolt is divided into two separate groups. One group consists of the bolthead which supports the cartridge and which contains the extractor, ejector, and two pivoting, locking cylinders. The other group consists of the plunger shaft which contains the firing pin assembly. This is generally similar to the German StG 45 (M) system.

When the recoil spring sets the plunger shaft into forward motion, the wedge-shaped head of the plunger shaft forces the pivoting, locking cylinders, on either side of the bolt, to swing out from their concealed seats in the bolthead, and to abut against recesses in the receiver wall, thus securing the bolt. The SIG rifle fires full or semiautomatically from a closed bolt. The fluted chamber prevents sticking of the case upon firing and is an aid to its rearward movement. The released gases thrust the case against the bolthead, moving it backward .008". This initial force is sufficient to cause the cylinders to pivot out of their geometrically-arranged, locking recesses in the receiver wall and to re-enter their niches in the bolthead. Pressure thus exerted against the shoulders of the wedge front of the plunger shaft causes it to travel backward about 1/4". At this point, the bullet has left the barrel. During the retracting action the plunger shaft absorbs sufficient kinetic energy to propel it rearward in unison with the bolthead, ejecting the expended case. The hammer is cocked and the recoil spring is compressed.

Travel of the bolt mechanism is about 8". Contraction of the recoil spring and special dampers act as brakes to the rearward movement of the bolt mechanism. The compressed recoil spring drives the bolt forward, stripping a cartridge from the magazine and chambering it. As the bolthead encounters the back of the barrel, its forward momentum is halted, but the plunger shaft continues onward until it forces out the pivoting cylinders from the bolthead into their locking recesses in the receiver wall. The weapon is now set for re-firing.

Recoil of the weapon is phenomenally light considering its weight and the use of the full-powered 7.5mm Swiss infantry cartridge (comparable with the U. S. .30-06 round) and is an important factor contributing to easy control of the weapon. By actual test, its recoil is only about one-third that of the Swiss K31 bolt action rifle. Light recoil can be attributed to (1) heavier weight of the SIG rifle, (2) use of a muzzle brake which would, in itself, reduce recoil by 25%, and (3) dispersal of the recoil force by the relatively massive, compounded bolt system which dissipates this force on its long return stroke, as well as by the resistance offered by the recoil spring.

The well-known tendency of automatic rifles to ascend at the muzzle when firing bursts has been minimized in this gun by use of a straight stock designed in line with the longitudinal axis of the barrel to reduce leverage force against the shoulder created by recoil. This control is evident when firing full automatic from the hip or in prone position. It is particularly noticeable when firing from the shoulder where control has always been difficult. Minimizing "climb" and recoil reduces the tendency to obscure the target, promising more accurate delivery of rapid fire.

Accuracy of the SIG rifle is, at least, on a par with their very fine bolt action K31 rifle and is one of its outstanding features. A special accuracy test in which a SIG rifle was selected at random, placed in a machine rest, and fired at 100-meter target, resulted in a 6 shot 2⅜″ group. At the conclusion of controlled tests conducted at Swiss Army shooting schools, marksmanship badges were awarded to 19% of the recruits firing the K31 bolt action rifle, as compared with 29% using the SIG StGw 57 automatic assault rifle—evidence of easy mastery and control of the weapon by men not particularly skilled in shooting.

Swiss Model 57 7.5mm Assault Rifle.

The StGw 57 is equipped with a carrying handle as well as an adjustable, folding bipod. Normally the bipod is located in the forward position near the muzzle. However, the bipod can be quickly relocated centrally under the barrel for a greater arc of fire and wider maneuverability.

A composition rubber butt imparts a certain amount of resiliency to the stock during grenade launching when the butt is backed up by a solid object, such as a building wall, curbstone, etc.

In view of the straight-line design of the stock, the sights are located high on the weapon; however, they may be folded down out of the way. For the

Swiss StGw Model 57 Assault Rifle, Stripped.

first time the Swiss have, in this particular instance, adopted a rear aperture sight.

The SIG automatic rifle was designed for low-cost mass production, making almost complete use of sheet metal stampings. Plain carbon steels are used for

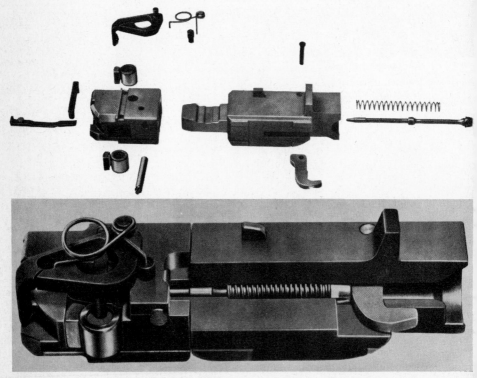

Bolt of Swiss 7.5mm Model 57 Assault Rifle. Top, bolt disassembled; Bottom, bolt assembled.

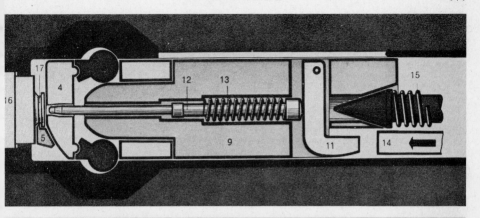

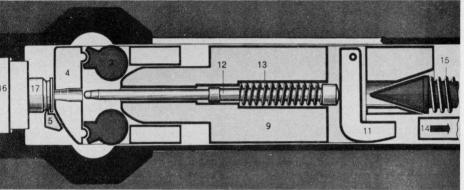

Schematic View of Bolt of Swiss 7.5mm Model 57 Assault Rifle. Top, bolt in locked position; Bottom, bolt unlocked.

the few machined parts since the supply of high-alloy steels is, generally, the first to become critical during shortages.

It has proved economically feasible, as well as detrimental to the formation of an arms cartel, to manufacture weapons in parts (barrels, receivers, magazines, screws, stocks, etc.) in many different plants throughout Switzerland. Decentralization of industry serves also as an effective defense measure in the event of attack. SIG lets contracts on their assault rifle to more than 200 subcontractors who produce the various components, shipping 90% of their output to the Swiss Federal Arsenal in Berne for final assembly. The remaining 10% of output is assembled by SIG as a control check on the production of the component parts.

The StGw 57 is relatively easy to maintain. Field stripping is fast and simple. To do so, remove butt stock from receiver by depressing bolt catch and rotating stock counterclockwise about one-eighth turn; then withdraw it back out of the receiver. Withdraw the recoil spring. Remove operating handle by pulling it rearward out of the receiver. The bolt assembly now protrudes about 3/4" from the receiver. Grasp it firmly and remove it from the receiver. Then remove trigger mechanism. The gun can be reassembled by reversing these steps.

SPECIFICATIONS OF THE SWISS STGW 57 ASSAULT RIFLE
Caliber: 7.5mm Swiss
Total length of weapon: 43.3".
Length of barrel including muzzle brake: 27.17".
Length of barrel excluding muzzle brake: 20.47".
Depth of rifling: .0098".
Number of grooves: 4.
Width of rifling: .1456".
Weight of barrel: 3.04 lbs.
Weight of weapon without magazine: 12.56 lbs.
Weight of magazine fully loaded with 24 rounds: 1.98 lbs.

FORMER MILITARY RIFLES: 7.5mm Schmidt Rubin M1889, M1889/1900, M1896/11, and M1911 rifles. Carbines: 7.5mm M1893 Mannlicher, M1905, and M1911 Schmidt Rubin.

Description of the Schmidt-Rubin Rifles

Major, later Lieut. Col. Rubin, then director of the Swiss Laboratory at Thun, was among the first to recognize the tremendous potentialities of the small bore high velocity military cartridge. As early as 1883, he submitted his 7.5mm cartridge to the Swiss Government. He introduced the then novel idea of using a lead bullet core completely enclosed in a copper jacket. Smokeless powder had not appeared at that time, but Rubin presented a load consisting in large part of a compressed black powder which was surprisingly effective. With the introduction of smokeless powder in 1886, Rubin intensified his development of his 7.5mm cartridge. The boat-tailed bullet design introduced in the Model 11 cartridge nearly doubled the effective range of the military bullet.

Meanwhile, Col. Rudolf Schmidt, one of the most scientific arms researchers and writers of all time, had made a complete survey of every type of rifle design then in existence. According to his own contemporaneous works, he was responsible for the rifle design basically, while Rubin was responsible for the cartridge and ballistic designs of the new rifle which the Swiss officially adopted in 1889.

Model 1911, Caliber 7.5mm

The first model of this rifle introduced in 1889, and long since obsolete, had a magazine capacity of 12 cartridges loaded from two clips. All later patterns hold 6 cartridges.

The early designs have the following characteristics:

The receiver is exceptionally long because of the straight pull action employed. At rear it comprises a complete cylinder form of bridge behind the magazine well. The length of this bridge is about 4.25 inches.

The receiver forging is bored with a second complete cylinder on the right rear, leading into the larger one. The point of the bolt stop, which prevents the bolt mechanism from being jerked out of the rifle as it is drawn to the rear, passes through a cut in the bottom of the smaller cylinder.

The larger cylinder is also provided with a bottom cut to receive the stud of the striker. The sear nose passes through a vertical cut in the bottom of this striker stud cut.

Longitudinal grooves are provided on the inside of the main receiver cylinder as travel guides for the two bolt lugs.

A diagonal groove extends from each longitudinal travel groove into the re-

Swiss 7.5mm Rifle and Carbine. These are the Schmidt-Rubin straight pull designs. The photographs are typical. There are several variations of the carbines, or short rifle, though mechanically they differ very little. M1911 rifle and carbine in picture.

cesses in the receiver for the lugs. These lug seats are cut on a screw pitch. The locking is to the rear of the magazine. The lugs are not carried on the bolt itself in customary fashion but on a bolt sleeve. The rear section of the receiver forms the customary tang for attachment to the stock.

The barrel is heavily reinforced at the point of screwing into the receiver. Diameter is reduced in two successive steps forward of the chamber and then tapers to the muzzle, a slight swelling being allowed at the point of mounting of a barrel sleeve which carries the sight ring. This barrel sleeve is not found on any other rifle. It is a copper alloy tube fitting around the reinforce in the barrel which is gripped between the fore-end and the handguard.

The bolt assembly is a complex unit consisting of (1) a long bolt cylinder; (2) a removable locking sleeve which fits over the rear half of the bolt cylinder and carries the locking lugs; (3) a bolt cap mounted over the rear of the assembly and designed to be operated by a side rod to which a handle is attached; and (4) the striker and safety mechanism.

The bolt cylinder proper is bored out through its entire length. The striker and the mainspring are inserted from the rear. The right side of the bolt cylinder has a cut to permit the stud of the operating rod to enter. Almost at its center a circular flange is machined which forms the forward bearing for the locking sleeve when it is in place. The cylinder is grooved on either side forward of this flange to permit it to travel through the folded-in edges of the magazine on forward and rearward stroke.

The bolt cylinder is cut with a groove on the left for the ejector; and on top to the right it has a flat to receive the extractor.

The bolt *face* is also *a separate piece* in this design, but is screwed in and *permanently* attached. It gives the general affect of a solid bolt head. The bolt head is recessed to completely enclose the head of the cartridge case.

The locking sleeve, which carries the lugs, is mounted loosely behind the flange on the bolt cylinder. The dual lugs are at the forward end of this sleeve on the M1911 rifle, the M1896/11 rifle, and the M1911 carbine. The M1889 rifle, M1889/96 rifle, M97 cadet rifle, and M89/00 short rifle have their locking lugs mounted toward the rear of the locking sleeve. The upper lug is somewhat ahead of the lower one. The front and rear faces of both lugs are cut to a screw pitch. A helical cut runs along part of the sleeve wall to receive the stud at the end of the operating rod, which works in this helical cut.

The bolt cap screws to the rear end of the bolt cylinder after the sleeve is mounted. It is bored for the striker to pass through it. The mainspring rear bears against an inner shoulder on this bolt cap. There is a broad flange at the rear of the cap having a clearance for the operating rod. A slot is also provided in the cap for the cocking stud of the striker. The safety slot for the striker stud is at right angles to this stud slot.

A rib with an undercut groove is provided in the right side of the cap to receive the stud on the operating rod. The forward end of the cap seats against the locking sleeve to provide a bearing.

The operating rod itself travels *in the secondary cylinder* in the receiver. It has a lever at its rear to serve as a hand piece, drawing knobs being provided on both sides of the lever. A groove on the underside of the rod receives the point of the bolt stop. Two projections are provided in this groove. The bolt stop

Model 1911 Swiss Service Rifle bolt. The upper picture shows details of the operating system. Note that this design uses a two piece firing pin. The ring on the rear of the striker assembly permits cocking the rifle without opening the action. When this ring is pulled back and turned, it withdraws the striker from sear contact and locks it against accidental discharge.

The lower picture shows detail of bolt assembly and independent view of the operating handle. The assembly is shown in rear position. The operating rod can travel only in a straight line in its own receiver groove. As it moves forward it works against the cam cut in the bolt, compelling the bolt to turn into locking engagement. The lugs lock to the rear of the magazine well in their receiver seats. (Note: Bolt construction differs slightly in earlier designs.)

bears against first one and then the other when in opened or closed position, holding the operating rod ready for forward or rearward thrust.

A dovetailed stud on the left side of the operating rod travels in the undercut groove on the bolt cap; while the rib travels in a slot between the main receiver cylinder (in which the bolt mechanism travels) and the secondary receiver cylinder on the right (in which the operating rod travels).

The operating rod stud working in the helical groove in the locking sleeve provides the means of revolving that element. The stud passes into the bolt cylinder through a slot and rests ahead of the forward section of the striker.

The bolt stop holds the bolt mechanism in place. As the operating rod is pulled back, the point on the bolt stop locks into the front end of the groove in the operating rod. A thumb piece is provided to depress this point to permit the bolt to be withdrawn.

The extractor is a plain flat spring type with front claw which projects beyond the face of the bolt. It is locked into the bolt cylinder by means of a stud having a circular stem and an oval head, which can be locked into place by starting the extractor at right angles into the bolt cylinder, then turning the extractor parallel with the bolt.

The ejector passes through the left side of the receiver, where it is secured by a screw. It is a pin having a broad head and a flat point. It does not move.

The striker is a two-part unit. The firing pin is at the forward end of the front section. A button at the end of the rear section fits into a recess in the forward part. The striker cocking stud, which works in the slot in the bolt cap, is on the underside of the rear striker section. A ring at the end of the rear striker section projects from the rear of the bolt cap and can be used to pull the striker back. Turning it operates the safety.

The sear pivots on a pin in a slot cut in a projection below the receiver. A

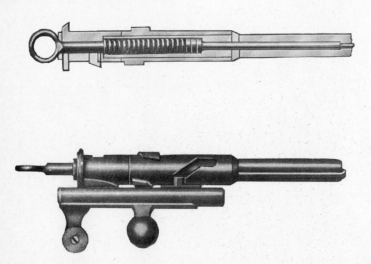

M1889 Swiss Service Rifle bolt. Note that position of lugs and shape of cam slot in bolt as well as operating handle details differ from later pattern.

spiral spring raises the sear nose, passing it through a cut in the bottom of the receiver into the groove where the striker stud travels.

The trigger is a simple element pivoted on a pin in a fork at the rear of the sear.

The magazine is a detachable steel box strengthened by a steel strap which is brazed on. Two openings are provided in the bottom at each side to permit escape of rain or water from melting snow.

The top edges of the magazine are slightly folded in to retain the double column of 3 cartridges each. The magazine follower is bent to raise one side just enough above the other to insure the feeding of cartridges from alternate sides, one at a time. A zigzag wire spring provides the motive power for elevating the follower.

The magazine is designed to be loaded either with single cartridges pressed down in standard fashion, or from a special clip. This clip is of papier maché. Its bottom edges have a tinned strip of iron with two tongues on either side bent over to retain the cartridges firmly in the clip. (This is a modification of a very early American clip, the Russell-Livermore.)

This clip is placed vertically over the exposed magazine with its mouth downwards. There is a wide slot in the papier maché section of the clip to permit passage of the thumb between the front and rear sections of the clip, as the thumb forces the cartridges down from above into the magazine.

The triggerguard in this design is very long. The forward end of the true triggerguard screws to a guard extension at the front, while its rear is fastened with a long screw passing through the stock into the tang. Two screws passing through the guard into projections in the receiver fasten the guard, the receiver and the stock together.

The stock is a one piece design, having finger grooves for gripping. The bed of the rear sight is screwed to the barrel. It is in the form of a ring which encircles the barrel.

Operation

Opening the Bolt: This rifle is operated by drawing straight back on the operating handle, to unlock, extract, eject with one direct pull.

While in theory this action can be operated more rapidly than a turning bolt design, in field use the difference in extracting power of the two designs very often upsets the theory involved. Furthermore, while the lock to the rear of the magazine well is entirely adequate for the cartridge used, it does not compare in strength with the Mauser or turning bolt Mannlicher either for strength of breech support, for certainty of primary extraction, or for bolt closing.

The initial pull on the operating handle draws the operating rod back in its travel cylinder parallel with the bolt in the main receiver cylinder.

As the rod starts back, its unlocking stud travels in the straight section of the locking sleeve in which it is engaged, hence there is no unlocking motion of the bolt assembly at this point.

However, the pull stud on the rod now engages the cocking stud of the striker and starts to draw it back, thus pulling its point free from the primer of the cartridge case in the chamber and back inside the bolt cylinder. The projection in the operating rod groove pushes down the projecting point of the bolt stop.

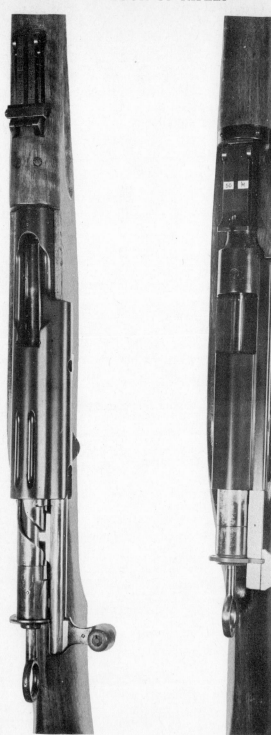

Comparison of Swiss Service Rifle Cal. 7.5mm, Model 11, and Swiss .22 Trainer, actions open. This trainer is also manufactured commercially for match shooting by Hämmerli in Switzerland.

As the rearward travel of the operating rod continues, its pull stud is compelled to move in a straight line, since its rib is travelling in a slot between the two parallel cylinders bored in the receiver. When this stud emerges from the straight cut in the bolt locking sleeve and hits the curved section, it provides a cam action which compels the locking sleeve to rotate. The locking lugs on the sleeve are thus turned out of their recesses in the receiver, and enter the diagonal grooves which connect the locking recesses with the longitudinal lug travel grooves.

Since both the lugs and their recesses are cut to a screw pitch, the opening action forces the entire bolt assembly back about .0625 inch to start the cartridge from the chamber, effecting a comparatively weak primary extraction. (The extraction results from a straight pull, and does not have the advantage of the leverage found in the turning bolt designs.)

At this point the pull stud on the operating rod is at the rear of the slot in the locking sleeve and has completely withdrawn the striker.

The locking lugs enter the longitudinal grooves after passing out of the diagonal grooves and completing rotation of the locking sleeve. The sleeve recess is now forward of the cocking stud. This action is brought about when the mainspring forcing against the head of the striker pushes against the stud. The stud is then in position to drive the bolt assembly forward.

The projection in the operating rod groove now forces the point of the bolt stop down until it hits the end of its groove and halts the rearward motion of the bolt assembly. The operating rod is held parallel with the bolt by the dovetailed stud on the rod which works in the groove in the bolt cap.

The magazine spring pushing against the follower feeds the cartridges up, the top one being lined up for chamber feeding.

Closing the Bolt: When the handle of the operating rod is pushed ahead, the projection in its groove forces the bolt stop down and permits the entire bolt mechanism to be thrust ahead.

The bolt face hits the top cartridge ready to be fed and starts it towards the chamber. When the bolt proper reaches its forward position against the head of the cartridge case, the spring extractor claw snaps into the cannelure around the head of the cartridge.

The lugs pass out of their longitudinal travel grooves in the receiver and enter their diagonal rotating grooves which start the turning motion of the locking sleeve. The sleeve rotates enough to let the stud on the rod leave its sleeve recess. The action is not yet locked however.

As the bolt cap flange nears the receiver bridge, the sear nose catches the striker stud. Since the sear nose holds the striker firmly, the mainspring is compressed by the final thrust. At this point the bolt sleeve lugs have reached the entrances to their recesses in the receiver.

The final thrusting motion causes the straight moving operating rod stud to travel along the helical cam groove in the bolt sleeve. Since the stud does not turn, the sleeve must, thereby rotating the sleeve to bring the locking lugs on it firmly into their receiver recesses. The point of the bolt stop is forced up behind the projection in the groove of the operating rod, thereby preventing the rod from slipping to the rear.

A large ring at the rear of the striker projects from the rear of the bolt cap.

Comparison of actions of Swiss M1911 7.5mm carbine and the cal. .22 Trainer, actions closed.

This forms a grip for the fingers. Pulling this back draws the striker back to cock the action without opening or unlocking it. This is of value in case of a misfire.

This ring device also acts as a manual safety. When the ring is pulled back and twisted to the left, it pulls the striker (of which it is a part) back with it; and the turning motion twists the striker cocking stud until it enters the safety slot provided for it. This prevents the striker from going forward to fire the cartridge and also prevents the bolt assembly from being pulled to the rear, since the rear face of this stud is caught in a shoulder in the groove and also in the bolt cap.

No magazine cutoff is provided in this design.

7.5mm M31 Carbine

The Model 31 has an action which is considerably altered from the Model 1911. Rather than having a long bolt body and a shorter locking sleeve encircling the bolt body which mounts the locking lugs, as on the M1889 and M1911 actions, the Model 31 action uses the short bolt sleeve section as the bolt. The

Swiss 7.5mm Model 31 Carbine (K31).

bolt on the Model 31 has its locking lugs mounted at the front and is only a bit over half as long as the Model 1911 bolt. The Model 31 is a much stronger and better weapon than the earlier rifles because of its modernized bolt. The locking lugs, being frontally placed, provide a stronger action. Since the bolt is shorter, the receiver is also shorter and the M31 as a result has a barrel about 2.5 inches longer than the Model 1911 carbine although its overall length is about the same. This shortening of the bolt has also allowed placing of the magazine just forward of the trigger guard on the M31 instead of being far forward as on the older rifles.

Swiss Bolt Action Service Rifles 1889-1931

7.5mm M1889. First of the Schmidt Rubin straight pull rifles. It has a long staggered row magazine and the bolt sleeve has its locking lugs mounted toward the rear. This is not a particularly strong action.

Swiss 7.5mm M1889 Schmidt Rubin Rifle.

7.5mm M1889/1896. In this weapon the 1889 action was shortened slightly and the lug system was strengthened.

7.5mm M1893 Carbine. This is a Mannlicher straight-pull weapon and did not last long in Swiss service. Only about 4000 were made by SIG at Neuhausen for the Swiss government.

Swiss M93 Mannlicher Cavalry Carbine. Only a few were made.

7.5mm M97 Cadet Rifle. A single shot version of the M1889/96.

7.5mm M1889/1900. A short rifle designed for the use of fortress artillery, signal, balloon, and bicycle troops. This weapon weighs about seven pounds.

7.5mm M1905 Carbine. Same action as M1889/96 rifle, weighs about 7.5 pounds.

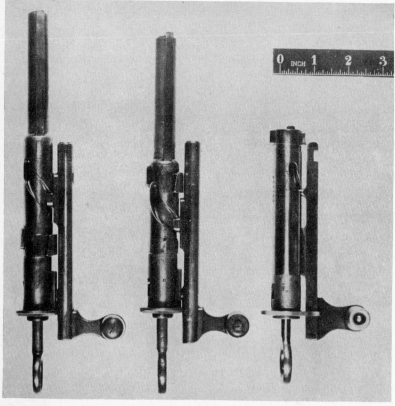

Schmidt Rubin Bolts. Left: M1889 with locking lugs at rear of sleeve. Center: M1911 with locking lugs at front of sleeve. Right: M31 with locking lugs at front of bolt.

7.5mm M1911 Rifle. First Schmidt Rubin specifically built to take the high pressure M11 cartridge. The action is stronger than the earlier actions, having the locking lugs mounted at the front of the bolt sleeve. The M1911 also has a bolt holding open device.

7.5mm M1889/11. A conversion of the M1889/96 rifle to make it suitable for use with the Model 11 cartridge. Some of the earlier carbines were also converted.

7.5mm M1911 Carbine. Short version of the M1911 rifle. Its sight is graduated to 1500 meters rather than 2000 meters as on the rifle. This weapon is used as a reserve weapon in Switzerland at present.

7.5mm M1931 Carbine. (Covered above.)

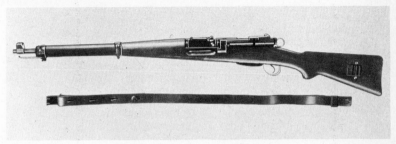

Swiss 7.5mm Model 31/42 Sniper Rifle.

View of Telescope on Model 31/42 Sniper Rifle.

7.5mm M1931/42 Carbine. Sniper version of the M31, having a 1.8 power scope permanently attached to the left side of the receiver. The head of the scope is movable and can be moved up when in use or folded down against the side of the carbine when not in use.

7.5mm M1931/43 Carbine. Same as M1931/42 but scope is 2.8 power.

7.5mm M1931/55 Sniper Rifle. The 7.5mm M1931 carbine with muzzle brake, bipod, shortened sporter type stock with very full pistol grip, and sporting type scope mounted on top of the receiver.

Swiss 7.5mm Model 1931/55 Sniper Rifle. The telescope is a 3.5 power hunting type.

Characteristics of the Significant Schmidt Rubins

	M1889 Rifle	M1911 Rifle	M1911 Carbine	M1931 Carbine
Caliber:	7.5mm	7.54mm	7.54mm	7.51mm
Land Diameter:	.295"	.2968"	.2968"	.2956"
Weight:	9.8 lbs.	10.15 lbs.	8.6 lbs.	8.83 lbs.
Length, Overall:	51.25"	51.6"	43.4"	43.5"
Barrel Length:	30.7"	30.7"	23.3"	25.67"
Magazine:	12-rd. detachable box	6-rd. detachable box	6-rd. detachable box	6-rd. detachable box
Chamber pressure:	38,400 p.s.i.	45,500 p.s.i.	45,500 p.s.i.	45,500 p.s.i.
Muzzle Velocity:	2033 f.p.s.	2640 f.p.s.	2490 f.p.s.	2560 f.p.s.

Swiss 7.5mm Ammunition

The 7.5mm Model 90 cartridge was loaded with semi-smokeless powder and had a long, round-nosed, hollow-based, paper-patched, lead bullet. This round was soon replaced by the Model 90/03; this cartridge has a paper patched, steel capped bullet. The 90/23 cartridge, the next of the series, is loaded with 34 grains of smokeless powder and has a copper or steel jacketed bullet. This is the only one currently available from Switzerland which should be used with the early Schmidt Rubin models i.e. those prior to the M1896/11. The 7.5mm Model 11 is the current Swiss service cartridge—it should not be used in the older Swiss rifles! This cartridge has a boat-tailed, nickel steel-clad, jacketed bullet. The Swiss 7.5mm cartridge may be seen referred to as the 7.45mm, 7.54, or 7.51 Swiss.

Swiss Sporting Arms

The Swiss themselves have never engaged extensively in the field of sporting small arms manufactures for export. The Societe Industrielle Suisse of Neuhausen manufactured submachine guns for export. In general however, very few small arms of Swiss manufacture ever leave that country. Even the elementary Schmidt-Rubin Army rifle was essentially a collector's item outside of Switzerland.

So called "Swiss Mausers" are actually rifles built usually on Belgian F. N. actions barreled and stocked in Switzerland. Instead of the conventional Mauser cocking piece and safety, these are often made with a modified cocking piece

Upper picture Swiss Hämmerli-Mauser, superior sporting rifle built on F.N. (Belgian) action in Switzerland. Lower picture shows a typical Hämmerli sporting bolt action .22. Hämmerli rifles are famous for fine construction.

Left side view of Hämmerli-Mauser action. Note that the bolt plug and safety differ from the standard Mauser design. The safety works on the Mauser principle, but does not lock the bolt down. Current Czech rifles are copying this bolt plug and safety.

carrying a low mounted modification of the Mauser safety on the left side to permit use of low telescope sight.

These rifles are made up in many calibers, since they are essentially built-up custom rifles. The favorite stock reaches below the barrel to the muzzle. These rifles are high priced even for the amount of hand work they entail.

The Swiss single shot .22 trainer is almost a duplicate in appearance and external characteristics of the Service Rifle. It is straight pull, but has a simplified locking system. It is one of the finest .22 precision rifles made, though again the price is high.

Some of the finest block action single shot rifles ever designed for target work have been built by custom gunmakers in Switzerland. Arms of this type vary so much in caliber and design that it is impossible to classify them for practical purposes. As a class they are merely modifications of the so-called Martini-Henry, Aydt and Sharps block actions, operated by levers of varying designs.

Hämmerli currently manufactures several first-class match rifles. These weapons are exported to the United States and have been used fairly extensively in free matches in this country. The Hämmerli Tanner 300 meter match rifle is a heavy single-shot free rifle with thumb-hole type stock, adjustable hook type butt plate, and palm rest. This bolt action rifle can be obtained in any of the common calibers used in the Olympic 300 meter match. The Model 503 and 504

Swiss Hämmerli caliber .22 Model 503 Match Rifle.

are .22 caliber match rifles. They differ only in triggers, the 504 having a 5 lever set trigger which has a finer adjustment than the 503. These rifles weigh 15.5 pounds, are 49.5 inches long and have a 27.5 inch barrel. These rifles are, of course, fitted with micrometer rear sights and "tunnel" type front sights.

Common single shot calibers for target work are .22 long rifle, 22 extra long and 7.5mm Swiss.

Large numbers of early Schmidt-Rubin rifles, particularly the 1889 through 1911 patterns have been converted to handle 22 caliber extra long ammunition. These are extensively used as training rifles.

Swiss manufactured and Swiss assembled rifles are imported here by Firearms International Corp. of Washington, D. C.

EARLIER BREECHLOADERS: In 1867 Switzerland equipped some of her troops with the Amsler. This was a lifting block, exposed hammer conversion design along the general lines of the familiar American Single Shot Springfield.

This rifle was followed by a line of Vetterli Rifles.

F. Vetterli, Director of the Neuhausen arms works recognized the inherent value of the bolt action for military service. He combined the idea of the turning bolt action with an adaptation of the Henry-Winchester principle of a tube below the barrel serving as a cartridge magazine. His initial repeating rifle was ready in 1869, the Swiss Confederation having voted on the adoption of such a system in 1868. In 1870 a single shot version of the Vetterli for the .41 Rim Fire Swiss cartridge was introduced. An improved version of the repeating rifle was developed in 1871 and a Cadet in 1878. The final modification was known as the 1881. This rifle was the standard of the Swiss forces until the official adoption of the straight pull Schmidt-Rubin in 1889 for a new small bore cartridge, the 7.5mm.

The Vetterli Model 1881

This rifle is a turning bolt action repeating rifle with a magazine tube in the fore-end. The magazine capacity is 11 cartridges, plus one in the elevating cage. The bolt is locked by lugs to the rear of the boltway in the receiver. The magazine is loaded through a right side opening in the receiver. This opening is covered by a sliding hinged plate. The rifle is loaded as in the case of the Winchester, except that this side plate cover is moved aside to expose the loading opening. Cartridges are thrust in bullet first to compress the magazine spring by forcing the follower ahead in the hollow magazine tube.

The cartridge elevating system in this design follows very closely that of the early 1866 Winchester. Turning the bolt handle up revolves the locking lugs out of their seats. When the bolt is pulled straight back, a stud on the bottom of the bolt cylinder works against a rising arm of a bell crank lever hinged in the receiver below it. As this upper arm is drawn back, a lower arm extending forward below the lifting cage for the cartridge (which has been fed back by the magazine spring) is elevated in line with the bolt. When the bolt handle is thrust forward, the bolt chambers the cartridge by stripping it forward out of the lifting cage. The stud on the bell crank lever is then forced ahead, depressing the extending forward arm and lowering the cage in line to permit the magazine spring to feed another cartridge back into the cage for the next lifting movement.

The Vetterli repeater was officially adopted in 1881. It carries 11 cartridges in the tube, one in the carrier or elevating cage, and a 13th in the chamber.

Large quantities of these rifles were sold here early in the century by Bannerman of N. Y. after the Swiss had discarded the model. Thousands are still in use on American farms.

Swiss Model 1869-81 Vetterli

Caliber: 10.4mm R.F.
Overall length, rifle without bayonet: 52″   *With bayonet attached:* 70.2″
Overall weight, rifle without bayonet: 9.75 lbs.   *With bayonet attached:* 11.62 lbs.
Type of action: Turnbolt   *Type of Bolt:* Lugs at rear
Type of Magazine: Tubular   *Capacity:* 12
Barrel Length: 33.2″   *No. Grooves:* 4   *Direction of Twist:* Right
Bore Diameter: .4095″   *Groove Dia.:* .4273″   *Rate of Twist:* 26″

Notes:

1. When the Swiss Army discarded this rifle huge quantities were sold to U. S. dealers. Many were converted to 5-shot sporters by shortening the fore-end and the magazine tube. These rifles were so widely distributed in the U. S. that the so-called .41 Swiss Rim Fire cartridge was manufactured here until quite recently.

.41 Swiss Cartridge

Other Names: 10.4 x 38R Vetterli M1867
Type: Rimmed, Necked, Rimfire
Overall Length: 2.22"
Type Powder: Nitrocellulose
Approximate Charge :
Type Primer: Rim Cavity

BULLET

Type: Lead (Round Nose)
Diameter: .426"
Weight: 310 grs.

CARTRIDGE CASE

Length Overall: 1.55"
Length Head to Shoulder: .99"
Length of Shoulder: .40"
Length of Neck: .16"
Diameter at Rim: .625"
Diameter at Base: .537"
Diameter at Neck: .435"
Diameter at Shoulder: .520"

BALLISTICS (approximate)

Muzzle Velocity: 1325 f.s.

Notes: This is the U. S. Commercial Load.

Swiss 10.4mm Vetterli M1867 Cartridge

Other Names: .41 Swiss. 10.4x38R. 10.2mm
   Vetterli
Type: Rimfire, Copper Case, Necked
Overall Length: 2.20"
Average Wt.: 470 gr.
Type Powder: Black
Approximate Chg.: 57-58 gr.
Type Primer: Rim Cavity

BULLET

Type: Lead
Diameter: .425"
Weight: 313 gr.
Length: .996"

CARTRIDGE CASE

Length Overall: 1.55"
Length Head to Shoulder: 1.00"
Length of Shoulder: .39"
Length of Neck: .158"
Diameter at Rim: .622"
Diameter at Base: .540"
Diameter at Neck: .444"
Diameter at Shoulder: .530"

BALLISTICS (approximate)

Muzzle Velocity: 1427 f.s.

Notes: The 10.4mm M67-71/78 round used a charge of semi-smokeless powder and a paper patched bullet.

Swiss Cal. 7.5mm Model 11 Cartridge

Other Names: 7.5mm Schmidt-Rubin
Type: Rimless, Necked, Centerfire
Overall Length: 3.05"
Average Wt.: 404 gr.
Type Powder: Nitrocellulose
Approximate Chg.: 49.3 gr.
Type Primer: Berdan

BULLET

Type: Jacketed, Pointed
Diameter: .3086"
Weight: 174 gr.
Length: 1.37"

CARTRIDGE CASE

Length Overall: 2.18"
Length Head to Shoulder: 1.15"
Length of Shoulder: .11"
Length of Neck: .32"
Diameter at Rim: .496"
Diameter at Base: .494"
Diameter at Neck: .335"
Diameter at Shoulder: .452"

BALLISTICS (approximate)

Muzzle Velocity: 2560 f.s.
Pressure: About 43,000 lbs./sq. in.

Chapter 54

TURKEY

(Turkiye Cumhuriyeti)

PRINCIPAL GOVERNMENT PLANTS: Kirikkale.
PRINCIPAL PRIVATE PLANTS: None of consequence.
PRINCIPAL MILITARY RIFLES: U.S. rifle cal. .30 M1. Mauser 1905, 7.92mm. Also earlier patterns, primarily M1893 converted to 7.92mm; British No. 1 and No. 4 rifles; Czech Model 24 Mausers, cal. 7.92mm; German Gew. 98 and Czech M98/22, 7.92mm.

Mausers of all the German 98 series in caliber 7.92mm were in use in Turkey at the beginning of World War II.

Model 1887 (Mauser Repeater)

In 1887 Turkey adopted the last of the black powder Mausers, a caliber specially designed by Paul Mauser as representing the best ballistic performance possible with the powders he knew before the coming of smokeless. This rifle was outmoded in the year it was designed (1886) by the French invention of an efficient smokeless powder. It was replaced by the Model 1890.

Description of the 7.65mm Model 1890 Turkish Mauser

This is a typical turn-bolt Mauser, similar to that described under Belgium, Model 1889, with the following exceptions:

1. The barrel does not have a metal jacket type handguard; a short wooden handguard is used.

2. Buttress threads are used on the bolt sleeve and a one piece sear is used.

The cocking system is similar to the Spanish Model 1893, depending on manual thrust on the bolt to complete compression of the mainspring on the forward thrust. No camming action is provided to assist in this effort.

The bolt stop and bolt stop latch are similar to the Belgian Mauser, being of the flat, swing-out type lying along the left side of the receiver bridge.

The magazine is of the single column, vertical type holding the conventional five cartridges. The follower rises to hold the bolt open when the magazine is empty.

The 7.65mm Model 1893 Turkish Mauser

A slightly modified version of the Spanish model 1893, this arm differs in caliber and in having a magazine cut-off.

EARLIER OFFICIAL BREECHLOADERS: The early American Peabody and Peabody-Martini rifles used jointly by Roumania and Turkey are described under Roumania.

Martini-Henry rifles of the British pattern and caliber were also among the early breechloaders in Turkey.

The Winchester 1866 in Caliber .44 Turkish rim fire proved a deciding factor because of its firepower in early battles against Russia.

The earliest Mausers used by Turkey are listed in the Mauser Chronology in appendix VIII.

Types of Turkish Mausers (Box Magazine Types)

(1). Model 1890. This model has a single line detachable box magazine. Locking is effected by dual front lugs on bolt. Cocking is on forward thrust of bolt handle. Caliber 7.65mm.

(2). Model 1890 Conversion. Specimens of the 1890 will be encountered altered to caliber 7.9mm. Rifles of this type were used in Yugoslavia in World War II.

Turkish 7.65mm M1890 Mauser Rifle. The straight line box magazine holds 5 cartridges.

(3). Model 1893. This is essentially the Spanish Model 1893 with caliber changed to 7.65mm and cutoff incorporated. Dual front lugs, cocking on closing thrust, built-in staggered magazine.

(4). Models 1903 and 1905. Caliber 7.65mm, but otherwise the same as the German Gewehr 98 except for sights, handguard, upper band, longer cocking piece and firing pin, and modified bolt stop. Many of these have been converted to 7.9mm.

(5). Czech-made Model 24 Mauser System Rifles, caliber 7.9mm. (See under *Belgium.*)

(6). Note: All forms of German rifles and carbines in caliber 7.9mm were provided to the Turks in the period of World War I or later. Any German equipment may be encountered.

(7). Since the end of World War II, both British and U. S. equipment have been made available to Turkey.

Turkish Model 1890 Mauser

Caliber: 7.65mm
Overall length, rifle without bayonet: 48.6″
Overall weight, rifle without bayonet: 8.8 lbs.
Type of action: Turnbolt
Type of Magazine: Box—Single Column
Barrel Length: 29.1″   *No. Grooves:* 4
Bore Diameter: .302″   *Groove Dia.:* .311″

With bayonet attached: 66.6″
With bayonet attached: 10.75 lbs.
Type of bolt: 1 piece, rotating head
Capacity: 5
   Direction of Twist: Right
   Rate of Twist: 9.84″

Yugoslav 7.92mm M90T; this is the Turkish 7.65mm cut down and rebarreled to 7.92mm.

Turkish M. 1893, Cal. 7.65mm Rifle. Mauser. This is one of the many Mauser forms in Turkish use. It is essentially the same as the Spanish Mauser 1893, except for caliber and the use of a magazine cut-off.

The early Turkish Mausers are the only general production Mausers to employ magazine cut-offs. Turkish patterns from 1903 on are the same as the German service arms of the same periods in most mechanical characteristics.

Turkish Model 1893 Mauser

Caliber: 7.65mm
Overall length, rifle without bayonet: 48.6"
Overall weight, rifle without bayonet: 8.8 lbs.
Type of action: Turnbolt
Type of Magazine: Box—Staggered Column
Barrel Length: 29.1"   *No. Grooves:* 4
Bore Diameter: .301"   *Groove Dia.:* .312"

With bayonet attached: 66.4"
With bayonet attached: 10.2 lbs.
Type of bolt: 1 piece—rotating head
Capacity: 5
   Direction of Twist: Right
   Rate of Twist: 9.84"

Notes:

1. This is the first Turkish rifle to use the now-common flush type staggered magazine.
2. This model has a cut-off.

Turkish 7.65mm Mauser Cartridge

Type: Rimless, Necked, Centerfire
Overall Length: 3.06"
Average Wt.: 370 gr.
Type Powder: Nitrocellulose
Approximate Chg.: 49.2 gr.
Type Primer: Berdan

BULLET

Type: Jacketed, Pointed
Diameter: .311"
Weight: 154.3 gr.
Length: 1.06"

CARTRIDGE CASE

Length Overall: 2.09"
Length Head to Shoulder: 1.75"
Length of Shoulder: .10"
Length of Neck: .24"
Diameter at Rim: .474"
Diameter at Base: .470"
Diameter at Neck: .340"
Diameter at Shoulder: .425"

BALLISTICS (approximate)

Muzzle Velocity: 2720 f.s.
Pressure: About 45,000 lbs./sq. in.

Notes: 1. This cartridge is interchangeable with the Belgian 7.65mm, Peruvian 7.65mm and Argentine 7.65mm Military cartridges.

Turkish Model 1905 Carbine. Although these weapons were originally made in 7.65mm, the specimen shown has been rebarreled to 7.92mm.

Turkish Model 1887 Mauser

Caliber: 9.5mm
Overall length, rifle without bayonet: 49.3"
Overall weight, rifle without bayonet: 9.3 lbs.
Type of action: Turnbolt
Type of Magazine: Tubular
Barrel Length: 29.9"   *No. Grooves:* 4
Bore Diameter: .374"   *Groove Dia.:* .386"

With bayonet attached: 67.8"
With bayonet attached: 10.8 lbs.
Type of bolt: 2 piece—Rotating head
Capacity: 8
   Direction of Twist: Right
   Rate of Twist: 19.7"

Notes:

1. This is a modification of the German Model 1871/84. It is an early Mauser turning bolt action with removable bolt head.

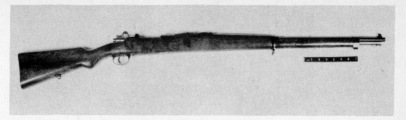

Turkish 7.65mm M1903 Rifle.

Turkish 9.5mm Mauser M1887 Cartridge

Other Names: 9.5x60R
Type: Rimmed, Necked, Centerfire, Type A Base
Overall Length: 2.973"
Average Wt.: 556 gr.
Type Powder: Black
Approximate Chg.: 69.4 gr.
Type Primer: Berdan

BULLET

Type: Lead, Paper Patched, Flat Nose
Diameter: .382"
Weight: 284 gr.
Length: 1.047"

CARTRIDGE CASE

Length Overall: 2.36"
Length Head to Shoulder: 1.55"
Length of Shoulder: .200"
Length of Neck: .61"
Diameter at Rim: .585"
Diameter at Base: .515"
Diameter at Neck: .407"
Diameter at Shoulder: .487"

BALLISTICS (approximate)

Muzzle Velocity: 1758 f.s.
Pressure: About 37,000 lbs./sq. in.

Notes: This was the last Mauser black powder cartridge.

Chapter 55
UNION OF SOVIET SOCIALIST REPUBLICS
(Rossija)

PRINCIPAL GOVERNMENT PLANTS: Tula, Sestoretsk, Izshevsky, and many others.

PRINCIPAL PRIVATE PLANTS: None.

PRINCIPAL MILITARY RIFLES: (a) 7.62mm AK-47 Assault Rifle. (b) Bolt action Model 1891/30, sniper version only.

Soviet 7.62mm AK-47 Assault Rifle

Shortly after World War II the U.S.S.R. adopted three squad level weapons for a new "intermediate" sized 7.62mm cartridge. These weapons are the 7.62mm SKS semiautomatic carbine, the 7.62mm AK-47 assault rifle, and the 7.62mm RPD light machine gun. The 7.62mm AK-47 assault rifle is now used as the basic Soviet rifle and the 7.62mm SKS carbine is no longer used by Soviet infantry.

Soviet 7.62mm AK-47 Assault Rifle, right side view.

System of operation: Gas, selective fire
Weight, loaded: 10.58 lbs.
Length, overall:
  w/fixed wooden stock: 34.25"
  w/folding stock extended: 34.25"
  w/folding stock folded: 25.39"
Barrel length: 16.34"
Feed device: 30-round, curved, staggered-row, detachable box magazine, not fillable with chargers

Muzzle velocity: 2329 f.p.s.
Cyclic rate: 600 r.p.m.
Bore diameter: .301"
Groove diameter: .311"
Direction of twist: Right, 1 turn in 9.45"
Sights, front: Protected post
  rear: Tangent leaf with open V-notch, graduated from 1-8 (100 M to 800 M) with battle-sight setting

The AK-47 Assault Rifle is considered even more efficient than the SKS Semi-automatic Carbine and is rated excellent in its class. It is comfortable to shoot and easily controlled in full automatic fire. This is attributed to its loaded weight (roughly 10.5 pounds) in relation to the medium-power 7.62mm x 39mm M43 cartridge it fires as compared with NATO-type rifles of similar weight where recoil is somewhat more pronounced because of the full-powered 7.62mm NATO cartridge used. It has a full automatic cyclic rate of fire of 600 rpm, obtainable when the selector lever on the right side of the receiver is centrally

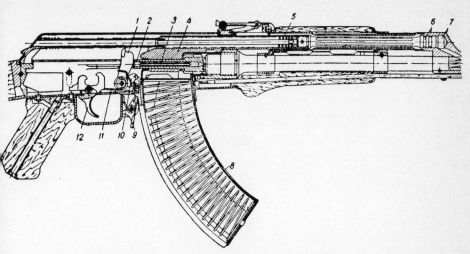

Section View of AK-47 Assault Rifle. 1, Hammer. 2, Bolt. 3, Firing pin. 4, Operating rod. 5, Recoil spring. 6, Gas piston. 7, Gas cylinder. 8, Magazine. 9, Magazine catch. 10, Full automatic sear. 11, Trigger and hammer spring. 12, Trigger.

located on the Cyrillic symbols: AB. In the lowest position, with the lever on OD, semiautomatic fire is possible. With the lever upright, the weapon is on "Safe."

The AK is simply constructed, yet sturdy, and machined in accordance with newly-elevated Soviet standards of manufacture, paralleling those of Western Europe and the United States. Internally, the full length of the barrel is

7.62mm AK-47 Assault Rifle (left side).

chromium-plated for greater wear and rustproofing. The gas cylinder being located above the barrel makes for an almost straight-line butt stock. In addition to the standard infantry pattern with wooden butt, a special AK is produced for paratroop and armored troop use. This has a folding metal butt similar to that of the German Schmeisser submachine gun of World War II fame.

The AK has a sliding, tangent-type rear sight, adjustable in 100-meter increments from 100-800 meters. A separate battlesight setting is provided. To zero in, the front sight is screwed up or down; lateral adjustments for windage are made with a special tool.

AK with folding stock.

The AK is gas operated as follows: Gas is tapped from the barrel and enters the gas port housing over the barrel via an orifice located 4.6″ from the muzzle; the gas impinges upon the gas piston contained within the gas cylinder to drive it rearward. The massive, machined bolt carrier with operating handle is attached to the rear part of the gas piston; the carrier houses the cylindrical bolt with recessed face. The bolt contains extractor, firing pin, two forward locking lugs, and camming lug. As the piston-carrier assembly retracts under pressure, excess gas is vented through holes in the forward end of the combined gas cylinder-handguard assembly, while the piston section of the gas piston-bolt carrier assembly slides back and through the rear sight.

During rearward travel, the camming groove machined in the carrier bears against the camming lug on the bolt causing it to rotate and unlock. The unlocking process is delayed inasmuch as about 1/4″ of free travel is permitted the bolt carrier before the camming surfaces engage. As the bolt rides back with the piston-carrier assembly, it extracts and ejects the expended case, and a cocking cam at the rear of the bolt carrier cocks the hammer. Firing pin is not spring actuated.

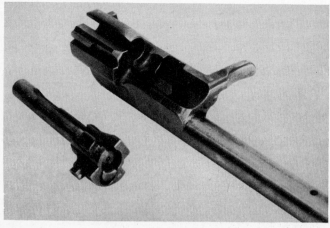

AK Bolt and Bolt Carrier.

The return spring, which has been compressed, exerts pressure on the bolt carrier and reverses its direction. Upon moving forward, a fresh round is stripped from the magazine and chambered. Pressure upon the camming surfaces causes the bolt to rotate and the two locking lugs to engage locking shoulders in the receiver to lock the action.

Like the SKS, the AK is very simple to field strip and maintain, particularly the gas mechanism. When field stripping, depress magazine catch situated below and forward of the triggerguard and pull magazine down and forward; remove cartridge from chamber. The cover catch is a component of the return spring assembly; when depressed, it permits removal of both receiver cover and return spring assembly. Pull back operating handle and slide gas piston-bolt carrier assembly, together with bolt, up and out of engaging slots in the receiver. As in the SKS, the upper handguard is an integral part of the gas cylinder. The lever on the right side of the rear sight locks in the handguard—turning it up releases the handguard, which can be pulled forward to free its rear end from the rear sight housing. Pull cleaning rod down slightly to remove it from stock. After turning front band lock, wooden forearm can be pulled forward. Reverse steps to reassemble the gun.

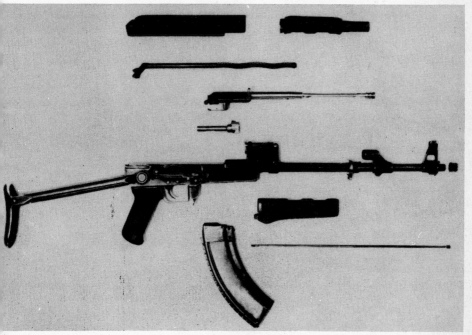

AK Stripped.

7.62mm SKS Carbine

The SKS is chambered for the same 7.62mm "intermediate" sized M43 cartridge as is used with the AK-47.

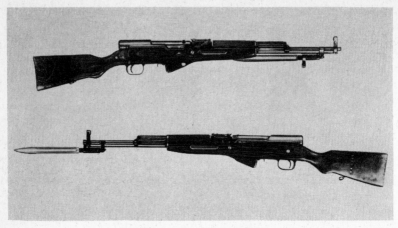

Soviet 7.62mm SKS Carbine.

System of operation: **Gas, semiautomatic fire only**

Weight, loaded: 8.84 lb.

Length, overall: 40.16"

Barrel length: 20.47"

Feed device: 10-round, fixed, staggered double-row, box magazine

Sights, front: **Hooded post**

   rear: **Tangent leaf, graduated from 100 M to 1000 M**

Muzzle velocity: 2411 f.p.s.

Type of bolt: 1 piece, tipping

Bore diameter: .301"

Groove diameter: .311"

Direction of twist: Right 1 turn in 9.45"

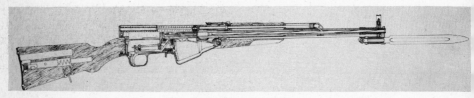

Section View of SKS Carbine.

The SKS was adopted before the AK. It is a gas-operated, semiautomatic rifle and might be referred to as a miniature version of the outstanding 14.5mm PTRS semiautomatic antitank rifle used during World War II. Because of its light recoil, 35 r.p.m. of aimed fire can be achieved.

Unlike its predecessor, the Tokarev, the SKS features an instantly dismountable gas system. The gas cylinder is an integral part of the handguard and contains the piston rod, tappet rod, and tappet rod return spring. The front end of the combined gas cylinder and handguard fits over a gas port housing pinned to the barrel approximately 7" from the muzzle. The rear end abuts against the rear sight. The latch located on the right side of this sight serves to lock the handguard-gas cylinder assembly into place. Its removal for field maintenance takes less than three seconds.

When the rifle is fired, gas enters the gas port housing under pressure to thrust the piston rod back against the short tappet rod. In moving back, the tappet rod slides through a hole in the rear sight base and a corresponding one in the top of the receiver to strike the bolt carrier. The claw-like arrangement of the bolt carrier cams the rear end of the bolt upward, unlocking it completely after 7/16″ of rearward travel. The kinetic energy imparted to the bolt carrier upon being struck by the tappet rod is sufficient to cause the bolt and bolt carrier to travel together 3⅞″ rearward to extract and eject the fired case and to compress the recoil spring. The compressed recoil spring forces the bolt and carrier forward to strip a cartridge from the magazine

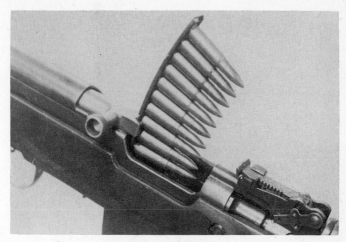

Loading SKS.

and chamber it. The camming surfaces within the carrier force the rear end of the bolt down into locked position. The lower rear end of the bolt then butts up against a crosspiece set in the receiver.

The bayonet of the SKS is attached to the barrel and folded back under the barrel when not in use. The stock and handguard of laminated beechwood are given a hard, clear lacquer, waterproof finish. The butt contains a combination cleaning tool and cleaning kit. The receiver, bolt carrier, bolt, and trigger group are closely-machined parts.

The magazine group is unusual and consists of a stamped and welded sheet metal housing, stamped sheet metal floor cap, and sheet metal follower. Both the follower arm and floor cap are hinged to the forward end of the magazine body. A coil spring set at the hinging point furnishes sufficient pressure to the follower arm to insure feed of cartridges. The weapon can be loaded from above with 10-shot stripper clips for which a guide groove has been provided in the forward face of the bolt carrier. It is important to exert thumb pressure against the cartridges as close to the clip as possible since pressure applied farther forward makes it difficult to strip the last three rounds. The stripper clip is a one-piece, spring-steel stamping—very sturdy and efficient. The magazine can also be loaded with single rounds.

When unloading the weapon for field stripping, rapid emptying of the magazine is accomplished by holding the hand under the floor cap to catch the loaded rounds as the cap drops open upon pulling back the magazine latch. After clearing the chamber, swing latch on right side of rear sight upward to the first stop. The gas cylinder-handguard assembly can be removed by lifting

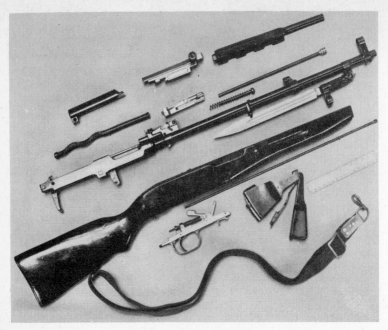

SKS Stripped.

up at the rear and withdrawing it from its forward contact with the gas port housing. By swinging up the latch to its second stop, plunger and spring can be released easily provided thumb pressure is maintained against tappet rod.

To dismantle the bolt assembly, swing latch pinned to the receiver on the right of the rear sight until it is upright and pull out as far as possible. Raise rear end of receiver cover, pulling back and out. Recoil spring can now be removed. By pulling bolt carrier up and out to the rear, bolt will be simultaneously extracted. Push safety lever into safe position. With point of bullet, press pocket of spring catch directly behind triggerguard and push forward. Trigger group will become unfastened and jump outward; swing out and pull back to remove. Pull magazine group down and to the rear. Gripping receiver latch pin, lift receiver up and out of stock. Pull handle of bayonet towards blade; pull bayonet down. Remove cleaning rod from under barrel.

By reversing these steps, the weapon can be reassembled. However, the following precautions must be observed. Reseat fore-end of stock properly within barrel band. When replacing the magazine, its forward end must engage the lug extending from the rear sight beneath the barrel. Hinge magazine upward and hold in position, while guiding projecting pins on trigger group into receiver lug. Apply pressure; if trigger group does not click into place, brace gun with one hand and, with the palm of the other, deliver a sharp blow against the triggerguard to insure full seating.

Earlier Russian Semiautomatic and Automatic Rifles

The Russians started working on semiautomatic rifles early in the 20th century. Some of the early efforts involved converting the bolt action M1891 Mosin Nagant into a self-loader. V. G. Fedorov produced a self-loading design in 1907 and Roshchepya converted a Mosin Nagant in 1905. The famed Russian designer F. V. Tokarev also produced a semiautomatic rifle in this period. The 1916 Fedorov was the first of Russian selective fire rifles that was produced in

Russian 6.5mm M1916 Fedorov "Avtomat," one of the first assault rifles."

quantity. This weapon was chambered for the 6.5mm Japanese cartridge. This recoil operated, selective fire weapon could be considered one of the first assault rifles. It is fed by a 25-round box magazine, weighs 9.7 lbs. and is 39 inches long. In 1926 a number of designs were tested, among them the products of Tokarev, Degtyarev, Federov, Koleshnikov, and Konovalov; these trials continued until 1932.

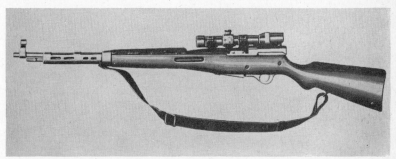

Early Soviet Semiautomatic 7.62mm M1931 Simonov Rifle.

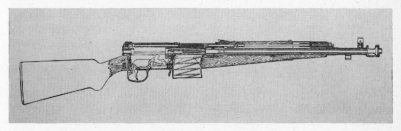

Section View of Soviet 7.62mm M1932 Tokarev Carbine.

Limited production of a few types were carried out. Among these was a 1931 Model believed to be a design of Sergei Gavrilovich Simonov and a Model 1932 Tokarev carbine. Both of these weapons are gas operated and chambered for the Russian 7.62mm rimmed cartridge. The first selective fire rifle produced in significant quantity was the 7.62mm M1936 Simonov (AVS). The Simonov was followed by the semiautomatic 7.62mm Tokarev M1938 (SVT-38) and the semiautomatic and selective fire 7.62mm M1940 Tokarevs (SVT-40) and (AVT-40).

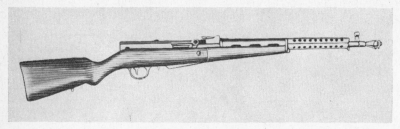

Soviet Semiautomatic 7.62mm Model 1938 Carbine.

Differences Between the Various Models of the Tokarev Rifle

7.62 Tokarev Semiautomatic Rifle Model 1938 (SVT-38). a. Has a two-piece stock and two stock bands.

b. A groove is cut out on the right side of the stock for the cleaning rod. The two stock bands serve as cleaning rod retainers.

c. This rifle has a one-piece magazine release.

d. It has a sheet metal guard forward of the wooden handguard.

e. It has a six-baffle muzzle brake.

7.62mm Tokarev Semiautomatic Sniper Rifle M1938. This model is the same as the semiautomatic rifle M1938 except that the barrel has been selected and the receiver has been drilled and tapped for a telescope mount.

7.62mm Tokarev Semiautomatic Rifle M1940 (SVT-40). a. It has top and bottom sheet metal guards forward of the stock and handguard.

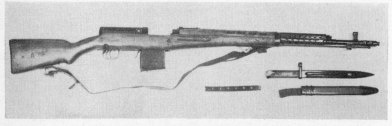

Soviet 7.62 Selective Fire Tokarev M1940 Rifle.

Soviet 7.62mm Semiautomatic Tokarev M1940 Rifle.

b. The full length cleaning rod is fitted into the stock under the barrel, and is held in place by a spring catch on the bayonet lug.

c. The stock is of one piece design.

d. The magazine release is of two-piece design.

e. The bayonet is shorter than the M1938 bayonet.

f. It has a two or three baffle muzzle brake.

7.62 Tokarev Automatic Rifle M1940 (AVT-40). The automatic rifle M1940 is almost identical in appearance to the semiautomatic rifle M1940. A notch has been cut into the right side of the stock, at the rear of the trigger guard, to allow the safety lever to swing to the right for automatic fire.

7.62 Tokarev Semiautomatic Sniper Rifle M1940. This model is the same as the semiautomatic rifle M1940 except that the barrel has been selected and the receiver has been drilled and tapped for a telescope mount.

Description of the Soviet Tokarev Models 1938 and 1940

These are gas operated semiautomatic rifles. The basic operating system is the same in all models. Differences lie in stock design and in minor changes in compensators and magazine catches. The bolt is held open in position for recharging of the magazine after the last cartridge has been ejected.

The design has a somewhat unusual feature, a "false muzzle" in the form of a sleeve screwed over the barrel and pinned in place. The "compensator" or "muzzle brake" is formed as a part of this sleeve. The front sight stud and the bayonet stud are integral with this false muzzle instead of being attached to the barrel as is the usual practice. The gas port housing is also formed at the rear of the sleeve where it screws over the muzzle of the barrel.

The breech action assembly consists of (1) the gas valve and operating rod assembly (2) the operating slide or "bolt carrier" (3) the bolt assembly (4) the breech cover or "housing" and (5) the recoil or "bolt return" spring.

A gas port is drilled through the top of the barrel a short distance from the true muzzle. It is covered by the gas port housing. The forward wall of the gas port housing is drilled and tapped to accept a small lag-bolt. The inner end of this bolt projects over the gas port and is provided with five cuts of varying dimension. The outer end of the bolt projects forward out of the housing and is provided with five flat surfaces, instead of the conventional square head. A number, from 1 to 5 inclusive, is stamped on each flat surface. By turning this bolt the flow of gas from the gas port upward into the gas port housing can be controlled to provide more or less thrust on the operating rod.

A round steel cylinder bored through from end to end is threaded into the rear of the gas port housing so that it lies over the barrel and parallel to it with the open end of the cylinder to the rear. We will refer to this as the "gas cylinder." A bottle necked steel sleeve, bored out from front and rear so as to leave a solid steel wall inside the cylinder at the bottle neck, is slipped over the open end of the gas cylinder to form a sleeve valve.

The operating rod assembly consists of a two-piece steel rod and a coiled return-spring. The short rear section of the operating rod is surrounded by the coiled return-spring and lies under the rear sight base, extending to the rear through a tunnel drilled through the rear sight-base lug on top of the receiver ring. As it emerges the end of the rod impinges on the forward nose of the bolt carrier. The forward portion of the rod is enlarged to form a collar. The return spring bears against this collar and, to the rear, against the rear sight-base lug. The forward end of the rod is bored out inside the collar to form a slip-fit coupling which accepts the rear end of the longer section of the operating rod. This longer section extends forward on top of the barrel and slips into the bottlenecked portion of the sleeve valve.

As the bullet passes the gas port some of the gas forces its way upward into the gas port housing and expands to the rear through the gas port cylinder. Emerging from the rear of the cylinder it is trapped inside the sleeve valve and forces the sleeve sharply to the rear. This movement of the sleeve valve forces the operating rod to the rear for a distance of about $1\frac{1}{2}$ inches. Further movement of the rod is stopped at this point by the full compression of the return spring against its rear bearing. The spring then returns the rod and sleeve valve to their forward positions.

In the meantime the operating rod has forced the bolt carrier sharply rearward for a distance equal to about half the full travel distance of the carrier and bolt. The carrier and bolt continue to the rear under their own momentum. The extraction of the cartridge case is completed, the hammer cocked, and the recoil spring is fully compressed. The recoil spring then returns the carrier and bolt to their forward positions. As the bolt moves forward it strips a cartridge from the top of the stack in the magazine, chambers it, the bolt locks and the gun is ready to fire.

The bolt carrier or operating slide is a rugged steel housing about $4\frac{3}{4}$ inches long and, when viewed from the rear, roughly of a figure 8 shape with the bottom of the eight cut away to form a semi-cylindrical housing which fits down over the bolt. The top of the figure 8 section is bored out from the rear to take the forward portion of the two-piece coil spring which is the recoil spring. The solid forward end of this section forms the "nose" of the bolt carrier which takes the thrust of the operating rod when the action is opened. Guide ribs running along the outside of the bottom edge of the housing engage grooves in the receiver to hold the carrier as it slides backward and forward. The groove on the right side of the receiver is milled away at the rear, under the breech cover, so that when the cover is removed the carrier and bolt may be lifted out of the receiver. About $\frac{3}{4}$ of an inch from the rear of the housing it is cut away on each side to provide for the camming lugs on the bolt. The front and rear surfaces of these cuts are made at an angle to provide camming surfaces for the bolt camming lugs. The bolt handle projects straight out to the right from the forward end of the carrier.

The bolt is of one piece design. The bolt face is recessed. Dual opposed camming lugs (not locking lugs) are situated on the right and left side at the bottom rear of the bolt. The firing pin is of one piece, two diameter, design with its larger diameter at the rear. It is inserted into the bolt from the rear. A coil spring mounted around the forward portion of the firing pin bears against the inside of the bolt head and presses backward against the shoulder formed by the larger diameter of the firing pin at the rear. This spring keeps the nose of the firing pin constantly retracted into the bolt face except when it is forced sharply forward by the impact of the hammer. The firing pin is held in place in the bolt by a drift pin which passes through the bolt from left to

Russian Model 1938 Tokarev (SVT) caliber 7.62mm. This is a gas operated rifle. The gas system resembles that of the Simonov. The rear of the bolt is lowered and raised to lock. Locking engagement is to the rear of the magazine. This weapon has a two-piece stock and can be easily distinguished from the Model 1940 Tokarev by the full length cleaning rod mounted on the right side of the stock.

right. A slot is cut across the top of the enlarged rear portion of the firing pin and the drift pin passes through this slot. The slot is wide enough to permit the firing pin to move forward and backward under the drift pin for the distance required to fire the cartridge. The bottom rear surface of the bolt is the locking surface. The head of the bolt is unsupported. When the action is open the bolt fits snugly up into the semi-cylindrical under portion of the bolt carrier. The camming lugs on the bolt are up in the cam-shaped notches in the rear under sides of the carrier. As the carrier is pushed forward by the recoil spring the engagement of the camming lugs in the notches of the carrier carry the bolt forward. The rear end of the barrel extends backward through the receiver ring about $\frac{1}{4}$ inch. Its perimeter is beveled from the chamber face to the receiver ring. The flanged face of the recessed bolt head comes into contact with the face of the chamber and the bolt stops its forward motion. The carrier continues forward about $\frac{1}{4}$ inch until it contacts the receiver ring. During this last $\frac{1}{4}$ inch of forward motion of the carrier the camming notches in the carrier act on the camming lugs on the bolt to force the rear of the bolt down into the bottom of the receiver where the locking surface at the bottom rear of the bolt engages the locking surface in the bottom of the receiver. A special steel block is inserted in the receiver at this point of thrust to minimize wear and to make it possible to compensate for the development of excess headspace without having to discard the bolt or receiver.

When the rifle is fired and the operating rod forces the carrier to the rear the above cycle is reversed. During the first $\frac{1}{4}$ inch of rearward travel of the carrier the camming notches exert a lifting force on the camming lugs, raising the rear end of the bolt, disengaging the locking surfaces and permitting the carrier to move the bolt to the rear.

The extractor is a sturdy steel claw inlet into the upper right quadrant of the bolt and actuated by a coil spring. The outside of the extractor lies flush with the outside of the bolt. The flange on the recessed bolt face is cut away under the extractor. To assist in extraction the neck of the chamber is fluted.

The ejector is merely a finger-like projection extending upward into the bolt raceway from the floor of the receiver at the left rear of the magazine well. The lower left quadrant of the bolt is grooved to accommodate the ejector and the flange around the recessed bolt face is cut away to allow the ejector to strike the head of the cartridge case.

The recoil spring is of two-piece design. The rear half is mounted around a guide rod $3\frac{5}{8}$ inches long having a bearing shoulder at its rear end. The rear end of this rod takes its bearing against the standing breech. A tube about 3 inches long with a collar around its middle serves as a guide for the front spring and as a coupling for the rear and front halves of the recoil spring. It is inserted into the front end of the rear spring, which bears against one side of the collar, and into the rear end of the front spring which bears against the other side of the collar. The front spring is then inserted in the tunnel in the top of the carrier and takes its bearing against the forward end of the tunnel. When the spring is compressed the hollow coupling tube slides to the rear, sleeve fashion, over the guide rod so that the springs are always well supported to prevent buckling.

The breech cover or housing covers the receiver from the rear of the magazine

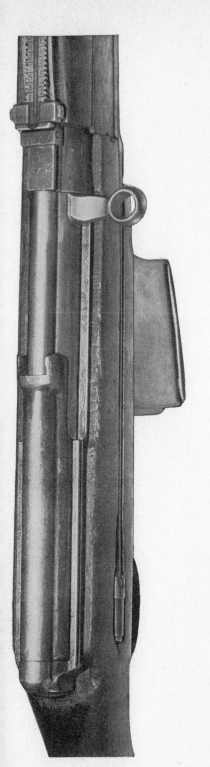
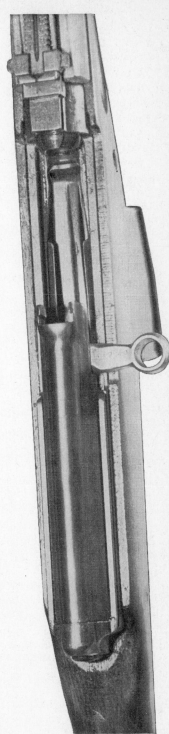

Russian Model 1938 and 1940 Series (Tokarev) action closed and open. The true bolt is housed inside the bolt carrier. Bolt handle is a part of the bolt carrier. The true bolt is housed inside the carrier. Note cut in barrel face for extractor. There is no primary extraction in this design, and in most models the chamber is fluted to assist in extraction. While this gives effective extraction it also results in mutilation of the fired cases. (Note: Closed rifle is 1940. Open one is 1938. Systems practically identical.)

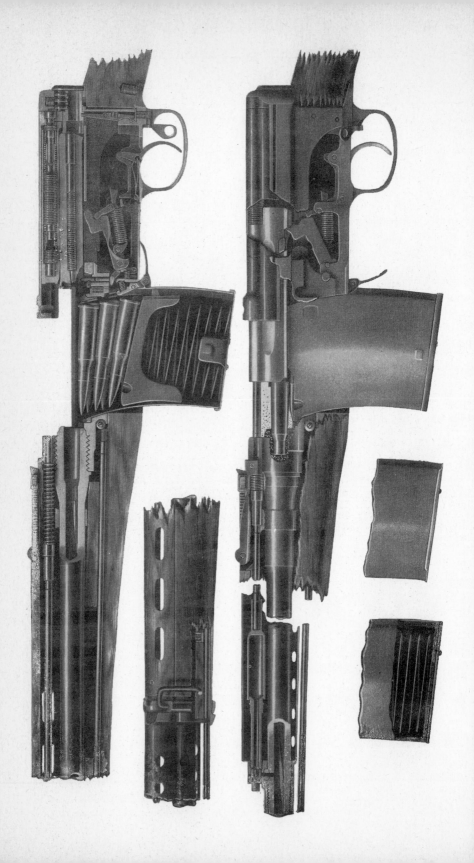

well to the standing breech. Flanges along its lower edges engage grooves in the receiver to hold it in place. It is prevented from sliding to the rear by the standing breech. At the rear it has a semi-circular groove which engages over the top half of the collar at the rear of the recoil spring guide rod so that the pressure of the recoil spring prevents the cover sliding forward except when firmly gripped and pushed forward by hand.

The hammer is of conventional design. To prevent firing if the bolt is not securely locked a semi-cylindrical steel block is mounted to rotate just forward of the lower end of the hammer and a notch is cut into the hammer at a point which will be adjacent to the block when the hammer is cocked. A curved rocker arm at the end of the block extends forward and upward to bear against a plunger which goes up through the receiver into the bolt locking recess. A small coil spring maintains constant pressure on the rocker arm forcing it upward against the plunger. So long as the plunger is at the top of its stroke, projecting into the locking recess, the semi-cylindrical block is engaged in the hammer notch and the hammer cannot move even though the trigger is pulled and the hammer hook disengaged. When the rear of the bolt is cammed down into its locking recess it forces the plunger down against the spring loaded rocker arm. As the rocker arm is pressed downward it rotates the semi-cylindrical block out of its engagement in the hammer notch and the hammer is free to strike.

The disconnector which operates to prevent "doubling" or full automatic fire is the beveled projecting end of the mainspring guide rod which extends rearward through the hammer hook. As the hammer is cocked and the mainspring compressed the end of this rod is forced back. If pressure has been maintained on the trigger so that the trigger bar is forward where it would exert pressure on the hammer hook to prevent its engaging in the cock-notch on the hammer, the camming surface on the mainspring guide rod pushes the trigger bar downward out of engagement with the hammer hook. This occurs before the hammer has reached its full-cock position so that when that position is reached the hammer hook is free to engage and hold the hammer. When the trigger is released the trigger bar is moved back slightly so that it clears the holding notch into which the mainspring guide rod pressed it. The trigger bar then rises to its operating position under pressure from the flat spring which lies under it in the triggerguard and serves also as the trigger spring.

The safety is a pivoted trigger block mounted inside the triggerguard behind the trigger. When swung down it prevents any rearward trigger movement. In

---

Russian Tokarev System, showing operational and construction details.
Upper drawing shows magazine partly loaded and action open ready to load chamber. Pulling back on operating handle frees the bolt assembly to be driven forward by the operating spring. The disconnector prevents release of the hammer until the action is fully forward and locked. The elementary construction of the trigger block safety may be seen in this drawing. The pivoted lever at the extreme rear of the receiver is part of the takedown system. The operating rod is furnished with its own return spring housed in its tunnel in the receiver above the chamber.
Line two shows details of the hand guard and cooling construction.
The third line shows the action unlocked as the operating rod is driven back through its cut in the receiver. The rod driving the bolt carrier back, causes cam movement to lift the bolt out of blocking engagement with the receiver insert. The bolt is then carried back in straight line action by the carrier. The carrier must not be confused with the metal housing which covers it and which encloses the bolt return spring and guide.
Other details show magazine construction.

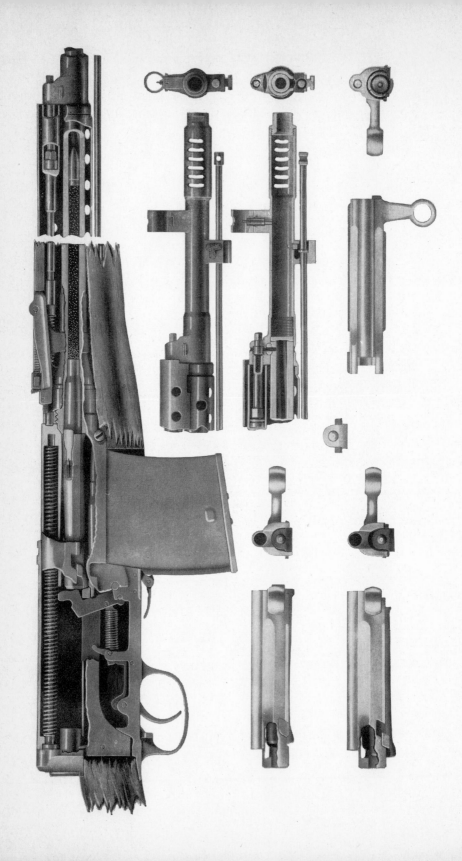

actual practice it is very simple and efficient, although from a design standpoint the only truly safe device is one which will remove the firing device from trigger contact and lock it there. In full automatic versions the safety can be swung completely to the right.

The entire triggerguard assembly, which includes the firing mechanism is removable by pressure on a spring loaded collar reached through a latch in the rear of the standing breech.

The magazine is removable through the bottom of the magazine well. The magazine catch is attached to the forward edge of the triggerguard which, as indicated above, extends forward to serve as the floor plate for the hammer assembly. Magazine is the staggered box type holding ten cartridges. The magazine may be loaded from charger clips through the top of the receiver. There is no magazine cut-off. The action remains open in loading position after the last round has been ejected. A projection from the magazine follower through the rear wall of the magazine engages a latch which raises a bolt stop in the raceway in front of the bolt face to hold the action open. When the magazine has been loaded the bolt stop does not release because of the pressure of the recoil spring against the bolt but a slight tug to the rear on the bolt handle releases this pressure, the bolt stop drops and the action closes.

The front sight is a cylindrical, flat topped, post. It is hooded with a light hole in the top of the hood. Sight and hood are dovetailed into a front sight stud which is integral with the false muzzle or sleeve which also forms the compensator.

The rear sight is of the ramp leaf type with vertical sided, round bottomed notch in a flat topped leaf.

Telescopic sights of 3.5 (Model PU) and 4 power (Model PE) are commonly mounted on these rifles.

Model 1936 (Simonov) Rifle (AVS)

This is a gas-operated semiautomatic with a unique locking system for the straight-line bolt. Officially adopted in 1936 it was quickly superseded by the

---

Russian Tokarev System, showing details of action at moment of firing, and details of locking and gas operating systems.

Bullet is still in barrel and approaching the gas port. Action is still firmly locked.

Bolt details at left show bolt assembly in unlocked and locked positions, right side views and rear views. Bolt is shaped to nest in bolt carrier. When rear of bolt is cammed up and the camming lugs on either side are in their cuts in the bottom of the bolt carrier, the action is unlocked and the bolt can move back and forth. When the action is locked, the bolt carrier is advanced beyond the face of the bolt and its rear surfaces cam the bolt down into receiver insert seats. When the operating rod starts the bolt carrier back, the first carrier movement does not affect the bolt itself. When pressure drops, the carrier is back far enough in its guides that it can cam the bolt up within it. On forward movement of the action as the cartridge is seated, the carrier can still be driven farther forward into a receiver recess. During this continued travel it cams down the rear of the bolt into locking engagement.

The muzzle drawings show details of the muzzle brake and gas port construction. The gas port has an adjusting nut which permits regulating the amount of gas tapped off to function the action.

Details of front sight mounting and cleaning rod fastening unit are shown opposite the muzzle views.

The smallest detail shows the positioning pin which secures the firing pin and regulates the length of its movement. Top and front bolt assembly details are shown at lower right. Note that a seating is provided in the front face of the carrier above the line of the bolt to receive the operating rod.

Russian Model 1936 (Simonov) caliber 7.62mm rifle (AVS). This is a gas operated rifle with top operating rod driven back by gas escaping through a barrel port into a gas cylinder. The locking design is very unusual and in field service did not prove practical.

This arm is commonly encountered with a full automatic switch. The muzzle brake is a rudimentary form which is not particularly effective.

simpler, more reliable Model 1938 Tokarev. The Model 1936 is now something of a collector's piece. These rifles were equipped with a change lever to make it possible to deliver either semiautomatic or full-automatic fire. Such weapons come under the restrictions imposed by federal firearms laws in the United States. They must be registered with the Treasury Department and may not be legally transferred without notification to the Treasury Department.

Generally similar in appearance to the Tokarev, the Simonov can be immediately recognized because of its artillery-type muzzle brake and by the fact that the breech cover is cut away on the right side to allow the bolt handle to move backward and forward—an arrangement which exposes the recoil spring and provides a wide open doorway through which sand and water can enter the action.

The gas port, cylinder, sleeve valve and operating rod are similar to the Tokarev assembly. The rear end of the operating rod of the Simonov is formed into a two-pronged fork, the prongs passing to the rear on either side of the rear sight base and thence through the receiver ring into contact with the bolt carrier.

The bolt lock is a hollow square steel unit which moves vertically in slots cut in the receiver ring. The forward end of the bolt moves longitudinally through the hollow square. The top section of the square is provided with cam faces which are engaged by suitable camming surfaces on the underside of the bolt carrier. As the bolt and carrier move forward the bolt head comes up against the face of the chamber as in the Tokarev. The carrier continues forward, as in the Tokarev, and the camming lug on its underside engages the camming surface at the top of the bolt lock lifting it in its slots in the receiver ring until the lock has engaged the bolt. Thus the head of the bolt is locked to the receiver ring. When the gun is fired and the operating rod is forced to the rear the camming surface on the bolt carrier forces the hollow square locking member down in its slots in the receiver ring, disengaging it from the bolt which then moves back with the carrier.

The Russian Mosin Nagant Bolt Action Rifles and Carbines

The Model 1891 is the first of the Russian Mosin Nagant rifles. It was developed by Colonel S. I. Mosin of the Russian Artillery and by Nagant, a Belgian. Mosin developed the action and Nagant the magazine. Mosin's name has been transliterated as Mossin, Mouzin, Moisin, and Mossine. Original M1891 rifles varied in many details from later production. They had no handguards, had sling swivels on the front of the magazine and on the upper band, and the rear sight was graduated for the round-nosed M1891 ball. Early drawings of the 1891 show the rear of the trigger guard continued beyond the rear tang screw and formed into a small finger rest under the small of the stock. At some time beween 1891 and 1908 a handguard was added to the M1891 and the rear sight was changed to one graduated for the M1908 light pointed ball. All Russian rifles manufactured prior to 1930 have their sights graduated in "Arshins"—an arshin is equivalent to .78 yards. These weapons are also known as the "3 line rifles"—a line being an old Russian measurement equivalent to about one-tenth of an inch—3 lines = .30. After the revolution, Russian adopted the metric system and the sights for the M1891/30 and later carbines are graduated in meters.

CHARACTERISTICS OF SOVIET PRE-WORLD WAR II 7.62MM AUTOMATIC AND SEMI-AUTOMATIC RIFLES

Characteristics	Automatic rifle M1936	Semi-automatic rifle M1938	Semi-automatic rifle M1940	Automatic rifle M1940	Semi-automatic sniper rifle M1938	Semi-automatic sniper rifle M1940
Weight—						
w/o bayonet & magazine	8.93 lb.	8.70 lb.	8.59 lb.	8.35 lb.	9.52 lb.	9.18 lb.
w/bayonet & magazine	....	10.8 lb.	9.48 lb.	9.24 lb.	....	....
Length—						
w/o bayonet	48.6 in.	48.1 in.	48.1 in.	48.1 in.	48.1 in.	48.1 in.
w/bayonet	59.3 in.	60.84 in.	57.1 in.	57.1 in.	60.84 in.	57.1 in.
Barrel length	24.16 in.	25 in.	24.6 in.	24.6 in.	25 in.	24.6 in.
Magazine capacity	15 rounds	10 rounds	10 rounds	10 rounds	10 rounds	10 rounds
Instrumental velocity at 78 ft. w/hvy ball	2519 f.p.s.	2519 f.p.s.	2519 f.p.s.	2519 f.p.s.	2519 f.p.s.	2519 f.p.s.
Rate of fire (semi-automatic)	30-40 r.p.m.	25 r.p.m.	25 r.p.m.	30-40 r.p.m.	25 r.p.m.	25 r.p.m.
Maximum sighting range	1500 meters	1500 meters	1500 meters	1500 meters	Iron sights: 600 m. (660 yd.) Telescope: 1300 m. (1430 yd.)	Iron sights: 600 m. (660 yd.) Telescope: 1300 m. (1430 yd.)
Front sight	Open guard blade	Hooded post	Hooded post	Hooded post	Hooded post	Hooded post
Rear sight	Tangent	Tangent	Tangent	Tangent	Tangent and telescope	Tangent and telescope
Principle of operation	Gas	Gas	Gas	Gas	Gas	Gas
Ammunition	*	*	*	*	*	*

* 7.62mm U.S.S.R. rifle and ground machine gun rimmed ammunition.

7.62mm M1891 Mosin Nagant Rifle of early manufacture. Note sling swivels and flat leaf rear sight.

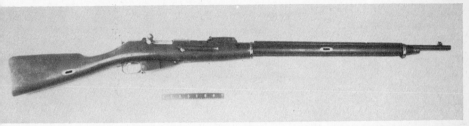

7.62mm M1891 Mosin Nagant Rifle of later manufacture. Note sling slots through stock and rounded sight leaf.

The Model 1891 was first made in quantity at Chatellerault in France; it has also been made by SIG in Switzerland and Steyr in Austria. It can also be found with a bayonet lug sleeve mounted on the barrel. This work was done by the Germans in World War I to enable them to use their Mauser-type knife bayonets on the Mosin Nagant. The Model 1891 has a hexagonal receiver.

The M1891 Mosin Nagant was made in the United States by Remington Arms at Ilion, N. Y. and by New England Westinghouse at Springfield, Mass. These two firms produced over 1,500,000 rifles which were delivered to the Imperial Russian and the Kerensky governments during the period 1915-17. The United States government bought 280,049 of these rifles, mainly for training purposes. A rather unusual fact that is not commonly known is that some of these American made 1891s were used on active service by American troops. The American expedition to Archangel, Russia in 1918 carried these rifles. These troops were sent to Russia to help protect Allied supplies stored in that port during the Russian Civil War. Some publications refer to the American made Mosin Nagant as the M1916. Many publications refer to various models of the Mosin Nagant which, insofar as Russian publications are concerned, don't really exist. Although

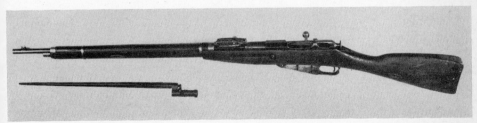

7.62mm M1891 Mosin Nagant Dragoon Rifle. Bayonet shown is late model with spring loaded catch.

many variations may be found among Mosin Nagants, especially the M1891s, the official Russian model designations are as given in this book.

Later models are the following:

7.62mm Dragoon Rifle M1891. This was used by mounted troops before the issue of carbines. The Dragoon has a shorter barrel than the M1891 and, like the later M1891's, has slots through the stock for mounting the sling. The Dragoon rifle has a hexagonal receiver and uses the same cruciform section bayonet with old fashioned locking ring as does the M1891.

7.62mm M1910 Mosin Nagant Carbine.

7.62mm Carbine M1910. This was the first true Mosin Nagant carbine. It has a leaf-type rear sight, is stocked almost to the muzzle, has a hexagonal receiver, and does not use a bayonet. This model is comparatively rare.

7.62mm M1891/30 Mosin Nagant Rifle.

7.62mm Rifle M1891/30. This rifle is about the same length as the M1891 Dragoon but has a tangent-type rear sight sighted in meters and a rounded receiver. The front sight of the M1891/30 is a hooded post rather than a barleycorn as on earlier models. The bayonet for the M1891/30 has a spring loaded catch rather than a locking ring as that of the M1891; both bayonets are interchangeable, however.

7.62mm M1891/30 Mosin Nagant Sniper Rifle with "PE" Scope.

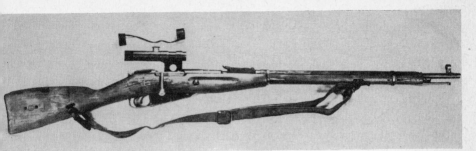

7.62mm M1891/30 Mosin Nagant Sniper Rifle with "PU" Scope.

7.62mm Sniper Rifle M1891/30. This rifle is the same as the M1891/30 but comes equipped with either the 4 power "PE" or the 3.5 power "PU" scope. The "PU" is the most common scope at present. The M1891/30 sniper rifle is still used by the U.S.S.R.

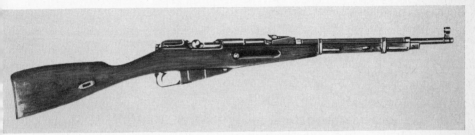

7.62mm M1938 Mosin Nagant Carbine.

7.62mm M1938 Carbine. This carbine is similar in most respects, except length, to the M1891/30 rifle. It has a rounded receiver and sights similar to the M1891/30 but does not take a bayonet. The common carbine of World War II and frequently, and erroneously called the Model 24/27, this weapon was extensively used by the Communist forces in Korea.

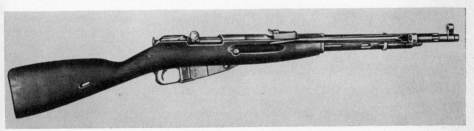

7.62mm M1944 Mosin Nagant Carbine. Note bayonet folded along stock.

7.62mm M1944 Carbine. The last of the Mosin Nagant Service weapons; this carbine is basically the same as the M1938 carbine, but has a cruciform section bayonet permanently fixed to its right side. This was the principal shoulder weapon of the Communist Forces in Korea. It still may be found in some of the satellite forces.

The 1891 Series are turn-bolt rifles. The bolt is of complex three-piece design. The bolt assembly consists of (1) the bolt cylinder carrying the straight bolt handle (2) the recessed bolt head carrying dual opposed locking lugs and the extractor (3) a bolt coupling unit which serves also as a bolt guide and (4) the striker assembly. The bolt handle is mid-way of the bolt cylinder, locking down forward of the split receiver bridge. The coupling unit is unique. It consists of a steel cylinder fractionally over one inch in length, the rear of which slips into the forward end of the bolt cylinder while the forward end slips into the back end of the bolt head to provide a rotatable sleeve joint. Practically mid way of the length of this connecting cylinder a collar surrounds it. The collar is about 1/4 inch wide and its diameter is the same as the outside diameter of the bolt. Its rear face rides against the front end of the bolt cylinder while its front face rides against the rear end of the bolt head so that it serves as a sort of "washer" or friction bearing between bolt cylinder and bolt head. A long guide rib is mounted on this collar, hollow-ground on its under side to fit closely over the bolt cylinder and bolt head. The length of the guide rib is such that it goes from the rear of the locking lugs on the bolt head all the way back over the bolt cylinder then extends about an inch further to the rear. This extension is slotted to form a two-pronged fork inside which the cocking piece stud slides backward and forward. Near the forward end of the guide rib on its under side, where it extends over the bolt head, a small lug engages a lateral groove in the outside of the bolt head to lock together the bolt head and the coupling. The guide rib rides in a raceway cut in the bottom of the receiver bridge and does not turn as the bolt is rotated.

As is customary in bolt action designs employing the split receiver bridge there is a sizeable guide rib or lug, on the outside of the bolt cylinder, the bolt handle projecting from the top of this rib. At its forward end this rib extends about 3/4 inch beyond the face of the bolt cylinder, over the bolt coupling and part way over the bolt head. It has a lateral undercut at the point where it passes over the collar on the coupling. A lug on the collar engages in this undercut so as to lock together the bolt cylinder and the coupling. Thus the bolt cylinder is locked to the coupling by one lug and the bolt head is locked to the coupling by another lug as explained in the preceding paragraph and a three-piece assembly is formed.

In the underside of the forward nose of the bolt handle guide rib a longitudinal cut is made. A small lug on the outside of the bolt head engages in this cut when the bolt cylinder, coupling and bolt head are assembled. Thus when the bolt handle is lifted, rotating the bolt cylinder, the bolt head is also rotated.

The locking lugs cam into recesses on either side of the receiver ring instead of into recesses at the top and bottom of the ring as is the case in the Mauser. Thus when the bolt handle is turned up and the locking lugs disengaged they are situated at the top and bottom of the bolt. Hence no raceways for the locking lugs are cut into the sides of the receiver. The long guide rib which is a part of the bolt coupling lies along the underside of the bolt as it is inserted in the receiver. The bottom locking lug rides just in front of this guide rib and travels in the same raceway.

The striker is of one-piece design. It passes to the rear through the bolt

Russian Model 1936, showing details of muzzle end and brake construction.

Russian Model 1936, showing details of breech construction and cocking handle. The exposed travel port permits dirt to enter the action very readily which results in unreliable performance. This design was not put into extensive production.

ylinder and is threaded into the cocking piece which has a large, easy-to-grasp ead. The forward end of the striker passes through the bolt coupling cylinder, hen forward through the bolt head. A collar on the striker comes up against he rear face of the bolt coupling to limit the forward travel of the firing pin. Flat surfaces on the striker bear on flat surfaces on the inside of the bolt coupling to prevent the rotation of the striker. The mainspring takes its rear bearing against the inside rear end of the bolt cylinder and its forward bearing against the collar on the striker. The conventional camming surfaces on the cocking piece and bolt cylinder provide most of the mainspring compression and cocking action as the bolt handle is lifted. Final compression is effected by the camming action of the rear nose of the bolt handle rib engaging a camming surface on the forward side of the receiver bridge as the bolt handle s turned down to seat the locking lugs.

The extractor is of the flat steel spring type mounted in the upper right quadrant of the bolt head. Primary extraction is obtained by the camming action of the forward nose of the bolt handle rib bearing against a camming surface on the receiver ring as the bolt handle is lifted.

The ejector is a small projection on the upper edge of the magazine "interruptor" or cartridge control device.

The cartridge control device in this rifle is another unique feature. Through the left wall of the magazine projects a $\frac{1}{4}$ inch wide flat steel "finger" or latch so positioned that it lightly engages the upper left quadrant of the cartridge case next to the top one of those stacked in the magazine. Thus this latch, by holding the second cartridge in the stack, takes the pressure of the magazine follower spring off of the top cartridge—the one which is being stripped off the top of the stack and pushed into the chamber by the bolt. The cartridge which is being chambered is free to slide forward with a minimum chance of jamming. This is the Russian answer to the problem of feeding rimmed cartridges from a charger-type box magazine. This "interruptor" latch is the downward extension of a horizontal flat steel piece mounted in a slot cut through the lower left side of the receiver. It extends from the rear of the magazine well (where the projection that forms the ejector is located) forward along the top of the magazine for half its length. Its upper edge curves inward slightly to serve as a guide for the rim of the cartridge as it is stripped off the stack in the magazine and pushed forward toward the chamber. The opposite (right) wall of the receiver is milled with a corresponding guide lip. Forward from the termination of these horizontal guides the receiver is milled with ramp guides to assist in the chambering of the rimmed case. The bolt cylinder and bolt head are grooved longitudinally to provide for their travel over the projecting upper lip of the interruptor and its attached ejector. When the bolt handle is lifted the upper lip of the interruptor and the ejector are held in the bottom of this groove by spring pressure. As the bolt is drawn fully to the rear the ejector emerges through the face of the bolt to knock the empty case out of the rifle. The lower side of this longitudinal groove in the bolt is cut with a sloping face from the bottom of the groove up to the normal diameter of the bolt cylinder. When the bolt handle is turned down to lock the bolt the bolt cylinder rotates and the interruptor and ejector are forced back into their cut in the receiver by the sloping surface on the lower side of the groove. This withdraws the latch into its cut in the side of the magazine well and permits the stack of cartridges to move upward under the pressure of the follower spring. As the bolt handle is lifted the interruptor and ejector press into the groove on the bolt and the interruptor latch again engages the next-to-the-top cartridge in the magazine. No magazine cut-off is provided. The magazine is charged through the top of the action using charger type clips which must be pulled up out of the clip guides and cannot be knocked out of the way by pushing the bolt forward. The projecting magazine well is formed by a forward extension of the triggerguard. A hinged floor-plate is provided with a latch at the rear. The magazine spring and follower are of conventional design.

The trigger is pivoted in the receiver. A lug on the top surface of the trigger is the bolt stop. It projects into the raceway in the bottom of the receiver in which the guide rib slides. The outer surface of the guide rib is channeled out so that it will clear the bolt stop and sear as the bolt is drawn to the rear. The channel ends forward just at the point where the bolt cylinder and bolt head are coupled. When the bolt has been withdrawn to this point the bolt stop comes up against the end of the channel in the guide rib and the bolt is held. Pulling the trigger depresses the bolt stop so that the bolt may be fully withdrawn from the rifle.

The sear is a flat steel spring with a square projection at one end which forms the sear nose and rises through a cut in the bottom of the receiver into the raceway provided for the above mentioned guide rib and for the travel of the cocking stud. The sear passes forward through a square cut in the trigger and is fastened to the lower side of the receiver by a screw. As the trigger is pulled and rotates on its pivot pin it depresses the nose of the sear at the same time that the bolt stop lug is depressed. The sear engages the conventional cocking stud on the lower side of the cocking piece. The design of the cocking stud varies from the conventional in that it is undercut to engage the fork on the rear of the guide rod which extends along the bottom of the bolt from the collar on the bolt coupling. Thus it holds the rear end of this guide rib securely against the bolt cylinder while the guide rib, not the raceway in the bottom of the receiver, prevents the cocking stud from turning as the bolt is rotated.

The safety is simple and effective but difficult to apply. The cocking piece is drawn to the rear against the tension of the mainspring until the cocking stud is clear of its engagement in the guide rod, then rotated counter-clockwise as far as it will turn—something less than an eighth-turn. As this point a projection on the underside of the nose of the cocking piece slips into a safety notch cut in the rear of the bolt cylinder and is held there by the tension of the mainspring. The cocking stud has been rotated to the right and rests against a square face at the rear of the receiver bridge. In this position it is impossible for the striker to move forward although the trigger and sear are fully operative.

EARLIER OFFICIAL BREECHLOADERS

In 1868 the American designed Berdan I was adopted. This was made for the .42 Russian C. F. cartridge, the first C. F. cartridge with outside Berdan primer and bottle neck case. This primer type is still the European standard.

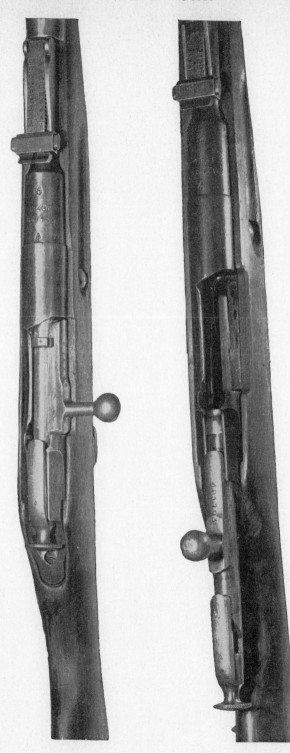

Soviet Model 1891/30, action closed and open. This is a special two piece bolt design. The dual lugs lock to right and left in the receiver ring. The lugs are carried on a separate bolt head.
This is a split receiver bridge design. Note that the bolt handle root is extended to bear against the front of the receiver bridge. The cocking piece can be turned to make a simple positive safety.
Note rounded receiver which identifies 1891/30 and later models.

CHARACTERISTICS OF SOVIET 7.62MM MOSIN-NAGANT BOLT ACTION RIFLES AND CARBINES

Characteristics	Rifle M1891	Dragoon Rifle M1891	Rifle M1891/30	Sniper Rifle M1891/30	Carbine M1910	Carbine M1938	Carbine M1944
Weight—							
w/o bayonet & sling	9.62 lb.	8.75 lb.	8.7 lb.	11.3 lb.	7.5 lb.	7.62 lb.	8.9 lb.
w/bayonet & sling	10.63 lb.	9.7 lb.	9.7 lb.		7.7 lb.		
Length—							
w/o bayonet	51.37 in.	48.75 in.	48.5 in.	48.5 in.	40 in.	40 in.	40 in. (folded)
w/bayonet	68.2 in.	65.5 in.	65.4 in.	65.4 in.			52.25 in. (extended)
Barrel length	31.6 in.	28.8 in.	28.7 in.	28.7 in.	20 in.	20 in.	20.4 in.
Magazine capacity	5 rounds	5 rounds	5 rounds	5 rounds	5 rounds	5 rounds	5 rounds
Instrumental velocity at 78 ft. w/hvy ball	2660 f.p.s.	2660 f.p.s	2660 f.p.s	2660 f.p.s	2514 f.p.s	2514 f.p.s	2514 f.p.s.
Rate of fire	8-10 r.p.m.	8-10 r.p.m.	8-10 r.p.m.	8-10 r.p.m.	8-10 r.p.m.	8-10 r.p.m.	8-10 r.p.m
Maximum sighting range	3200 arshins (2496 yd.)	3200 arshins (2496 yd.)	2000 meters (2200 yd.)	2000 meters* (2200 yd.)	2000 arshins (1560 yd.)	1000 meters (1100 yd.)	1000 meters (1100 yd.)
Front sight	Unprotected blade	Unprotected blade	Hooded post	Hooded post	Unprotected blade	Hooded post	Hooded post
Rear sight	Leaf	Leaf	Tangent	Tangent	Leaf	Tangent	Tangent
Ammunition**	....	....	....	....	....	....	....

* For iron sights when scope is dismounted. Maximum sighting range for the telescopic sight on this weapon is: PE scope—1400 meters (1540 yd.); PU scope—1300 meters (1420 yd.).

** Soviet 7.62mm rifle and ground machine gun rimmed ammunition.

The Krnka 1869 was merely a lifting block conversion for muzzle loaders. In 1870 the Berdan II was adopted.

The Russian "Berdan I" is commonly confused with the Spanish Berdan. Where the Spanish Model resembles the typical hinged lifting block, *outside hammer* type of construction widely associated in the U. S. with the old single shot Springfield, the Russian Berdan I is a different design entirely.

The block of this rifle is hinged forward and is raised to extract and load as in the single shot Springfield. However, instead of the typical hammer, this rifle uses a center plunger system modeled after the French Chassepot. This straight line plunger type bolt has a center cocking thumbpiece which must be drawn straight back to cock the arm. The block can be hinged up only when the action is cocked. When the trigger is pulled, the mainspring drives the bolt attached to the firing plunger forward into a seating in the breech-block where it hits the true firing pin and transmits the blow to the primer of the cartridge in the chamber. Thus this driving bolt serves as a combination hammer and breech lock.

This rifle is about 53 inches long and weighs about 9.75 pounds. Sights are set in Russian paces from 300 to 1400 (287 to 1148 yards).

The "Berdan II" adopted in 1870 is again an entirely different rifle. This is a single shot rifle with a turning bolt action. It too uses the .42 Russian Center Fire cartridge.

The Berdan II bolt action was the most widely used single shot rifle in early Russian service. In battle use against the Turks it was commonly equipped with the "Krnka Quick Loader," a device attached to the side of the rifle and holding a number of cartridges with heads up to permit rapid reloading.

Russian Model 1870 Berdan II Single Shot

Caliber: 10.66mm, .42 Caliber
Overall length, rifle without bayonet: 53"   *With bayonet attached:* 73.2"
Overall weight, rifle without bayonet: 9.8 lbs.   *With bayonet attached:* 11 lbs.
Type of action: Turnbolt
Barrel Length: 32.8"   *No. Grooves:* 6   *Direction of Twist:* Right
Bore Diameter: .42"   *Groove Dia.:* .435"   *Rate of Twist:* 22"

Russian 10.66mm (.42 cal.) Berdan II Rifle.

Foreign Rifles Used by the Russians

The armament production capability of Imperial Russia never matched their wartime requirements. Therefore the Russians were dependent on imports to sustain their World War I efforts. Large quantities of foreign rifles were used by the Russians in World War I. Winchester produced 300,000 of the Musket

Russian M 91 System with action open ready for loading. The interruptor which prevents more than one cartridge from rising into line for feeding is seen in the left side receiver wall. The bolt head construction may vary somewhat in models manufactured at different periods or places.

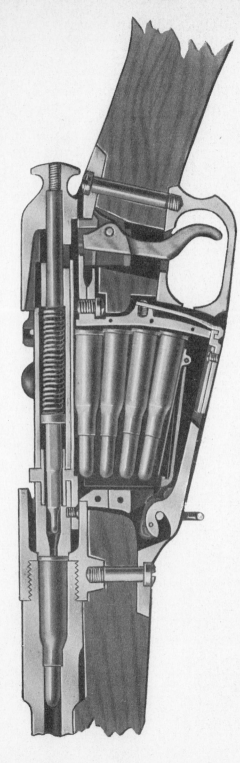

Russian M 91 System loaded and locked, ready to fire. The lugs in this design lock into the right and left side walls of the receiver ring. Pulling back and turning the cocking piece not only removes it from contact with the sear nose, but also locks the nose of the cocking piece against the rear surface of the receiver bridge. This provides a safety that is practically impossible to jar off. The old pre-1908 cartridge is shown.

Model of the M1895 Winchester lever action rifles for the Russians in World War I. This is a full stocked M1895 with bayonet lug and with charger guide added to the sides of the receiver. These rifles were made in 1915-16, and Winchester reports that 293,818 rifles were actually delivered to the Russians. (A Soviet publication says that 299,000 were delivered.) Soviet Russian seized large quantities of 7.92mm Polish Mausers and 1924 FN Mausers used by Lithuania these rifles were apparently issued to Russian partisans during World War II A quantity of Canadian Ross Mark III (M-10) rifles were given to the U.S.S.R. by Great Britain. Some of these rifles (action only) were used by the Soviets to make their 7.62mm MTs-16 match rifles. These rifles have been used by the Soviets in the Olympic running deer contest, where a smooth, fast action is necessary.

Foreign Made Rifles Delivered to or Ordered by Russia During World War

Caliber and Type Rifle	Origin	Quantity	Years Delivered
7.62mm M1891 Mosin Nagant	Remington	840,307	1916-17
7.62mm M1891 Mosin Nagant	N.E. Westinghouse	769,520	1916-17
7.62mm M1895 Win.	Winchester	293,818/299,000	1915-17
7mm Arisaka (Mexican Type)	Japan	35,400	1914
6.5mm Arisaka Type 38	Japan	600,000	1914-15
11mm M1878 Gras	France	450,000	1915-16
11mm M1878 Kropatchek	France	105,000	1915-16
6.5mm Arisaka Type 38*	England	128,000	1915-16
8mm Lebel M1886	France	86,000	1915-16
10.4mm Vetterli M1871	Italy	400,000	1915-16

* This is as reported in a Russian publication; these rifles were not made in England and may have been rifles ordered by England from Japan in 1914 for possible use by British forces, but not actually ever used by the British. This is pure conjecture, but large quantities of 6.5mm Japanese ammunition were made by Kynoch of England for Russia during World War I.

Russian 10.67mm M1870 Cartridge

Other Names: 10.67mm Berdan II (.42 Russian)
Type: Rimmed, Necked, Centerfire
Overall Length: 2.95"
Average Wt.: 610 gr.
Type Powder: Black
Approximate Chg.: 77.1 gr.
Type Primer: Berdan

BULLET

Type: Lead, Paper patched
Diameter: .430"
Weight: 370 gr.
Length: 1.063"

CARTRIDGE CASE

Length Overall: 2.24"
Length Head to Shoulder: 1.58"
Length of Shoulder: .17"
Length of Neck: .49"
Diameter at Rim: .635"
Diameter at Base: .567"
Diameter at Neck: .450"
Diameter at Shoulder: .506"

BALLISTICS (approximate)
Muzzle Velocity: 1444 f.s.

Notes: 1. A large percentage of this ammunition was made in the United States for the Russian Government. None manufactured in recent years.

7.62mm Russian Cartridge

Type: Rimmed, Necked, Centerfire
Overall Length: 3.015"
Average Wt.: 350 gr.
Type Powder: Nitrocellulose
Approximate Chg.: 48 gr.
Type Primer: Boxer (Large Rifle)

BULLET

Type: Expanding
Diameter: .311"
Weight: 150 gr.
Length: 1.08"

CARTRIDGE CASE

Length Overall: 2.06"
Length Head to Shoulder: 1.55"
Length of Shoulder: 21"
Length of Neck: .33"
Diameter at Rim: .570"

Diameter at Base: .489"
Diameter at Neck: .3368"
Diameter at Shoulder: .456"

BALLISTICS (approximate)
Muzzle Velocity: 2810 f.s.
Pressure: 44,000 lbs./sq. in.

Notes: Formerly commercially manufactured in the United States for use in rifles made here in 1916 for Russia which were never shipped, but were sold through Government channels. This cartridge, as pre-1930 Soviet service ammunition, was made with a rounded base.

Soviet 7.62mm Light Ball M1908 Type "L" Cartridge

Other Names: 7.62mm Mosin-Nagant
Type: Rimmed, Necked, Beveled Head, Centerfire
Overall Length: 2.12"
Average Wt.: 330 gr.
Type Powder: Nitrocellulose
Approximate Chg.: 48 gr.
Type Primer: Berdan

BULLET

Type: Pointed
Diameter: .311"
Weight: 148 gr.
Length: 1.12"

CARTRIDGE CASE

Length Overall: 2.11"
Length Head to Shoulder: 1.55"
Length of Shoulder: .21"
Length of Neck: .35"
Diameter at Rim: .564"
Diameter at Base: .489"
Diameter at Neck: .336"
Diameter at Shoulder: .450"

BALLISTICS (approximate)
Muzzle Velocity: 2800 f.s.
Pressure: 45,000 lbs./sq. in.

Notes: 1. As military ammunition, this is made also in tracer, armor-piercing, incendiary ranging (HE), armor piercing tracer, armor piercing incendiary tracer, armor piercing incendiary and heavy ball types. 2. This cartridge has a bevelled base for ease in feeding in automatic weapons.

Soviet Sporting Rifles

The Soviets have a complete line of sporting rifles, from relatively cheaply-made caliber .22 weapons to expensive match weapons. These weapons are rare in the United States and are quite expensive in this country, but are widely used throughout the Soviet Bloc. The Soviets have especially concentrated on free-type match rifles suitable for Olympic competition. By competing in the Olympics with first-class shooters and first-class equipment of native design, the Soviets have attempted to make match shooting into a propaganda arm of Communism just as they have with all other sports. Listed below are the characteristics of some Soviet match rifles.

Soviet 7.62mm Match Rifle Model MTs-13. This rifle, as all other Soviet High Power Match Rifles, is chambered for the 7.62mm rimmed full power cartridge (7.62mm x 53mm). No Soviet match weapon is chambered for the new 7.62mm M43 Service cartridge (7.62mm x 39mm).

Characteristics of Soviet Match Rifles

Class Weapon	Caliber	Barrel Length inches	Rifle Length inches	Rifle Weight pounds	Sight Type	No. of Grooves	Trigger Mechanism
MTs-13	7.62mm	29.9	50.6	17.6	Peep	4	Set trigger
TsV-52	7.62mm	28.7	50.6	14.7	Peep	4	Set trigger
TsV-55 Zenit	7.62mm	28.7	50.6	17.2	Peep	4	Set trigger
Tallin Arsenal	7.62mm	29.9	46.1	17.6	Peep	4	Conventional
Zenit-2	7.62mm	28.7	47.2	14.6	Peep	4	Set trigger
MTs-16 5-shot	7.62mm	27.6	49.6	9.9-11.1	Peep	4	Conventional
MTs-12	.22	29.5	49.2	14.3	Peep	6	Set trigger
MTsV-52	.22	28.7	48.4	14.3	Peep	6	Set trigger
Tallin Arsenal	.22	29.4	48.2	15.4	Peep	6	Conventional
Strela	.22	28.7	48.4	15.4	Peep	6	Set trigger
Tayga	.22	26.8	43.3	12.0	Peep	4	Set trigger
TOZ-10	.22	29.0	46.5	11.9	Peep	4	Conventional
TOZ-20	.22	27.6	48.4	13.4	Peep	6	Conventional
TOZ-8	.22	25.2	43.8	6.9	Open & peep	4	Conventional
TOZ-9 5-shot	.22	25.2	43.8	6.9	Open & peep	4	Conventional
TOZ-12	.22	25.2	43.3	7.7	Peep	4	Conventional

Soviet Caliber .22 (5.6mm) Match Rifle Model MTs-12.

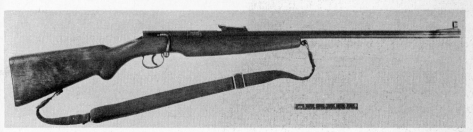

Soviet Caliber .22 TOZ-8 Single Shot Training Rifle. (Top, left side view.)

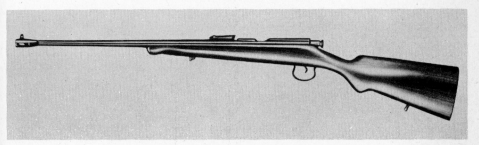

Soviet Caliber .22 TOZ-16 Bolt Action Hunting Rifle.

Soviet Caliber .22 TOZ-18 Bolt Action Hunting Rifle with Scope. It is Box Magazine Fed.

Soviet Caliber .22 TOZ-21 Semiautomatic Box Magazine Fed Hunting Rifle with Scope.

Chapter 56

UNITED STATES OF AMERICA

The development of military and sporting rifles in the U. S. has been touched upon in Part I. It is impractical to recapitulate and describe generally all the early forms of even military metallic cartridge breech loaders. We can deal here only with comparatively recent types.

The Springfield Single Shot

The Springfield single shot breech loading cam-lock design began with E. S. Allin's alteration of Civil War Springfield muzzle loaders. This design of hinged breechblock is unlocked at the rear and lifted up on its hinge above the barrel breech for loading and unloading. The design was the subject of many patent suits. Literally scores of breechblocks of this hinged design were evolved both here and abroad.

In 1873 this rifle in a somewhat improved design was introduced in caliber .45. With essential changes confined to sights and bayonets, this was the U. S. Service Rifle in use by the regular army until 1894. It was used by Militia and Home Guard units as late as 1919. With the introduction of the 1884 Model, the cartridge was changed from .45-70-405 to .45-70-500. The additional bullet weight was provided to delay barrel travel time long enough to effect complete combustion of the powder charge, since unburned powder was a common occurrence with the lighter bullet.

The last model of this famous old Springfield single shot line was the Model 1888. The 1884 and 1888 were the common Volunteer and Militia rifles in the Spanish-American War, although the Regulars were armed with Krags.

These rifles have the following general characteristics: Caliber .45-70-500 black powder. Straight taper brass case with rim, center fire.

Length of barrel 32.6 inches, overall length 51.92 inches, weight 9.30 pounds.

The rifling is 3 concentric grooves of .005 inch depth with a twist of one to the right in 22 inches.

The muzzle velocity is 1315 feet per second and maximum range about 3500 yards.

The U. S. Krag-Jorgensens

After extensive tests of various magazine rifles, the U. S. Ordnance Department in 1892 officially adopted a slightly modified form of the rifle invented in Norway by Ole Krag, Captain of Artillery and Superintendent of the Kongsberg Armory in Norway, and by an engineer, Erik Jorgensen. The Krag had been officially adopted in 1889 in caliber 8mm (.315) as the official rifle of the Danish Army. (See *Denmark* for sectional drawings.)

The American and Norwegian magazines differ from the Danish M89 in that the loading gate is hinged at the bottom. This arrangement provides a loading platform and makes it less likely that the cartridges will be dropped as they are individually placed in the magazine.

All American Krags were designed for the .30/40 rimmed cartridge officially

U. S. Model 1898 (Krag-Jorgensen), action closed and open. Upper photo shows American Krag remodeled as a sporter. Lower shows Norwegian military finish. Instead of the bolt stop common to most military actions, the K-J design bolt travel is halted by the single forward locking lug hitting the receiver bridge.

The bolt is a modified form of the original Danish K-J. The manual safety differs radically from all the Danish systems. The magazine loading gate which houses the cartridge propelling mechanism hinges down in the American version, and to the front on the original Danish.

Extractor lies on top of bolt. Magazine cutoff can be seen rising from left receiver wall in lower picture.

designated as "Cartridge, ball, caliber .30, Model 1898." Unofficially this cartridge has been designated by a confusing variety of names—".30/40", ".30 Army" and ".30 Government." After the adoption of the .30/06 rimless cartridge it, too, was dubbed ".30 Government" and some ordinary citizens naturally thought of it as the ".30 Army." Probably the best designation for today's use is ".30/40 Krag."

The Model 1892

Although officially adopted in 1892 the first shipment of rifles to troops was not made by Springfield Armory until October 1894. The Fourth Infantry received this shipment and made the field tests of the new weapon. The overall length was 49.14 inches with a 30 inch barrel. The weight was 9.35 pounds. As field use developed the usual minor defects in materials and design, changes were made. As the minor changes accumulated it was decided to adopt a new model designation.

The Model 1896

This model had an over-all length of 49.1 inches. The barrel length remained at 30 inches for the rifle and 22 inches for the carbine. Overall length of the carbine was 41.15 inches. Weight of the rifle 8.94 pounds, carbine 7.75 pounds. The magazine cut-off on the 1896 model, plus 1892's modified per instructions of the Chief Ordnance issued in 1895, turned down to lock off the magazine feed intead of turning up as in the model 1892. A spiral spring and spindle were substituted for the flat spring in the magazine cut-off. The square cut on the muzzle of the 1892 was also rounded on the 1896, and modified 1892's.

The Model 1898

Similar in essential dimensions and weight to the Model 1896 the Model 1898 rifle and carbine merely embodied further minor structural changes. Interest in individual marksmanship for the soldier also resulted in numerous changes in rear sights and less obvious changes in the dimensions of the front sight. No good purpose would be served here by going into almost endless detail concerning this obsolete arm. Most of them now in use by Americans have been converted into sporters to which purpose they are admirably suited when used with modern hunting cartridges.

The description of operation as given under *Denmark* applies to the American Krag. There is also a Model 1898 and 1899 Carbine, a Cadet Rifle, and a .22 Caliber Gallery Rifle.

The U. S. Rifle, Caliber .30, Model 1903

Shortly after the adoption of the Krag-Jorgensen in 1892 the U. S. Army Ordnance Department began the study of the Mauser system. Five thousand of a first model, designed with a 30 inch barrel and having a muzzle-length stock were ordered for experimental purposes in 1901. Before they were ready the barrel length was ordered reduced to 24 inches. This was in the direction of providing a weapon suitable for both infantry and cavalry use, eliminating the long standard combination of rifle and carbine. The cartridge was rimless and had a round-nosed 220 grain bullet. Designated the Model 1903, the new rifle and cartridge were issued for field tests in 1905. In the same year the U.S. paid

$200,000 to Mauser for some of their rifle and charger patents which had been used in the design of the weapon.

As a result of these tests the customary minor structural changes were made in the rifle; but the outstanding change was in the adoption of a 150 grain pointed bullet to replace the 220 round nosed bullet. The shorter bullet required shortening the neck of the cartridge case but no change was made in the shoulder or outside diameter of the case. To properly seat the shorter pointed bullet in the throat of the chamber some redesign was also necessary at that point. The required changes were made by cutting an additional thread in the receiver ring so that the barrel could be screwed back an additional

U. S. Model 1898 (K-J), sectional drawings showing operating mechanism.

Receiver detail shows rifle loaded ready for firing. Note position of long spring extractor, which is secured at rear to bolt sleeve; and of single forward locking lug which engages below chamber. The sear spring is housed within the extreme forward end of the sear, to the rear of the front guard screw seat.

Magazine detail shows rear view with magazine loaded and gate closed. Rear of firing units seen above center cartridge.

complete turn and then reworking the chamber to properly accommodate the new cartridge. All Model 1903 rifles issued up to the time of this conversion were recalled and reworked in this manner. Thus the U. S. Rifle, caliber .30, Model 1903, chambered for the cartridge, ball, caliber .30, Model 1906, popularly known as the ".30/06 Springfield" came into being.

Except for changes in manufacturing methods, processes for hardening the receivers, and types of steel employed in the construction, practically no changes were made in this original design until 1929.

In 1918 as a result of war experience, the bolt handle was bent slightly to the rear to permit faster operation of the NS bolt.

U. S. Rifle, Caliber .30 M1903A1

In December 1929 the straight stock of the earlier Springfield was replaced by a pistol grip stock. The finger grooves in the fore-end were also eliminated. The buttplate was checkered to give better support on the shoulder, and a serrated trigger was fitted.

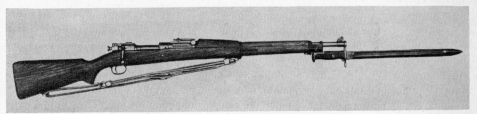

U.S. Caliber .30 M1903A1 Springfield Rifle.

U. S. Rifle, Caliber .30 M1903A2

This design is *not* a shoulder rifle. It consists of a receiver and barrel mounted within the open breech of an artillery piece on a tank to be used for sub-caliber practice.

U. S. Rifle, Caliber .30 M1903 Mark 1

This designation indicates the standard Model 1903 rifle as altered to accommodate the Pedersen Device. It is designed to permit removal of the regular bolt and instant replacement by a special bolt assembly to convert the rifle into a blowback automatic weapon. The device shoots a .30 caliber straight taper rimless cartridge of pistol type. The bullet takes the rifling of the standard Model 1903 rifle. Very few of these devices are now in existence. The current French Service 7.65mm MAS pistol uses a cartridge very like the obsolete Pedersen, cal. .30 M1918.

U. S. Rifle, Caliber .30 M1903 NM

Until the approach of World War II, this Model was designed for target shooting at the National Matches.

This is the standard M1903A1 rifle except for the following: Barrel is star-gauged. Type C pistol grip stock is specially selected. Bolt is bright metal and numbered. Ejector is nickel steel.

The late models of this design had a reversed safety lock and a cocking piece without a projecting head. Early National Match rifles had the straight

The U. S. 30-06 Springfield M1903: Shown with M1905 Bayonet.

grip type "S" stock. The Model 1928 National Match had the 1922 M1 cal. .30 stock which was called the type "B," 1929 and later National Match Rifles had type "C" stocks.

U. S. Rifle, Caliber .30 M1903, Other Models

Style SB: This is the standard M1903 rifle as fitted to the 1922M1 cal. .30 stock (Type B).

Style NRA: This is the "Springfield Sporter." It employs the Model 1922, (NRA), stock, Caliber .30. This is the short sporting design without handguard and with a rounded shotgun buttplate. The barrel and receiver are browned in this design. A special lower band fastens the short fore-end of the stock to the barrel. A Lyman 48 receiver rear sight replaces the military design.

Style NBA: This is the same as the NRA except for the stock, which is a M1922M1, Caliber .22 design with added stock grooves. The pistol grip of the M1922M1 stocks differ from all others. The NBA design is the short sporting stock but is provided with finger grooves in the front end.

Style T: This is a heavy barrel target design fitted to a stock like the NRA. Barrel exteriors are 1.250 inch diameter at the breech, tapering to .860 at the muzzle. Barrel length is 28 inches. All rifle components are specially selected for accuracy and durability. Telescope sight seats are attached to the top of the barrel. The Lyman 48 receiver sight, and a special Winchester globe front sight are standard. This rifle design averages about 12 pounds 6 ounces in weight.

Style U. S. Rifle, Caliber .30, Special Match Rifles

In addition to the various models of the Springfield National Match Rifle, limited quantities of special Match Rifles were made at Springfield mainly for use in the Olympics and other international competitions. Special Cal. .30 Match Rifles with set triggers were made for the 1921 International Matches. For the 1922 Matches, Springfield made a number of special rifles. These had an adjustable upper band, stocks specially fitted to the team members, a butt hook, a cork palm rest, headless cocking piece, and set triggers manufactured by the Marine Small Arms Arsenal and Armory in Philadelphia. A Lyman 48 rear sight was used with this rifle as with the 1921 rifle. Another special Match rifle was made for the 1924 International Matches. This rifle also had a palm rest and butt hook, but also had a new speed-firing mechanism developed by John C. Garand. Some were fitted with German set triggers and some with a set trigger developed by Frank Rinkuna of the Marine Armory at Philadelphia. The International Match Rifle Cal. .22 M1924 was basically the same as the caliber .30 rifle described above. The caliber .30 International Match Rifle Model 1927 was similar to the M1924, but had a 28-inch barrel rather than a 30-inch barrel, a different type palm rest, and had the Woody set trigger.

A number of other target and sporting models of the Springfield were made from World War I to about 1937. They were all made in small quantities.

U. S. Rifle, Caliber .30 M1903A3

This modification was approved on 21 May 1942. While essentially the same as the original standard Rifle, it was modified to permit faster mass production

U. S. Caliber .30 M1903A3 Springfield Rifle.

and to lower cost without interfering with the accuracy or performance of the regular M1903A1.

One major difference between this rifle and the earlier design is the use of a new receiver rear sight.

A longer handguard (called a barrel guard) covers the area occupied by the old leaf sight of the early models.

Pistol grip is optional in this design. While very early Model 1903A3 rifles had stock screw pins passing laterally through the center of the stock to reinforce triggerguard and magazine well, late models have stock screws and nuts similar to the M1903.

The upper band assembly, lower band and its swivel, and triggerguard magazine assemblies are all stampings. Triggerguard and magazine units are staked and welded. The extractor collar is also stamped.

Buttplate group is the same as the M1903A1 except that it is made of stampings, and buttplate cap is not easily removed. Butt swivel groups consist of two plates with the swivel between welded together and fastened with two butt swivel screws.

Front sight groups consists of a flat front sight pinned into a slot in a ring-type sight base. The base is keyed and pinned to the muzzle; 5 heights of sight are provided, varying from .477 to .537 inch.

Rear sight is a receiver type mounted on the rear of the receiver bridge. It has a dovetailed base, a windage yoke with range scale graduated in 100 yard divisions and with 50 yard adjustments. The slide aperture can be raised or lowered from 200 to 800 yards. A windage knob moves the yoke to either side in clicks which represent a shift of one minute of angle. This represents a shift in the point of impact of one inch for each 100 yards of range involved.

The magazine follower is a sheet steel stamping. A straight ridge extends longitudinally on its top side. The front end is narrower than the rear and a section there is bent down and in on both sides to retain the magazine spring. A projection at the rear end holds the spring in position (although the 1903 follower is a machined piece, the stamped groups just described are interchangeable with it).

Some of the bolt parts of the 1903A3 are differently made than those of the

1903. In Oct. 1942 two groove barrels were approved for the 1903A3. There were 945,856 M1903A3 rifles produced by Remington and L. C. Smith Corona.

U. S. Rifle, Caliber .30, M1903A4 (Sniper)

This rifle was adopted in December 1942.

This rifle is the same as the 1903A3 except as follows: Telescope sight in bridge type mount over receiver (these mountings are attached to the re-

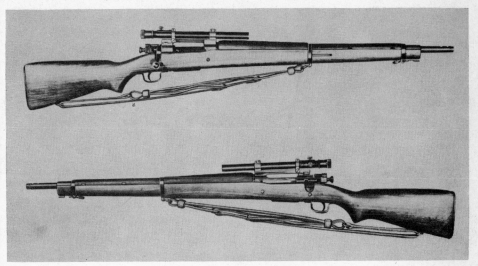

U. S. Caliber .30 M1903A4 Sniper Rifle.

ceiver itself). No metallic sights are used on this rifle. Stock has a full pistol grip and notch for the bolt handle which is altered in shape as required by telescope mounted above. Bolt handle curves downward and is cut away on outside to provide clearance for the telescope as the bolt handle is raised. Since the telescope blocks the clip guides in the receiver bridge, this rifle can be loaded only with single cartridges. No bayonet mounting is provided. The Weaver 330C is the common telescope sight employed. This 2.5 power telescope can be elevated to 1200 yards and was called M73B1 in the Government Service.

Government Made .22 Bolt Action Rifles

U. S. Rifle Caliber .22: The Ordnance Department together with the National Rifle Association developed a series of rifles built around the M1903 action to use the .22 long rifle cartridge. These were designed to stimulate training with the bolt action service rifle not only in service units, but also in rifle clubs, schools and colleges; and were developed before the adoption of the semi-automatic rifle. Early models which were made in prototype form were the Model 1 and Model 2.

U. S. Magazine Gallery Rifle, Model 1922: This design has a 5-shot detachable magazine, 24 inch barrel, Lyman NRA No. 48B rear sight. It weighs 9 pounds and has a shotgun type butt plate.

U. S. Magazine Gallery Rifle Model 1922M1: This improved design was

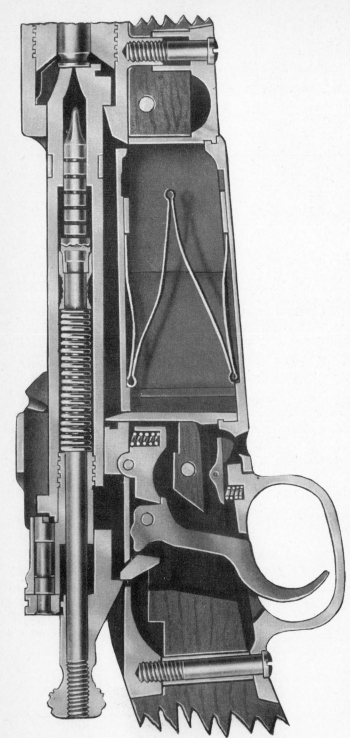

U. S. Model 1903, sectional view of receiver with magazine empty, chamber loaded, action ready to fire. The two-piece striker assembly held together by the firing pin sleeve is clearly shown.

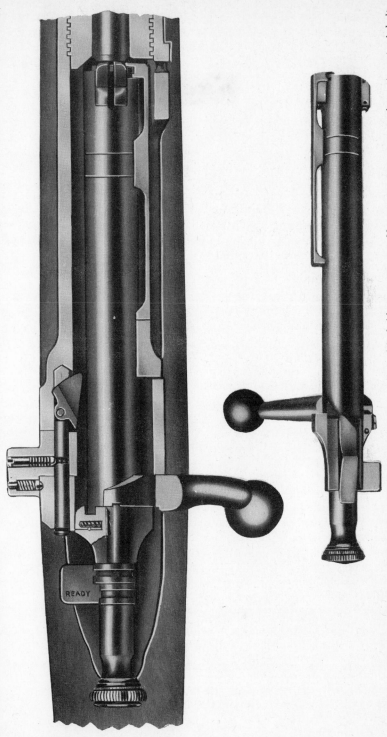

U. S. (Springfield) Model 1903. Sectional view through receiver top with bridge cut away. Note extracting cam surface at root of bolt handle which works in receiver bridge as action is opened, and gives primary extraction as it forces the entire bolt assembly back. Magazine cutoff and bolt stop assembly, together with ejector, are seen at top of main drawing. Note that the top locking lug (left lug locks in top of receiver ring when bolt is rotated down) is split to permit passage of ejector on opening bolt stroke. Details of manual bolt lock (safety) are seen at rear.

Lower detail shows view of assembled bolt. Note how extractor head straddles bolt lug. When the bolt handle is raised and lowered, the extractor does not turn with the bolt cylinder. Instead the bolt cylinder turns within the extractor collar. Sear notch and cocking cam surfaces can be seen on underside of cocking piece.

first produced in 1925. It differs from the earlier model in having a shorter chamber with a longer throat. A flush 5 round type magazine is provided. A single striker replaces the double one used in the earlier model. The firing pin rod and the ejector are of new design. The outside of the barrel is a straight taper from the curve ahead of the chamber to the front sight stud. The new bolt allows more accurate head space adjustment for improved accuracy. A Lyman 48C rear sight replaces the 48B.

U. S. Rifle, Caliber .22, M2: This design follows that of the M1 (1922) with further modifications as follows: Bolt redesigned to provide adjustable head space (an adjusting screw with a locking plug provides for this). The outstanding advance is in the speeding up of the firing lock. The firing pin travel is about one-half that of previous designs. Feeding was improved.

Note: The .22 caliber Springfield when stamped "M1922M2" indicates early Models to which the M2 features were added. Those marked M1922 MII indicate the 1922M1 design with the M2 bolt firing mechanism and bolt.

The M2 designs are the ones commonly encountered. They are parkerized to give a gray finish. Stocks are encountered with and without hand grooves.

Description of Basic Model 1903 Rifle

This is a turning bolt action rifle of general Mauser pattern. The magazine is a fixed vertical double line box. It may be loaded with single cartridges or from a charger clip. It is provided with a magazine cut-off. Magazine capacity is 5 cartridges.

The barrel is .30 caliber (7.62mm).

Barrel length is 23.79 inches. Bore diameter is .30 inch. Exterior barrel diameter at breech is 1.114 inch and at muzzle .619 inch. Chamber diameter at rear end is .4716 and at front end .442 inch. Diameter of chamber neck at rear is .442 inch and at front .3425 inch. Total length of chamber is 2.4716 inches. This is composed of the length of the chamber body (1.9356 inch), length of chamber shoulder (.16 inch) and length of chamber neck (.376 inch).

The length of bullet travel in the bore is 21.697 inches.

Rifling: M1903 and M1903A1 designs are rifled with 4 grooves having a uniform twist of one turn in 10 inches. Depth of groove is .004 inch. Width of grooves is .1767 and width of lands is .0589.

During World War II, to speed up manufacture, Springfields were provided with 2-groove as well as 4-groove barrels, the specifications being optional with the manufacturer. These 2-groove barrels were manufactured to the same accuracy specifications as the 4-groove.

The rifle weighs 8.69 pounds on an average with oiler and thong case in butt. The overall length is 43.21 inches.

Sights: The front sight on the Model 1903 and the 1903A1 is a blade type. The flat front sight and a movable stud are fitted into a ring type fixed stud which is splined and pinned at the muzzle. The 1903A3 group has the blade pinned in a slot in a ring type sight base which is pinned and keyed at the muzzle.

The rear sights on the earlier Models are mounted forward of the receiver on the rear end of the barrel, giving a sight radius of 22.14 inches.

Receiver: Springfield receivers made at Springfield Armory bearing numbers

U. S. Model 1903. Left side sectional view with bolt in full rear position, cutoff off, and magazine ready for loading. Note safety lug on bolt cylinder.

Sear nose is in position to stop forward movement of cocking assembly on forward bolt stroke, and to hold the cocking piece back while the bolt itself is turned and forced forward to seat the cartridge as the bolt handle is turned down. The sleeve lock engaged in the extracting cam on the bolt cylinder near handle works in receiver bridge to force assembly back as handle is lifted. Cam surface on the bolt cylinder shows clearly.

below serial 800,000 were made of Springfield Armory class C steel. These are commonly considered "brittle" receivers. They should not be used with modern or stepped-up loads.

Receivers between 800,000 and 1,275,767 serial numbers are Springfield Armory class C steel which were specially heat treated by improved methods. These are not as desirable as the later numbers, though far superior to the earliest manufacture.

All receivers between serial number 1,275,767 to 3,000,000 are made of nickel steel WD 2340 and represent the most advanced type of receiver designed. Between March, 1942 and July 5, 1942 WD steel No. 4045 was used. After July 5, 1942 WD steel No. 8620, modified, was used.

Springfield receivers made at Rock Island from serial No. 1 to Serial No. 285,507 were made of Springfield Armory class C steel. From No. 285,507 to 319,921 were made of Springfield Armory class C steel with improved treatment. Receivers over serial No. 319,921 were made of both class C steel and hot rolled nickel steel WD 35NS.

The receiver ring is threaded to screw to the end of the barrel in customary fashion. The right side of the boltway is cut to help loading and ejection. Below the boltway the receiver is cut through and shaped to form the upper section of the magazine.

Longitudinal grooves are cut on either side of the inside of the receiver walls to serve as travel guides for the locking lugs on the forward end of the bolt during bolt movement. The grooves turn into locking lug recesses in the receiver ring. The locking lugs turn into these locking recesses when the bolt handle is turned fully down.

To the rear of the magazine well, the receiver forms a solid bridge as in Mauser practice. A groove is cut in the under face of the bridge at the top to allow the safety lug on the bolt to pass through when the unlocked bolt is drawn to the rear. The right forward face of the receiver bridge provides a resistance shoulder for this special lug when the action is locked. Clip guides are machined into the front of the receiver bridge. They are sloped so that the bolt being pushed home can eject the empty clip without it being manually withdrawn after cartridges have been stripped down into the magazine.

The bolt stop and the ejector are positioned in the left of the rear of the receiver. Inside the rear of the receiver bridge a cam is machined to provide primary extraction as the bolt handle is raised. The handle as it is lifted works against this cam to move the complete bolt assembly and the case in the chamber back as soon as the lugs are turned out of their locking seats.

The rear extension of the receiver behind the bridge forms the customary tang having the usual longitudinal groove in which the sear notch (or stud) of the cocking piece operates. The rear of the tang has an underscrew thread to receive the screw from below which locks the triggerguard and woodwork to the receiver.

The barrel is reinforced over the chamber. It tapers to the muzzle from a shoulder 2 inches forward of the receiver.

The bolt is of one-piece design with a turned down bolt handle at the rear and dual opposed locking lugs at the front end. It is bored out from the rear in standard Mauser practice. Its face is recessed to receive the base of the rim-ess cartridge. It is pierced to permit the firing pin to protrude to fire the cartridge. While the lower lug is solid, the upper lug is slit for ejector travel, and its forward face is hook shaped to help support the cartridge in the chamber. Cam surfaces are provided at the rear of both lugs. A large solid lug on the right side of the bolt cylinder (when the action is closed) bears against a shoulder in the receiver to act as a safety lug in the unlikely event of the two forward lugs letting go. When turned down, the handle near the end of the bolt cylinder locks down into the receiver behind the rear bridge.

The two gas escape holes (there is only one on early models) are bored at the front of the bolt cylinder to exhaust any gas which might blow back through the firing pin hole into the interior of the bolt cylinder, in the event of a pierced primer.

At the rear of the bolt cylinder is a flange which goes partly around the rear of the cylinder and which has a recess for the spring catch which secures the bolt sleeve (or plug). The rear of the cylinder has a cam cut which operates against the face of the non-turning cocking piece stud to drive the stud and cocking piece back as the bolt handle is raised; and also a small cut which receives the point of the cocking piece sear notch (or stud) when the action is open.

Unlike the Mauser, the Springfield uses a two-piece striker. The firing pin rod carries the conventional cocking stud and is threaded at its rear end into the round, milled cocking knob. Its forward end is cut to form a mortise and tenon fit into the rear of the striker. The firing pin sleeve fits over the forward end of the firing pin rod and over the after end of the striker, covering the mortise and tenon joint and giving it rigidity. The mainspring is mounted around the firing pin rod, taking its rear bearing against the cocking piece sleeve and its forward bearing against the firing pin sleeve. A collar on the striker provides a forward bearing for the firing pin sleeve. The bolt sleeve screws into the rear of the bolt cylinder to hold the firing assembly in place. A spring loaded plunger mounted in the bolt sleeve engages a notch in the bolt cylinder to prevent the accidental unscrewing of the sleeve when the action is open. The rotary safety lock latch is mounted on the top rear of the bolt sleeve.

The safety has a thumb piece with the word "Ready" on the right side and "Safe" on the left. A stem or spindle to which it is riveted works in a hole on top of the bolt sleeve. A small spring stud on the underside of the thumb piece at the front end works in a groove in the bolt sleeve. It projects over the sleeve. This groove has three notches, one on each side and one on top.

The forward end of the stem is cut away at two points. When the thumb piece reaches the "Intermediate" stage, the safety cams enter the cuts in the top of the cocking piece and force it to the rear out of sear contact. If the thumb piece is turned to the right or "Safe" position, an uncut section of the stem is turned into a cut in the rear of the bolt. The bolt handle cannot be raised when the safety is in this position.

The ribs running around the bottom of the thumb piece are cut away at one point. When the safety is set at "Safe," these ribs revolve into recesses in the cocking piece to prevent that unit from moving forward.

When the thumb piece is in the "Ready" position the cocking piece can move freely and the bolt handle can be raised and lowered. When the thumb piece is in "Intermediate" position, the bolt handle can be lifted and the bolt pulled back, but the cocking piece is blocked and the rifle cannot be fired. When the thumb piece is turned completely to the "Safe" position, the bolt is locked to prevent opening and the cocking piece is also locked to prevent movement.

The extractor is a wide, long spring fastened by a dovetail to a split ring working in a cannelure cut around the bolt cylinder to the rear of the locking lugs. There is a projection in the front of the extractor which works in a second small cannelure in the front of the bolt cylinder to prevent the extractor being pulled off to the front. The extractor is mounted clear of the bolt so that the bottom (right) locking lug can turn up under the extractor spring as the bolt handle is lifted.

This system of extractor mounting permits the bolt cylinder to revolve as the handle is lifted, while the extractor remains in stationary position throughout the period of primary extraction, since the extractor body is held securely in its groove in the right side of the receiver. The full effect of the powerful leverage is thus applied to starting the fixed case back out of the chamber.

The ejector is mounted in the left side of the receiver just ahead of the magazine cutoff and while it resembles the Mauser in design, it works without a spring. It is pivoted near its rear end. As the bolt is withdrawn, the rear of the left locking lug hits the rear broad section of the ejector; that unit turns on its pivot and forces its front thin tip into the lug cut. Continued rearward bolt travel brings the ejector tip against the base of the cartridge case to eject it from the rifle.

The sear is pivoted on a pin to the receiver on two projections. The sear nose projects into the slot cut in the tang of the receiver and is pushed up by a small spiral spring which is fitted into a recess ahead.

The trigger is pivoted by a pin to the sear. There are two projections on its upper surface which bear in succession against the lower side of the receiver to give the standard military type double pull. This trigger design was originally used on the M. 1886 Mannlicher straight pull rifle.

The magazine is the Mauser design. It is flush with the bottom of the receiver and carries its 5 cartridges in two columns. The magazine lower section forms part of the triggerguard and is fastened to the stock and receiver by screws.

The magazine follower has a raised rib at its left side to elevate the column of cartridges there to almost the level of the right column. This permits the cartridges to position so that the advancing bolt can strip and chamber a cartridge alternately from either column. The follower is operated by a Z-spring positioned between it and the detachable magazine bottom. The upper section of the magazine is machined into the receiver and provides overhanging edges so that cartridges are stripped down individually and then stacked to right and left in the wider magazine below. This retains the double column effectively and prevents double loading, since only one cartridge at a time can either enter or leave the magazine.

The one-piece stock extends almost to the muzzle. Two "guard screws" passing through the ends of the triggerguard fasten the stock to the tang and

eceiver ring. The handguard extends from the rear sight base to the upper
)and.

The bolt stop performs the duties of a magazine cutoff also. This unit con-
ists of a spindle (or stem) with a thumb piece. The spindle lies longitudinally
n a cut in the left side of the receiver at the bridge. A spring stud of similar
)attern to that of the thumb safety controls the distance of action of the cutoff.

This spindle is cut away longitudinally in two places. At one section it is
:ut its entire length, and at the other for only a portion of its length. When
he thumb piece is turned down and the word "Off" can be seen on it, the
incut section of the spindle interferes with the rearward passage of the left
)olt lug. This prevents the bolt from being drawn back far enough over the
op of the magazine to allow a cartridge to feed up.

When the thumb piece is turned up so the word "On" shows, the spindle
1as been revolved so that the section which is partly cut away is projecting
into the bolt way. This permits the bolt to travel farther back before its left
.ug hits the stop spindle, and exposes the magazine so that a cartridge is fed
ip into line for chambering.

If the thumb piece is turned to a *horizontal* position, the completely cutaway
section of the spindle is lined up with the boltway. There is nothing to interfere with the passage of the left locking lug so the bolt can be pulled clear
back out of the receiver. This is one of the simplest and most effective magazine
:utoff and bolt stop systems ever designed.

Operation

As the bolt handle is turned up, the extractor is held in fixed position, since
its long surface is locked into the groove in the right side of the receiver. The
dual locking lugs are turned up out of their locking seats in the receiver.

As the locking lugs clear their seats, the extracting cam at the root of the
bolt handle hits against the corresponding cam face on the receiver bridge. This
affords powerful primary extraction for the cartridge case. (Note that while
this primary extraction system is as efficient as the Mauser, its system of applying the cam force is not exactly the same.) When the bolt is drawn back, the
extractor hook engaged in the extracting groove in the head of the cartridge
case carries the case back with it.

Near the end of the rearward bolt stroke the front end of the pivoted ejector
is traveling through a slot in the left lug. The rear of the split left lug hits
the broad rear of the pivoted ejector, thereby bringing the front tip of the
ejector sharply against the head of the cartridge case. Since the extractor is
still gripping the case, it serves as a pivot, so that as the case is torn from the
extractor grip it is hurled to the right and up.

The final .5-inch of the rearward bolt movement carries the bolt back over
the top of the magazine. The spring below forces the cartridges up into contact with the overhanging receiver sides. The magazine spring tension working
against the staggered follower, forces the cartridges up until the top cartridge
(which may feed up either from right or left depending on the number in the
magazine) will be in the path of the bolt. The left bolt lug hits the stop
spindle behind it, and bolt travel is halted.

When the bolt handle is lifted, the cam surface cut deeply into the rear of
the bolt cylinder bears on the camming surface at the front end of the cocking

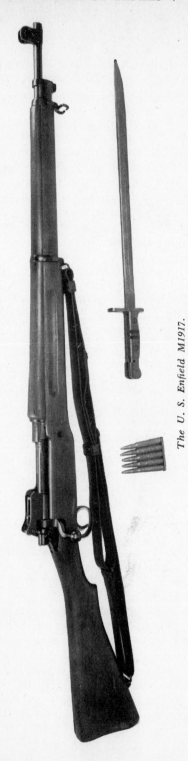

The U. S. Enfield M1917.

tud. It cams it to the rear in its groove far enough to pull the firing pin point back inside the bolt cylinder. This starts mainspring compression. The cocking piece cannot rotate; hence the curved surface of the cam-cut in the bolt cylinder forces the cocking piece to the rear and compresses the mainspring. In the Springfield design, this first cocking action produces the principal mainspring compression, though final compression occurs when the locking lugs cam down into their recesses as the bolt handle is locked down.

As the rotation of the bolt is completed the nose of the cocking piece passes out of the deep camming notch into a holding notch where it is retained by the tension of the compressed mainspring. As the bolt is retracted the sear notch on the cocking stud rides back over the sear nose which rises through a cut in the groove in the tang.

As the bolt is pushed ahead, its lower face strikes against the top of the base of the cartridge to be fed. The nose of the bullet rises as the bolt moves ahead, striking and riding up a guide (or ramp) machined into the receiver, which leads it into the chamber. When the cartridge has entered the chamber far enough so that the case is free from the overhanging magazine lips of the receiver, the continuing forward travel forces the base of the cartridge up into the grip of the extractor hook.

At the end of the forward thrust, the bolt lugs have traveled down the length of their longitudinal receiver grooves. The rear resistance (safety) lug, having passed through its cut in the underside of the receiver bridge, is now in front of the bridge, ready to be turned down into locked position. As the bolt handle is turned down, camming faces on the lugs and on their recesses (or locking seats), force the entire bolt assembly forward slightly to seat the cartridge in the chamber. The final turning action brings the lugs completely into their locking recesses in the receiver to support the head of the cartridge case. The rear safety lug is against the forward face of the receiver bridge.

When the bolt is moved forward to the point where it is ready to be turned down, the sear nose engages the sear notch on the cocking stud and holds it. Hence, as the bolt cams forward and downward, the holding notch disengages from the cocking piece nose. The rotation of the bolt brings the deep cocking cam recess into line with the cocking stud. When the trigger is pulled the sear is lowered, the disengaged cocking stud moves forward under the pressure from the mainspring and slides into the deep cocking cam notch. The cartridge fires and the operations cycle is ready to be repeated.

U. S. Rifle, Caliber .30, M1917

The description of this rifle, except for unimportant minor details, covers also that of the original British No. 3 Mark I .303 (commonly called the Pattern 14).

This rifle was designed originally in Great Britain. It was developed before World War I and was intended as a new design to replace the SMLE. A new rimless cartridge was designed for it there, but with the coming of war the caliber change idea was discarded.

With the outbreak of World War I, Great Britain decided to put the rifle into production in the standard .303 rim cartridge to prevent complication of ammunition supply.

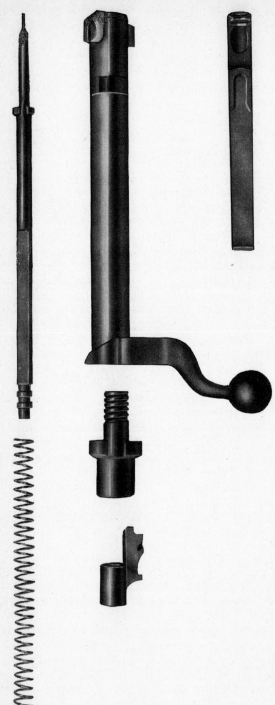

U. S. Model 1917 (Enfield). Bolt assembly dismounted. The extreme simplicity of design can be seen from the few and sturdy parts.

(1) 1-Piece striker with forward shoulder for mainspring seat, and interrupted rings at rear to lock cocking piece. Mainspring which is mounted over striker.

(2) Cocking piece which is secured to rear of striker. Bolt sleeve which is screwed loosely into rear of bolt cylinder. Bolt cylinder with extractor collar in place. Dual front lugs machined into bolt.

(3) Extractor which is easily removed from collar on bolt.

Contracts were placed with U. S. arms companies by Great Britain for manufacture of this rifle.

When the U. S. entered World War I in 1917, the shortage of Springfields (M1903) and the difficulty of tooling up additional factories for that rifle induced our Ordnance Department to turn to the three U. S. rifle makers then manufacturing rifles for Great Britain.

The British rifle M1914 (or P-14) was then modified to use the .30 U. S. Government M1906 rimless cartridge. This changeover required the manufacture of new barrels. The face of the bolt was changed to receive the rimless cartridge, while the magazine and follower required alterations because of the overall differences in cartridge lengths.

These rifles were manufactured by the Eddystone Rifle Plant, Pennsylvania, an organization originally owned by Remington Arms Co. but later purchased by Midvale Steel and Ordnance Co. Eddystone manufactured 1,181,908 rifles to the 9th of November 1918.

Remington Arms and Union Metallic Cartridge Co., Ilion, New York, manufactured 545,541 of these rifles to the same date.

Winchester Repeating Arms Co., at New Haven, Conn., produced 465,980 of these rifles in the same period. None has been made since 1918, but over 1,000,000 on hand were shipped to Great Britain during World War II.

This rifle is commonly known as the "Enfield" in the U. S. after the name of the great British Armory at which it was developed.

Characteristics

This is a modified Mauser design with one piece bolt bored out from the rear and with dual opposed locking lugs at the extreme forward end. It has a fixed vertical staggered box magazine of 5 shot capacity, loaded through the top of the action from standard U. S. Springfield charger clips. This rifle weighs about 9.5 pounds and has an overall length of approximately 46 inches. The nominal barrel length is 26 inches.

Barrels made in 1917 were rifled with five grooves, left-hand twist, one turn in ten inches. Rifles barreled during World War II may have two grooves or four grooves.

This rifle's principal variations from the Springfield are that it cocks on the closing motion of the bolt; utilizes a simplified, one-piece striker; has no magazine cut-off; the safety is of the "rocker" type mounted on the right rear of the receiver; the rear sight is mounted on the receiver and both front and rear sights are protected by stout "wings"; the bolt stop is of the Mauser type, a swing-out latch mounted on the left side of the receiver.

A camming and holding notch in the rear of the bolt cylinder operates on the nose of the cocking piece to withdraw the point of the firing pin and to hold it retracted when the bolt handle is lifted. This compresses the mainspring slightly but does not cock the piece.

As the bolt is closed the sear nose engages and holds the sear notch on the cocking stud when the bolt has about an inch of remaining forward travel. As the bolt is pressed forward and cammed down into locked position the mainspring is compressed and the rifle is cocked.

The sear has a safety stud which must enter a slot in the bottom of the

U. S. Model 1917 (Enfield). Action open and magazine loaded ready for forward bolt stroke. This construction differs considerably from the M 1903 (Springfield). The cocking and mechanical safety systems of this Model derive from the Spanish 1892 Mauser. 1-piece bolt with dual front locking lugs. This is one of the simplest and sturdiest bolt action rifles ever made.

closed bolt before the trigger can disengage the sear nose from the sear notch on the cocking piece stud. The bolt must be completely closed and locked down before the safety stud can enter this "interlock slot" in the bolt cylinder.

The thumb operated safety lock operates a half-round spindle which passes through a slot cut in the underside of the cocking piece. When the thumb latch is rotated the camming surface engages and pushes back the cocking piece holding it away from engagement with the sear. At the same time a plunger is moved into engagement with a hole in the rear surface of the bolt handle, locking the bolt. When the safety is rotated to the "Ready" position the cocking piece can ride over the flat side of the spindle and the piece may be fired.

The U. S. Rifle, Caliber .30 M1 (Garand)

An outline of the development of the Garand is given in Part I. As originally issued the rifle employed a false muzzle in which the gas port was drilled and to which the gas cylinder was attached. All of these rifles have been recalled. Numerous other modifications have been incorporated in the rifle but it is still designated the "M1"—a variation from the practice in other nations.

This is a gas operated semiautomatic, turn-bolt rifle. The design is notable among semiautomatics because of the relatively short receiver. This is made possible by the fact that the bolt return spring is not housed behind the bolt but is mounted inside the operating rod under the barrel. Thus, the receiver needs to be only long enough to accommodate the rearward travel of the comparatively short bolt. The standing breech and bolt housing at the rear of the receiver are integral with the receiver.

The bolt is of one-piece design with dual opposed locking lugs set back about $\frac{3}{16}$ inch from the bolt head. The lugs rotate into locking recesses cut into the sides of the receiver immediately to the rear of the receiver ring. The bolt-head, projecting forward of the locking lugs, is firmly seated inside the receiver ring when the action is closed. The firing pin is of one-piece, free floating design. It is L-shaped, the long arm of the L constituting the striker while the short arm of the L rides in a cut in the rear face of the bolt and projects about ⅛ inch beyond the perimeter of the bolt. This projecting arm of the firing pin bears against the rear face of the lower left quadrant of the receiver bridge until the bolt has rotated into fully locked position. In that position the firing pin arm lies opposite a slot cut in the receiver bridge so that the firing pin is free to move forward. It is positively blocked from forward movement except when the bolt is rotated into fully locked position. As the bolt is rotated and unlocked, a camming surface on the receiver works against the firing pin arm to withdraw the striker within the bolt face.

The extractor is a rugged, spring loaded claw mounted in the upper right quadrant of the bolt. Its pivot pin passes through a slot in the firing pin and ejector pin to hold them in the bolt.

The ejector is a sturdy, spring loaded pin mounted in the lower left quadrant of the bolt head. Forced back inside the bolt face by the head of the cartridge case, this efficient ejector is constantly exerting pressure on the case head. This ejector design makes it unnecessary to slot one of the locking lugs to permit ejector functioning as in many other designs.

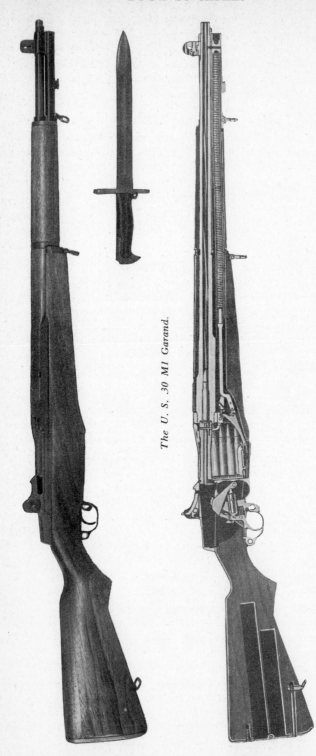

The U. S. .30 M1 Garand.

U. S. Caliber .30 M1 (Garand). Full length sectional view with magazine and chamber loaded and action ready to fire. Note that gas port is very far forward and on the under side of the barrel in this design. The magazine works off the operating rod and its spring through an unusual system of leverage.

The operating cam projects from the outside of the right-hand locking lug and extends into the operating rod raceway cut in the outside of the receiver.

The gas port is drilled through the bottom of the barrel about 1½ inches from the muzzle. It is covered by a gas chamber housing ("gas cylinder") which extends about 5 inches to the rear along the underside of the barrel. This gas cylinder is held in place by barrel bands at either end. The upper barrel band carries the front sight stud. The stacking swivel and bayonet stud are on the underside of the gas cylinder. Another barrel band called the "gas cylinder lock" is mounted immediately forward of the gas cylinder. It carries a threaded plug which screws into the gas cylinder and thus seals the forward end.

That portion of the operating rod which lies under the barrel is of tubular section. The forward end of the operating rod tube is closed and forms the gas piston when the operating rod is inserted in the gas cylinder from the rear. The operating rod spring (the action closing spring) is carried inside the tubular section of the operating rod, taking its front bearing against the inside of the piston head. Its rear bearing is against the magazine follower rod. To the rear of the tubular section of the operating rod is welded an offset to the right which rises and extends to the rear along the right side of the receiver in the form of a flat rod ending in a hook which forms the operating rod handle. Just forward of the handle a hump on the rod is milled on its inner surface to form the camming surfaces which engage the operating cam on the outer surface of the right hand bolt lug. The outside of the receiver and the inside of the operating rod are formed to provide a sliding mortise and tenon, holding the operating rod snugly to the side of the receiver as the rod travels backward and forward.

The magazine well is integral with the receiver. The follower mechanism is built into the magazine well. The rifle magazine is not complete in itself but requires the insertion of a clip holding cartridges in order to function. The bottom of the magazine well is closed by a floor plate which is a part of the trigger housing group. The magazine follower, its slide, its arm, a bullet guide and the operating rod catch (to which the accelerator is pinned) are all mounted within the receiver. A follower arm pin holds the assembly and serves as a pivot for both the follower arm and the rod catch.

There are small lugs at the long end of the follower arm which slide in grooves in the follower itself. The follower slides vertically in grooves in the sides of the receiver walls. Thus rear or forward movement of the follower arm works the follower straight up or down in the receiver.

The upward motion of the magazine follower is produced by the main operating rod spring. This spring also furnishes the force which imparts upward pressure to the operating rod catch. This operating rod catch is forced up to grasp the operating rod and hold the bolt open when the last shot has been fired and the empty clip expelled from the action. This notifies the shooter his rifle is empty, and permits quick insertion of a loaded clip.

The clip latch, mounted in a groove in the left side of the receiver, is pivoted on a long pin which passes through lugs on the receiver at each end of the latch. A thumb piece is provided at the rear of the latch and a spring under it bears against latch and receiver. Its normal function is to hold the latch

U. S. M1 (Garand). Details of operating mechanism.

(1) Rifle at moment of firing. Hammer has been driven ahead by spring within plunger tube, and firing pin driven forward. Bullet is still in barrel and action is locked by dual front lugs.

(2) Top view of details of bolt, operating rod and piston assemblies. Cartridge case is firmly held to face of bolt by extractor. Operating rod is shaped to work around corner of receiver. Rod spring is housed within hollow rod. Front end of rod is gas piston.

(3) Gas system details. Bullet has passed over port and some gas under pressure is expanding in gas cylinder to drive piston-operating rod units back. Since rod has some free travel before unlocking begins, breech is locked until bullet is out of barrel.

(4) Right side view showing actual appearance of operating rod parts on exterior of rifle, with hammer and trigger units shown in phantom. Hammer is cocked by bolt as it rides back and over it. Rear hook on hammer is caught and held by sear. When action closes, this feature prevents hammer from going forward. When trigger is released, front trigger lug grabs and holds front hammer hook. This system makes it necessary to pull the trigger once for each shot, a very necessary factor in a semi-

way from the receiver. The latch retains the clip in the action. When the
action is open, pressing the latch thumbpiece will release the clip and the
operating rod spring, functioning through the follower arm, will drive the
follower up and expel the clip and its cartridges from the action. When the
last shot has been fired, the clip ejector forces the empty clip out the top of
the open action. There is no magazine cut-off.

The trigger housing assembly consists of the housing itself, the trigger, the
triggerguard, hammer and sear, safety and their related springs and pins.

The housing is fastened to the receiver through lugs which engage with
corresponding lugs on the triggerguard. The triggerguard in turn is held in
position on the housing by the hammer retaining pin. When the triggerguard
lugs are engaged with those of the receiver, a squeezing action results which
also holds the stock securely to the receiver by lips on the trigger housing.

The clip ejector is mounted in the trigger housing assembly. It is placed
under a lug on the inner left face of the trigger housing. This clip ejector
is merely a looped spring. One end extends forward through the housing
where it bears against the cartridge clip forced down from above.

The hammer rotates about its pin. The mainspring (or hammer spring) is a
coil enclosed in a tubular housing which is open at the side near the safety.
A clevis at the rear of this housing is pinned to the trigger.

The trigger and sear rotate about the trigger pin. A safety bar is pivoted in
a hole in the left side of the trigger housing. The lug at its side serves as a pin.
The lower end of this safety bar extends down through the trigger housing
through a cut in the triggerguard. A spring engaged in the trigger housing
above holds the safety bar in whichever position it is pushed. This manual
safety can easily be pushed forward or back through the triggerguard cut to
"On" or "Off" position.

The hammer spring housing contains the coil hammer spring and a spring
guide plunger inserted through the center of the spring coil.

The hammer itself is split at the rear to enable it to ride down over the
manual safety. It has dual hooks protruding from the rear. The upper rear
hooks are engaged to hold the hammer as the bolt rides over it on rearward
movement. This prevents the hammer from going forward with the bolt to
fire in full automatic fashion. After the arm has locked, releasing the trigger
slightly in normal fashion, permits the upper hooks to disengage while the
lower forward hooks are immediately engaged by the trigger lugs ready for
the trigger pull.

If the bolt is not fully turned down into locked position a camming surface
on the hammer will, as it falls, strike a camming surface on the rear of the
bolt and turn the bolt into locked position. If the bolt does not turn the
hammer will not fall far enough to hit the firing pin.

The stock group is composed of the stock proper in which the barrel and
receiver rests; (the stock extends only midway along the barrel where it joins
the lower band) ; a rear handguard extending from the front of the receiver
to the lower band; a front handguard enclosing the top of the barrel, its front
held securely by the gas cylinder and its rear end by the lower band; and the
butt plate at the rear of the stock.

The butt plate is recessed, the butt setting into the plate itself. A trap in

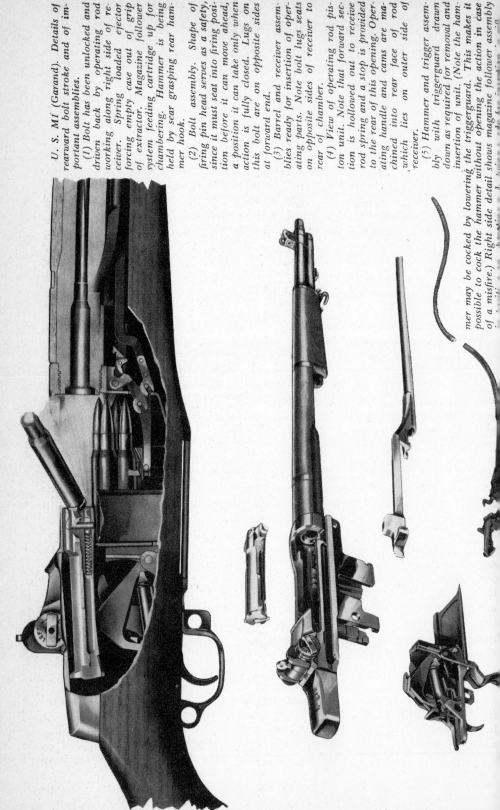

U. S. M1 (Garand). Details of rearward bolt stroke and of important assemblies.

(1) Bolt has been unlocked and driven back by operating rod working along right side of receiver. Spring loaded ejector forcing empty case out of grip of extractor. Magazine follower system feeding cartridge up for chambering. Hammer is being held by sear grasping rear hammer hook.

(2) Bolt assembly. Shape of firing pin head serves as a safety, since it must seat into firing position before it can move ahead, a position it can take only when action is fully closed. Lugs on this bolt are on opposite sides at forward end.

(3) Barrel and receiver assemblies ready for insertion of operating parts. Note bolt lugs seats on opposite sides of receiver to rear of chamber.

(4) View of operating rod piston unit. Note that forward section is hollowed out to receive rod spring and a stop is provided to the rear of this opening. Operating handle and cams are machined into rear face of rod which lies on outer side of receiver.

(5) Hammer and trigger assembly with triggerguard drawn down as required for removal and insertion of unit. (Note the hammer may be cocked by lowering the triggerguard. This makes it possible to cock the hammer without opening the action in case of a misfire.) Right side detail shows magazine follower assembly

he butt has a hinged cover. Two wells in the butt store the combination tool, he oiler and thong.

Early types of Garands have a plain buttplate mounted flat on the end of he buttstock and do not have a trap.

The cartridge clip is an integral part of the operating system of this rifle. The clip has side walls extending to right and left from the rear clip base. An opening is provided at either end of the clip permitting it to be inserted n the magazine either end up. The clip carries 8 cartridges in slightly staggered double rows of 4. The extraction grooves in the cartridge case heads engage an inner rib on the clip. They are thus held firmly in place between the rib and the individual side walls. The clip base is provided with projections on which the clip latch can engage to retain the clip in the magazine. This is a modified form of the familiar Mannlicher loading clip.

The rear sight is of the aperture type with protecting wings mounted on the bridge of the receiver. Large knurled knobs provide click adjustments for both elevation and windage.

The front sight is of the blade type, protected by wings on either side.

Operation

When the rifle is fired and the bullet passes the gas port some of the gas passes through the port down into the gas chamber where it impinges on the piston at the end of the operating rod. The operating rod is forced to the rear. It has about $\frac{5}{16}$ inch of free travel which gives the bullet time to clear the muzzle and allows the breech pressure to drop. Then the camming surfaces on the inside of the hump on the operating rod engage the camming surfaces on he operating lug and rotate the bolt counter-clockwise until the locking lugs are disengaged. Residual pressure in the gas cylinder and the momentum of the operating rod and bolt then carry the bolt fully to the rear, extracting and ejecting the cartridge, and over-riding and cocking the hammer. The operating rod spring is compressed between the inner face of the operating rod piston and the magazine follower rod. The pressure of the operating rod spring on the magazine follower rod forces a cartridge up into feeding position as soon as the bolt has moved far enough to the rear to clear the top of the magazine well. As rearward travel of the bolt is halted by the standing breech the compressed operating rod spring asserts itself and the operating rod is pressed forward. It carries the bolt with it, feeding a cartridge from the magazine into he chamber. At the forward end of the bolt stroke the cam surfaces on the operating rod engage the cams on the operating lug and force the locking lugs down into their locking recesses in the receiver, at the same time seating the bolt head in the receiver ring and engaging the extractor claw in the cannelure of the rimless cartridge case.

Production of the M1 Rifle

During World War II, the M1 rifle was produced by Springfield Armory and he Winchester Repeating Arms Co. A total of over 4,040,000 rifles were produced from the beginning of production in 1937 through 1945. Springfield made by far the greater amount, Winchester making 513,582 during World War II. After the war, an additional 600,000 were made by Springfield, Inter-

national Harvester, and Harrington and Richardson. In addition to this pro
duction the M1 was made by Beretta and Breda in Italy during the early
fifties. Beretta-made M1's, in addition to being supplied to the Italian Army
were sold to Denmark and Indonesia.

Variations of the M1 Rifle

A number of variations of the M1 have been produced, usually only in
limited quantity or in prototype form. A number of these weapons are listed
below with their outstanding characteristics.

M1E1 Rifle: It differs from the M1 only in having a more gradual cam angle
in the operating rod handle—few were made.

M1E3 Rifle: A roller lug was attached to the bolt cam lug and the cam angle
of the operating rod was altered to match. Few of these weapons were made
but this system was used in the later selective fire T20E2 rifle and the current
M14 rifle.

M1E4 Rifle: In order to provide a "softer action" by increasing action dwell
time and to decrease the rearward velocity of the operating rod, the gas system
of the M1E4 was altered from that of the M1. The M1 uses an impinging gas
system; that of the M1E4 is a gas cut-off expansion system. The gas port is
located approximately 8 inches from the muzzle and the gas, after filling the
expansion chamber, is cut off from the gas port and is allowed to expand. Im
mediately after the hammer was cocked by the recoiling bolt, the gas was
allowed to escape. This gas system is similar in concept to that used on the
current M14 rifle.

M1E9 Rifle: This rifle also has a gas expansion cut-off system; however, the
piston was divided from the operating rod and served as a tappet to the oper
ating rod. This avoided the overheating of the combined piston operating rod
experienced with the M1E4. This system is very similar to that used with the
current M14 rifle.

M1E5 Rifle: This was a shortened version of the M1 using a pantograph-type
folding stock. The barrel was 18 inches long and although accuracy was com
parable to the M1 at ranges up to 300 yards, blast and muzzle flash were ex
cessive.

T26 Rifle: In July 1945 the Pacific Theater of Operations requested 25,000
shortened M1 rifles. To meet this requirement the M1E5 barreled action was
fitted with a standard M1 stock. An order for 15,000 of these rifles was given
but was cancelled in August 1945.

M1E2 Rifle: This is the first experimental M1 Sniper rifle. It was equipped
with an International Industries telescope and mounts. At the same time an
M1 equipped with a Weaver 330 scope and Stith mounts was tested.

M1E6 Rifle: This was an M1 Sniper model with offset telescope designed to
allow use of the iron sights in addition to the telescope. None were made.

M1E7 Rifle: This weapon had a Griffin and Howe scope mount and an M7,
(Lyman Alaskan) or M73B1 (Weaver 330) scope. A removable leather cheek
piece was fitted to the stock. This weapon was standardized in June 1944 as the
U. S. Rifle Caliber .30 M1C (Snipers). A removable flash hider was adopted in
January 1945.

U. S. Caliber .30 M1C Sniper Rifle.

M1E8 Rifle: This is similar to the M1E7, but the scope mount is a block-type developed by Springfield Armory. A leather cheek piece on the stock was also used with this rifle. The M1E8 was adopted as substitute standard in September 1944 as the *U. S. Rifle Caliber .30 M1D (Snipers).* The M73 (Lyman) telescope with cross-wire type reticle and rubber eye piece is called the Telescope M81. When equipped with tapered post reticle and rubber eye piece, it is designated as the M82. A later telescope used with the M1C and M1D is the M84.

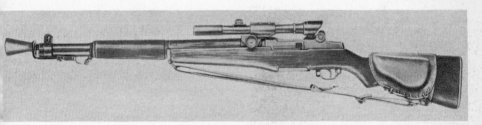

U. S. Caliber .30 M1D Sniper Rifle.

M1 National Match Model: This is similar to the issue M1 but has a special National Match barrel, sight parts, and a few other special components. Specially assembled for accuracy.

Predecessors to the 7.62mm M14 Rifle

In early 1944 Springfield Armory and Remington Arms were directed to develop a selective fire weapon having the following characteristics:
a. Weight—9 pounds less magazine.
b. Magazine—20-round.
c. Bipod equipped.
d. Semi-automatic fire on closed bolt.
e. Full-automatic fire on open bolt.
f. Suitable for launching grenades.
g. Use standard M15 grenade launcher sight.
h. Weapon to have a folding stock.
The development weapon at Springfield was designated the T20 and that at Remington was designated the T22. Winchester developed a weapon of their own. In September 1944, Headquarters Army Ground Forces requested that the M1 be modified to: (a) selective fire, (b) use a bipod, (c) that the mechanism

be simple and capable of field stripping, and (d) that a suitable 20-round magazine loaded from the bottom of the piece be developed. Accordingly Springfield and Remington were instructed to change the original requirements they received dropping those for a short barrel and folding stock.

Cal. .30 T20 Rifle: This rifle had selective fire, originally with closed bolt on semiautomatic fire and open bolt on automatic fire. The first models were delivered to Aberdeen Proving Ground in 1944 for test. A modified 20-round Browning Automatic Rifle (BAR) magazine was used. The gas cylinder was locked into position with a muzzle brake. Aberdeen tests indicated the need for a better magazine and better method of holding it in place.

Cal. .30 T20E1 Rifle: This model fired from the closed bolt in both semiautomatic and automatic fire. A new magazine catch and new magazine were also used. A new muzzle brake was also used; the muzzle brake of the T20 did not allow the use of a bayonet, grenade launcher, or flash hider. Two heat flow arresting grooves were put on the barrel before the chamber. The T20E1 had an adjustable bipod which was not easily removable. The weapon was tested at Aberdeen in January 1945 and the tests were successful. As a result 100 of an improved version were ordered from Springfield Armory.

Cal. .30 T20E2 Rifle: This rifle differs from the T20E1 in the following: the muzzle brake has been further modified to use a new grenade launcher which, with a new valve, is designed to permit semi- or full-automatic fire without the removal or manual adjustment of the launcher by the firer. A new bipod with longer legs was adopted, the bolt was slightly modified, and a roller lug added to the bolt lug (similar to the M1E3). The receiver is slightly longer than that of the T20 and the bridge has been modified to mount an operating rod lock to hold the bolt open when desired. The magazine was usable in the BAR, but BAR magazines could not be used in the T20E2. There were numerous minor changes made as well. In May 1945 the Ordnance Committee recommended that 100,000 of these rifles be procured, but no action was taken because of the ending of the war.

Cal. .30 T22 Rifle: This was one of the Remington developments and had a bipod, flash hider and 20-round magazine. Tests indicated that minor modifi-

U. S. Rifle Caliber .30, T22. A selective fire prototype developed by Remington from the M1.

cations were needed to improve functioning, the magazine release, and retention of the bolt in the open position.

Cal. .30 Rifle T22E1: The required modifications to the T22 were made in this model and several were tested at Aberdeen.

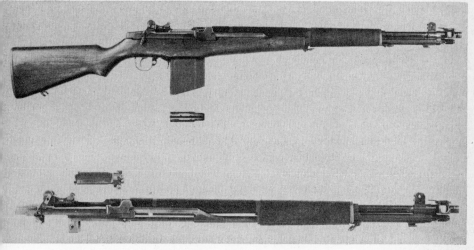

U. S. Rifle Caliber .30 T22E2.

Cal. .30 Rifle T22E2: This weapon had a new magazine catch and a slightly changed trigger group. It incorporated the gas cylinder, gas cylinder valve screw, muzzle brake, flash hider, and bipod as used on the T20E2. The T22E2, like all the Remington modifications, used the M1 receiver without lengthening.

Cal. .30 Rifle T23: This Remington modification of the M1 incorporates selective fire control by means of an independent hammer release. This weapon fired full automatic from an open bolt and semiautomatic from a closed bolt; however the Proving Ground test indicated that it would fire from the open bolt only 20 percent of the time. More change was required and it was decided to use a closed bolt for both full and semiautomatic fire. T23 used the standard M1 stock and early test models used the M1 8-round "en bloc" clip. Later models used a BAR magazine, but were not too successful and it was decided that a new magazine should be designed.

Cal. .30 T24: The T24 was another Remington modification of the M1 to selective fire in which selective fire control is obtained by means of an independent sear release. The T24 fired from a closed bolt in both semiautomatic and full automatic fire and used the 8-round "en bloc" clip in test models. It was equipped with a straight high comb stock.

Winchester Automatic Rifle: Winchester developed this weapon on their own initiative. It was based on the carbine gas system and had a bipod and flash hider. Ten specimens were procured in May 1945 for test.

Cal. .30 T25 Rifle: This was a postwar Springfield Armory design using a gas cut-off and expansion system. It is a selective fire weapon having a straight line stock. The bolt is a tipping type which locks on the top of the receiver. The T25 fires on a closed bolt in semiautomatic fire and an open bolt in full

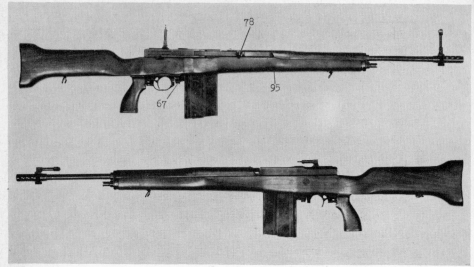

U. S. Caliber .30 T25 Rifle.

automatic. It was later altered to fire selectively from a closed bolt. T25 was chambered for the T65 series caliber .30 case; this case later was developed into the 7.62mm NATO case.

Cal. .30 T27 Rifle: This was an M1 converted to automatic fire by an auxiliary device that could be inserted in the field. It was subsequently redesigned so that it was capable of selective fire. It uses the M1 8-round "en bloc" clip.

Cal. .30 T37: Chambered for the NATO cartridge, this rifle evolved from the T20E2. A few minor differences, beyond the change of cartridge, differentiate this rifle from the T20E2.

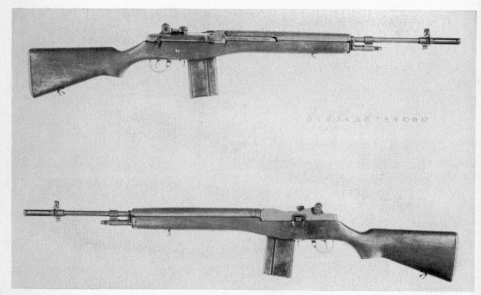

U. S. 7.62mm T44E4 Rifle (M14).

Cal. .30 T44: Chambered for the NATO cartridge, the T44 is basically the T37 with gas cut-off expansion system. The T44 is the first of the prototypes which directly resulted in the M14 rifle. T44E1 was a heavy-barrel version of the T44. The T44E4 was adopted as the 7.62mm Rifle M14 in June 1957. Two differences of the T44E4 from the production M14 are a plastic ventilated hand guard in the M14 as opposed to a wooden handguard in the T44E4, and M14 has an aluminium hinged butt plate as opposed to a standard steel butt plate in the T44E4. The T44E5 was adopted as the 7.62mm Rifle M15; a heavy-barrel

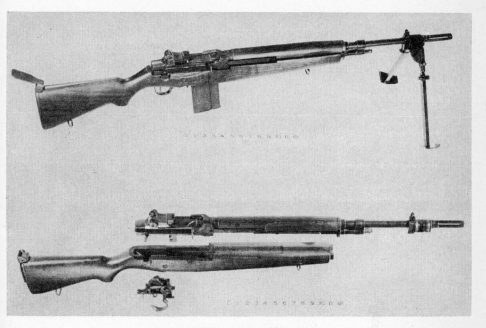

U. S. T44E5 (7.62mm Rifle M15).

version of the M14, it was dropped shortly after adoption and never mass produced. It was decided that the selective fire M14 when fitted with bipod and hinged butt would be used to fill the squad automatic role formerly filled by the Browning Automatic Rifle. The T44E6 is a light-weight form of the M14 which was produced only as a prototype.

Cal. .30 T47 Rifle: Chambered for the NATO cartridge, the T47 is a redesign of the T25 to use a conventional stock.

Cal. .30 T47E1 Rifle: The heavy barrel version of the T47 rifle; chambered for the NATO cartridge.

Cal. .30 T48 Rifle: Chambered for the 7.62mm NATO cartridge, this is the U. S. experimental model designation for the Belgian FN "FAL" rifle. In addition to a quantity purchased from FN, 500 were manufactured by Harrington and Richardson, Worcester, Mass. The T48 competed against the T47, the British EM2, and the T44 during the early 50's.

U. S. Caliber .30 T47 Rifle.

U. S. 7.62mm Rifle M14, Production Version.

U. S. 7.62mm Rifle M14. Production version fitted with bipod.

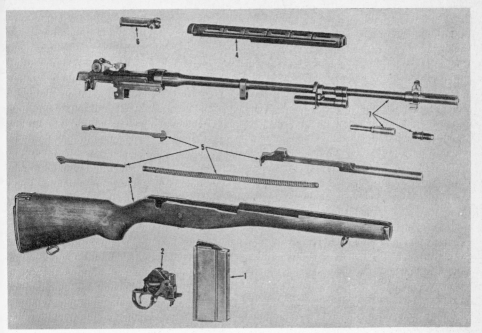

U. S. 7.62mm Rifle M14, Field Stripped. 1, Magazine. 2, Trigger mechanism. 3, Stock. 4, Handguard. 5, Operating Rod Assembly. 6, Bolt. 7, Gas Piston, Gas Cylinder Valve, and Barrel.

The 7.62mm M14 Rifle

The gas cut-off and expansion system of the M14 operates as follows: Gas is tapped 8″ from the muzzle of the barrel which is only 22″ in length, 2″ shorter than the M1 rifle. Gas descends into the gas cylinder through a gas port and enters the snugly-enclosed, hollow gas piston through an orifice in the top. In moving back, further supply of gas to the piston is cut off, insuring constant gas pressure against the piston. Gas vented from the bottom of the cylinder as the piston nears the end of its 1½″ stroke. One half of the gas piston is rectangular and bears against the operating rod; the other half is rounded with shallow rings cut in its surface to collect fouling from the cylinder during travel of the piston. To clean the cylinder and piston, removal of the plug at the front end of the cylinder is necessary. A manual gas cutoff on the right side to the rear of the cylinder is used when grenades are to be launched. The operating rod looks like that of the M1 Garand, except that it has been reduced proportionately for the shorter gas system.

The front and rear sights remain the same as on the M1 Garand rifles but are graduated in meters. The left side of the M14 receiver has been milled out to form an integral telescope mount base. The barrel is fitted with a removable, 5-prong, flash suppressor, which is remarkably efficient, particularly at night. The bottom prong is wider than the rest and helps reduce climb. To load the M14, a fully-loaded, 20-round magazine may be substituted for the empty one, or it may be loaded from the top with 5-round, Springfield-type stripper clips. However, 2-stud, 03 Springfield stripper clips are not interchangeable with those of the M14, as they have only one centrally-located stud on each side of the clip. A special sleeve is fitted over the rear end of the magazine to permit insertion and stripping of the 5-round M14 clips directly into the 20-round capacity magazine.

After careful consideration and experimentation, the conventional pistol-grip stock of the M1 rifle was retained for the M14 in preference to the straight-line submachine gun style stock where the butt stock and pistol grip are separate units as typified by the SIG Stgw 57, CETME, EM2, and FN NATO Assault Rifles. The principal advantage of the straight-line submachine gun style stock is reduced recoil and climb. The M1 type of grip stock avoids high line of sights, slow handling in assuming shooting position, and deliberation required to position rifle and align sights.

Most M14's are fitted with the selector locked on semiautomatic fire. By replacing this lock with a fire selector and spring, the gun can be quickly converted from a semiautomatic to selective fire, since it contains all the necessary components. It will apparently be left to the discretion of local commanders to order this conversion to meet the tactical situation. The high cyclic rate of fire, 750 r.p.m., of the 10-pound, fully-loaded M14 makes control extremely difficult during full automatic fire. A hinged, BAR-type butt plate and bipod are provided as special issue, affording the M14 greater support when used as a squad automatic weapon. By actual timing, it takes just 1.6 seconds to empty an M14 20-round magazine on full automatic fire. Under the circumstances, the Army's decision to issue the M14 as a semiautomatic is quite understandable.

The automatic firing mechanism of the M14 consists of the following parts mounted on the right side of the receiver and positioned by the selector lock: selector lever, selector eccentric, sear tripper, selector shaft, and connector arm. The trigger mechanism of the M14 is identical with that of the M1 rifle except for the rear sear which is elongated to permit tripping.

To fire full automatic, depress selector lever and rotate it until it snaps into position with face marked "A" to the rear and with projection upward. This eccentric movement of the selector lever causes the sear tripper to move rearward to contact the elongated trigger sear. Simultaneously, the connector arm moves rearward and its hook-shaped front end contacts the operating rod. When the trigger is pulled to fire a shot, the operating rod is forced by the gases to move to the rear and unlock the bolt. As the bolt moves back, it extracts and ejects the expended case. The compressed operating rod spring forces the operating rod forward along with the bolt which strips a cartridge from the magazine and chambers it. After the operating rod locks the bolt, it strikes the hook-shaped front end of the connector arm causing it to move forward slightly. This forward movement causes the sear tripper to disengage the elongated rear sear from the hammer, permitting the hammer to fall and strike the firing pin. Unless the trigger is released, this cycle of fire will continue until all 20 rounds from the magazine are expended.

To switch over to semiautomatic fire, depress and rotate the selector lever until it snaps into position with blank face to rear and projection downward. The connector assembly is rendered inoperable in this position since the connector arm is held forward and out of engagement with the operating rod, as is the case when the rifle is issued with the blank stud.

Dissassembly. Proceed as with the M1 Garand. Remove trigger group from butt stock and remove stock from barrel and receiver. With connector assembly upright, depress and turn selector until letter "A" faces rear sight knob. Press connector arm forward with thumb, lifting it off connector lock. Rotate connector arm clockwise until slot at rear aligns with elongated slot on sear release. Lifting front end slightly disengages connector arm from sear release. With barrel and receiver group upside down, pull operating spring forward to relieve pressure on connector lock. Pull lock outward to disconnect and remove operating spring and guide. With barrel and receiver group rightside up, retract operating rod until lug on underside coincides with dismounting opening in receiver. Lift up and pull back operating rod to free it from its guide. Bolt is removed from the receiver by tilting, as in the M1. Reassembly is accomplished by reversing this procedure.

SPECIFICATIONS OF M14 RIFLE

Total length of weapon with flash suppressor: 44.14".
Total weight of rifle with 20-round loaded magazine: 10.0 lbs.
Weight of rifle with empty magazine: 8.7 lbs.
Total length of barrel: 22.00".
Groove diameter: .308" plus .002" tol.
Bore diameter: .300" plus .002" tol.
Number of grooves: 4.
Rifling, righthand twist, 1 turn in: 10".
Cyclic rate of fire: 750 r.p.m.
Muzzle velocity: 2,800 f.p.s.
Maximum chamber pressure: 50,000 p.s.i.

SPECIFICATIONS OF M15 RIFLE

Total weight of rifle fully loaded with 20 rounds: 14.80 lbs.
Total weight of rifle with bipod and empty 20-round magazine: 13.75 lbs
Total length of rifle with flash suppressor: 45.5".
Total length of barrel: 22.0".
Total weight of barrel: 3.5 lbs.

U. S. Carbines, Caliber .30, M1 and M1A1

The story of the development of these arms has been dealt with in Part I.

The carbine form of a service rifle is normally merely a cut-down version of the rifle, receivers and calibers being identical. It is necessary, therefore, to emphasize that the U. S. Carbines M1 and M1A1 are distinctive arms differing in all their parts, either in design or size, from the standard U. S. M1 Rifle. The carbine cartridge, while of .30 caliber, is a short straight tapered case not interchangeable with the rifle cartridge.

Carbine, Caliber .30, M1

This model is the basic form. It has a one-piece wood stock extending somewhat over half the length of the barrel. The single handguard extends from the receiver forward on top of the barrel to the front band which fastens it and the stock to the barrel at their forward ends. The stock itself protrudes in this design beyond the front band. A recoil plate is screwed into position in the rear of the receiver cut in the stock. A sling swivel is provided on the left side of the front band. The buttstock is pierced to provide a positioning point for

The U. S. 30 M2 Carbine.

the oiler. The rear of the sling is passed around this oiler, holding it in the stock cut at the same time that the oiler serves as an anchor point for the sling. The butt plate is screwed to the stock.

The front sight is a blade attached to the muzzle end of the barrel; while the first issue rear sight consisted of two integral leaves set at right angles to each other. They are set for 150 and 300 yards respectively. The current rear sight is a ramp-type similar to that of the M1903A3. Graduated to 300 yards. The M1 Carbine was adopted in October 1941. Overall length of this carbine form is 35.6 inches, and weight with sling and unloaded magazine is about 5.2 pounds. Magazine capacity 15 cartridges held in double staggered rows.

Carbine, Caliber .30, M1 A1

This is identical with the M1 style except for the stock. A wood stock is fitted with a wood grip resembling that of a standard automatic pistol. A folding metal skeleton stock extension is hinged to the grip at the bottom and to the rear of the stock at the top. The rear of the sling in this design is secured to an eye on the lower hinge assembly at the bottom of the grip. This skeleton can fold forward along the left side of the rifle. This design was intended primarily for use by paratroopers.

With stock extended, the carbine M1A1 is about the same length as the M1. When the extension is folded, the length is about 25.4 inches. The weight with unloaded magazine is about 6.19 pounds.

Carbine, Caliber .30, M2

This is the same basic arm except that it has been modified for full automatic fire. This places it in the category of machine weapons.

The M2 carbine is the result of a project initiated in May 1944 to develop the carbine into a selective fire weapon. The T4 carbine, as the developmental

U. S. Caliber .30 Carbine M2 with Bayonet and 30-round Magazine.

carbine was known, had a modified sear, hammer, operating slide, trigger housing, trigger housing pin, and magazine catch. Added parts were the selector, sear trip lever, sear trip, sear trip plunger with spring, and selector spring. The M2 was adopted as standard in September 1944. The M2 is usually used with a 30-round magazine and its cyclic rate of fire is 750-775 rounds per minute. With loaded magazine, it weighs 6.60 pounds. When the selective fire M2 carbine was adopted as standard, the M1 and M1A1 were reclassified as limited standard. All carbines are to be replaced by the M14 rifle.

Carbine Caliber .30 M3

This weapon is an M2 carbine with receiver designed for an infra-red sniperscope. It does not have iron sights. It was adopted in August 1945 and was previously designated as the Carbine caliber .30 T3.

Carbine Characteristics

The U. S. Carbines, M1 and M1A1 are semiautomatic carbines. Barrel length is 18 inches. Rifling is right hand, 4 grooves one turn in 20 inches. The sight radius is 21.46 inches.

The cartridge is .30 caliber with a straight taper brass case and a round nose gilding metal jacketed bullet. The loaded ball cartridge weighs 193 grains; its overall length is about 1.67 inches. The approximate weight of the bullet is 110 grains. Maximum chamber pressure is approximately 40,000 pounds. Muzzle velocity is 1970 feet per second; maximum range is about 2000 yards and effective range for use against military targets about 300 yards. Magazine capacity is 15 rounds, held in a double column detachable box inserted through the bottom of the action. The 30-round magazine can also be used.

While the various designs are basically the same, they may vary in some manufacturing details. These differences stem from the fact that the carbines

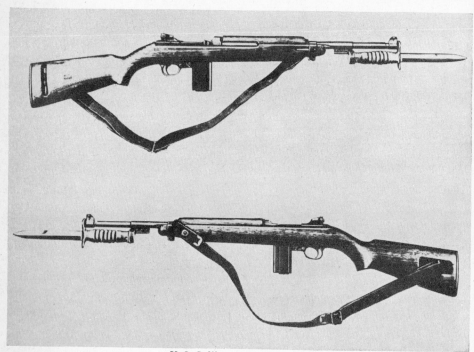

U. S. Caliber .30 Carbine M1.

were made in several plants and production occasionally required alteration of original specifications because of machinery differences and the like; minor changes invariably encountered on all new models after field tests also were required on the carbines.

In the M1 and M1A1 designs, the variations are principally in the stock.

Some of the Type 1 receivers were manufactured without the disengaging notch for the rear end of the operating slide. In these a slot is cut in the bottom of the operating slide guideway to permit disengagement and engagement of the rear end of the slide when removing or assembling. A lug pressed out of the operating slide spring housing tub fills the bottom of this slot.

Carbines of later manufacture eliminated this modification. The original dismounting notch and spring housing without lug were utilized.

The gas cylinder may be swedged on the barrel; or in the second ("alternative") design may be an integral part of the barrel forging.

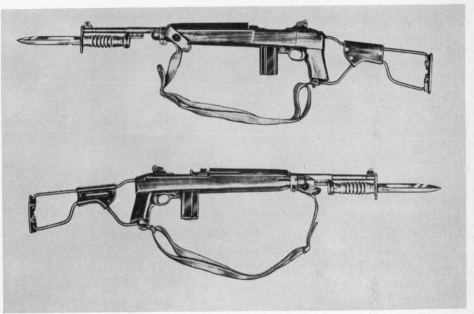

U. S. Caliber .30 Carbine M1A1.

Description and Operation of M1 Carbine

This is a gas operated, semiautomatic, turn-bolt design. It operates on the short-stroke or "tappet" principle instead of on the long-stroke or "piston" principle employed in the Garand. The gas port is in the bottom of the barrel about 3 inches forward of the chamber. The port is covered by a gas chamber which is integral with the barrel. Into the rear of this gas chamber is threaded a gas cylinder carrying a piston which has a $\frac{3}{16}$ inch stroke. The operating slide is a U-shaped steel piece with tenons on the inside top edges of the U which slide in grooves cut on either side of the barrel forging. This piece is open forward so as to slide over the gas cylinder. It is closed at the rear to provide a buffer surface against which the piston can bear. The operating slide spring has its forward bearing against the rear face of the slide and in its rear bearing in the tunnel drilled for it in the receiver. Extending from the top left side of the slide is a rod which ends in a hook to form the operating slide handle. The rod rides in a cut on the right side of the receiver with a sliding mortise and tenon effect. A camming cut on the inside of the operating slide engages camming surfaces on the operating lug on the bolt as in the case of the Garand.

The bolt is of one piece design with dual opposed lugs set back slightly from the face of the bolt similarly to the Garand bolt. The extractor, ejector, and striker are similar to the Garand.

The trigger housing assembly consists of the hammer, trigger and sear mechanisms and the holding framework.

The housing is attached to the receiver at the rear by its T-shaped lug engaging the facing L-shaped mating lugs on the receiver. It is retained at its forward end by the retaining pin passing through the mating lugs at the forward end of the receiver and the trigger housing.

The hammer rotates on its pin and the trigger and sear rotate together about a second pin.

The hammer pin is straight and has a head on one side for positioning. A hammer plunger is seated in a notch in the rear face of the shank of the hammer, extending back into an aperture in the rear of the trigger housing. The hammer spring (or mainspring) is seated in a counter bore in the trigger housing; it bears on a collar on the hammer spring plunger. The left face of the hammer has a stop lug which limits both forward and rearward movement.

The trigger spring is U-shaped. It is a torsion spring with a straight section seating in a slot in the rear end of the trigger, and a coiled center section housed in an aperture in the rear end of the trigger housing.

The rear end of the sear spring is seated in a recess in the body of the trigger. The front end of the sear spring seats in a recess in the rear face of the sear itself.

The manual safety is in the shape of a push-through cylinder having a notch. It is mounted in the forward end of the trigger housing just ahead of the bow.

The safety cylinder is so shaped that it can clear or block the forward end of the trigger as it is pushed from side to side in its cut. A spring operated plunger which can seat in either one of two indents in the safety locks it in the position to which it is pushed.

The magazine catch is mounted on the right side of the trigger housing ahead of the safety. It functions in a T-shaped guide way and is kept in engagement with two small lugs at the rear of the magazine by pressure of the magazine catch spring and plunger.

When the magazine catch is pushed to the left it moves in far enough to disengage it from the magazine lugs. This frees the magazine, allowing it to be drawn down out of the action. When released, the catch is sprung back into place to hold the next magazine inserted. (A plunger like the safety plunger holds the magazine catch.)

Operation

When the carbine is fired, as the bullet passes over the gas port gas is forced through the barrel port into the gas cylinder below. It expands and acts against the head of the short piston.

The piston is driven sharply back about .140 inch. Its travel is then halted when it hits the piston nut which locks it to the gas cylinder. When the piston hits this nut, it serves as a dam to prevent any additional gas loss from the barrel.

The piston hits the front face of the operating slide body, which has been resting against it, a very sharp blow. This starts the operating slide assembly to the rear.

The operating slide travels freely to the rear without affecting the bolt assembly for about .3125 inch. During this free travel of the slide, the chamber pressure drops to permit extraction.

The front face of the cam recess in the cam lug on the operating slide bar now acts against the cam face on the bolt cam. This rotates the bolt far enough to the left to raise its right lug out of engagement in its receiver recess and lower the left lug below its locking shoulder. This unlocks the bolt from the receiver.

The rotation of the bolt provides primary extraction of the empty case by loosening the case in the chamber. The turning movement also causes the cam face on the tang of the firing pin to work against the cut in the interior of the receiver bridge to withdraw the firing pin within the bolt. A rear cam surface on the bolt also acts against the lug on the hammer to draw the hammer back away from the head of the firing pin.

The slide travelling in its travel grooves carries the bolt back in its guides. The cartridge case is drawn out of the chamber by the extractor in the head of the bolt.

When the forward end of the empty case is clear of the receiver, the ejector constantly bearing against the under face of the cartridge case as it is forced forward by its spring, is able to force the cartridge up, tearing it loose from the grip of the extractor and hurling it out of the rifle. The extractor spring snaps the extractor back into place.

The lower rear face of the bolt thrusting against the forward face of the hammer pushes it back and down. The hammer is thus rotated about its pin. It in turn forces the hammer plunger attached to it back to compress the mainspring (or hammer spring). (Note that the hammer, trigger and safety designs in the carbine differ radically from those in the M1 Rifle.)

The hammer is pushed down until the notch for the sear in the hammer is in position to be caught by the nose of the sear. This sear nose engaging in the sear notch in the hammer is held by pressure of the sear spring which causes elongation of the pivot hole in the sear. The bolt rides back over the cocked hammer.

While the trigger is still held back after firing a shot, the rear end of the trigger is elevated and the trigger spring is compressed.

Since the sear spring has forced the sear ahead, when disengaged from the hammer when the pivot pin hole in the sear was elongated, the sear is holding the hammer, but is not in contact with the trigger. Hence the arm cannot fire automatically.

Forward movement of the sear causes the rear end of the sear to drop below the level of the lip at the rear top face of the trigger. This elongated pivot pin hole in the sear therefore permits the sear to stay in engagement with the hammer when the hammer is forced back past the cocking point as the bolt rides over it. (This obviates the necessity for the rear and front hammer hook system of the M1 Rifle.)

Releasing the trigger permits the trigger spring to push the rear end of the trigger down. The hammer spring acts through the hammer to lever the sear to the rear. The elongated pivot pin hole in the sear permits this. As the trigger is released, the lip on the rear top face of the trigger drops low enough for the sear to ride over and rest upon it.

A pull on the trigger will now elevate its rear end and carry the rear end of the sear with it. When the sear turns about the trigger pin, its forward end will be forced down out of engagement with the sear notch in the hammer.

The freed hammer, forced ahead by the hammer spring plunger which is driven by the expanding hammer spring, rotates the hammer on its pin to strike the rear end of the firing pin.

Return Stroke of Action

At the end of the recoil stroke, the magazine is completely exposed. The compressed spring forcing up the follower pushes the columns of cartridges up. The cartridges rise alternately from each side of the magazine, being caught and held by the overhanging magazine lips. One cartridge is slightly above the other and is in the path of the forward movement of the bolt.

The operating slide spring compressed during the rearward movement now reasserts itself. It forces the operating slide forward. The bolt is drawn ahead by the operating slide with which it is engaged.

The lower face of the bolt hits the top cartridge in the magazine and starts it toward the firing chamber.

When the bolt has chambered the cartridge, the rear face of the cam cut in the camming lug at the rear of the operating slide bar works against the cam on the bolt. This rotates the bolt from left to right, bringing its locking lugs into position in front of their respective locking shoulders in the receiver cuts.

At this point the firing pin tang mates with its cut in the interior of the receiver bridge, and only then can the hammer hit the firing pin.

The forward end of the slide is again in contact with the rear end of the floating piston.

When the bolt chambers the cartridge, the extractor in the top face of the bolt is cammed up by the edge of the cartridge case. Its hook, driven by its spring, snaps into the extracting groove in the face of the cartridge case. The cartridge case forces the ejector back into the bolt and compresses the ejector spring.

Pressing the trigger will now fire the cartridge in the chamber and repeat the cycle just described.

The manual safety in the bow of the trigger housing ahead of the trigger can be pushed through from side to side. When pushed to the left, a slot in the safety allows the forward end of the trigger to be depressed; this elevates the rear end, carrying the sear up to release the hammer. When the safety is pushed through to the *right,* its solid face provides a positive block for the forward end of the trigger. Since the front end of the trigger cannot be lowered, the rear end cannot be elevated; hence the sear cannot release the hammer.

The magazine in this arm is detachable as in a standard automatic pistol. It consists of the customary steel body, the follower on which the cartridges rest, follower spring and floor plate. Compression of the spring as cartridges are slid in under the overhanging magazine lip and pushed down into the magazine tube provides the motive power for elevating the cartridges for feeding. There is no magazine cut-off.

Production of the Carbine

Approximately 7,130,000 carbines of all models were manufactured. Manufacturers were Inland (by far the largest), Winchester, Underwood, Rochester Defense Corp., Quality Hardware, Saginaw Steering Gear, Rock-Ola, National Postal Meter, Standard Products, and I.B.M.

Survival Rifles

These are guns developed for the use of Air Force personnel for hunting if forced down in uninhabited or hostile territory. The M6 is a combination rifle-shotgun using a .22 Hornet and .410 gauge. It is a folding-type weapon weighing 3.75 pounds with a 14-inch barrel. When unfolded in firing position, it

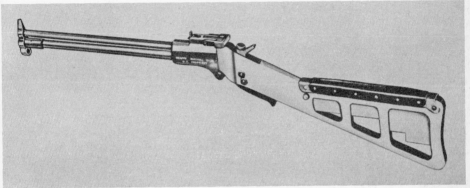

M6 Survival Rifle—Shotgun, .22/.410.

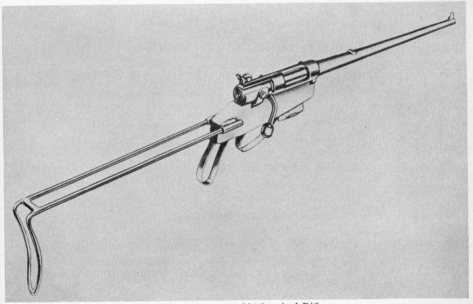

Caliber .22 Hornet M4 Survival Rifle.

is 27.75 inches long and when folded it is 15 inches long. The M4 Survival Rifle is bolt action and chambered for the .22 Hornet cartridge; it has a 5-round box-type magazine and a collapsible wire stock. The barrel is removable for packing purposes. The rifle weighs 4 pounds and has a 13.75-inch barrel. The AR-5 is a semiautomatic survival rifle that floats; the stock is made of fiber glass and the barrel and action are packed in the stock when dismounted.

The Johnson Semiautomatic Cal. .30 M1941 Rifle

This is a short-recoil, turn bolt design, with 10-shot, clip-loaded rotary-type magazine. Unique features include an instantly removable air-cooled barrel; an 8-lug turning bolt rotating 20 degrees, which gives great locking strength, yet provides fast unlocking time; a magazine which permits both clip and single loading with the bolt closed or open, thereby allowing selective reloading of a partially empty magazine without opening the breech.

The principal units in this 9½ pound arm are the barrel, receiver, bolt, butt, and magazine assemblies.

The slide mounted 22-inch barrel is carried in the cylindrical receiver sleeve, supported by the breech-end locking bushing and the guide collar nine inches from the breech. Holes in the receiver sleeve permit heat radiation. A spring assembly in the lower radiator sleeve keeps the barrel in battery and serves as a quick-release retaining latch.

The receiver includes the bolt and barrel sections. The bolt section includes a ⅞-inch diameter hole for the bolt, with an inside enclosed cam channel on the top. The hinged ejector is housed on the left. The ejection port is on the right. The top of the receiver is entirely covered. The forestock is screwed to the radiator sleeve. A back plate assembly secures the rear of the receiver.

The bolt includes the flat-leaf extractor with spring-tensioned claw recessed in the bolt head, retained in place by the cocking handle which is assembled in the bolt slot and held by a plunger. The unlocking cam lug is on top of the bolt, and mates with the locking cam of that assembly, which also carries the key-locked firing pin and mainspring strut.

The eight locking lugs on the head of the bolt are circumferentially displaced and equi-distant. The ninth lug of this 20-degree turning assembly is removed to provide the extractor recess. The bolt lugs engage with corresponding abutments in the locking bushing which is threaded to the barrel. The eight lugs and their abutments are respectively over one-half inch long, and the locking area thus obtained in this design gives it unusual strength.

The butt assembly includes the hammer, sear, and trigger block to which the butt stock with mainspring tube is screwed. The block is held by its longitudinal slots to the receiver, and secured by a cross pin shaft. The double hooks of the hammer operate on the sliding double hooks of the sear to provide semiautomatic fire. The safety lever extending through the block to a point ahead of the triggerguard secures the sear unit to prevent discharge, but permits manual bolt operation to remove cartridges. The hammer is actuated by a coil spring on the hammer shaft.

The mainspring plunger in the tang of the stock is completely covered by the receiver lock plate extension so that the shooter's face is fully protected.

The ten-shot rotary magazine is held by two shafts to the receiver; also, it is supported in the hammer block and receiver by the follower shaft. The rotary follower tube assembly is actuated by a round wire torsion spring. The loading cover is held closed by a leaf spring. The cover is pressed inward by seating a clip in the receiver clip-seat, or by pressing in single rounds. When the rounds are stripped off, the cover is closed by the cover spring which also ejects the clip.

The rear sight is of the aperture type with windage. The leaf is raised by the notched sight slide which provides locking notches for each hundred meters up to 1200 meters.

The front sight is a square post protected by curved ears.

Operation

As the bullet passes through the barrel, the bolt and barrel commence the primary recoil phase of 3/16 of an inch. When the bullet is some two or three feet from the muzzle, the unlocking cam on the bolt contacts the corresponding cam face in the receiver. The second phase includes rotation of the bolt within one millisecond, withdrawal of the firing pin, primary extraction aided by the tapping action of the locking cam unit, and completion of the barrel recoil stroke which totals 3/8 of an inch. After completing the recoil and unlocking stroke, the barrel, aided by the recoil spring, returns to battery.

The bolt and locking cam assembly continue rearward due to recoil plus some residual blow-back force. During this phase the hammer is cocked, the mainspring is compressed, the empty case is withdrawn from the chamber, and is ejected to the right forward side of the receiver as the ejector blade contacts the rim. The bolt is arrested on the bolt stop, and a fresh cartridge is positioned in the feed lips of the receiver by the rotary magazine follower and feed ramp of the cover.

In the closing phase the mainspring pushes the bolt assembly forward, feeding the cartridge into the chamber. When the bolt has entered the barrel locking bushing, the locking cam is permitted to rotate the bolt into the locked position. This locking cam movement permits the blocked-off firing pin to move forward so that its point can reach the primer of the fresh round when the trigger has moved the sear for the next blow by the released hammer. Johnson Automatics Trust made 50,000 of these weapons for the Netherlands East Indies Army and limited quantities were used by the U. S. Marines and the Special Service Force during World War II.

Armalite—AR-10

Fairchild Engine and Airplane Corporation entered the armament field through its division of Armalite whose first major offering was the AR-10 Assault Rifle in caliber 7.62mm NATO. This rifle looks somewhat like the FN NATO Assault Rifle. It is capable of full or semiautomatic fire, and is gas operated. Use of the Swedish Ljungman AG42-type of gas system avoids expensive, complicated, and fragile construction. Plastics are used for the forearm, butt, and pistol grip, and non-ferrous alloys are used extensively. Steel is used for the bolt and bolt carrier. Wood has been totally eliminated. Aluminum parts, like the frame and magazine, are given a black anodized coating. The chamber is the conventional-type—not fluted. A pronged flash suppressor is an integral part of the barrel. The aluminum magazine is detachable but no provision is made to load the weapon by stripper clips. The muzzle section of the barrel can be used as a grenade launcher.

7.62mm Armalite AR-10 Rifle as usually found.

A concave carrying handle is an integral part of the receiver. Between this handle and the receiver is the operating handle, positioned like an upright trigger. An aperture rear sight is fitted to the rear section of the carrying handle frame; elevation is controlled by a knurled knob in graduations from 200-500 yards; the sight also has a windage feature. Straight-line construction of the butt in relation to the long axis of the barrel necessitates the high line of sights which tunnel through the carrying handle; the handle tends to narrow the field of view considerably. Because of the close proximity of the sighting eye to the carrying frame, shooters complain of being struck frequently by this portion while firing. Recoil is reported mild as compared with guns of similar weight and caliber; it has a cyclic rate of 700 rounds per minute.

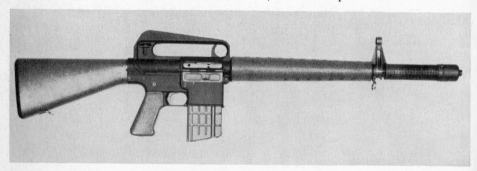

7.62mm AR-10 Rifle, as it was first made.

The massive bolt weighs approximately one pound and consists of the bolt-head with 7 locking lugs, extractor, and ejector—all seated within a cylindrical bolt carrier. The bolt mechanism is completely enclosed by the receiver, with the exception of the ejection port which has a hinged cover to keep out foreign matter when not firing. This is similar to the German Sturmgewehr, snapping open after the first shot is fired. A camming stud extends from the bolthead through the top of the carrier directly beneath the gas tube. Two allen screws fasten the gas tube to the top of the bolt carrier.

When the rifle is fired, gas is tapped from the barrel into the gas tube; gas

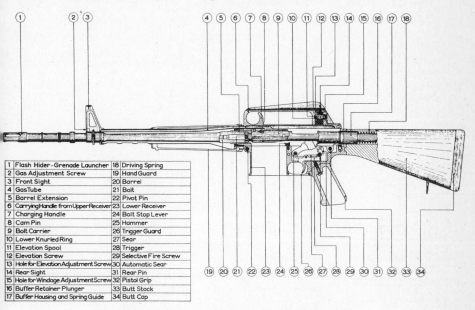

1	Flash Hider - Grenade Launcher	18	Driving Spring
2	Gas Adjustment Screw	19	Hand Guard
3	Front Sight	20	Barrel
4	Gas Tube	21	Bolt
5	Barrel Extension	22	Pivot Pin
6	Carrying Handle from Upper Receiver	23	Lower Receiver
7	Charging Handle	24	Bolt Stop Lever
8	Cam Pin	25	Hammer
9	Bolt Carrier	26	Trigger Guard
10	Lower Knurled Ring	27	Sear
11	Elevation Spool	28	Trigger
12	Elevation Screw	29	Selective Fire Screw
13	Hole for Elevation Adjustment Screw	30	Automatic Sear
14	Rear Sight	31	Rear Pin
15	Hole for Windage Adjustment Screw	32	Pistol Grip
16	Buffer Retainer Plunger	33	Butt Stock
17	Buffer Housing and Spring Guide	34	Butt Cap

Section View of 7.62mm AR-10 Rifle.

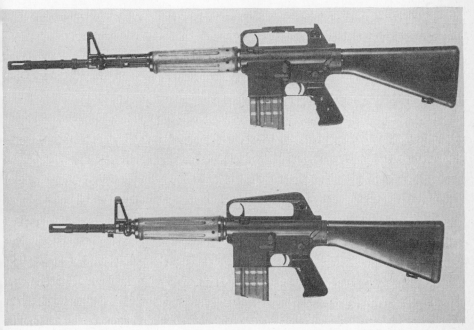

Late Prototypes of the 7.62mm AR-10 Rifle made at Artillerie Inrichtingen.

passing through the short gas tube over the bolt carrier forces it rearward about ⅛″. At this point, gas, being cut off, is unable to enter the tube, and the bullet leaves the barrel. Gas trapped within the chamber formed by the bolt and carrier is vented through ports in the carrier sleeve. But sufficient kinetic energy has been imparted to the carrier to continue its travel to the rear, during which time the geometrically-arranged camming slot acts against the bolthead stud, forcing it to turn and unlock the bolt. Released, the bolt joins the carrier in moving to the rear.

Briefly, the weapon can be field stripped as follows: Insert a cartridge up to the neck to drive out the pin above the grip on the left side of the gun. Like the FN and in shotgun manner, the weapon will hinge apart in two sections. Pull back cocking piece. In reassembly, bolthead must be in forward position before exerting pressure on the bolt to seat it.

Manufacturing rights for the AR-10 were acquired by Artillerie-Inrichtingen, Zaandam, Holland. This government arsenal, better known as Hembrug, became a private concern to avoid war work under Nazi occupation. Several years ago it reverted to government ownership but, under Dutch law, this tax-supported arsenal is permitted to compete with private enterprise. Only limited quantities of the weapon have been produced to date. It failed to pass tests in West Germany and, despite its novel, lightweight construction, has been unable to gain a foothold except for a limited quantity in the Sudan.

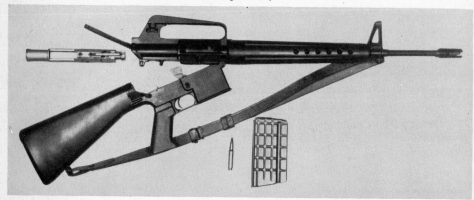

AR-10 Broken for Stripping.

The AR-10 is no longer in production.

SPECIFICATIONS OF AR-10
Caliber 7.62mm NATO

Total length of weapon: 41.25″.
Weight of weapon with sling and empty 20-round magazine: 7.5 lbs.
Weight of weapon with loaded 20-round magazine: 8.4 lbs. approx.
Length of barrel with flash suppressor: 21.4″.
Muzzle velocity: 2723 f.p.s.

Armalite—AR-15

Armalite Corporation submitted the AR-15 (a smaller version of the AR-10 in caliber .223) which fires full or semiautomatically. An L-shaped, dual-range peep sight is standard with the AR-15, but basically the mechanics and operation are the same as the AR-10.

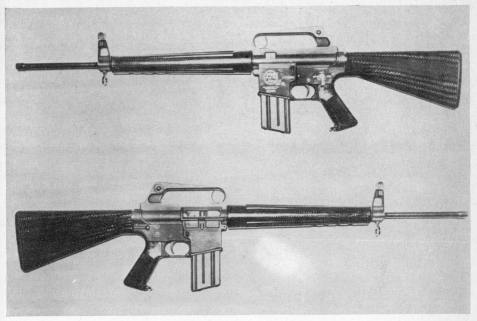

Cal. .223 AR-15 Rifle as first produced.

Cal. .223 AR-15 Rifle of current production. Grenade launcher sight is in fixed position.

The U. S. Air Force has purchased AR-15 rifles for the use of guards at SAC bases.

SPECIFICATIONS OF AR-15
Caliber .223

Total length of weapon: 38.0".
Weight of weapon with 20-rd. magazine: 6 lbs.
Length of barrel: 20.0".
Magazine capacity: 20 rds.
Muzzle velocity: 3300 f.p.s.
Cyclic rate: 750 r.p.m.

New Developments

The Armalite Corp. of Costa Mesa, California has developed a new selective fire rifle for the 7.62mm NATO cartridge. This gas operated weapon is composed mainly of steel stampings. It weighs 8.75 pounds, has a cyclic rate of 650 rounds per minute and in the rifle version is 41.5 inches long. The barrel is 20 inches long; the weapon is fed with a 20-round detachable box magazine. This rifle is called the AR-16.

Winchester Lightweight Military Rifle

The lightweight military rifle submitted by Winchester Arms Company looks like a larger version of the U. S. Army .30 caliber M1 carbine and fires a high-velocity cartridge designed by Winchester called the .224. While there is only a minute difference between the .22 round developed by the Remington Arms

Winchester Cal. .224 Rifle.

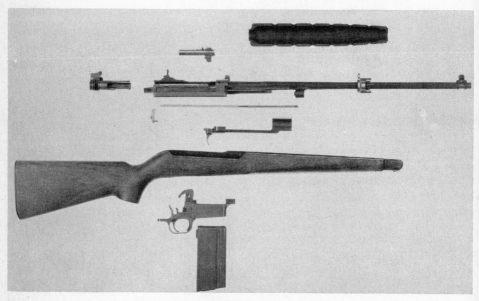

Winchester Rifle Stripped.

Company and the one designed by Winchester, they are not interchangeable in the Winchester model as they are in the AR-15.

The Winchester prototype operates like the M1 carbine since it incorporates the M1 Garand-type bolt and Williams short-stroke gas system. An M2 carbine-type, full or semiautomatic fire selector is on the forward, lefthand side of the receiver. Safety is at the rear of the receiver. Triggerguard and magazine are aluminum alloy composition. A fluted barrel reduces weight without unduly sacrificing strength.

SPECIFICATIONS OF WINCHESTER LIGHTWEIGHT MILITARY RIFLE

Caliber .224 Winchester E2 Ammo

Total weight of weapon with loaded 20-round magazine: 5.5 lbs.
Total weight of weapon without magazine: 4.9 lbs.
Weight of empty magazine: .14 lbs.
Weight of stock: 1.4 lbs.
Weight of rifle action group: 3.5 lbs.
Total length of weapon: 37.6".
Length of barrel: 20.0".
Total number of individual components: 71.

AMMUNITION

Caliber: .224 Winchester E2   Maximum pressure: 52,000 lbs. per sq. in.
Bullet: Flat base spitzer.   Maximum cartridge length: 2.17".
Weight of bullet: 53 grains.

Range (in yards)	Velocity (feet p.sec.)	Energy (ft. lbs.)	M.R. Ordinate (in inches)
Muzzle	3,300	1,280	..
100	2,795	920	0.5
200	2,340	645	2.5
300	1,930	440	6.0
500	1,275	190	25.5

Sporting Rifles

The outstanding characteristics of the basic American sporting rifle types are in the following tabular data which covers the essential specifications of each of the great variety of commercial models now in production.

The products of the several manufacturers are covered alphabetically by manufacturers and serially by model number for each manufacturer.

No attempt has been made to show bore diameter, groove diameter and twist for each of the American sporting rifles. These specifications have been changed slightly from time to time in the individual models and there is variation from rifle to rifle. The following figures, however, are representative. The groove and bore diameters in most American sporting weapons will be within two thousandths of an inch of those listed.

Cartridge for which rifle is chambered	Groove diameter (inches)	Bore diameter	Twist (rifling) No. of inches per turn
.22 Short R.F.	.223	.217	20–24
.22 Long R.F.	.223	.217	20–24
.22 Long Rifle R.F.	.223	.217	16
.22 W.R.F. R.F.	.226	.220	14
.25 Stevens R.F.	.256	.248	17
.22 Hornet	.223	.217	16
.218 Bee	.224	.219	16
.219 Zipper	.224	.219	16
.22 Savage H.P.	.227	.221	12
.220 Swift	.224	.219	14
.6mm Lee Navy	.242	...	7½

Cartridge for which rifle is chambered	Groove diameter (inches)	Bore diameter	Twist (rifling) No. of inches per turn
.25-20	.256	.248	12–14
.25-35	.256	.249	14
.25 Rem. Auto.	.256	.249	10
.250-3000 Savage	.257	.250	14
.257 Roberts	.257	.250	10
.270 W.C.F.	.277	.270	10
7mm Mauser	.285	.276	10
.30-30 W.C.F.	.308	.300	12
.30 Rem. Auto.	.308	.300	12
.30-40 Krag	.308	.300	10
.30 Rem.	.308	.300	12
.30-'06	.308	.300	10
.300 Savage	.308	.300	12
.300 H&H Magnum	.308	.300	10
8mm Mauser	.318	.311	9–10
.303 British	.312	.303	10
.303 Savage	.308	.300	12
.32 Short and Long R.F. ...	.313	.305	20–26
.32 Rem. Auto.	.320	.312	14
.32 Win. Special	.320	.315	16
.32 Win. Self-Loading	.320	.315	16
.32-20 W.C.F.	.311	.305	20
.32-40	.320	.315	16
.33 W.C.F.	.338	.330	12
.348 Win.	.348	.340	12
.35 Win. Self-Loading	.351	.345	16
.351 Win. Self-Loading	.351	.345	16
.35 Rem. Auto.	.357	.349	16
.35 W.C.F.	.358	.350	12
.375 H&H Magnum	.376	.366	12
.38-40 W.C.F.	.400	.394	36
.401 Win. Self-Loading	.407	.399	14
.405 Winchester	.413	.405	14
.44-40 W.C.F.	.428	.422	36
.45-70 Gov't.	.458	.450	22

Colt Model 1-22

Caliber: .22 Short, Long or Long Rifle
Type of action: Turnbolt
Manual safety: Thumb lever
Magazine type and capacity: Single shot
Barrel length and style: 22" round
Overall length: 41.75"
Weight: 5.25 lbs.
Sights: open rear, post on ramp front, adapted for scope
Stock: 1 piece Monte Carlo with pistol grip

Notes: Also made in Boys Model 20 with 20" barrel and in a model chambered for the .22 Winchester Magnum.

Colt Lever Action

Caliber: .22 Short, Long or Long Rifle
Type of action: Lever action, hammerless
Manual safety: Cross bolt
Magazine type and capacity: Tubular, 15-rounds

Barrel length: Approx. 20"
Overall length: 39"
Weight: Approx. 5 lbs.
Sights: Open rear, post on ramp front
Stock: 2 piece with pistol grip

Colt Autoloader Carbine

Caliber: .22 Long rifle
Type of action: Blowback, semiautomatic
Manual safety: Cross bolt
Magazine type and capacity: Tubular, 15-rounds
Barrel length: approx. 20"

Overall length: 37"
Weight: 4.75 lbs.
Sights: open rear, hooded ramp, adapted for scope
Stock: 2-piece, straight grip

Colt Standard Hi-Power

Caliber: .222, .222 Magnum, .243,
.264, .270, .308, .30-06, .300 H&H
Magnum, .375 H&H Magnum
Type of action: Turnbolt
Manual safety: Roll over or sliding type
Magazine type and capacity: Box-staggered
column—4 or 5 rounds

Barrel length and style: 22"-26"
Overall length: Average 42"
Weight: Average 7.5 lbs.
Sights: Adjustable leaf rear, hooded ramp
front, tapped for scope
Stock: 1 piece with full pistol grip

Notes: The Coltsman Custom Hi-Power has a checkered Monte Carlo type stock, rubber recoil pad, Q.D. swivels, and hinged floor plate.

Harrington and Richardson Model 60

Calibers: .45 A.C.P.
Type of Action: Blowback semiautomatic.
Magazine type and capacity: Detachable box
(clip) 12 rounds.

Barrel Length and style: 18.25"
Overall length: 40.25"
Weight: 7.4 lbs.
(Discontinued)

Harrington and Richardson Models 65 and 165

Calibers: .22 Long Rifle
Type of Action: Blowback semiautomatic.
Magazine type and capacity: Detachable box
(clip) 10 rounds.
Rate of Twist: 1x16
Model styles: Military training rifle, full
stock, sling swivels (Model 65). Sporter
type, no swivels (Model 165)

Barrel Length and style: 23"
Overall length: 43"
Weights: 9 lbs. (Model 65). 7.5 lbs.
(Model 165)
Sights: Military blade front. Micrometer,
receiver type, rear.
Stock types: One piece. Pistol grip.
(Discontinued)

Harrington and Richardson Models 150 and 151 "Leatherneck"

Calibers: .22 Long Rifle
Type of Action: Blowback, semiautomatic.
Magazine type and capacity: Detachable
boxes (clips,) 5 and 10 rounds.
Model styles: Models 150 and 151 are the
same with the exception of the rear sight.
Barrel Length and style: 23" round
Overall length: 43"

Weight: 7.5 lbs.
Sights: Model 150 has open sights. Model
151 has micrometer aperture rear and open
front.
Stock types: One piece. Composition butt
plate. Semi-beavertail fore-end. Half
pistol grip.
(Discontinued)

Notes: This rifle is the same design as the rifle used by the U. S. Marine Corps as a training rifle during World War II and referred to as the Model 65. The Model 65, however, weighed 9 lbs. The lighter weight sporter model was known as the Model 65 previous to the Models 150 and 151 designation.

Harrington and Richardson Models 250 and 251 "Sportster"

Calibers: .22 Long Rifles or Longs (interchangeably) (functions with Shorts)

Type of Action: Turnbolt.

Manual Safety: Thumb lever at rear and under receiver.

Magazine type and capacity: Detachable boxes, (clips.) 5 and 10 rounds.

Model styles: Models 250 and 251 are the same with the exception of the rear sight.

Barrel Length and style: 22" round.

Overall length: 40"

Sights: Model 250 has open sights. Model 251 has aperture rear and open front.

Stock types: One piece. Composition butt plate. Semi-beavertail fore-end. Half pistol grip.

(Discontinued)

Harrington and Richardson Model 265 "NRA Targeteer Jr." (Target Rifle)

Calibers: .22 Long Rifle (functions with Longs or Shorts)

Type of Action: Turnbolt.

Manual Safety: Thumb lever at rear and under receiver.

Magazine type and capacity: Detachable box (clip), 5 rounds.

Direction of Twist: Right.

Barrel Length and style: 20" round.

Overall length: 36.75"

Weights: 7 lbs.

Sights: Micrometer aperture rear and hooded front with interchangeable inserts.

Stock types: One piece. Composition butt plate. Half pistol grip. Buttstock measures 11.75" from trigger to butt.

First issued: 1948

(Discontinued)

Notes: This is a rifle designed to fit the junior shooter. The rifle and sights meet the requirements for precision target shooting.

Harrington and Richardson Models 450 and 451 "Medalist" (Target Rifle)

Calibers: .22 Long Rifle (functions with Longs or Shorts)

Type of Action: Turnbolt.

Manual Safety: Thumb lever at rear and under receiver.

Magazine type and capacity: Detachable Box (clip), 5 and 10 rounds.

Model styles: Models 450 and 451 are the same with the exception that the Model 450 comes without sights.

Barrel Length and style: 26" round.

Overall length: 44"

Weight: 10.5 lbs.

Sights: Micrometer aperture rear and hooded front with interchangeable inserts.

Stock types: One piece. Steel butt plate. Semi-beavertail fore-end. Pistol grip. Adjustable front sling swivel.

First issued: 1948

(Discontinued)

Harrington and Richardson Model 550 "Pal"

Note: New .22 auto is replacing this.

Calibers: .22 Long Rifle, Longs and Shorts (interchangeably)

Type of Action: Turnbolt.

Manual Safety: Thumb lever at rear and under receiver.

Magazine type and capacity: Single shot.

Barrel Length and style: 22" round.

Overall length: 40"

Sights: Open.

Stock types: One piece Composition butt plate. Semi-beavertail fore-end. Half pistol grip.

(Discontinued)

Hi-Standard Sport King Carbine

Calibers: .22 Short, Long, or Long Rifle

Type of action: Blowback, semiautomatic

Manual safety: Thumb lever on receiver

Magazine type and capacity: Tubular, 12 Long Rifles, 14 Longs, and 17 Shorts

Barrel length and type: approx. 19" round

Overall length: 38.5"

Weight: 5.5 lbs.

Sights: Open rear, patridge front, dovetailed for scope

Stock: 1-Piece straight grip

Hi-Standard Sport King Rifle

Calibers: .22 Short, Long or Long Rifle
Type of action: Blowback, semiautomatic
Manual safety: Thumb lever on receiver
Magazine type and capacity: Tubular, 15
  Long Rifles, 17 Longs, and 21 Shorts
Barrel length and type: 22.25" round

Overall length: 42.75"
Weight: 5.5 lbs.
Sights: Open rear, patridge front, dove-
  tailed for scope
Stock: 1-piece Monte Carlo with pistol grip,
  semi-beavertail fore-end

Notes: The rifle described above is the Sport King Special—the Sport King Field is the same but does not have Monte Carlo stock or semi-beavertail fore-end and has an 18" barrel.

Hi-Standard Hi-Power Deluxe

Calibers: .270, 30-06
Type of action: Turnbolt
Manual safety: Thumb lever
Magazine type and capacity: Box, staggered
  column, 4 rounds
Barrel length and type: approx. 22" round

Overall length: 42.75"
Weight: 7 lbs.
Sights: Open rear, ramp front, tapped for
  micrometer sights & scopes
Stock: Checkered 1-piece Monte Carlo

Notes: Standard Model does not have Monte Carlo Stock or Q.D. Swivels.

Harrington and Richardson Model 865 "Plainsman"

Calibers: .22 Short, Long, or Long Rifle
Type of action: Turnbolt
Manual safety: Thumb lever on right of
  receiver
Magazine type and capacity: Detachable box,
  5 rounds

Barrel length and style: 24" round
Overall length: 41"
Weight: 5 lbs.
Sights: Open rear and bead front, grooved
  for scope or rear peep
Stock: 1-Piece Monte Carlo

Harrington and Richardson Model 750 "Pioneer"

Calibers: .22 Short, Long or Long Rifle
Type of action: Turnbolt
Manual safety: Thumb lever on right of re-
  ceiver
Magazine type and capacity: Single shot
Barrel length and style: 24" round

Overall length: 41"
Weight: 4.75 lbs.
Sights: Open rear and bead front, grooved
  for scope or rear peep
Stock: 1-Piece Monte Carlo

Marlin Model A-1

Note: New .22 auto is replacing this.

Calibers: .22 Long Rifle.
Type of Action: Blowback, semiautomatic.
Manual Safety: Thumb lever at right of
  receiver.
Magazine type and capacity: Detachable box
  (clip) 6 rounds.

Model styles: AL-C is the standard rifle.
  AL-DL is the "deluxe" version.
Barrel Length and style: 24" round tapered.
Weight: 6 lbs.
Sights: Aperture rear.
Stock types: One piece, Rubber butt plate,
  pistol grip.
(Discontinued)

Notes: This action is designed for use only with lubricated bullets.

Marlin Model 36A

Note: New Marlin 336A with cylindrical bolt replacing this model.

Calibers: .30/30-.32 Special.
Type of Action: Lever, exposed hammer,
  solid top receiver.
Manual Safety: Exposed hammer.
Magazine type and capacity: Tubular—6
  rounds. Except Carbine—7 rounds. Sporting Carbine—6 rounds. 36A—DL—6
  rounds.

Model styles: 36A—Sporting rifle. 36A-DL
  is the "deluxe" version with sling swivels
  and stock checkering. 36 Carbine. 36
  Sporting Carbine.

Barrel Length and style: Rifles—24" round,
  crowned muzle. Carbines—20" round,
  crowned muzle.

Overall lengths: Rifles—42". Carbines—38".
All are round.
Weights: Rifles—6.75 lbs. Carbines 6.5 lbs.

Sights: Open.
Stock types: Two piece. Composition butt
plate. Semi-beavertail fore-end.
(Discontinued)

Marlin Model 39-A "Mountie"

Calibers: .22 Short, Long or Long Rifle
Type of action: Lever, exposed hammer,
solid top receiver
Manual safety: Half cock notch
Magazine type and capacity: Tubular. 26,
Shorts; 21, Longs; 19, Long Rifles

Barrel length and style: 20" round
Overall length: approx. 37"
Weight: approx. 6 lbs.
Sights: Open rear, hooded ramp front,
drilled and tapped for peep and scopes
Stock: Two-piece straight grip type

Marlin Model 336-C, 336-T, 336-SC, and Marauder

Calibers: .30/30, .32 Special and .35 Reming-
ton
Type of action: Lever, exposed hammer,
Solid top receiver
Manual safety: Half cock
Magazine type and capacity: Tubular—6
rounds in carbine models, (336-C, 336-T,
and Marauder) 5 rounds in 336-SC

Barrell length and style: 20" except Marau-
der—16.25" round
Overall length: Approx. 37" except
Marauder
Weight: 6.5 lbs.; Marauder—6.25 lbs.
Sights: Open rear, hooded ramp front
Stock: 2 piece with pistol grip except 336-T
and Marauder

Notes: 336-ADL is rifle model having 24 inch barrel and weighing 7.5 lbs. It has Q.D.
swivels and sling, stock with Monte Carlo type cheek piece, and semi-beavertail fore-end.

Marlin Model 99C

Calibers: .22 Long Rifle
Type of action: Blowback, semiautomatic
Magazine type and capacity: Tubular, 18-
rounds
Manual safety: cross bolt
Barrel length and style: 22" round

Overall length: 42"
Weight: 5.5 lbs.
Sights: Open rear, hooded front, tapped for
scope
Stock: 1 piece with pistol grip

Marlin Model 989

Calibers: .22 Long Rifle
Type of action: Blowback, semiautomatic
Magazine type and capacity: Detachable box,
8-round
Manual safety: Cross bolt
Barrel length and style: 22", round

Overall length: 42"
Weight: 5.5 lbs.
Sights: Open rear, hooded front, tapped for
scope
Stock: 1 piece with pistol grip

Marlin Model 56

Calibers: .22 Short, Long or Long Rifle
Type of action: Lever-action, inclosed ham-
mer, solid top receiver
Manual safety: Thumb lever
Magazine type and safety: Detachable box,
8 rounds

Barrel length and style: 22" round
Overall length: 42"
Weight: 6.25 lbs.
Sights: Open rear, hooded ramp front,
tapped for scope
Stock: 1-Piece Monte Carlo with pistol grip

Notes: Model 57 is the same as above but has tubular magazine for 27 shorts, 21 longs,
or 19 long rifles. Model 57-M is chambered for the .22 Winchester Magnum cartridge and has
15-round tubular magazine.

Marlin Model 980

Calibers: .22 Winchester Magnum
Type of action: Turnbolt
Manual safety: Thumb lever on right side
of receiver
Magazine type and capacity: Detachable box,
8 and 12 rounds

Barrel length and style: 24" round
Overall length: Approx. 44"
Weight: 6.25 lbs.
Sights: Open rear, Hooded ramp front,
tapped for micrometer sight and telescope
Stock: 1-Piece Monte Carlo with pistol grip

Marlin Model 122

Calibers: .22 Short, Long, and Long Rifle
Type of action: Turnbolt
Manual safety: Thumb lever
Magazine type and capacity: Single shot
Barrel length and style: 22" round
Overall length: 40"

Weight: 5 lbs.
Sights: Open rear, hooded ramp front, tapped for micrometer rear
Stock type: 1-Piece Monte Carlo with pistol grip

Marlin Model 39-A

Calibers: .22 Long Rifle, Longs or Shorts (interchangeably)
Type of Action: Lever, exposed hammer, solid top receiver.
Manual Safety: Exposed hammer.
Magazine type and capacity: Tubular. Long Rifles—18 rounds, Longs—20 rounds, Shorts—25 rounds.
Direction of Twist: Right.

Barrel Length and style: 24" round.
Overall length: 41"
Weight: 6.5 lbs.
Sights: Open.
Stock types: Two piece. Composition butt plate. Semi-beavertail fore-end. Half pistol grip.
First issued: 1897.

Notes: "Golden 39-ADL" is the deluxe model of the 39-A; it has hand checkered woodwork.

Marlin Model 80

Calibers: .22 Long Rifle, Long or Short (interchangeably)
Type of Action: Turnbolt.
Manual Safety: Thumb lever at right of receiver.
Magazine type and capacity: Detachable box (clip)
Model styles: 80-C is the standard rifle. 80-DL is the "deluxe" version.
Barrel Length and style: 24" round.

Overall length: 42-5"
Weight: 6 lbs.
Sights: Model 80-C has open sights. Model 80-DL has aperture rear and hooded front.
Stock types: One piece. Composition butt plate. Semi-beavertail fore-end. Half pistol grip.
First issued: 1937

Marlin Model 81

Calibers: .22 Long Rifle, Long or Short (interchangeably)
Type of Action: Turnbolt.
Manual Safety: Thumb lever at right of receiver.
Magazine type and capacity: Tubular. Long Rifles—18 rounds, Longs 20 rounds, Shorts —25 rounds.
Model styles: 81-C is the standard rifle. 81-DL is the "deluxe" version.

Barrel Length and style: 24" round.
Overall length: 42.5"
Weight: 6.5 lbs.
Sights: Model 81-C has open sights. Model 81-DL has aperture rear and hooded front.
Stock types: One piece. Composition butt plate. Semi-beavertail fore-end. Half pistol grip.
First issued: 1934.

Marlin Model 101

Calibers: .22 Long Rifle, Long or Short (interchangeably)
Type of Action. Turnbolt, single shot.
Manual Safety: Thumb lever at right of receiver.
Model styles: 101-C is the standard rifle. 101-DL is the "deluxe" version. 101-SB

is bored and sighted for the use of .22 short cartridges.
Barrel Length and style: 24" round.
Overall length: 42.5"
Weight: 5 lbs.
Sights: Aperture rear and hooded front.
Stock types: 1 piece—rubber butt plate.

Mossberg Model 26 B

Calibers: .22 Long Rifles, Longs and Shorts (interchangeably)
Type of Action: Turnbolt, single shot.
Breechblock: Single lug at bolt handle position on bolt.
Manual Safety: Thumb lever at rear of receiver.
Model styles: Standard

Barrel Length and style: 26" round tapered.
Overall length: 51.75"
Weight: 5.5 lbs.
Sights: Micrometer aperture rear and hooded front with selective posts. Also is equipped with open rear.
Stock types: 1 piece. Composition butt plate. Half pistol grip.
(Discontinued)

Mossberg Model 42 B

Calibers: .22 Long Rifle, Long or Short (interchangeably)
Type of Action: Turnbolt.
Manual Safety: Thumb lever at rear of receiver.
Magazine type and capacity: Detachable box (clip) 5 rounds.
Direction of Twist: Right
Barrel Length and style: 24" round.

Overall length: 41.5"
Weight: 5.25 lbs.
Sights: Micrometer aperture rear and hooded front with selective posts. Also is equipped with open rear.
Stock types: One piece. Composition butt plate. Half pistol grip.
First issued: 1938
(Discontinued)

Mossberg Model 42 M

Calibers: .22 Long Rifle, Long or Short (interchangeably)
Type of Action: Turnbolt.
Manual Safety: Thumb lever at rear of receiver.
Magazine type and capacity: Detachable box (clip) 7 rounds.
Direction of Twist: Right
Model styles: Takedown

Notes: Trap in butt for spare magazine.

Barrel Length and style: 23" round.
Overall length: 40"
Weight: 6.75 lbs.
Sights: Micrometer aperture rear and hooded front with selective posts.
Stock types: Two piece. Steel butt plate. Mannlicher type. Half pistol grip.
First issued: 1939
(Discontinued)

Mossberg Model 44 U. S.

Calibers: .22 Long Rifles (functions with Longs or Shorts)
Type of Action: Turnbolt.
Manual Safety: Thumb lever at rear of receiver.
Magazine type and capacity: Detachable box (clip) 7 rounds.
Direction of Twist: Right

Notes: This rifle is an improvement over the former 44B.

Barrel Length and style: 25" round.
Overall length: 43"
Weight: 8.5 lbs.
Sights: Micrometer, aperture rear and hooded front with selective inserts.
Stock types: One piece. Steel butt plate. Half pistol grip.
First issued: 1945
(Discontinued)

Mossberg Model 46 B

Calibers: .22 Long Rifle, Longs or Shorts (interchangeably)
Type of Action: Turnbolt.
Manual Safety: Thumb lever at rear of receiver.
Magazine type and capacity: Tubular. 20 Long Rifles, 23 Longs or 30 shorts.
Direction of Twist: Right

Barrel Length and style: 26" round
Overall length: 43.25"
Weight: 7 lbs.
Sights: Micrometer aperture rear and hooded front with selective inserts.
Stock types: One piece. Composition butt plate. Half pistol grip.
First issued: 1938
(Discontinued)

Mossberg Model 46 M

Calibers: .22 Long Rifle, Long or Short (interchangeably)

Type of Action: Turnbolt.

Manual Safety: Thumb lever at rear of receiver.

Magazine type and capacity: Tubular. Long Rifles—15 rounds, Longs—18 rounds, Shorts—22 rounds.

Note: There are also two Mossberg semiautos.

Barrel Length and style: 23" round.

Overall length: 40"

Weight: 7 lbs.

Sights: Micrometer aperture rear and hooded front with selective inserts.

Stock types: Two piece. Composition butt plate. Mannlicher type. Half pistol grip.

First issued: 1939

(Discontinued)

Mossberg Model 642K

Calibers: .22 Winchester Magnum

Type of action: Turnbolt

Manual safety: Thumb lever

Magazine type and capacity: detachable box 5 rounds

Barrel length and style: Approx. 20" round

Overall length: 38.5"

Weight: Approx. 5 lbs.

Sights: Open rear, bead front, grooved for scope

Stock: 2-Piece Monte Carlo with full pistol grip and hinged fore-arm

Mossberg Model 640K

Calibers: .22 Winchester Magnum

Type of action: Turnbolt

Manual safety: Thumb lever

Magazine type and capacity: Detachable box, 5 rounds

Barrel length and style: 24" round

Overall length: 44.75"

Weight: 6 lbs.

Sights: Open rear, bead front, tapped for micrometer and grooved for scope

Stock: 1-Piece Monte Carlo with pistol grip

Notes: The Model 640KS is the same as the Model 640K except that it has a checkered stock and gold plated trigger. The Model 620K is the single shot version of the 640K.

Mossberg Model 320K

Calibers: .22 Short, Long, and Long Rifle

Type of action: Turnbolt

Manual safety: Thumb lever

Magazine type and capacity: Single shot

Barrel length and style: 24" round

Overall length: 43.5"

Weight: 5.75 lbs.

Sights: Open rear, bead front, tapped for micrometer and grooved for scope

Stock: 1-Piece Monte Carlo with pistol grip

Notes: Model 320B is the same as Model 320K but has a micrometer type rear sight, hooded ramp front sight, and is fitted with sling swivels.

Mossberg Model 340B

Calibers: .22 Short, Long, or Long Rifle

Type of action: Turnbolt

Manual safety: Thumb lever

Magazine type and capacity: Detachable box, 7 rounds

Barrel length and style: 24" round

Overall length: 43.5"

Weight: 6.5 lbs.

Sights: Micrometer rear, ramp front

Stock: 1-Piece Monte Carlo with pistol grip

Notes: The Model 340K is the same as the 340B but has open sights.

Mossberg Model 144LS

Calibers: .22 Short, Long, or Long Rifle

Type of action: Turnbolt

Manual safety: Thumb lever

Magazine type and capacity: Detachable box, 7 rounds

Overall length: 43"

Weight: Approx. 8 lbs.

Sights: Micrometer rear, hooded target front, grooved for scope

Stock: 1-Piece with pistol grip and hand stop

Mossberg Model 346K

Calibers: .22 Short, Long and Long Rifle
Type of action: Turnbolt
Manual safety: Thumb lever
Magazine type and capacity: Tubular, 25
  shorts, 20 longs, and 18 long rifles
Barrel length and style: 24" round

Overall length: 43.5"
Weight: 6.5 lbs.
Sights: Open rear, bead front, tapped for
  micrometer and grooved for scope
Stock: 1-Piece Monte Carlo with pistol grip

Notes: Model 346B is the same as 346K but has a micrometer rear sight and ramp front sight.

Mossberg Model 350K

Calibers: .22 Long and Long Rifle
Type of action: Blowback, semiautomatic
Manual safety: Thumb lever
Magazine type and capacity: Detachable box,
  7 rounds
Barrel length and style: 23.5" round

Overall length: 43.5"
Weight: 6 lbs.
Sights: Open rear, bead front, grooved for
  scope
Stock: 1-Piece Monte Carlo with pistol grip

Notes: Model 351K is the same as 350K but has a tubular magazine—capacity: 15 long rifles—and is 43" long.

Mossberg Model 342K

Calibers: .22 Short, Long, and Long Rifle
Type of action: Turnbolt
Manual safety: Thumb lever
Magazine type and capacity: Detachable box,
  7 rounds
Barrel length and style: 18", round

Overall length: 38"
Weight: Approx. 5 lbs.
Sights: Open rear, bead front, grooved for
  scope
Stock: 2-Piece Monte Carlo with pistol grip
  —hinged fore-end

Notes: Model 352K is the same as 342K but has a blowback semiautomatic action.

Mossberg Model 402 (Palomino)

Calibers: .22 Short, Long, and Long Rifle
Type of action: Lever action, hammerless
Manual safety: Cross bolt
Magazine type and capacity: Tubular, 20
  short, 15 long and 13 long rifles
Barrel length and style: 20" round

Overall length: 36.5"
Weight: 4.75 lbs.
Sights: Open rear, bead front
Stock: 2-Piece Monte Carlo type butt; butt
  and fore-end checkered

Notes: Model 400 (Palomino) is the same as Model 402 but has a 24" barrel and the tubular magazine holds 22 shorts, 17 longs, and 15 long rifles.

Remington Model 37 "Rangemaster" (Target Rifle)

Calibers: .22 Long Rifle (functions with
  Longs and Shorts)
Type of Action: Turnbolt, adjustable trigger, speed lock.
Manual Safety: Thumb lever on left side
  of receiver.
Magazine type and capacity: Detachable box
  (clip)—5 rounds.
Direction of Twist: Right

Barrel Length and style: 28" round.
Overall length: 46.5"
Weight: 12 lbs.
Sights: Micrometer aperture rear and
  hooded aperture front.
Stock types: One piece. Steel butt plate.
  Wide beavertail fore-end. Pistol grip. Adjustable front swivel.
First issued: 1937
  (Discontinued)

Remington Model 81 "Woodsmaster"

Calibers: .30, .32 or .35 Remington and .300
  Savage.

Type of Action: Semiautomatic.
Breechblock: Rotating bolt head having

double lugs locks in barrel extension. Barrel recoils inside of jacket while locked to bolt.

Manual Safety: Thumb lever on right of receiver.

Magazine type and capacity: Detachable box—Staggered column. 5 rounds.

Direction of Twist: Right.

Model styles: Takedown. Sold in 5 grades.

Barrel Length and style: .22" round.

Overall length: 41"

Weight: 8.25 lbs.

Sights: Open

Stock types: Two pieces. Shotgun style butt plate. Semi-beavertail fore-end. Half pistol grip.

First issued. 1936

(Discontinued)

Notes: The Model 81 is basically the same as the Remington Model 8 with improvements. The Model 8 was discontinued in 1936.

Remington Model 121 "Fieldmaster"

Calibers: .22 Long Rifle, Longs or Shorts (interchangeably) and for the .22 Remington Special (.22 W.R.F.)

Type of Action: Slide.

Breechblock: Breechblock tips up in closed position placing single lug on forward top end of breechblock into recess in receiver.

Manual Safety: Crossbolt at rear of triggerguard.

Magazine type and capacity: Tubular—20 Shorts, 15 Longs, 14 Long Rifles, or 12

Remington Specials.

Direction of Twist: Right

Model styles: Takedown

Barrel Length and style: 24" round

Overall length: 41"

Weight: 6 lbs.

Sights: Open

Stock types: Two piece. Shotgun style butt plate. Semi-beavertail grooved fore-end. Half pistol grip.

First issued: 1936

(Discontinued)

Notes: Basically the same but revised version of Model 12 which was discontinued in 1936.

Remington Model 141 "Gamemaster"

Calibers: .30, .32 and .35 Remington.

Type of Action: Slide

Breechblock: Breechblock tips up in closed position placing single lug on forward top end of breechblock into recess in receiver.

Manual Safety: Cross bolt at rear of triggerguard.

Magazine type and capacity: Tubular—5 rounds.

Direction of Twist: Right

Model styles: Takedown. A carbine type with 18½" barrel has been produced in this model.

Barrel Length and style: 24" round.

Overall length: 42.75"

Weight: 7.75 lbs.

Sights: Open

Stock types: Two piece. Shotgun type butt plate. Semi-beavertail grooved fore-end. Half pistol grip.

First issued: 1936.

(Discontinued)

Notes: Basically the same but revised version of the old Remington Model 14 which was discontinued in 1935.

Remington Model 241 "Speedmaster"

Calibers: .22 Long Rifles or Shorts.

Type of Action: Blowback—semiautomatic.

Manual Safety: Cross bolt locks trigger.

Magazine type and capacity: Tubular (in butt stock) 15 Long Rifles or 10 Shorts.

Direction of Twist: Right

Model styles: Takedown. 241 SA for Shorts only. 241 LA for Long Rifles only. 5 grades of rifles for each of the two cartridges.

Barrel Length and style: 24" round.

Overall length: 41.5"

Weight: 6.25 lbs.

Sights: Open

Stock types: Two piece. Shotgun style butt plate. Semi-beavertail fore-end. Half-pistol grip.

First issued: 1938

(Discontinued)

Remington Model 510 "Targetmaster" Single Shot

Calibers: .22 Long Rifles, Longs or Shorts (interchangeably)
Type of Action: Turnbolt
Breechblock: Bolt system with double lugs at bolt handle position on bolt.
Manual Safety: Thumb lever on right of receiver.
Direction of Twist: Right
Barrel Length and style: 25" round

Overall length: 43"
Weight: 5.75 lbs.
Sights: 510-A with open sights. 510-P has rear peep sight.
Stock types: One piece. Composition butt plate. Semi-beavertail fore-end. Half pistol grip.
First issued: 1938

Notes: Model 510C has 21" barrel; 510B has smooth bore barrel for use with shot cartridges.

Remington Model 511 "Scoremaster"

Calibers: .22 Long Rifles, Longs or Shorts (interchangeably)
Type of Action: Turnbolt
Manual Safety: Thumb lever on right of receiver.
Magazine type and capacity: Detachable Box (clips) —6 rounds.
Direction of Twist: Right
Barrel Length and style: 25" round.

Overall length: 43"
Weight: 5.75 lbs.
Sights: 511-A with open sights. 510-P has peep sights.
Stock types: One piece. Composition butt plate. Semi-beavertail fore-end. Half pistol grip.
First issued: 1939

Remington Model 512 "Sportsmaster"

Calibers: .22 Long Rifles, Longs or Shorts (interchangeably)
Type of Action: Turnbolt.
Manual Safety: Thumb lever on right of receiver.
Magazine type and capacity: Tubular. 15— Long Rifles, 17—Longs, 22—Shorts.
Direction of Twist: Right
Barrel Length and style: 25" round.

Overall length: 43"
Weight: 6 lbs.
Sights: 512-A with open sights, 512-P has rear peep sight.
Stock types: One piece. Composition butt plate. Semi-beavertail fore-end. Half pistol grip.
First issued: 1940

Remington Model 513 S "Sporter"

Calibers: .22 Long Rifle (functions with Longs or Shorts)
Type of Action: Turnbolt.
Breechblock: Bolt system with double lugs at bolt handle position on bolt.
Manual Safety: Thumb lever on right side of receiver.
Magazine type and capacity: Detachable Box (clip) 6 rounds.

Direction of Twist: Right
Barrel Length and style: 27" round.
Overall lengths: 45"
Weight: 6.25 lbs.
Sights: Open or aperture rear and open ramp front.
Stock types: One piece. Sporter style. Fore-arm and pistol grip checkered.
First issued: 1940
(Discontinued)

Remington Model 513 T "Matchmaster"

Calibers: .22 Long Rifle (functions with Longs or Shorts)
Manual Safety: Thumb lever at right side of receiver.
Magazine type and capacity: Detachable Box (clip) 6 rounds.
Direction of Twist: Right
Barrel Length and style: 27" round

Overall length: 45"
Weight: 9 lb.
Sights: Micrometer aperture rear and hooded aperture front.
Stock types: One piece. Steel butt plate. Beavertail fore-end. Pistol grip. Adjustable front swivel.
First issued: 1940

Remington Model 514

Calibers: .22 Long Rifles, Longs and Shorts (interchangeably)
Type of Action: Turnbolt.
Manual Safety: Rotary thumb safety on cocking piece.
Magazine type and capacity: Single shot.
Barrel Length and style: 24.75" round.
Note: Model 514A has 20" barrel.

Overall length: 42"
Weight: 5.25 lbs.
Sights: Open.
Stock types: One piece. Composition butt plate. Semi-beavertail fore-end. Half pistol grip.
First issued: 1948

Remington Model 521 T "Junior Special"

Calibers: .22 Long Rifle (functions with Longs and Shorts)
Type of Action: Turnbolt.
Breechblock: Bolt system with double lugs at bolt handle position on bolt.
Manual Safety: Thumb lever on right side of receiver.
Magazine type and capacity: Detachable box (clip) 6 rounds.

Barrel Length and style: 25" round.
Overall length: 43"
Sights: Micrometer, aperture rear and open partridge front.
Stock types: One piece. Composition butt plate. Beavertail fore-end. Pistol grip. Adjustable front swivel.
First issued: 1947

Remington Model 550

Calibers: .22 Long Rifles, Longs and Shorts (interchangeably)
Type of Action: Blowback semiautomatic.
Manual Safety: Thumb lever on right side of receiver.
Magazine type and capacity. Tubular. 15 Long Rifles, 17 Longs or 22 Shorts.
Direction of Twist: Right.
Barrel Length and style: 24" round.

Overall length: 43.5"
Weight: 6.25 lbs.
Sights: Open or aperture rear and open front.
Stock types: One piece, composition butt plate. Semi-beavertail fore-end. Half pistol grip.
First issued: 1941

Remington Model 40X

Calibers: .22 Long Rifle, .222 Rem., .222 Rem. Mag., 7.62mm NATO, .30-06
Type of action: Turnbolt
Manual safety: Thumb lever
Magazine type and capacity: Single shot
Barrel length and style: 28" round
Note: Originally made in .22 Long Rifle only.

Overall length: 46.75"
Weight: Heavy barrel—12.75 lbs. Standard barrel—10.62 lbs.
Sights: Micrometer rear, hooded target front
Stock: 1-Piece with pistol grip, built-in adjustable bedding device, hand stop

Remington International Free Rifle

Calibers: .22 Long Rifle, .222 Rem., .222 Rem. Mag., 7.62mm NATO, .30-06, others on order
Type of action: Turnbolt
Manual safety: Thumb lever
Magazine type and capacity: Single shot

Barrel length and style: 28" round
Overall length: Approx. 47"
Weight: 15.5 lbs.
Sights: Tapped for micrometer sights
Stock: 1-Piece thumbhole type with adjustable butt plate, palm rest and hand stop

Remington Model 572A

Calibers: .22 Short, Long, and Long Rifle
Type of action: Slide action
Manual safety: Cross bolt
Magazine type and capacity: Tubular. 20, shorts; 17, longs; and 15, long rifles
Barrel length and style: 25" round

Overall length: 42"
Weight: 5.5 lbs.
Sights: Open rear, bead front, grooved for scope
Stock: 1-Piece butt with pistol grip, sliding fore-end

Remington Model 552

Calibers: .22 Short, Long, and Long Rifle
Type of action: Blowback, semiautomatic
Manual safety: Cross bolt
Magazine type and capacity: Tubular, 20, shorts; 17 longs; and 15 long rifles
Barrel length and style: 21" round

Overall length: 38"
Weight: 5.25 lbs.
Sights: Open rear, bead front, grooved for scope
Stock: 2-Piece butt with pistol grip

Notes: Model 552A has 25" barrel and Model 552-GS is chambered for .22 shorts.

Remington Model 66 Nylon

Calibers: .22 Long Rifle
Type of action: Blowback, semiautomatic
Manual safety: Thumb lever
Magazine type and capacity: Tubular. 14, long rifles
Barrel length and style: 19.5" round

Overall length: 38.5"
Weight: 4 lbs.
Sights: Open rear, blade front, grooved for scope
Stock: 2-Piece with pistol grip, made of nylon

Remington Model 76 Nylon

Caliber: .22 Long Rifle
Type of action: Lever action, hammerless
Manual safety: Thumb lever
Magazine type and capacity: Tubular. 14, long rifles
Barrel length and style: 19.5" round

Overall length: 38.5"
Weight: 4.5 lbs.
Sights: Open rear, blade front, grooved for scope
Stock: 2-Piece with pistol grip, made of nylon

Remington Model 11 Nylon

Calibers: .22 Short, Long, or Long Rifle
Type of action: Turnbolt
Manual safety: Thumb lever
Magazine type and capacity: Detachable box, 6 rounds
Barrel length and style: 19.62" round

Overall length: 38.5"
Weight: 4.25 lbs.
Sights: Open rear, blade front, grooved for scope
Stock: 1-Piece with full pistol grip, made of nylon

Remington Model 12 Nylon

Calibers: .22 Short, Long, and Long Rifle
Type of action: Turnbolt
Manual safety: Thumb lever
Magazine type and capacity: Tubular, 22, shorts; 17, long; and 15, long rifles
Barrel length and style: 19.62 round

Overall length: 38.5"
Weight: 4.5 lbs.
Sights: Open rear, blade front, grooved for scope
Stock: 1-Piece with full pistol grip, made of nylon

Remington Model 700ADL

Calibers: .222., .222 Rem. Mag., .243 Win. Mag. 7mm Rem. Mag., .270 Win., .280 Rem., .30-06, .308 Win.
Type of action: Turnbolt
Magazine type and capacity: Staggered box, 6—.222 Rem. and Rem. Mag.; 4—.264 Win. Mag. and 7mm Rem. Mag.; 5—all other calibers
Barrel length and style: 24" for 7mm Rem. Mag. and .264 Win.; 22"—all others
Overall length: 39.5"—.222 Rem., .222 Rem. Mag.; 40.37"—.270 Win. .280 Rem., .30-06,

.308 Win.; 44.37"—7mm Rem. Mag., .264 Win. Mag.
Weight: 6.5 lbs.—.222 Rem. and Rem. Mag.; 6.75 lbs.—.243 Win., .270 Win., .280 Rem., .30-06, .308 Win.; 7.75 lbs.—7mm Rem. Mag., .264 Win. Mag.
Sights: Open rear, ramp type front, tapped for scope
Stock: 1-Piece Monte Carlo with pistol grip Recoil pad on 7mm Rem. Mag. and .264 Win. Mag.

Notes: Model 700BDL is generally the same but also chambered for .375 H&H Mag. and .458 Win. Mag. in which calibers it weighs 9 lbs., is 46.37" overall, and has a 26" barrel with muzzle brake. Stock has white spacers, fore-end tip, and Q.D. swivels with sling.

Remington Model 742A

Calibers: .280 Rem., .308 Win., .30-06
Type of action: Gas operated, semiautomatic
Manual safety: Cross bolt
Magazine type and capacity: Detachable box,
   4 rounds
Barrel length and style: 22″ round

Overall length: 42″
Weight: 7.5 lbs.
Sights: Open rear, ramp type front, tapped
   for scope
Stock type: 2-Piece, butt with pistol grip,
   grooved fore-end

Notes: Model 742ADL is Deluxe Version of 742A and has checkered stock, engraved receiver, swivels, and pistol grip cap. Model 742C is carbine version with 18.5″ barrel and is 38.5″ overall. Model 742CDL is deluxe version of the carbine.

Remington 760A

Calibers: .270 Win., .280 Rem., .30-06, .308
   Win., and .35 Rem.
Type of action: Slide action
Manual safety: Cross bolt
Magazine type and capacity: Detachable box,
   4 rounds
Barrel length and style: 22″ round

Overall length: 42″
Weight: 7.5 lbs.
Sights: Open rear with ramp front, tapped
   for scope.
Stock type: 2-Piece butt with pistol grip,
   grooved movable fore-end.

Notes: Model 760ADL is deluxe version with sling swivels; checkered stock, engraved receiver, and pistol grip cap. Model 760C is carbine with 18.5″ barrel, 38.5″ overall, and weighs 6.75 lbs. Model 760CDL is deluxe version of carbine. "D" and "F"—Peerless and Premier grades exist as in the Model 742 series.

Remington Model 720

Calibers: .257 Rem. Roberts. .270 Winchester and .30-'06.
Type of Action: Turnbolt.
Breechblock: Double lugs at bolt head.
Manual Safety: Thumb lever on right of receiver.
Magazine type and capacity: Box—staggered column. 5 rounds.
Direction of Twist: Right.
Model styles: Selection of barrel lengths and types of sights.

Barrel Length and styles: 20″, 22″ or 24″
Overall length: 40.5″ (with 20″ bbl.)
Weights: 8 lbs.
Sights: A wide selection of open or micrometer aperture rear sights and open front sights.
Stock types: One piece. Shotgun style butt plate. Semi-beavertail fore-end. Pistol grip.
First issued: 1941
(Discontinued)

Remington Model 721

Calibers: .30-'06, .270 Winchester or 300 Magnum.
Type of Action: Turnbolt.
Breechblock: Double lugs at bolt head.
Manual Safety: Thumb lever on right of receiver.
Magazine type and capacity: Box. Staggered column. 4—.30-'06 or 270 Winchester cartridges. 3—300 Magnum cartridges.

Barrel Lengths and styles: 24″ for .30-'06 and 270 Winchester. 26″ for 300 Magnum.
Overall length: 44.25″
Weight: 7.25 lbs.
Sights: Open
Stock types: One piece. Steel shotgun style butt plate. Semibeavertail fore-end. Pistol grip.
First issued: 1948
(Discontinued)

Notes: This rifle has a recessed bolt head with enclosed extractor which permits encasing the entire cartridge head when the bolt is closed. This design of bolt has proven to be extremely strong.

Remington Model 722

Calibers: 257 Roberts or 300 Savage, .222 Rem., .222 Rem. Mag., 244 Rem. and .308 Win.
Type of Action: Turnbolt.
Breechblock: Double lugs at bolt head.
Magazine type and capacity: Box. Staggered column. 4 rounds.
Barrel Length and style: 24" round.

Overall length: 43.25"
Weight: 7 lbs.
Sights: Open
Stock types: One piece Steel shotgun style butt plate. Semi-beavertail fore-end. Pistol grip.
First issued: 1948
(Discontinued)

Notes: This rifle is the same as the Model 721 with the exception that the action is shorter.

Ruger Carbine

Calibers: .44 Magnum
Type of action: Gas operated, semiautomatic
Manual safety: Cross bolt
Magazine type and capacity: Tubular, 4 rounds
Barrel length and style: 18.5" round

Overall length: 36.75"
Weight: 5.75 lbs.
Sights: Open rear, blade front, tapped for scope
Stock type: 1-Piece with pistol grip

Savage Models 3 and 3-S

Calibers: .22 Long Rifle, Long or Short (interchangeably)
Type of Action: Turnbolt, single shot.
Manual Safety; Knurled cocking piece.
Direction of Twist: Right
Model styles: Models 3 and 3-S differ in sights only.
Barrel Length and style: 26" round.

Overall length: 43"
Weight: 5 lbs.
Sights: 3 has open sights. 3-S has aperture rear and hooded front with selective inserts.
Stock types: One Piece, steel butt plate, checkered pistol grip.
First issued: 1931
(Discontinued)

Savage Model 4

Calibers: .22 Longs, Long Rifles or Shorts. (interchangeably)
Type of Action: Turnbolt.
Manual Safety: Thumb lever at right of receiver.
Magazine type and capacity: Detachable box (clip) 5 rounds.
Direction of Twist: Right.

Model styles; 4 and 4S. These are the same except for the sights.
Barrel Length and style: 24" round tapered.
Weights: 5.5 lbs.
Sights: 4 has open sights. 4S has aperture rear and hooded front sight with selective inserts.
Stock types: 1 piece. Rubber butt plate. Pistol grip.

Note: Model 4M is chambered for .22 Winchester Magnum.

Savage Model 5

Calibers: .22 Long Rifle, Longs or Shorts (interchangeably).
Type of Action: Turnbolt.
Manual Safety: Thumb lever at right of receiver.
Magazine type and capacity: Tubular. Longs —17 rounds, Long Rifles—15 rounds, Shorts—21 rounds.
Direction of Twist: Right.
Model styles: 5 and 5-S. These are the

same except for the sights.
Barrel Length and style: 24" round.
Overall length: 43.5"
Weights: 6 lbs.
Sights: 5 has open sights. 5-S has aperture rear and hooded front with selective inserts.
Stock types: One piece. Hard rubber butt plate. Checkered pistol grip.
(Discontinued)

Savage Model 6

Calibers: .22 Long Rifle.
Type of Action: Blowback, semiautomatic.
The bolt is equipped with a cross-bolt which can be used to eliminate the blowback feature permitting the rifle to be operated as a bolt action repeater.
Manual Safety: Thumb lever at right of receiver.
Magazine type and capacity: Tubular, 15 rounds.

Model styles: Takedown: 6 and 6S. These are the same except for the sights. 602 for Shorts only.
Barrel Length and style: 24" round.
Weights: 6 lbs.
Sights: 6 has open sights. 6-S has aperture rear and hooded front with selective inserts.
Stock types: One piece. Hard rubber butt plate. Checkered pistol grip.

Notes: This arm is designed to function only with lubricated bullets.

Savage Model 7

Calibers: .22 Long Rifle.
Type of Action: Blowback, semiautomatic. with "lock-out" feature similar to the Model 6.
Manual Safety: Thumb lever at right of receiver.
Magazine type and capacity: Detachable box (clip) 5 rounds.
Direction of Twist: Right.

Model styles: 7 and 7S. These rifles are the same except for the sights.
Barrel Length and style: 24" round.
Weight: 6 lbs.
Sights: 7 has open sights. 7-S has aperture rear and hooded front with selective inserts.
Stock types: One piece. Hard rubber butt plate. Checkered pistol grip.

Notes: This arm is designed to function only with lubricated bullets.

Savage Model 23

Calibers: 23A-.22 Long Rifle (functions with Longs or Shorts). 23B-.25/20, 23C-.32/20 and 23D-22 Hornet.
Type of Action: Turnbolt.
Manual Safety: Thumb lever at right of receiver.
Magazine type and capacity: Detachable box 23A—5 rounds. 23 B and 23C—4

rounds. .23D—5 rounds.
Direction of Twist: Right.
Barrel Length and style: 25" round tapered.
Weights: 6.5 lbs.
Sights: Open.
Stock types: 1 piece. Steel butt plate. Pistol grip.
First issued: 1923
(Discontinued)

Savage Model 23 AA

Calibers: .22 Long Rifle, Long or .22 Shorts (interchangeably).
Type of Action: Turnbolt.
Breechblock: Double lugs at bolt handle position on bolt.
Manual Safety: Thumb lever at right of receiver.
Magazine type and capacity: Detachable box

(clip) 5 rounds.
Direction of Twist: Right.
Model styles: Standard only.
Barrel Length and style: 23" round.
Weights: 6.5 lbs.
Sights: Open.
Stock types: One piece. Pistol grip. British type fore-end.
(Discontinued)

Savage Model 29

Calibers: .22 Long Rifles (functions with Longs and Shorts).
Type of Action: Slide action.
Manual Safety: Pushbutton through rear of triggerguard.
Magazine type and capacity: Tubular, 15 Long Rifles, 17 Longs, 20 Shorts.
Note: Current production is called 29G.

Direction of Twist: Right.
Model styles: Takedown.
Barrel Length and style: 24" octagon.
Weights: 5.75 lbs.
Sights: Open, grooved for scope
Stock types: 2 piece. Hard rubber butt plate. Checkered pistol grip and fore-end.

Savage Model 40

Calibers: .250-300 and .300 Savage. .30/30 and .30-'06.

Type of Action: Turnbolt.

Manual Safety: Thumb lever at right of receiver.

Magazine type and capacity: Detachable box.

Direction of Twist: Right.

Model styles: Standard.

Barrel Length and style: .250-300 and .30/30 round tapered. .300 Savage and .30-'06 24" round tapered.

Weights: 7.5 lbs.

Sights: Open.

Stock types: 1 piece. Steel butt plate. Pistol grip. British type fore-end.

First issued: 1920

(Discontinued)

Savage Model 24

Calibers: .22 Short, Long, or Long Rifle and 20 or .410 gauge

Type of action: Top break over and under—rifle barrel on top—shotgun barrel on bottom

Magazine type and capacity: no magazine

Barrel length and style: 24" round, over and under

Overall length: 40"

Weight: 6.75 lbs.

Sights: Open rear and ramp front

Stock type: 2-Piece, butt with pistol grip

Notes: Model 24M same as Model 24 but rifle barrel is chambered for .22 Winchester Magnum. Model 24DL has Monte Carlo type butt stock; Model 24 MDL is the same but rifle barrel is chambered for .22 Winchester Magnum.

Savage Model 110

Calibers: .243 Win., .308 Win., .30-06, and .270

Type of action: Turnbolt, long action for .30-06 and .270—short action for .243 and .308

Manual safety: Thumb lever

Magazine type and capacity: staggered box, 4 rounds

Barrel length and style: 22" round

Overall length: 42.5"

Weight: 6.75 lbs.

Sights: Open rear, ramp type front, tapped for micrometer sights and scope

Stock type: 1-Piece with pistol grip, checkered

Notes: Model 110MC has a Monte Carlo type stock; Model 110MCL has left hand action; this is the only mass production left hand bolt action currently available.

Savage Model 340

Calibers: .222 Rem., .22 Hornet, and .30-30 Win.

Type of action: Turnbolt

Manual safety: Thumb lever

Magazine type and capacity: Detachable box, .222 Rem. and .22 Hornet—4 rounds .30-30 —3 rounds

Barrel length and style: .222 Rem.—24" .22

Hornet and .30-30—22"

Overall length: 42"—.222 Rem. 40"—.22 Hornet and .30-30

Weight: 6.75 lbs.—.222 Rem. and .22 Hornet 6.5 lbs.—.30-30

Sights: Open rear, ramp type front, tapped for micrometer and scope

Stock type: 1-Piece with pistol grip

Notes: Springfield Model 840 is basically similar, but is chambered for .30-30 only.

Savage Model 99

Calibers: 99F, 99G, 99EG, 99T-.22 Hi-Power, .30/30, .303 Savage, 250-3000 or .300 Savage. 99H-.30/30, .303 Savage or 250-3000. 99R-250-3000, .303 Savage or .300 Savage. 99RS-250-3000 or .300 Savage. 99K-.22 Hi-Power, .30/30, .303 Savage, 250-3000 Savage or .300 Savage.

Type of Action: Lever, enclosed hammer.

Breechblock: Entire breechblock unit wedged into receiver.

Magazine type and capacity: Rotary box, 5 rounds.

Direction of Twist: Right.

Model styles: Models 99F, 99G and 99K are takedown and the others are solid frame.

Model 99K is Deluxe model. Model 99H is a Carbine.

Barrel Length and style: Model 99E-20" .22 Hi-Power, .30/30, .303 Savage, .250-3000 Savage—22" barrels with exception of Model 99H whose barrel is 20". .300 Savage has a barrel of 24".

Weights: Model 99F-6.5 lbs. Model 99H-6.5

lbs., Model 99T—7 lbs. others vary from 7.25 to 7.75 lbs.

Sights: Open with exception of Models 99Rs and 99K which have tang peep sights.

Stock types: 2 piece. Steel butt plate. All styles have a pistol grip with the exception of the 99F and 99H.

First issued: 1899.

Notes: Model 99DL, 99F, and 99E are current production. 99DL uses .300 Sav., .308 Win., and .243 Win., as does M99F. M99E uses .300 Sav., .243, and .308 Win.

Savage Model 219

Calibers: .22 Hornet, .25/20, .32/20 and .30/30.

Type of Action: Hinged frame, hammerless, single shot.

Manual Safety: Top tang safety.

Direction of Twist: Right.

Model styles: Takedown.

Barrel Lengths and styles: 26" round tapered.

Weights: 6 lbs.

Sights: Open.

Stock types: 2 piece shotgun type, hard rubber butt plate, pistol grip.

Notes: Shotgun barrel in 12, 16 and 20 gauge were also available for this weapon.

Stevens Model 15

Calibers: .22 Short, Long, and Long Rifle

Type of action: Turnbolt

Manual safety: Half cock on bolt

Magazine type and capacity: Single shot

Barrel length and style: 24", round

Overall length: 40"

Weight: Approx. 5 lbs.

Sights: Open rear, blade front, grooved for scope

Stock type: 1-Piece with pistol grip

Notes: Model 15Y—youth model—has 20" barrel; is 35.25" overall and weighs 4.75 lbs. Springfield model 120 is similar to Model 15.

Stevens Models No. 26 and 26½

Calibers: .22 Long Rifles, .32 Long Rimfire, also .22 or .32 shot cartridges.

Type of Action: Lever, single shot.

Manual Safety: Exposed hammer.

Model styles: Takedown. The No. 26½ is the same as the 26 with the exception that the former has a smooth bore full choked barrel for use with shot cartridges.

Barrel Length and style: .22" round, crowned muzzle.

Overall lengths: 36"

Weights: 3.5 lbs.

Sights: Open (not adjustable).

Stock types: Two piece. Steel butt plate.

First issued: 1913

Discontinued: 1939

Stevens Models No. 53 and 053

Calibers: .22 Long Rifles, .22 W.R.F., or .25 Stevens Rimfire (Rifles chambered for .22 Long Rifles will also function with Longs or Shorts).

Type of Action: Turnbolt, single shot.

Model styles: The Models 53 and 053 differ in sights only.

Barrel Length and style: 24" round.

Overall lengths: 41.25"

Weights: 5.5 lbs.

Sights: Model 53 has open sights. Model 053 has aperture rear and hooded front with selective inserts.

Stock types: One piece. Rubber butt plate. Pistol grip. Black fore-end tip.

First issued: 1935

(Discontinued)

Stevens Models Nos. 56 and 056

Calibers: .22 Long Rifle (functions with Longs or Shorts).

Type of Action: Turnbolt.

Manual Safety: Thumb lever at right of receiver.

Magazine type and capacity: Detachable box (clip) 5 rounds.

Model styles: The Models 56 and 056 differ in sights only.

Barrel Length and style: 24" round.

Overall lengths: 43.5"
Weights: 6 lbs.
Sights: Model 56 has open sights. Model 056 has aperture rear and hooded front with

selective inserts.
Stock types: One piece. Rubber butt plate. Pistol grip. Black fore-end tip.
First issued: 1935
(Discontinued)

Notes: This is the same model number which was originally assigned to the No. 56 ladies rifle introduced in 1906 and discontinued in 1916. The two rifles differ in many respects.

Stevens Models 57 and 057

Calibers: .22 Long Rifles (functions as repeater with Longs or Shorts).
Type of Action: Blowback, semiautomatic with "lock-out" feature same as Savage Model 6.
Type of Action: Turnbolt.
Manual Safety: Thumb lever at right of receiver.
Magazine type and capacity: Detachable box (clip) 5 rounds.

Model styles: The Models 57 and 057 differ in sights only.
Barrel Length and style: 24" round.
Sights: Model 57 has open sights. Model 057 has aperture rear and hooded front with selective inserts.
Stock types: One piece. Composition butt plate. Pistol grip. Black fore-end tip.
First issued: 1939
(Discontinued)

Notes: These arms are designed to function only with lubricated bullets.

Stevens Model No. 066

Calibers: .22 Long Rifles (Functions with Longs or Shorts).
Type of Action: Turnbolt.
Manual Safety: Thumb lever at right of receiver.
Magazine type and capacity: Tubular. Long Rifles—15 rounds, Longs—17 rounds, Shorts—15 rounds.
Model styles: Standard. Differs in design from No. 66.

Barrel Length and style: 24" round.
Overall lengths: 43.5"
Weights: 6 lbs.
Sights: Open rear and hooded front with selective inserts.
Stock types: One piece. Rubber butt plate. Pistol grip. Black fore-end tip.
First issued: 1931
(Discontinued)

Stevens Model No. 66

Calibers: .22 Long Rifles, Longs or Shorts (interchangeably).
Type of Action: Turnbolt.
Manual Safety: Thumb lever at right of receiver.
Magazine type and capacity: Tubular. Long Rifles—15 rounds, Longs—17 rounds, Shorts—21 rounds.
Model styles: Standard. The No. 66 differed

in design from the No. 066 and is therefore dealt with separately.
Barrel Length and style: 24" round.
Overall lengths: 39.5"
Weights: 5 lbs.
Sights: Open.
Stock types: One piece. Steel butt plate. Military type.
First issued: 1930
(Discontinued)

Stevens Models 76 and 076

Calibers: .22 Long Rifle (functions as repeater with Longs and Shorts).
Type of Action: Blowback, semiautomatic with "lock-out" feature same as Savage Model 6.
Manual Safety: Thumb lever at right of receiver.
Magazine type and capacity: Tubular 15 rounds.
Model styles: The Models 76 and 076 are

different in sights only.
Barrel Length and style: 24" round.
Weights: 6 lbs.
Sights: Model 76 has open sights. Model 076 has aperture rear and hooded front with selective inserts.
Stock types: One piece. Hard rubber butt plate. Pistol grip. Black fore-end tip.
First issued: 1938
(Discontinued)

Notes: These arms are designed to function only with lubricated bullets.

Stevens Models Nos. 84 and 084 Springfield

Calibers: .22 Long Rifles, Longs and Shorts (interchangeably).

Type of Action: Turnbolt.

Manual Safety: Thumb lever at right of receiver.

Magazine type and capacity: Detachable box (clip) 5 rounds.

Model styles: Models 84 and 084 are the same except for sights.

Barrel Length and style: 24" round.

Overall lengths: 43.5"

Weights: 6 lbs.

Sights: Model 84 has open sights. Model 084 has aperture rear and hooded front with interchangeable inserts.

Stock types: One piece. Rubber butt plate. Pistol grip.

First issued: 1935

Notes: These are commercially produced rifles of competitive grade and must not be confused with the rifles produced at the United States Armory at Springfield, Massachusetts. Springfield 084 discontinued.

Stevens Models Nos. 85 and 085 Springfield

Calibers: .22 Long Rifle.

Type of Action: Blowback, semiautomatic with "lock-out" feature same as Savage Model 6.

Manual Safety: Thumb lever at right of receiver.

Magazine type and capacity: Detachable box (clip) 5 rounds.

Model styles: Takedown Nos. 85 and 085

differ in sights only.

Barrel Length and style: 24" round.

Weights: 6 lbs.

Sights: No. 85 has open sights. No. 085 has aperture rear and hooded front with interchangeable inserts.

Stock types: One piece. Composition butt plate. Pistol grip.

First issued: 1939 (Discontinued)

Notes: These are commercially produced rifles of competitive grade and must not be confused with the rifles produced at the United States Armory at Springfield, Massachusetts. These rifles are basically the same as the Nos. 57 and 057.

Stevens Models Nos. 86 and 086 Springfield

Calibers: .22 Long Rifles, Longs or Shorts (interchangeably).

Type of Action: Turnbolt.

Manual Safety: Thumb lever at right of receiver.

Magazine type and capacity: Tubular. Shorts—21 rounds, Long Rifles—15 rounds, Longs—17 rounds.

Model styles: Nos. 86 and 086 differ in sights only.

Barrel Length and style: 24" round.

Overall lengths: 43.5"

Weights: 5.5 lbs.

Sights: Model 86 has open sights. Model 086 has aperture rear and hooded front with interchangeable inserts.

Stock types: One piece. Rubber butt plate. Pistol grip.

First issued: 1935

Notes: These are commercial rifles of competitive grade trademarked "Springfield" and must not be confused with the rifles produced at the United States Armory at Springfield, Massachusetts. (086 Springfield is discontinued.)

Stevens Models Nos. 87 and 087 Springfield

Calibers: .22 Long Rifle (functions as repeater with Longs and Shorts).

Type of Action: Blowback, semiautomatic with "lock-out" feature same as Savage Model 6.

Manual Safety: Thumb lever at right of receiver.

Magazine type and capacity: Tubular, 15 rounds.

Model styles: Takedown. Nos. 87 and 087 differ in sights only.

Barrel Length and style: 24" round.

Weights: 6 lbs.

Sights: Model 87 has open sights. Model 087 has aperture rear and hooded front with interchangeable inserts.

Stock types: One piece. Steel butt plate. Pistol grip.

First issued: 1938

Notes: These are commercially manufactured rifles of competitive grade and must not be confused with the rifles produced by the United States Armory at Springfield, Massachusetts. Model 087 Springfield is now known as Model 187. Model 87K "Scout Carbine" is the same as Model 87 but has a 20" barrel.

Stevens Model 325

Calibers: 30/30.
Type of Action: Turnbolt.
Manual Safety: Thumb lever at right of receiver.
Magazine type and capacity: Box.
Model styles: Standard.
Barrel Length and style: 21" round.

Overall lengths: 39½"
Weights: 6.75 lbs.
Sights: Open.
Stock types: One piece. Composition butt plate. Pistol grip.
First issued: 1947
(Discontinued)

Stevens Models Nos. 416-2 and 416-3

Calibers: .22 Long Rifle (functions with Longs or Shorts).
Type of Action: Turnbolt.
Manual Safety: Thumb lever at right of receiver.
Magazine type and capacity: Detachable box (clip) 5 rounds.
Model styles: Models 416-2 and 416-3 are identical with the exception that the

latter comes without sights.
Barrel Length and style: 26" round.
Weights: 9.5 lbs.
Sights: Model 416-2 has micrometer aperture rear and hooded front with selective inserts.
Stock types: One piece. Steel butt plate. Semi-beavertail fore-end. Pistol grip.
First issued: 1937
(Discontinued)

Stevens Models Nos. 417, 417-1, 417-2 and 417-3

Calibers: .22 Long Rifle (Functions with Longs or Shorts).
Type of Action: Lever, dropping block, single shot, exposed hammer.
Manual Safety: Half cock.
Model styles: The different models differ in sighting equipment.
Barrel Length and styles: 28" round. 29" extra heavy, round also available.

Overall lengths: 44" with 28" barrel.
Weights: 10.5 lbs. with 28" barrel.
Sights: Models 417, 417-1 and 417-2 have micrometer aperture rear sights and hooded front with selective inserts. Model 417-3 comes without sights.
Stock types: Two piece. Steel butt plate. Semi-beavertail fore-end. Pistol grip.
First issued: 1932
(Discontinued)

Notes: Models 417-4 and 417-5 used to be included in the series but these have been discontinued.

W.R.A. Model Lee Straight Pull

Calibers: 6mm (.236).
Type of Action: Straight Pull Bolt.
Breechblock: Block cammed up and down by rearward and forward bolt handle pull.
Manual Safety: Firing pin lock on left of receiver locks the striker.
Magazine type and capacity: Box. 5 cartridges.
Model styles: U. S. Navy Model Musket with or without bayonet. Sporting rifle first listed 1897.

Barrel Length and style: Musket-28" and Sporting Rifle 24" round. Nickel steel.
Weights: Musket—8.5 lbs. and sporting rifle 7.5 lbs.
Stock types: One piece musket type has steel butt plate and pistol grip. Sporting rifle type has finger grooves in front section of fore-end and a pistol grip.
First issued: 1895 for Navy.
Discontinued: Final clean up 1916.

Notes: These rifles were ahead of their time. They were not well received. The bolt handle was a cam lever. Pulling it straight back unlocked and opened the action. The clip was inserted either end up into the action with the cartridges. The clip dropped out the bottom of the magazine. During firing thrusting the bolt forward sharply chambered a cartridge and locked the action. When the gun was cocked the action could be opened only by pressing down the bolt release or pulling the trigger. Cartridges could be singly inserted by forcing them under the extractor and in front of the clip release ways.

W.R.A. Model Single Shot

Calibers: These rifles were made for all the old standard calibers from .22 cal. to 50 cal. Rim and center fired types were included. All calibers as manufactured by Winchester used cartridges with rims. Also made for 20 gauge shotgun shell in 1914.

Type of Action: Triggerguard lever, vertical dropping block. Exposed hammer.

Breechblock: A rising and falling block traveling in receiver guides.

Manual Safety: Half cock notch on hammer.

Mechanical Safety: Can be fired only when action is closed.

Magazine type and capacity: Single shot.

Model styles: Plain and special sporting rifles, special target rifle, Schuetzen rifle, carbine, musket and shotgun.

Barrel Length and style: Round, octagon and ½ octagon in various styles and lengths. 1886 catalogue lists by number 5 barrel weights which vary the rifle weight from 7 to 12 lbs.

Weights: 7 to 12 lbs. according to caliber and specifications.

Stock types: Two piece sporting rifle—rifle type with straight grip. Special sporting rifle—rifle type with pistol grip. Schuetzen rifle—special Schuetzen. Musket—musket type.

First issued: Announced 1885.

Discontinued: About 1920.

Notes: Some models were made as take down, though most were solid frame. Set triggers and special sights were provided to order. It is impossible to list all the variants of this design.

This rifle was purchased from Browning Bros. It marks the beginning of the association between John Browning and the Winchester Company which resulted in a long line of the world's outstanding rifle designs.

W.R.A. Model 1900 Rifle

Calibers: .22 Long and Short (interchangeably).

Type of Action: Turnbolt.

Breechblock: Bolt handle locking into receiver.

Manual Safety: Cocking piece must be pulled back manually after loading.

Magazine type and capacity: Single shot.

Model styles: Sporting rifle.

Barrel Length and style: 18" round.

Weights: 2.75 lbs.

Stock types: One piece gum wood straight grip.

First issued: announced August 1899

(Discontinued: 1902)

Notes: This was a very low priced plinking rifle. It did not have a butt plate. The model was not extensively manufactured, being redesigned as the Model 02. This rifle was made on the basic Browning Patent issued in 1900.

W.R.A. Model 02 (1902)

Calibers: Originally .22 Long and Short (interchangeably). Altered in 1914 to take 22 extra longs, 22 longs, and 22 shorts interchangeably. Altered again in 1927 for 22 long rifles, 22 longs and 22 shorts interchangeably.

Type of Action: Turnbolt.

Breechblock: Same as 1900.

Manual Safety: Same as 1900.

Mechanical Safety: Same as 1900.

Magazine type and capacity: Single shot.

Model styles: Standard rifle only.

Barrel Length and style: 18" round only.

Weights: About 3 lbs.

Sights: Peep rear until 1904, when open rear was standard.

Stock types: One piece gumwood with steel buttplate. Buttplate changed to composition in 1907.

First issued: 1902

Discontinued: 1931

Notes: This rifle had a very wide export sale because of its low price and the quality of the construction.

W.R.A. Model 1903

Calibers: .22 Winchester automatic.

Type of Action: Semiautomatic blowback. A heavy breech closing mechanism and spring is proportioned in relation to the weight and velocity of the bullet to counterbalance the shock of recoil at the instant of firing.

Breechblock: Inertia locked. No formal locking mechanism required with this cartridge.

Mechanical Safety: Sear contact only when breechblock is fully forward.

Magazine type and capacity: Tube in butt. 10 rounds.

Model styles: Plain and fancy rifle.

Barrel Length and style: 20" round only.

Weights: 5.75 and 6 lbs.

Sights: Open.

Stock types: Two piece standard rifle had straight grip and fancy rifle had pistol grip.

First issued: 1904

Discontinued: 1932

Notes: This rifle was invented by Thomas C. Johnson, Winchester engineer. To obtain satisfactory performance, it was necessary to develop a special cartridge for this early semi-automatic rifle. While the design requires much more machine work than the late elementary types, this early model represents one of the best of the low power blowback designs. It was the first Winchester self-loading rifle.

W.R.A. Model 1904

Calibers: .22 Long and Short (interchangeably). In 1914 altered to chamber .22 Long, extra long and short interchangeably. Altered again in 1927, to take .22 Long, Long Rifle and Short interchangeably.

Type of Action: Same as 02.

Breechblock: Same as 02.

Manual Safety: Same as 02.

Mechanical Safety: Same as 02.

Magazine type and capacity: Single shot.

Model styles: Standard rifle only.

Barrel Length and style: 21" round only.

Weights: About 4 lbs.

Sights: Open.

Stock types: One piece varnished gumwood, blued steel buttplate changed to hard rubber in 1925. Triggerguard shaped to serve as a pistol grip.

First issued: 1904

Discontinued: 1931

Notes: This rifle closely resembled the Model 02 and its price was materially higher. As a result it was not very well received.

W.R.A. Model 1905

Calibers: .32 and .35 Winchester self loading.

Type of Action: Blowback semiautomatic on Johnson system. Takedown. Enclosed hammer construction.

Breechblock: Counterbalances only, no formal lock.

Manual Safety: Push through type.

Mechanical Safety: Sear contact only when breechblock is fully forward.

Magazine type and capacity: Detachable box inserted from below, 5 cartridges. 10

shot magazine first listed in 1911.

Model styles: Sporting and fancy sporting models.

Barrel Length and style: 22" round.

Weights: 7.5 and 8 lbs.

Sights: Open.

Stock types: Two piece Sporting rifle originally issued with straight grip, changed to pistol grip in 1908. Fancy rifle issued with pistol grip.

First issued: 1905

Discontinued: 1920

Notes: Special cartridges with short stubby cases were required to operate this action satisfactorily. The trigger must be released after each shot. Because of the comparatively low velocity cartridges employed, and the relatively high price of the rifle, this model was not commercially very successful.

W.R.A. Model 1906

Calibers: Originally .22 Short only. Altered in 1908 to handle Short, Long and Long Rifle cartridges (interchangeably).

Type of Action: Browning slide fore-arm. Exposed hammer.

Breechblock: Browning system.

Manual Safety: Half cock notch on hammer.

Mechanical Safety: Sear contact only when action is locked.

Magazine type and capacity: Tubular. 15

Shorts, 12 Long or 11 Long Rifle rounds.

Model styles: Takedown standard sporting rifle and "Expert."

Barrel Length and style: 20" round.

Weights: About 5 lbs.

Sights: Open.

Stock types: Two piece. Composition butt plate. Straight grip on standard and pistol grip on "Expert."

First issued: 1906

Discontinued: 1932

Notes: The operating mechanism of the rifle is practically identical with the Model 90. Changes include the shotgun type butt replaced with composition buttplate, and a 20" round barrel and composition buttplate. Sales of this model were greatly accelerated when the arm was chambered to take the three .22 cartridges interchangeably.

W.R.A. Model 07 (1907)

Calibers: .351 Winchester self-loading.

Type of Action: Blowback.

Manuel Safety: Pushbutton in triggerguard.

Mechanical Safety: Sear contact only when action is fully closed.

Magazine type and capacity: Detachable box. Either 5 or 10 rounds types.

Model styles: Standard rifle, deluxe sporting rifle and Police model, authorized in 1934. Equipped with Army type sling.

Barrel Length and style: 20" round.

Weights: 7.75 to 10.8 lbs.

Sights: Blade front. Open, ramp type, rear.

Stock types: Pistol grip.

First issued: 1906

Discontinued: Police Rifle discontinued 1937. Other types also discontinued.

W.R.A. Model 10

Calibers: .401 Winchester self-loading.

Type of Action: Same as M07.

Manual Safety: Same as M07.

Mechanical Safety: Same as M07.

Magazine type and capacity: Detachable box. 4 cartridges.

Model styles: Standard and deluxe sporting rifles.

Barrel Length and style: 20" round.

Weights: 8.25 to 8.5 lbs.

Sights: Open.

Stock types: Two piece pistol grip.

First issued: 1910

Discontinued: Last rifle sold 1936

W.R.A. Model 52

Calibers: .22 Long Rifle (functions with Longs and Shorts).

Type of Action: Turnbolt, adjustable trigger, speed lock.

Manual Safety: Thumb lever at right of receiver.

Magazine type and capacity: Detachable box (clip) 5 or 10 rounds optional. Single shot adaptor to replace magazine, optional.

Model styles: Standard barrel, heavy barrel and extra heavy barrel (bullgun) target rifles. Standard sporting type.

Barrel Length and style: Target rifles 28". Sporter 24"

Weights: Target rifles 8.75 lbs. to 13.5 lbs. Sporters 7.25 lbs.

Sights: Target rifles, hooded front interchangeable blade and apertures; micrometer receiver rear. Sporters—micrometer aperture rear, hooded bead front.

Stock types: Two piece target rifles, one piece, beaver tail fore-end, pistol grip. Sporters, standard sporter fore-end, pistol grip.

First issued: 1920

Notes: Speed lock first added in 1929, new type adopted in 1937. Original safety on left side of receiver discontinued in 1937. Adjustable trigger and new bolt handle designed to clear telescope sight adopted in 1937. Currently made in Model 52 Standard, Model 52 Heavyweight, Model 52 Bull Gun, and Model 52 Sporter.

W.R.A. Model 53

Calibers: 25, 32 and 44 Winchester centerfire.

Type of Action: Lever same as Model 92.

Breechblock: Same as Model 92.

Manual Safety: Same as Model 92.

Mechanical Safety: Same as Model 92.

Magazine type and capacity: Same as Model 92. 6 rounds.

Model styles: Takedown of Solid Frame. Sporting rifle only.

Barrel Length and style: 22" round only.

Weights: 5.5 to 6 lbs.

Sights: Open.

Stock types: Two piece walnut straight grip, rifle or shotgun butt stocks.

First issued: 1924

Discontinued: 1932

Notes: The principal changes from the M92 were in the barrel length, butt type and sighting equipment. This rifle did not meet the success accorded to the Model 92, principally because the cartridges no longer are the favorites they once were.

W.R.A. Model 54

Calibers: Originally 270 Winchester and .30-'06 Government. In 1928 caliber .30 Winchester was added. In 1930 calibers 7mm, 7.65mm and 9mm were added. In 1931 .250-3000. In 1933 caliber .22 Hornet. In 1936 .220 Swift and .257 Roberts.

Type of Action: Turnbolt, Modified Mauser.

Breechblock: Lugs on bolt lock into receiver.

Magazine type and capacity: Built in box. 5 cartridges.

Model styles: Standard rifle, carbine, snipers rifle, N.R.A. rifle, super grade, target rifle and National Match rifle.

Barrel Length and style: 20 to 26". Various weights.

Weights: 7.25 to 11.75 lbs.

Sights: Various.

Stock types: One piece walnut with pistol grip. Various designs and butt plates.

First issued: 1925

Discontinued: 1936

Notes: This rifle was designed by Winchester to meet the needs for a modern turnbolt, sporting rifle. After World War I the Military bolt action rifle system became a favorite with sporting shooters. While it cannot be operated as rapidly as a lever action, it permits the use of much more powerful cartridges. The .220 Swift was especially developed for this model. The caliber range was suited to a wide variety of small and big game shooting as well as target work.

W.R.A. Model 55

Calibers: Originally issued in 30 W.C.F. In 1927 also made in .25-35 and .32 Winchester Special.

Type of Action: Same as M94.

Breechblock: Same as M94.

Manual Safety: Same as M94.

Mechanical Safety: Same as M94.

Magazine type and capacity: Tubular, 3 rounds.

Model styles: Takedown or solid frame; sporting rifle only.

Barrel Length and style: 24" round only.

Weights: 6.75 to 7 lbs.

Sights: Open.

Stock types: Two piece, walnut, shotgun butt with straight grip for standard.

First issued: Take down Model in 1924. Solid frame model 1931.

Discontinued: 1932

Notes: The principal differences between the M55 and M94 are in the barrel lengths, butt types and sight equipment. The rifle model did not sell extensively, though the Carbine form of M94 is still manufactured and sold in large numbers.

W.R.A. Model 56 Rifle

Calibers: 22 Long Rifle. 22 Short was discontinued in 1929.

Type of Action: Turnbolt.

Breechblock: Bolt system.

Manual Safety:

Magazine type and capacity: Detachable box, 5 rounds. 10 round magazines also available.

Model styles: Sporting and fancy sporting rifles.

Barrel Length and style: 22" round only.

Weights: 4.75 to 5 lbs.

Sights: Various.

Stock types: One piece Walnut, pistol grip.

First issued: 1926

Discontinued: 1928

Notes: This was designed as a light-weight sporting rifle of small size. The bolt action did not prove popular in this size and at the price asked. This rifle was not very successful commercially.

W.R.A. Model 57

Calibers: .22 Long rifle. .22 Short was discontinued in 1930.

Type of Action: Turnbolt.

Breechblock: Bolt system.

Magazine type and capacity: Detachable box, 5 rounds. 10 round magazines also available.

Model styles: Target rifle.

Barrel Length and style: 22" round only.

Weight: 5 lbs.

Stock types: Target type. Walnut with pistol grip.

First issued: 1926.

Discontinued: 1936.

Notes: This model was designed as a light-weight bolt-action target rifle. The weight proved too light and the barrel too short to receive acceptance in the serious target shooting field.

W.R.A. Model 58

Calibers: .22 Long, Long rifle and Short, (interchangeably).

Type of Action: Turnbolt. Manually cocked by pulling back cocking piece after loading.

Magazine type and capacity: Single shot.

Model styles: Takedown. Standard rifle only.

Barrel Length and style: 18″ round only.

Weight: about 3 lbs.

Sight: Open.

Stock types: 1 piece plain wood. Straight grip. No butt plate.

First issued: 1928.

Discontinued: 1931.

Notes: This was a very cheaply manufactured arm. The stock was made from a flat board with corners edged. This model was not successful. Very few were sold.

W.R.A. Model 59

Calibers: .22 Long, Long Rifle and Short interchangeably.

Type of Action: Same as Model 58.

Breechblock: Same as Model 58.

Manual Safety: Same as Model 58.

Mechanical Safety: Same as Model 58.

Magazine type and capacity: Same as Model 58.

Model style: Standard rifle only.

Barrel Length and style: 23″ round only.

Weight: About 4.5 lbs.

Sights: Open.

Stock types: Plain wood, pistol grip, composition buttplate.

First issued: 1930.

Discontinued: 1930.

Notes: This design proved unsuccessful. It was redesigned.

W.R.A. Model 60

Calibers: .22 Long, Long Rifle and Short interchangeably.

Type of Action: Same as M59.

Breechblock: Same as M59.

Manual Safety: Same as M59.

Mechanical Safety: Same as M59.

Magazine type and capacity: Same as M59.

Model styles: Sporting rifle only.

Barrel Length and style: 23″ round tapered. Increased to 27″ in 1933.

Weight: About 4.25 lbs.

Sights: Open.

Stock types: 1 piece, plain wood, shotgun butt and pistol grip.

First issued: 1930.

Discontinued: 1934.

Notes: This was a redesigned M59. In 1932 bolt and trigger were chromium-plated. Trigger spring was added to hold trigger forward. An opening was added to the top of the bolt. Words "safe" or "fire" were visible through this opening as a safety factor. Firing pin shank was changed. Extra sear notch was added to relieve pressure on sear spring when sear was in retracted position. This permitted ejection of .22 Long cartridges.

W.R.A. Model 60-A

Calibers: .22 Long Rifle (functions with Longs or Shorts).

Type of Action: Same as Model 60.

Breechblock: Same as Model 60.

Manual Safety: Same as Model 60.

Mechanical Safety: Same as Model 60.

Magazine type and capacity: Same as Model 60. Single shot.

Model styles: Standard rifle only.

Barrel Length and style: 27″ round tapered.

Weight: About 5.5 lbs.

Sights: Micrometer aperture rear and open front.

Stock types: 1 piece, walnut, military type with sling.

First issued: 1932.

Discontinued: 1939.

Notes: Mechanically this was the same as the Model 60. It was specially designed for accuracy. Opening in top of bolt showed word "safe" in black and "fire" in red. Bolt, bolt handle and trigger were chromium plated.

W.R.A. Model 61

Calibers: .22 Long Rifle, .22 Long Rifle shot. .22 Short. .22 Long, interchangeably.

Type of Action: Slide. Enclosed hammer.

Breechblock: Breech bolt locks in breech-

ing shoulder located in top of receiver when action slide is pushed forward.

Manual Safety: Pushbutton in forward part of triggerguard.

Mechanical Safety: Hammer can reach firing pin only when action is fully locked.
Magazine type and capacity: Tubular .22 Short—20 rounds. .22 Long—16 rounds. .22 Long Rifle—14 rounds.
Model styles: Takedown.

Barrel length and style: 24" round
Weight: 5.75 lbs.
Stock types: 2 piece Sporter type, pistol grip.
First issued: 1932.

Notes: This rifle is normally classed as hammerless. Actually it has a conventional rotating hammer housed inside the solid receiver. Ejection is through a port in the right side. This rifle is also made chambered for the .22 Win. Mag. cartridge.

W.R.A. Model 62

Calibers: .22 Short only, or .22 Short, Long and Long Rifle interchangeably.
Type of Action: Slide with exposed hammer.
Manual Safety: Half cock notch on hammer.
Mechanical Safety: Sear contact only when action is locked.
Magazine type and capacity: .22 Short—20 rounds, .22 Long—16 rounds, .22 Long Rifle—14 rounds.

Model styles: Takedown Gallery rifle (.22 Short) and sporting rifle.
Barrel Length and style: 23" round.
Weight: 5.5 lbs.
Sights: Bead front. Open ramp type, rear.
Stock types: Two piece, straight grip, steel butt plate. Composition butt plates supplied in 1934.
First issued: 1932.
(Discontinued)

Notes: As originally issued the M62 lock required a slide handle movement of about .25" before the opening movement of the breechblock started. This was altered in 1938 to the system used on the old Model 90 rifle. In this type the first rearward movement of the handle begins the opening movement of the breechblock.

W.R.A. Model 63

Calibers: .22 Long Rifle high speed.
Type of Action: Blowback, semiautomatic.
Mechanical Safety: Sear contact only when action is fully closed.
Magazine type and capacity: Tube in butt, 10 rounds.

Model styles: Sporting rifle only.
Barrel Length and style: 23" round.
Weight: 5.75 lbs.
Stock types: 2 piece Sporting type, pistol grip.
First issued: 1933.
(Discontinued)

Notes: 20" barrel originally made was discontinued in 1936.

W.R.A. Model 64

Calibers: .25-35 Winchester, .30 Winchester, .32 Winchester Special.
Type of Action: Lever. Exposed hammer.
Breechblock: Sliding bolt with bolt locks operated by lever. Browning system.
Manual Safety: Half cock notch on hammer.
Mechanical Safety: Sear contact only when action is fully closed.

Magazine type and capacity: Tubular—5 rounds.
Barrel Length and style: 20" to 26" round.
Weights: 6.75 lbs. to 7.75 lbs.
Stock types: 2 piece shotgun butt plate, pistol grip.
First issued: 1933.
(Discontinued)

Notes: This model was produced in .219 Zipper caliber from 1938 to 1941.

W.R.A. Model 65

Calibers: .218 Bee, .25-20 and .32-20.
Type of Action: Lever.
Manual Safety: Half cock notch on hammer.
Mechanical Safety: Sear contact only when action is fully closed.
Magazine type and capacity: Tubular—7 rounds.
Barrel Length and style: 22" round. 24"

round on .218 Bee.
Weight: 6.5 lbs.
Sights: Blade or bead front. Open, ramp type, rear.
Stock types: 2 piece, shotgun butt plate with modified pistol grip.
First issued: 1933.
(Discontinued)

W.R.A. Model 66

Calibers: 44 flat and 44 pointed rimmed fire. Interchangeably.
Type of Action: Finger lever triggerguard.
Breechblock: Toggle joint operated. Lowering triggerguard breaks the toggle joint and draws the breechlock back.
Manual Safety: None.
Mechanical Safety: Trigger and sear contact only when breechblock is locked.
Magazine type and capacity: Tubular. Rifle and musket hold 15 rounds. Carbine holds 13.

Model styles: 1—Sporting Rifle, 2—Carbine. 3—Musket with angular or saber bayonet.
Barrel Length and style: Rifle 24", round or octagon. Carbine 20" round. Musket 20" round.
Overall lengths: 43" with 24" barrel.
Weights: Sporting Rifle—9 and 9.5 lbs. Carbine—7.75 lbs. Musket—8.25 lbs.
Stock types: Two piece rifle type. Straight grip. Curved brass butt plate.
First issued: 1866.
Discontinued: 1898.

Notes: A few early models were issued under the Henry name. The original receivers were cast brass. The firing pin had two prongs, which hit on either side of the rimmed fire case. These were called "breech pin snappers."

Some M 66 rifles made at Bridgeport had serial numbers and some do not. Those made at New Haven were serially numbered from 125,000 and up. While manufacture was halted in 1875, in 1891 1,000 rifles were assembled from parts on hand and chambered for 44 S & W American center fire cartridges. These were shipped to Brazil.

W.R.A. Models 67 and 677

Calibers: .22 Short, Long and Long Rifle inchangeably; .22 WRF; .22 Long Rifle shot smooth bore; .22 Long Rifle only.
Type of Action: Turnbolt.
Model styles: Takedown, Sporting rifle, smooth bore and junior rifle Models 67 and 677 are the same except for the sights.
Barrel Length and style: 20" round; 24"

round on .22 Long Rifle Target model; others 27" round.
Weights: 4.5 to 5.25 lbs.
Sights: Choice of sights on Model 67. Model 677 equipped for telescope sights only.
Stock types: One piece, pistol grip. Composition buttplate.
First issued: 1934.

Notes: Model 67 Boys Rifle has 20" barrel and weighs 4.5 lbs. Model 677 is no longer made.

W.R.A. Model 68

Calibers: .22 Short, Long and Long Rifle (Interchangeably). .22 W.R.F.

Notes: There are no essential points of difference between this model and the Model 67 except in sight equipment.

(Discontinued)

W.R.A. Models 69, 69A and 697

Calibers: .22 Long rifles, longs and shorts interchangeably.
Type of Action: Turn bolt.
Manual Safety: Thumb lever at right of receiver.
Magazine type and capacity: Detachable box (clip) 5 rounds. 10 round magazines are also available.
Model styles: Sporting, target and match rifles. Models 69 and 697 cock on closing

motion. Model 69A cocks on opening motion.
Barrel Length and style: 25" round.
Weight: About 5 lbs.
Sights: Various including telescope for which the Model 697 is equipped.
Stock types: 1 piece walnut with pistol grip. New type as semi-beavertail fore-end and pistol grip.
First issued: 1935.

Notes: A rebounding lock was added in 1935.
The M 69 was originally made to cock on closing motion of the bolt. In 1937 it was redesigned to cock on opening motion. The M 69 rifles with cocking on opening motion are listed as M 69 A. Model 69 (A), Model 69 with micrometer rear sight, and M69 Junior Target with Lyman M57 rear sight, are the currently produced rifles.

W.R.A. Model 70

Calibers: .22 Hornet; .220 Swift; .250/3000 Savage: .257 Roberts; .270 Winchester; .30/06; .300 H & H Magnum; .375 H & H Magnum 7mm and .35 Remington. .243 Win., .308 Win., .264 Win. Mag., .458 Win. Mag.

Type of Action: Turn bolt, speed lock, modified Mau er system.

Breechblock: Dual opposed forward lugs locking into receiver ring.

Manual Safety: Thumb lever at rear of receiver.

Magazine type and capacity: Box—Staggered

Column 5 rounds.

Model styles: Standard, super grade, target, National match and "Bull Gun."

Barrel Length and style: 20" to 28", standard to extra heavy weights in various models.

Weights: 7.5 to 13 lbs.

Sights: Various, open and aperature.

Stock types: 1 piece marksman and special types. Some with slings. .375 H & H Magnum are equipped with rubber recoil pads. Others have steel butt plate.

First issued: 1936.

Notes: A few rifles were chambered for 7.65mm and 9mm. Some sniping rifles were furnished using M 54 barrels. Currently made in: Featherweight (FMC), "RMC," Westerner Alaskan, African, Varmint, and Target rifles. Made in all Standard American calibers; the most versatile U. S. made bolt-action.

W.R.A. Model 71

Calibers: .348 Winchester.

Type of Action: Lever, exposed hammer.

Breechblock: Lever, exposed hammer.

Manual Safety: Lever, exposed hammer.

Magazine type and capacity: Exposed hammer—4 rounds.

Model styles: Sporting rifles, two types.

Barrel Lengths and styles: 20" and 24"

round. Forged ramp on barrel for front sight base.

Weights: 7.75 and 8 lbs.

Sights: Various. Open and aperature types.

Stock types: 2 piece walnut sporting type. Two lengths of comb.

First issued: 1935.

(Discontinued)

Winchester Model 100 Rifle

Calibers: .243 Win. and .308 Win.

Type of action: Gas, semiautomatic

Manual safety: Cross bolt

Magazine type and capacity: Detachable box 4 rounds

Barrel length and style: 22" round

Overall length: 42.5"

Weight: 7.25 lbs.

Sights: Open rear, ramp front, tapped for micrometer sights and scope

Stock type: 1-Piece with pistol grip

Winchester Model 88

Calibers: .243 Win., .308 Win., .358 Win. (Caliber .358 discontinued in 1962.)

Type of action: Lever action, hammerless rotary bolt

Manual safety: Cross bolt

Magazine type and capacity: Detachable box, 4 rounds

Barrel length and style: 22" round

Overall length: Approx. 42"

Weight: 6.5 lbs.

Sights: Open rear, ramp front, tapped for micrometer rear and scope

Stock type: 1-Piece with checkered pistol grip and fore-arm

W.R.A. Model 72 Rifle

Calibers: .22 Short only and .22 Long Rifles, Longs and Shorts interchangeably.

Type of Action: Turn bolt, cocking on opening bolt movement.

Manual Safety: Right side lever. Locks both sear and bolt handle.

Mechanical Safety: Sear contact only when action is closed.

Magazine type and capacity: Tubular. Long Rifles—15 rounds. Longs—16 rounds. Shorts—20 rounds.

Barrel Length and style: 25" round.

Overall length: 42".

Weight: 6 lbs.

Stock types: One piece, semi-beavertail pistol grip.

First issued: 1939.

(Discontinued)

W.R.A. Model 73

Calibers: Originally 44 W.C.F. (44-40). .38 W.C.F. .32 W.C.F. .22 Short R.F. .22 Long R.F. Winchester catalogue 1885 lists .22 W.C.F. caliber but factory doubts that actual manufacture was done.

Type of Action: Triggerguard finger lever. This is an improved form of the Model 1866 altered for center fire cartridges. Breechblock locked by toggle. Later altered for .22 R.F.

Breechblock: Sliding block locked by toggle behind it.

Manual Safety: Exposed hammer system. Half cock notch.

Mechanical Safety: Same as M 66.

Magazine type and capacity: Tubular. Sporting Rifle—15 rounds (with short mag. 6) Carbine—12. Musket—17. .22

Short—25 rounds. .22 Long—20 rounds.

Model styles: Sporting Rifle and special sporting rifle. Carbine. Musket with angular or saber bayonet.

Barrel Length and style: Sporting rifle—24" round, 20" and 24" octagon, 24" ½ oct. Carbine—20" round. Musket—30" round. (Note: 14, 16, 18 and 20" round and octagon barrels were specially furnished, particularly for South American export.

Weights: Sporting rifle—8.5 to 9 lbs. Carbine—7.25 to 7.5 lbs. Musket—9.5 lbs.

Stock types: Two piece Rifle type with straight grip and curved iron buttplate. Special shotgun butt available from 1879.

First issued: 1873.

Discontinued: 1919. Final sales in 1925.

Notes: The M 73 is the famous Winchester usually associated with the opening of the West. Rifles which made exceptionally fine targets were specially finished and provided with set triggers. These were sold as "One of a thousand" and were priced at $100. The next grade of barrels marked "One of a hundred" were sold at $20 above list. Original receivers were forged iron. These were later changed to steel.

W.R.A. Model 74 Rifle

Calibers: .22 Long Rifles or .22 Short.

Type of Action: Blowback. Semiautomatic.

Manual Safety: Pushbutton at rear of receiver.

Mechanical Safety: Sear contact only when action is closed.

Magazine type and capacity: Tube in stock. Long Rifles—14 rounds. Shorts—20 rounds.

Model styles: Sporting and Gallery. Gallery .22 Short has shell deflector.

Barrel Length and style: 24" round.

Weight: 6.5 lbs.

Stock types: Semi-beavertail fore-end. Checkered steel buttplate pistol grip.

First issued: Long Rifles in 1940; Shorts in 1939.

(Discontinued)

W.R.A. Model 75

Calibers: .22 Long Rifles (Functions with Longs and Shorts).

Type of Action: Turn bolt, recessed bolt head, "speed lock."

Manual Safety: Thumb lever at right rear of receiver. Locks sear and handle.

Magazine type and capacity: Detachable box, (clip) 5 or 10 shot optional.

Model styles: Target and Sporter.

Barrel Length and style: Target 28" round. Sporter 24" round.

Weights: Target 8.5 lbs. Sporter 5.75 lbs.

Sights: Various.

Stock types: One piece Winchester target and sporting types. Checkered buttplates.

First issued: 1938-39.

(Discontinued)

W.R.A. Model 76

Calibers: .45-75 W.C.F., .50-95 Express. .45-60 W.C.F. .40-60 W.C.F.

Type of Action: Same as 73 but larger.

Breechblock: Essentially an oversized Model 73.

Manual Safety: Same as 73.

Mechanical Safety: Same as 73.

Magazine type and capacity: Tubular. Sporting rifle—12 rounds, musket—13 rounds, carbine—9 rounds in full length magazines. Short magazines were also supplied.

Model styles: Sporting rifles, express rifle, musket and carbine.
Barrel Length and style: Sporting rifle—28" round, octagon or ½ octagon. Express rifle—26" round, octagon or ½ octagon. Carbine—22" round. Musket—32" round.
Weights: Sporting rifle—9.25 to 9.75 lbs. Musket—8.75 to 9 lbs. Carbine—8.25 lbs.

Stock types: Two piece rifle type with straight grip and curved iron buttplate. Pistol grip was standard on special sporting rifle. Furnished on other models as an extra.
First issued: 1876.
Discontinued: Manufacture ended in 1897.

Notes: The Model 76 was designed for more powerful ammunition than the earlier types. The extra length of the cartridges required some redesigning. These rifles were extensively sold to England and its colonies. The carbine in caliber 45-75 W.C.F. was officially adopted by the Royal North West Mounted Police.

W.R.A. Model 83

Calibers: .45-70-405 U. S. Government (While the 1884 catalogue lists a sporting rifle for .40-64 Hotchkiss cartridge, it is not definitely known if the rifle was issued.)
Type of Action: Turnbolt.
Breechblock: Cylindrical bolts, Hotchkiss.
Mechanical Safety: Sear contact only when both handles turn down.
Magazine type and capacity: Tube in buttstock. 6 cartridges.
Model styles: This was designed as a Military rifle. It received only limited use as a sporting arm. Made as sporting rifle, musket and carbine.

Barrel Length and style: Sporting rifle—26" round, octagon or ½ octagon. Musket—32" round, changed to 28" round in 1884. Carbine—24" round, changed to 22.5" round in 1884.
Weights: Sporting rifle—8.25 to 8.5 lbs. Musket—about 9 lbs. Carbine—about 8.25 lbs.
Stock types: One piece military style for muskets and carbines. Rifle type on sporting rifles. Straight grips were standard except for pistol grip on special sporting rifle.
First issued: Announced 1878.
Discontinued: 1899. Parts scrapped in 1913.

Notes: This was originally issued as the Hotchkiss Repeater. It was presented in 1878 to the Ordnance Board for testing. In 1883 several construction changes were made, and the name was changed to Winchester Model 1883. This was the first bolt action manufactured by Winchester.

W.R.A. Model 1886

Calibers: .45-70 U. S. Government, .40-82 W.C.F., .45-90, .40-65 W.C.F., .38-56 W.C.F., .50-110 Express, .40-70 W.C.F., .38-70 W.C.F., .50-100-45, or .33 W.C.F.
Type of Action: Triggerguard lever.
Breechblock: Sliding type locked to receiver by locks operated by lever.
Manual Safety: Half cock notch.
Mechanical Safety: Sear contact only when action is locked.
Magazine type and capacity: Tubular. Full and half length. Capacities varied.
Model styles: Sporting and fancy sporting rifles, half magazine rifle, carbine, muskets to order and extra light weight rifle (.45-70).

Barrel Length and style: Sporting and fancy sporting rifle 26" barrels. Extra light weight rifle—22" round nickel steel. Carbine—22" round. Special barrels and magazines furnished to specifications. This practice was discontinued in 1908.
Weights: Weights varying widely with specifications and caliber.
Sights: Open.
Stock types: Two piece sporting rifle had straight grip. Fancy sporting rifle had pistol grip. Carbine had carbine stock with straight grip. Half magazine rifle had shotgun butt with straight grip. Special butts and grips to order.
First issued: 1886.
Discontinued: Final sales 1935.

Notes: Winchester considers this design the strongest and smoothest operating lever action they ever manufactured. Its appearance halted American interest in bolt actions. The superiority of the operating and locking system soon outmoded the Model 76.

W.R.A. Model 90

Calibers: .22 long rifles only, .22 longs only, .22 short only, or .22 W.R.F.

Type of Action: Slide. Exposed Hammer.

Breechblock: Tipping breechblock operated by forearm slide.

Manual Safety: Half cock notch.

Mechanical Safety: Sear contact only when breechblock is locked down into receiver.

Magazine type and capacity: Tubular. .22 long rifle—11. .22 long—12. .22 short—15. .22 W.R.F.—12.

Model styles: Sporting and fancy sporting rifles. Originally issued as a solid frame but was soon altered to takedown.

Barrel Length and style: 24″ octagon.

Weights: 5.75 to 6 lbs.

Stock types: Two piece rifle type with straight grip and curved steel buttplate. Pistol grips furnished as specials.

First issued: 1890.

Discontinued: 1932. Cleanup in 1941.

Notes: This was the first popular shooting gallery rifle in this country. Its introduction paved the way for several later gallery type slide action rifles. These rifles were not intended for interchangeable cartridge use.

W.R.A. Model 92

Calibers: Originally issued for .32, .38 and .44 W.C.F. cartridges. .25 W.C.F. first listed in 1895.

Type of Action: Same as M 86.

Breechblock: Same as M 86.

Manual Safety: Same as M 86.

Mechanical Safety: Same as M 86.

Magazine type and capacity: Tubular. Standard rifle—13 rounds. Musket—17 rounds. Cabine—11 rounds with full magazines and 5 rounds with half magazine.

Model styles: Sporting rifle and fancy sporting rifle, musket and carbine.

Barrel Length and style: Rifles, 24″ round, octagon or ½ octagon. Musket—30″ round. Carbine—20″ round. Special barrels from 14 to 20″ were also provided, principally for South American export. Special lengths were also made up to 36″.

Weights: 5.5 to 8 lbs.

Sights: Ramp sight bases authorized in 1931 on M 92 carbines.

Stock types: 2 piece rifle, carbine and musket types according to model. Pistol grip on fancy sporting rifle. Extras to order.

First issued: 1892.

Discontinued: 1932. Final close out 1942.

Notes: This rifle was developed because of the popularity of the 32, 38 and 44 W.C.F. cartridges as used in the old Model 73. The stronger lock permitted use of cartridges with improved ballistics. The one millionth Model 92 was presented to U. S. Secretary of War Hurley in December 1932.

W.R.A. Model 94

Calibers: .25/35; .30/30; .32 Special; .38/55, or .32/40.

Type of Action: Lever, exposed hammer.

Manual Safety: Half cock notch on hammer.

Mechanical Safety: Sear contact only when action is fully closed.

Magazine type and capacity: Tubular, (half or full length) Rifle (full length) 6 rounds, Carbine—6 rounds.

Model styles: Rifle or Carbine sporter.

Takedown or solid frame.

Barrel Length and style: Rifle 26″ round, octagon or half octagon. Carbine Sporter —20″ round.

Weights: Rifle—7.7 to 8.0 lbs. Carbine—6.25 lbs.

Sights: Open.

Stock types: Two piece, rubber or steel butt plate.

First issued: 1894.

Notes: Originally produced for black powder .32/40 and .38/55. The .25/35 and .30/30 were added in 1895 when nickel steel was also made standard in order to safely handle the newly developed smokeless powder cartridges. The .32 Special chambering was begun in 1902. Manufacture of the Model 94 was discontinued in 1936. Renewed for three calibers as the result of popular demand in 1940. Currently made in carbine version chambered for .30/30 and .32 Special only.

W.R.A. Model 95 Rifle

Calibers: .30 U. S. Army (Krag), .38-72, .40-72 Winchester, .303 British, .35 Winchester, .405 Winchester, .30 government 1903, .30 government 1906 or 7.62mm Russian.

Type of Action: Triggerguard lever, exposed hammer, solid frame, carbines and muskets and takedown rifle. Original rifle was solid frame.

Breechblock: Browning system, sliding breechblock with locks operated by lever.

Manual Safety: Half cock notch on hammer.

Mechanical Safety: Sear contact only when action is locked.

Magazine type and capacity: Box—capacity varied 4 to 6 rounds.

Model styles: Sporting and fancy sporting rifles and carbines, muskets.

Barrel Length and style: Various. 24 to 36" barrels were commonly furnished.

Weights: Varied with specifications and caliber.

Stock types: Two piece standard for models.

First issued: 1896.

Discontinued: 1931. Final cleanup 1938.

Notes: This rifle was designed to meet the competition of bolt action rifles using very powerful cartridges. While the design was much stronger than any of the previous Browning patterns, the locking was too far to the rear of the cartridge case head for ultrapowerful calibers. While the design was popular with big game hunters, its locking and extracting factors could not compete with the turn bolt design. These rifles are entirely adequate for the cartridges originally used in them; but modern versions of the same calibers may be too powerful for sustained use.

W.R.A. Model 99
(Also called the Thumb Trigger Rifle.)

Calibers: .22 Long and Short interchangeably as originally issued. In 1914 chambering was changed to .22 Long, extra Long and Short, interchangeably.

Type of Action: Turn bolt single shot. Cocking piece on firing pin had to be pulled back manually after loading before rifle could be fired. Thumb operated trigger on small of stock.

Breechblock: Turn bolt handle.

Manual Safety: Manual cocking required.

Mechanical Safety: Action locked when cocked.

Magazine type and capacity: Single shot.

Model styles: Standard only.

Barrel Length and style: 18" round.

Weight: About 3 lbs.

Sights: Open.

Stock types: 1 piece gum wood shotgun butt. No trigger or triggerguard on stock. Checkered composition butt plate.

First issued: 1904.

Discontinued: 1923.

Notes: This rifle was developed from the Model 02. The name Model 99 was assigned arbitrarily to the design in the 1920 catalog.

A special thumb trigger replaced the standard mechanism. This trigger included the sear and extractor. It extended to the rear below the head of the firing pin. Pressing down its knurled end released the striker. This was the first Winchester rifle fitted with a rebounding lock.

DISCONTINUED MODELS OF WINCHESTER RIFLES

This is not a complete list of all discontinued Winchester models. It covers those models which have been discontinued since the turn of the century, many of which are therefore still found in use.

Model	Date Introduced	Date Discontinued	Type Action	Type Magazine	Capacity Magazine	Calibers
1873	1873	1919	Lever	Tube	6 to 15	.44/40
						.38/40 (1879)
						.32/40 (1882)
						.22 W.C.F. (1885)
						.22 R.F. (1884)
*Single Shot	1885	*	Drop Block	None	None	*

Model	Date Introduced	Date Discontinued	Type Action	Type Magazine	Capacity Magazine	Calibers
1886	1886	1935	Lever	Tube	Varied	.45/70 .40/82 .45/90 .40/65 (1887) .38/56 (1887) .50/110 (1887) .40/70 (1894) .38/70 (1894) .50/100 (1895) .33 W.C.F. (1903)
1890	1890	1932	Slide	Tube	11-15	.22 R.F.
Lee Straight Pull	1895	1916	Straight Pull Bolt	Box	5	6mm
1895	1896	1931	Lever	Box	Varied	.30/40 .38/72 .40/72 .303 Br. (1898) .35 Win. (1903) .405 (1904) .30/03 (1905) .30/06 (1908) †7.62mm (1916)
99	1904	1923	‡Bolt	None	None	.22 R.F.
1900	1899	1901	Bolt	None	None	.22 R.F.
1902	1902	1931	Bolt	None	None	.22 R.F.
1903	1904	1932	Blowback Semiauto	Butt Tube	10	.22 Win. Auto. Rimfire
1904	1904	1931	Bolt	None	None	.22 R.F.
1905	1905	1920	Blowback Semiauto	Detch. Box	Option 5-10	.22 R.F.
1906	1906	1932	Slide	Tube	11-15	.22 R.F.
53	1924	1932	Lever	Tube	6	.25 W.C.F. .32 W.C.F. .44 W.C.F.
54	1925	1936	Bolt	Box	5	.270 .30/06 .30/30 (1928) 7mm (1930) 7.65mm (1930) 9mm (1930) .250/3000 (1931) .22 Hornet (1933) .220 Swift (1936) .257 Roberts (1936)

Model	Date Introduced	Date Discontinued	Type Action	Type Magazine	Capacity Magazine	Calibers
55	1924	1932	Lever	Tube	3	.30/30 .25/35 (1927) .32 Spl (1927)
56	1926	1928	Bolt	Detch. Box	Option 5-10	.22 L.R. .22 Short
57	1926	1936	Bolt	Detch. Box	Option 5-10	.22 L.R.
58	1928	1931	Bolt	None	None	.22 R.F.
59	1930	1930	Bolt	None	None	.22 R.F.
60	1930	1934	Bolt	None	None	.22 R.F.
60-A	1932	1939	Bolt	None	None	.22 R.F.
677	1937	1939	Bolt	None	None	.22 R.F.
697	1937	1941	Bolt	Detch. Box	Option 5-10	.22 R.F.

---

*Rights to manufacture purchased from Browning Brothers, beginning the association of John Browning and Winchester. The first single shot made by Winchester, it was produced in all the old standard calibers, rim- and center-fire. Some were made in solid frame, some take-down. Set triggers and Schuetzen type stocks were available. Also made for 20 gauge shotgun shell in 1914. Discontinued about 1920 except the "Model 87 Musket" in .22 L.R. which was listed up to beginning of World War II.

†Made for Russia in Russian 7.62mm during World War I.

‡Thumb trigger on tang.

Note: Bayonet lengths varied.

Chapter 57

U. S. CARTRIDGES

AMERICAN MILITARY CARTRIDGES

7.62mm NATO

Other names: .308 Winchester, cal. .30 T65E3
Overall length: 2.80"
Type powder: Double base, ball
Type Primer: Boxer, F.A. #36, Rem. #9½, WRA #120

BULLET

Type: (1) Soft point, (2) Expanding, (3) Full jacket, (4) Expanding (5) Expanding
Weight: (1) 110 gr. (2) 150 gr. (3) 150 gr. (4) 190 gr. (5) 200 gr.
Diameter: .3090"

CARTRIDGE CASE

Length overall: 2.015"
Length of shoulder: .15"
Length of neck: .30"
Diameter at rim: .473"
Diameter at base: .4703"
Diameter at neck: .3435"
Diameter at shoulder: .454"

BALLISTICS (approximate)

Muzzle velocity: (1) 3340 f.p.s. (2) 2800 f.p.s. (3) 2860 f.p.s. (4) 2610 f.p.s. (5) 2450 f.p.s.

Notes: Service ammunition includes the M59 ball (mild steel cored boat tail), M80 ball (lead cored boat tail), M61 A.P., M62 tracer, M82 blank, M63 dummy, M60 high pressure and match.

.30-'06 Springfield

Other Names: .30 Government
Type: Rimless, Necked, Centerfire
Overall Length: 3.34"
Type Powder: Nitrocellulose
Type Primer: Boxer (Large Rifle)

BULLET

Type: (1) Hollow Pt. (2) Expanding (3) Expanding (4) Hollow Pt. (5) Full Jacketed (6) Expanding (7) Hollow Pt. (8) Soft Pt. (9) Expanding (10) Hollow Pt. (11) Full Jacketed (12) Soft Pt.
Diameter .3086"
Weight: (1) 110 grs. (2) 145 grs. (3) 150 grs. (4) 150 grs. (5) 150 grs. (6) 172 grs. (7) 180 grs. (8) 180 grs. (9) 180 grs. (10) 220 grs. (11) 220 grs. (12) 220 grs.

CARTRIDGE CASE

Length Overall: 2.494"
Length of Shoulder: .17"
Length of Neck: .370"
Diameter at Rim: .470"
Diameter at Base: .470"
Diameter at Neck: .338"
Diameter at Shoulder: .443"

BALLISTICS (approximate)

Muzzle Velocity: (1) 3380 f.s. (2) 2960 f.s. (3) 2960 f.s. (4) 2980 f.s. (5) 2800 f.s. (6) 2700 f.s. (7) 2710 f.s. (8) 2710 f.s. (9) 2690 f.s. (10) 2410 f.s. (11) 2410 f.s. (12) 2410 f.s.
Normal Pressure Level: 50,000 lbs./sq. in.

United States .30 Carbine Ball M1

Type: Rimless, Straight taper to neck, Centerfire
Overall Length: 1.68"
Average Wt.: 193 grs.
Type Powder: Nitrocellulose
Approximate Charge: 14.5 grs.
Type Primer: Boxer (Small Rifle)

BULLET

Type: (1) Full Jacketed (Round nose)
Weight: 111 grs.
Length: .690"

CARTRIDGE CASE

Length Overall: 1.28"
Length Head to Neck: .96"
Length of Neck: .32"
Diameter at Rim: .355"
Diameter at Base: .355"
Diameter at Neck: .332"

BALLISTICS (approximate)

Muzzle Velocity: 1970 f.s.
Normal Pressure Level: 40,000 lbs./sq. in.

AMERICAN SPORTING CARTRIDGES

.22 Short

Type: Straight, Rimfire
Overall Length: .695"
Average Wt.: Varies
Type Powder: Nitrocellulose
Type Primer: Rim Cavity

BULLET

Type: (1) Lead (2) Lead (Hollow Pt.)
(3) Disintegrating
Diameter: .225"
Weight: (1) 29 grs. (2) 27 grs. (3) 26 grs.
Length: Varies

CARTRIDGE CASE

Length Overall: .420"
Diameter at Rim: .278"
Diameter at Base: .226" under head
Diameter at Neck: .226"

BALLISTICS (approximate)

Muzzle Velocity: (1) 1130 f.s. (High Vel.)
(1) 1030 f.s. (Int. Vel.) (2) 1175 f.s.
(High Vel.) (3) 955 f.s. (Std. Vel.)
Normal Pressure Level: 16,000 lbs./sq. in.

Notes: Weights and lengths vary with type and manufacture.

.22 Long

Type: Straight, Rimfire
Overall Length: .887"
Type Powder: Nitrocellulose
Type Primer: Rim Cavity

BULLET

Type: (1) Lead. (2) Lead (Hollow Pt.)
Diameter: .225"
Weight: (1) 29 grs. (2) 27 grs.

CARTRIDGE CASE

Length Overall: .613"
Diameter at Rim .278"
Diameter at Base: .226" Under Head
Diameter at Neck: .226"

BALLISTICS (approximate)

Muzzle Velocity: (1) 1275 f.s. (High Vel.)
(1) 1080 f.s. (Int. Vel.) (1) 1030 f.s. (Std.
Vel.) (2) 1285 f.s. (High Vel.)
Normal Pressure Level: 18,000 lbs./sq. in.
(High Vel.)

Notes: Weights and lengths vary with type and manufacture.

.22 Long Rifle

Type: Straight, Rimfire
Overall Length: 1.00"
Type Powder: Nitrocellulose
Type Primer: Rim Capacity

BULLETS

Type: (1) Lead (2) Lead (Hollow Pt.)
Diameter: .2255"
Weight: (1) 40 grs. (2) 37 grs.
Length:

CARTRIDGE CASE

Length Overall: .613"
Diameter at Rim: .278"
Diameter at Base: .226" under head
Diameter at Mouth: .226"

BALLISTICS (approximate)

Muzzle Velocity: (1) 1375 f.s. (High Vel.)
(1) 1230 f.s. (Int. Vel.) (1) 1030 f.s.
(Std. Vel.) (2) 1400 f.s. (High Vel.)
Normal Pressure Level: 22,000 lbs./sq. in.

.22 Long Rifle Shot

Type: Rimfire
Overall Length: .990"
Type Powder: Nitrocellulose
Type Primer: Rim Capacity

BULLET

Type: #12 Shot

BALLISTICS (approximate)

Muzzle Velocity: 1115 f.s.

CARTRIDGE CASE

Length Overall: .99"
Length Head to Shoulder: .57"
Length of Shoulder: .03"
Length of Neck: .39"
Diameter at Rim: .278"
Diameter at Base: .226"
Diameter at Neck: .217"
Diameter at Shoulder: .226"

.22 W.R.F.

Other Names: .22 Remington Special
Type: Straight, Rimfire (Inside Lubricated)
Overall Length: 1.180"
Type Powder: Nitrocellulose
Type Primer: Rim Cavity

BULLET

Type: (1) Lead (Flat Nose). (2) Lead
(Hollow Pt.)
Diameter: .228"
Weight: (1) 45 grs. (2) 40 grs.

CARTRIDGE CASE

Length Overall: .965"
Diameter at Rim: .300"
Diameter at Base: .245" Under Head
Diameter at Mouth: .245"

BALLISTICS (approximate)

Muzzle Velocity: (1) 1450 f.s. (2) 1475 f.s.
Normal Pressure Level: 16,000 lbs./sq. in.

Notes: The .22 W.R.F. Hollow Point cartridge has been discontinued.

.22 Winchester Automatic

Type: Straight, Rimfire (Inside Lubricated)
Overall Length: .915"
Type Powder: Nitrocellulose
Type Primer: Rim Cavity

BULLET

Type: (1) Lead (Flat Nose). (2) Lead
(Hollow Pt.)
Weight: (1) 45 grs. (2) 45 grs.

CARTRIDGE CASE

Length Overall: .665"
Diameter at Rim: .300"
Diameter at Base: .245" Under Head
Diameter at Mouth: .245"

BALLISTICS (approximate)

Muzzle Velocity: (1) 1055 f.s. 2) 1055 f.s.
Normal Pressure Level: 15,000 lbs./sq. in.

Notes: The Winchester Automatic Hollow Point has been discontinued.

.22 Winchester Magnum Rimfire

Type: Straight rimfire
Overall length: 1.35"
Type powder: Nitrocellulose
Type primer: Rim cavity

BULLET

Type: Jacketed hollow point
Weight: 40 grs.

CARTRIDGE CASE

Length overall: 1.005"
Diameter at rim: .294"
Diameter at base: .242"

BALLISTICS

Muzzle velocity: 1550 f.p.s.
Maximum pressure: 24,000 p.s.i.

.218 Bee

Type: Rimmed, Necked, Centerfire
Overall Length: 1.68"
Average Wt.: 137 gr.
Type Powder: Nitrocellulose
Type Primer: Boxer (Small Rifle)

BULLET

Type: (1) Soft Pt. (2) Hollow Pt.
Diameter: .2245"
Weight: (1) 45 grs. (2) 46 grs.
Length: .535"

CARTRIDGE CASE

Length Overall: 1.345"
Length Head to Shoulder: .923"
Length of Shoulder: .166"
Length of Neck: .256"
Diameter at Rim: .408"
Diameter at Base: .3492"
Diameter at Neck: .2435"
Diameter at Shoulder: .3323"

BALLISTICS (approximate)

Muzzle Velocity: (1) 2860 f.s. (2) 2860 f.s.
Normal Pressure: Level 45,000 lbs./sq. in.

.219 Zipper

Type: Rimmed, Necked, Centerfire
Overall Length: 2.260"
Type Powder: Nitrocellulose
Type Primer: Boxer (Large Rifle)

BULLET

Type: (1) Hollow Pt. (2) Hollow Pt.
Diameter: .2245"
Weight: (1) 46 grs. (2) 56 grs.

CARTRIDGE CASE

Length Head to Shoulder: 1.35"
Length of Shoulder: .26"
Length of Neck: .31"
Diameter at Rim: .506"
Diameter at Base: .421"

Diameter at Neck: .253" Taper to .252"
Diameter at Shoulder: .364"

BALLISTICS (approximate)

Muzzle Velocity: (1) 3390 f.s. (2) 3050 f.s.
Normal Pressure: Level 39,000 lbs./sq. in.

.220 Swift

Type: Semi-rimmed, Necked, Centerfire
Overall Length: 2.68"
Type Powder: Nitrocellulose
Type Primer: Boxer (Large Rifle)

BULLET

Type: (1) Hollow Pt. (2) Soft Pt. (Pt'd.)
(3) Pointed
Diameter: .2245"
Weight: (1) 46 grs. (2) 48 grs. (3) 55 grs.

CARTRIDGE CASE

Length Overall: 2.20"
Length Head to Shoulder: 1.72"
Length of Shoulder: .183"
Length of Neck: .299"
Diameter at Rim: .473"
Diameter at Base: .443"
Diameter at Neck: .2615" taper to .260"
Diameter at Shoulder: .402"

BALLISTICS (approximate)

Muzzle Velocity: (1) 4140 f.s. (2) 4140 f.s.
(3) 3600 f.s.
Normal Pressure Level: 53,000 lbs./sq. in.

.22 Hornet

Type: Rimmed, Necked, Centerfire
Overall Length: 1.723"
Type Powder: Nitrocellulose
Type Primer: Boxer (Small Rifle)

BULLET

Type: (1) Hollow Pt. (2) Soft Pt. (3)
Soft Pt. Pt'd (4) Hollow Pt.
Diameter: .2235"
Weight: (1) 45 grs. (2) 45 grs. (3) 45 grs.
(4) 46 grs.

CARTRIDGE CASE

Length Overall: 1.40"
Length Head to Shoulder: .82"
Length of Shoulder: .25"
Length of Neck: .32"
Diameter at Rim: .350"
Diameter at Base: .298"
Diameter at Neck: .244" Taper to .242"
Diameter at Shoulder: .278"

BALLISTICS (approximate)

Muzzle Velocity: (1) 2650 f.s. (2) 2650 f.s.
(3) 2600 f.s. (4) 2650 f.s.
Normal Pressure Level: 44,000 lbs./sq. in.

.22 Savage

Other Names: .22 Savage High Power
Type: Rimmed, Necked, Centerfire
Overall Length: 2.51"
Type Powder: Nitrocellulose
Type Primer: Boxer (Large Rifle)

BULLET

Type: Soft Point
Diameter: .288"
Weight: 70 grs.

CARTRIDGE CASE

Length Overall: 2.05"
Length Head to Shoulder: 1.39"
Length of Shoulder: .200"
Length of Neck: .46"
Diameter at Rim: .506"
Diameter at Base: .416"
Diameter at Neck: .254"
Diameter at Shoulder: .357"

BALLISTICS (approximate)

Muzzle Velocity: 2780 f.s.
Pressure: 40,000 lbs./sq. in.

Notes: Powder charges vary by lot.

.222 Remington

Type: Necked, rimless, center fire
Overall length: 2.13"
Type powder: Nitrocellulose
Type primer: Boxer small rifle

BULLET

Type: Jacketed soft point
Diameter: .2245"
Weight: 55 gr.

CARTRIDGE CASE

Length overall: 1.70"
Rim diameter: .378"
Base diameter: .3759"
Neck diameter: .253"

BALLISTICS

Muzzle velocity: 3170 f.p.s.
Normal pressure: Approx. 45,500 p.s.i.

.222 Remington Magnum

Type: Necked, rimless, center fire
Overall length: 2.280"
Type powder: Nitrocellulose
Type Primer: Boxer Small Rifle

BULLET

Type: Jacketed, soft point
Diameter: .2245"
Weight: 55 gr.

CARTRIDGE CASE

Length overall: 1.85"
Rim diameter: .378"
Base diameter: .3754"
Neck diameter: .253"

BALLISTICS

Muzzle velocity: 3275 f.p.s.
Normal pressure: Approx. 50,000 p.s.i.

.223 Remington

Type: Necked, rimless, center fire
Overall length: 2.260"
Type powder: Nitrocellulose
Type primer: Boxer Small Rifle

BULLET

Type: Jacketed, soft point
Diameter: .2245"
Weight: 55 gr.

CARTRIDGE CASE

Length overall: 1.760"
Rim diameter: .378"
Base diameter: .3759"
Neck diameter: .253"

BALLISTICS

Muzzle velocity: 3250 f.p.s.
Normal pressure: 55,000 p.s.i.

.243 Winchester

Type: Necked, rimless, center fire
Overall length: 2.710"
Type powder: Nitrocellulose
Type primer: Boxer rifle

BULLET

Type: Jacketed soft point
Diameter: .2435"
Weight: 80 and 100 grs.

CARTRIDGE CASE

Length overall: 2.045"
Rim diameter: .473"
Base diameter: .4703"
Neck diameter: .276"

BALLISTICS

Muzzle velocity: 80 gr. bullet—3480 f.p.s.
100 gr. bullet—3050 f.p.s.
Normal pressure: Approx. 51,000 p.s.i.

.244 Remington

Type: Necked, rimless, center fire
Overall length: 2.750"
Type powder: Nitrocellulose
Type primer: Boxer (Large Rifle)

BULLET

Type: Jacketed,soft point
Diameter: .243"
Weight: 75 gr. and 90 gr.

CARTRIDGE CASE

Length overall: 2.233"
Rim diameter: .472"
Base diameter: .471"
Neck diameter: .276"

BALLISTICS

Muzzle velocity: 75 gr.—3480 f.p.s.
90 gr.—3180 f.p.s.
Normal pressure: Approx. 51,500 p.s.i.

6mm Lee Navy

Other Names: 6mm Lee. 6mm Navy
Type: Rimless, Necked, Centerfire
Overall Length: 3.11"
Average Wt.: 297 grs.
Type Primer: Nitrocellulose
Type Primer: Boxer

BULLET

Type: Soft Point (Round Nose)
Diameter: .244"
Weight: 112 grs.
Length: .996"

Notes: Obsolete.

CARTRIDGE CASE

Length Overall: 2.35"
Length Head to Shoulder: 1.62"
Length of Shoulder: .20"
Length of Neck: .535"
Diameter at Rim: .448"
Diameter at Base: .445"
Diameter at Neck: .278"
Diameter at Shoulder: .402"

BALLISTICS (approximate)

Muzzle Velocity: 2560 f.s.
Normal Pressure Level: 48,000 lbs./sq. in.

.25 Remington

Other Names: .25 Remington Automatic
Type: Rimless, Necked, Centerfire
Overall Length: 2.525"
Type Powder: Nitrocellulose
Type Primer: Boxer (Large Rifle)

BULLET

Type: (1) Hollow Pt. (2) Soft Pt.
Diameter: .258"
Weight: (1) 117 grs. (2) 117 grs.

CARTRIDGE CASE

Length Overall: 2.05"
Length Head to Shoulder: 1.50"
Length of Shoulder: .15"
Length of Neck: .40"
Diameter at Rim: .422"
Diameter at Base: .421"
Diameter at Neck: .288" Taper to .285"
Diameter at Shoulder: .390"

BALLISTICS (approximate)

Muzzle Velocity: (1) 2300 f.s. (2) 2300 f.s.
Normal Pressure Level: 36,000 lbs./sq. in.

Notes: Weights, lengths and powder charges vary as required by powder lot and bullet type.

.25-20 Winchester Single Shot (For .243 Winchester, see page 533.)

Type: Rimmed, Necked, Centerfire
Overall Length: 1.895"
Average Wt.: 153 gr.
Type Powder: Nitrocellulose
Type Primer: Boxer (Small Rifle)

BULLET

Type: (1) Lead. (2) Soft Pt.
Diameter: .2575"
Weight: (1) 86 grs. (2) 86 grs.
Length: (1) .685". (2) .745"

CARTRIDGE CASE

Length Overall: 1.635"
Length Head to Shoulder: 1.062"
Length of Shoulder: .180"
Length of Neck: .393"
Diameter at Rim: .380"
Diameter at Base: .3186"
Diameter at Neck: .279"
Diameter at Shoulder: .3036"

BALLISTICS (approximate)

Muzzle Velocity: (1) 1380 f.s. (2) 1380 f.s.
Normal Pressure Level: 20,000 lbs./sq. in.

Notes: 1. The Union Metallic Cartridge Co. introduced this cartridge in 1886 with the 86 grain bullet. Since World War II the cartridge has been discontinued from manufacture.

.250-3000 Savage Hi-Power

Other Names: .250 Savage
Type: Rimless, Necked, Centerfire
Overall Length: 2.515"
Type Powder: Nitrocellulose
Type Primer: Boxer (Large Rifle)

BULLET

Type: (1) Full Jacketed. (2) Soft Pt. Pt's.
(3) Hollow Pt. (4) Hollow Pt. (5) Expanding
Diameter: .2580"
Weight: (1) 87 grs. (2) 87 grs. (3) 87 grs.
(4) 100 grs. (5) 100 grs.

CARTRIDGE CASE

Length Overall: 1.91"
Length Head to Shoulder: 1.51"
Length of Shoulder: .12"
Length of Neck: .28"
Diameter at Rim: .473"
Diameter at Base: .468" @ .155"

Diameter at Neck: .285"
Diameter at Shoulder: .405"

BALLISTICS (approximate)

Muzzle Velocity: (1) 3000 f.s. (2) 3000 f.s.
(3) 3040 f.s. (4) 2810 f.s. (5) 2790 f.s.
Normal Pressure Level: 45,000 lbs./sq. in.

Notes: Popular European caliber as well as American.

.25-20 Winchester

Other Names: .25-20 W.C.F.
Type: Rimmed, Necked, Centerfire
Overall Length: 1.592"
Type Powder: Nitrocellulose
Type Primer: Boxer (Small Rifle)

BULLET

Type: (1) Hollow Pt. (2) Soft Pt. (3) Soft
Pt. (4) Full Jacketed. (5) Lead. (6)
Soft Pt.
Diameter: .2570"
Weight: (1) 60 grs. (2) 60 grs. (3) 86 grs.
(4) 86 grs. (5) 86 grs. (6) 86 grs.

CARTRIDGE CASE

Length Overall: 1.33"
Length Head to Shoulder: .83"
Length of Shoulder: .12"
Length of Neck: .38"
Diameter at Rim: .408"
Diameter at Base: .349"
Diameter at Neck: .276" Taper to .273"
Diameter at Shoulder: .325"

BALLISTICS (approximate)

Muzzle Velocity: (1) 2210 f.s. (2) 1710 f.s.
(3) 1710 f.s. (4) 1450 f.s. (5) 1450 f.s.
(6) 1450 f.s.
Normal Pressure Level: 28,000 lbs./sq. in.

Notes: Weights vary with powder lot and bullet type.

.25-35 Winchester

Other Names: .25-35 W.C.F.
Type: Rimmed, Necked, Centerfire
Overall Length: 2.550"
Type Powder: Nitrocellulose
Type Primer: Boxer (Large Rifle)

BULLET

Type: (1) Hollow Pt. (2) Full Jacketed.
(3) Soft Pt.
Diameter: .258"
Weight: (1) 87 grs. (2) 117 grs. (3) 117
grs. (4) 117 grs.

CARTRIDGE CASE

Length Overall: 2.04"
Length Head to Shoulder: 1.36"
Length of Shoulder: .20"
Length of Neck: .48"
Diameter at Rim: .506"
Diameter at Base: .4224"
Diameter at Neck: .2866" Taper to .2816"
Diameter at Shoulder: .364"

BALLISTICS (approximate)

Muzzle Velocity: (1) 2650 f.s. (2) 2280 f.s.
(3) 2280 f.s. (4) 2280 f.s.
Normal Pressure Level: 37,000 lbs./sq. in.

.25 Short Stevens

Other Names: .25 Short Rim Fire
Type: Straight, Rimfire (Inside Lubricated)
Overall Length: .885"
Average Wt.: 84 grs.
Type Primer: Nitrocellulose
Type Primer: Rim Cavity

BULLET

Type: Lead (Flat Nose)
Diameter: .257"
Weight: 65 grs.
Length: .540"

CARTRIDGE CASE

Length Overall: .610"
Diameter at Rim: .336"
Diameter at Base: .278"
Diameter at Mouth: .278"

BALLISTICS (approximate)

Muzzle Velocity: 925 f.s.

.257 Roberts

Other Names: .257 Remington Roberts
Type: Rimless, Necked, Centerfire
Overall Length: 2.750"
Type Powder: Nitrocellulose
Type Primer: Boxer (Large Rifle)

BULLET

Type: (1) Expanding. (2) Hollow Pt. (3)
Expanding. (4) Hollow Pt. (5) Hollow
Pt.
Diameter: .2575"
Weight: (1) 87 grs. (2) 87 grs. (3) 100
grs. (4) 100 grs. (5) 117 grs.

Notes: Weights and lengths vary with loadings.

CARTRIDGE CASE

Length Overall: 2.23"
Length Head to Shoulder: 1.72"
Length of Shoulder: .19"
Length of Neck: .32"
Diameter at Rim: .473"
Diameter at Base: .472"
Diameter at Neck: .290"
Diameter at Shoulder: .423"

BALLISTICS (approximate)

Muzzle Velocity: (1) 3180 f.s. (2) 3220 f.s.
(3) 2860 f.s. (4) 2900 f.s. (5) 2630 f.s.
Normal Pressure Level: 45,000 lbs./sq. in.

.264 Winchester Magnum

Type: Rimless, necked, belted, center fire
Overall length: 3.340"
Type powder: Nitrocellulose
Type primer: Large rifle

BULLET

Type: Jacketed, soft point
Diameter: .265"
Weight: 100 gr. and 140 gr.

CARTRIDGE CASE

Length overall: 2.50"
Rim diameter: .532"
Base diameter: .513"
Neck diameter: .298"

BALLISTICS

Muzzle velocity: 100 gr.—3675 f.p.s.
140 gr.—3185 f.p.s.
Normal pressure: Approx. 53,500 P.S.I.

.270 Winchester

Other Names: .270 W. C. F.
Type: Rimless, Necked, Centerfire
Overall Length: 3.340"
Type Powder: Nitrocellulose
Type Primer: Boxer (Large Rifle)

BULLET

Type: (1) Expanding. (2) Hollow Pt. (3)
Expanding. (4) Soft Pt. (5) Soft Pt.
Diameter: .2780
Weight: (1) 100 grs. (2) 130 grs. (3) 140
grs. (4) 150 grs. (5) 175 grs.

Notes: The .270 case is based on the .30-06, but is slightly longer and necked for the smaller bullet.

CARTRIDGE CASE

Length Overall: 2.54"
Length Head to Shoulder: 1.95"
Length of Shoulder: .20"
Length of Neck: .39"
Diameter at Rim: .473"
Diameter at Base: .470" @ .200"
Diameter at Neck: .310" Taper to .308"
Diameter at Shoulder: .435"

BALLISTICS (approximate)

Muzzle Velocity: (1) 3455 f.s. (2) 3140 f.s.
(3) 3120 f.s. (4) 2790 f.s. (5) 2560 f.s.
Normal Pressure Level: 54,000 lbs./sq. in.

.280 Remington

Type: Rimless, necked, center fire
Overall length: 3.30"—165 gr. bullet
Type powder: Nitrocellulose
Type primer: Large rifle

BULLET

Type: Jacketed, soft point
Diameter: .2845"
Weight: 100 gr.
125 gr.
150 gr.
165 gr.

CARTRIDGE CASE

Length overall: 2.54"
Rim diameter: .472"
Base diameter: .470"
Neck diameter: .315"

BALLISTICS

Muzzle velocity: 100 gr.—3550 f.p.s.
165 gr.—2800 f.p.s.
Normal pressure: Approx. 50,000 p.s.i.

.300 Savage

Type: Rimless, Necked, Centerfire
Overall Length: 2.600"
Type Powder: Nitrocellulose
Type Primer: Boxer (Large Rifle)

BULLET

Type: (1) Soft Pt. (2) Hollow Pt. (3) Expanding. (4) Soft Point
Diameter: .3085"
Weight: (1) 180 grs. (2) 150 grs. (3) 180 grs. (4) 150 grs.

CARTRIDGE CASE

Length Overall: 1.87"
Length Head to Shoulder: 1.56"
Length of Shoulder: .10"
Length of Neck: .21"
Diameter at Rim: .473"
Diameter at Base: .471"
Diameter at Neck: .33"
Diameter at Shoulder: .449"

BALLISTICS (approximate)

Muzzle Velocity: (1) 2380 f.s. (2) 2680 f.s. (3) 2380 f.s. (4) 2660 f.s.
Normal Pressure Level: 46,000 lbs./sq. in.

Notes: Lengths and weights vary with loadings.

.30 Remington

Other Names: .30 Remington Automatic
Type: Rimless, Necked, Centerfire
Overall Length: 2.525"
Type Powder: Nitrocellulose
Type Primer: Boxer (Large Rifle)

BULLET

Type: (1) Hollow Pt. (2) Hollow Pt. (3) Full Jacketed. (4) Hollow Pt. (5) Soft Pt. (6) Full Jacketed
Diameter: .307"
Weight: (1) 110 grs. (2) 125 grs. (3) 160 grs. (4) 165 grs. (5) 170 grs. (6) 170 grs.

CARTRIDGE CASE

Length Overall: 2.05"
Length Head to Shoulder: 1.50"
Length of Shoulder: .10"
Length of Neck: .45"
Diameter at Rim: .422"
Diameter at Base: .4207 @ .200
Diameter at Neck: .3326" Taper to .3317"
Diameter at Shoulder: .4019" @ 1.440"

BALLISTICS (approximate)

Muzzle Velocity: (1) 2720 f.s. (2) 2560 f.s. (3) 2200 f.s. (4) 2200 f.s. (5) 2200 f.s.
Normal Pressure Level: 35,000 lbs./sq. in.

Notes: This is the rimless equivalent of the rimmed .30-30 cartridge. It was designed without rim for autoloading use.

.38-56 W.C.F.

Type: Rimmed, Necked, Centerfire
Overall Length: 2.50"
Average Wt.: 474 grs.
Type Powder: Black
Approximate Chg.: 56 grs.
Type Primer: Boxer

BULLET

Type: Lead, Flat Nose
Diameter: .377"
Weight: 255 grs.
Length: .94"

CARTRIDGE CASE

Length Overall: 2.10"
Length Head to Shoulder: 1.21"
Length of Shoulder: .31"
Length of Neck: .555"
Diameter at Rim: .610"
Diameter at Base: .506"
Diameter at Neck: .403"
Diameter at Shoulder: .450"

BALLISTICS (approximate)

Muzzle Velocity: 1400 f.s.
Normal Pressure Level: 16,000 lbs./sq. in.

.30-30 Winchester

Other Names: .30 W.C.F.
Type: Rimmed, Necked, Centerfire
Overall Length: 2.55"
Type Powder: Nitrocellulose
Type Primer: Boxer (Large Rifle)

BULLET

Type: (1) Hollow Pt. (2) Hollow Pt. (3) Hollow Pt. (4) Full Jacketed. (5) Hollow Pt. (6) Soft Pt. (7) Full Jacketed
Diameter: .309"

Weight: (1) 100 grs. (2) 125 grs. (3) 150
grs. (4) 160 grs. (5) 165 grs. (6) 170
grs. (7) 170 grs.

CARTRIDGE CASE

Length Overall: 2.04"
Length Head to Shoulder: 1.45"
Length of Shoulder: .14"
Length of Neck: .45"
Diameter at Rim: .506"

Diameter at Base: .421"
Diameter at Neck: .3328" Taper to .3301"
Diameter at Shoulder: .391"

BALLISTICS (approximate)

Muzzle Velocity: (1) 2720 f.s. (2) 2560 f.s.
(3) 2380 f.s. (4) 2200 f.s. (5) 2200 f.s.
(6) 2200 f.s. (7) 2200 f.s.
Normal Pressure Level: 38,000 lbs./sq. in.

Notes: This famous cartridge takes its popular name (.30-30) from its caliber plus the fact that the original load was 30 grains of powder. The charge varies with modern improved powders.

.300 H&H Magnum

Other Names: .300 Magnum
Type: Belted, Necked, Centerfire
Overall Length: 3.600"
Type Powder: Nitrocellulose
Type Primer: Boxer (Large Rifle)

BULLET

Type: (1) Full Jacketed. (2) Expanding.
(3) Expanding. (4) Soft Pt.
Diameter: .309"
Weight: (1) 180 grs. (2) 180 grs. (3) 220
grs. (4) 220 grs.

CARTRIDGE CASE

Length Overall: 2.79"
Lenght Head to Shoulder: 2.27"
Length of Shoulder: .15"
Length of Neck: .37"
Diameter at Rim: .532"
Diameter at Belt: .532"
Diameter at Neck: .338"
Diameter at Shoulder: .456"

BALLISTICS (approximate)

Muzzle Velocity: (1) 3030 f.s. (2) 2930 f.s.
(3) 2610 f.s. (4) 2610 f.s.
Normal Pressure Level: 54,000 lbs./sq. in.

Notes: Designed in England by Holland & Holland.

.303 British

Other Names: .303 Mark VII
Type: Rimmed, Necked, Centerfire
Overall Length: 3.09"
Average Wt.: 437 grs.
Type Powder: Nitrocellulose
Type Primer: Boxer (Large Rifle)

BULLET

Type: (1) Soft Pt., (2) Full Jacketed,
(3) Hollow Pt.
Diameter: .3125"
Weight: (1) 215 grs., (2) 215 grs., (3)
174 grs.
Length: 1.221"

CARTRIDGE CASE

Length Overall: 2.21"
Length Head to Shoulder: 1.763"
Length of Shoulder: .13"
Length of Neck: .317"
Diameter at Rim: .529"
Diameter at Base: .4597"
Diameter at Neck: .341"
Diameter at Shoulder: .398"

BALLISTICS (approximate)

Muzzle Velocity: (1) 2160 f.s., (2) 2160 f.s.,
(3) 2470 f.s.
Normal Pressure Level: 45,000 lbs./sq. in.

Notes: 1. Commercially manufactured in the United States. British loadings, sporting and military, differ in weights, bullet types, etc.

.30-40 Krag

Other Names: .30 U. S. Army
Type: Rimmed, Necked, Centerfire
Overall Length: 3.089"
Type Powder: Nitrocellulose
Type Primer: Boxer (Large Rifle)

BULLET

Type: (1) Soft Pt. (2) Open Point. (3)
Expanding. (4) Expanding. (5) Full
Jacketed. (6) Full Jacketed. (7) Soft Pt.
Diameter: .3088"

Weight: (1) 180 grs. (2) 180 grs. (3) 190 grs. (4) 220 grs. (5) 180 grs. (6) 220 grs. (7) 220 grs.

Diameter at Rim: .545"
Diameter at Base: .457"
Diameter at Neck: .338"
Diameter at Shoulder: .423"

CARTRIDGE CASE

Length Overall: 2.31"
Length Head to Shoulder: 1.71"
Length of Shoulder: .10"
Length of Neck: .50"

BALLISTICS (approximate)

Muzzle Velocity: (1) 2480 f.s. (2) 2480 f.s. (3) 2480 f.s. (4) 2190 f.s. (5) 2460 f.s. (6) 2190 f.s. (7) 2190 f.s.
Normal Pressure Level: 40,000 lbs./sq. in.

Notes: This cartridge must not be confused with the present rimless .30 Government cartridge.

.32-40 Winchester

Type: Rimmed, Necked, Centerfire
Overall Length: 2.300"
Type Powder: Nitrocellulose
Type Primer: Boxer (Large Rifle)

BULLET

Type: Soft Point, Flat Nose
Diameter: .321"
Weight: 165 grs.

CARTRIDGE CASE

Length Overall: 2.130"
Length Head to Neck: 1.60"
Length of Shoulder: None
Length of Neck: .53"
Diameter at Rim: .506"
Diameter at Base: .424"
Diameter at Neck: .340"

BALLISTICS (approximate)

Muzzle Velocity: 1440 f.s.
Pressure: 30,000 lbs./sq. in.

Notes: 1. This was originally a black powder cartridge. Name came from the caliber (.32) plus the original powder charge (40 gr.) .

.32 Winchester Special

Other Names: .32 Special
Type: Rimmed, Necked, Centerfire
Overall Length: 2.565"
Type Powder: Nitrocellulose
Type Primer: Boxer (Large Rifle)

BULLET

Type: (1) Soft Point, Flat Nose; (2) Hollow Point; (3) Expanding; (4) Hollow Point
Diameter: .322"
Weight: (1) 170 grs., (2) 165 grs., (3) 170 grs., (4) 110 grs.

CARTRIDGE CASE

Length Overall: 2.040"
Length Head to Shoulder: 1.41"
Length of Shoulder: .12"
Length of Neck: .51"
Diameter at Rim: .506"
Diameter at Base: .421"
Diameter at Neck: .343"
Diameter at Shoulder: .403"

BALLISTICS (approximate)

Muzzle Velocity: (1) 2260 f.s., (2) 2260 f.s., (3) 2260 f.s., (4) 2630 f.s.
Normal Pressure Level: 35,000 lbs./sq. in.

Notes: This modern cartridge is in the .30-30 class.

.32-20 Winchester

Other Names: .32 Winchester
Type: Rimmed, Straight Taper, Centerfire
Overall Length: 1.592"
Type Powder: Nitrocellulose
Type Primer: Boxer (Small Rifle)

BULLET

Type: (1) Full Metal Jacketed; (2) Lead; (3) Soft Point, Flat Nose; (4) Hollow Point
Diameter: .3125"
Weight: (1) 115 grs., (2) 100 grs., (3) 100 grs., (4) 80 grs.

CARTRIDGE CASE

Length Overall: 1.31"
Diameter at Rim: .408"
Diameter at Base: .353"
Diameter at Neck: .327"

BALLISTICS (approximate)

Muzzle Velocity: (1) 1280 f.s., (2) 1280 f.s., (3) 1280 f.s., (4) 2050 f.s.
Normal Pressure Level: 28,000 lbs./sq. in.

Notes: 1. This was originally a black powder cartridge.
2. Low velocity cartridges loaded to a normal pressure level of 16,000 lbs./sq. in. can also be used in .32-20 revolvers. The higher pressure cartridges are dangerous in revolvers.

.32 Winchester Self-Loading

Other Names: .32 Winchester S.L.R.
Type: Semi-Rimmed, Straight Taper,
  Centerfire
Overall Length: 1.83"
Type Powder: Nitrocellulose
Type Primer: Boxer (Small Rifle)

BULLET
Type: Soft Point, Flat Nose
Diameter: .322"
Weight: 165 grs.

CARTRIDGE CASE
Length Overall: 1.29"
Diameter at Rim: .390"
Diameter at Base: .351"
Diameter at Neck: .348"

BALLISTICS (approximate)
Muzzle Velocity: 1390 f.s.
Normal Pressure Level: 27,000 lbs./sq. in.

Notes: Use confined to Win. auto rifle and a few European imitations. The U. S. Carbine .30 M1 cartridge derived from this case.

.32 Remington

Other Names: .32 Remington Automatic
Type: Rimless, Necked, Centerfire
Overall Length: 2.525"
Type Powder: Nitrocellulose
Type Primer: Boxer (Large Rifle)

BULLET
Type: (1) Soft Pt., (2) Expanding, (3)
  Hollow Pt., (4) Hollow Pt.
Diameter: .321"
Weight: (1) 170 grs., (2) 170 grs., (3) 165
  grs., (4) 110 grs.

CARTRIDGE CASE
Length Overall: 2.05"
Length Head to Shoulder: 1.50"
Length of Shoulder: .06"
Length of Neck: .49"
Diameter at Rim: .422"
Diameter at Base: .420"
Diameter at Neck: .344"
Diameter at Shoulder: .402"

BALLISTICS (approximate)
Muzzle Velocity: (1) 2200 f.s., (2) 2200
  f.s., (3) 2260 f.s., (4) 2630 f.s.
Normal Perssure Level: 35,000 lbs./sq. in.

.33 Winchester

Type: Rimmed, Necked, Centerfire
Overall Length: 2.795"
Average Wt.: 410 grs.
Type Powder: Nitrocellulose
Type Primer: Boxer (Large Rifle)

BULLET
Type: Soft Point, Flat Nose
Diameter: .3385"
Weight: 200 grs.
Length: 1.221"

CARTRIDGE CASE
Length Overall: 2.11"
Length Head to Shoulder: 1.57"
Length of Shoulder: .180"
Length of Neck: .36"
Diameter at Rim: .610"
Diameter at Base: .508"
Diameter at Neck: .3685"
Diameter at Shoulder: .4432"

BALLISTICS (approximate)
Muzzle Velocity: 2180 f.s.
Normal Pressure Level: 32,000 lbs./sq. in.

.338 Winchester Magnum

Type: Necked, rimless, belted, center fire
Overall length: 3.340"
Type powder: Nitrocellulose
Type primer: Large rifle

BULLET
Type: Jacketed, soft point
Diameter: .339"
Weight: 200 gr.
  250 gr.

CARTRIDGE CASE
Length overall: 2.50"
Rim diameter: .537"
Belt diameter: .532"
Base diameter: .513"
Neck diameter: .369"

BALLISTICS
Muzzle velocity: 200 gr.—2980 f.p.s.
  250 gr.—2650 f.p.s.
Normal pressure: Approx. 53,750 p.s.i.

.348 Winchester

Type: Rimmed, Necked, Centerfire
Overall Length: 2.80"
Average Wt.: 517 grs.
Type Powder: Nitrocellulose
Type Primer: Boxer (Large Rifle)

BULLET

Type: Soft Point (three weights)
Diameter: .3757"
Weight: (1) 150 grs., (2) 200 grs., (3) 250 grs.

CARTRIDGE CASE

Length Overall: 2.25"
Length Head to Shoulder: 1.65"
Length of Shoulder: .154"
Length of Neck: .521"
Diameter at Rim: .610"
Diameter at Base: .553"
Diameter at Neck: .375"
Diameter at Shoulder: .485"

BALLISTICS (approximate)

Muzzle Velocity: (1) 2880 f.s., (2) 2520 f.s., (3) 2320 f.s.
Normal Pressure Level: 40,000 lbs./sq. in.

Notes: 1. Other types of expanding bullets commercially manufactured for this cartridge.

.35 Winchester

Other Names: .35 WCF
Type: Rimmed, Necked, Centerfire
Overall Length: 3.175"
Average Wt.: 483 grs.
Type Powder: Nitrocellulose
Type Primer: Boxer (Large Rifle)

BULLET

Type: Soft Point, Flat Nose
Diameter: .359"
Weight: 250 grs.

CARTRIDGE CASE

Length Overall: 2.41"
Length Head to Shoulder: 2.00"
Length of Shoulder: .11"
Length of Neck: .30"
Diameter at Rim: .543"
Diameter at Base: .4613"
Diameter at Neck: .3854"
Diameter at Shoulder: .4276"

BALLISTICS (approximate)

Muzzle Velocity: 2160 f.s.
Normal Pressure Level: 39,000 lbs./sq. in.

.35 Winchester Self-Loading

Type: Semi-Rimmed, Straight Taper, Centerfire
Overall Length: 1:65"
Average Wt.: 273 grs.
Type Powder: Nitrocellulose
Type Primer: Boxer (Small Rifle)

BULLET

Type: Soft Point
Diameter: .351"
Weight: 180 grs.

CARTRIDGE CASE

Length Overall: 1.54"
Diameter at Rim: .405"
Diameter at Base: .381"
Diameter at Neck: .377"

BALLISTICS (approximate)

Muzzle Velocity: 1390 f.s.
Normal Pressure Level: 30,000 lbs./sq. in.

.35 Remington

Other Names: .35 Remington Automatic
Type: Rimless, Necked, Centerfire
Overall Length: 2.53"
Type Powder: Nitrocellulose
Type Primer: Boxer (Large Rifle)

BULLET

Type: (1) Soft Pt., (2) Hollow Pt., (3) Expanding, (4) Hollow Pt.
Diameter: .359"
Weight: (1) 200 grs., (2) 200 grs., (3) 200 grs., (4) 150 grs.

CARTRIDGE CASE

Length Overall: 1.92"
Length Head to Shoulder: 1.53"
Length of Shoulder: .04"
Length of Neck: .35"
Diameter at Rim: .457"
Diameter at Base: .454"
Diameter at Neck: .405"
Diameter at Shoulder: .420"

BALLISTICS (approximate)

Muzzle Velocity: (1) 2180 f.s., (2) 2180 f.s., (3) 2180 f.s., (4) 2360 f.s.
Normal Pressure Level: 35,000 lbs./sq. in.

Notes: A development of John M. Browning. Used also in autoloading Browning rifles made by F. N. in Belgium. European manufacture has Berdan primers.

.351 Winchester Self-Loading

Type: Semi-rimmed, Straight taper
Overall Length: 1.90"
Average Wt.: 290 grs.
Type Powder: Nitrocellulose
Type Primer: Boxer (Small Rifle)

BULLET

Type: (1) Full Jacketed, (2) Soft Point
Diameter: .352"
Weight: (1) 180 grs., (2) 180 grs.
Length: .77"
Notes: Used only in .351 W. S. L. rifles.

CARTRIDGE CASE:
Length Overall: 1.38"
Diameter at Rim: .410"
Diameter at Base: .3805"
Diameter at Mouth: .3805"

BALLISTICS (approximate)
Muzzle Velocity: (1) 1850 f.s., (2) 1850 f.s.
Normal Pressure Level: 45,000 lbs./sq. in.

.358 Winchester

Type: Necked, rimless, center fire
Overall length: 2.780"
Type powder: Nitrocellulose
Type primer: Large primer

BULLET

Type: Jacketed, soft point
Diameter: .3585"
Weight: 200 gr.
     258 gr.

CARTRIDGE CASE
Length overall: 2.015"
Rim diameter: .473"
Base diameter: .4703"
Neck diameter: .388"

BALLISTICS
Muzzle velocity: 200 gr.—2515 f.p.s.
              258 gr.—2235 f.p.s.
Normal pressure: Approx: 51,750 p.s.i.

.375 H&H Magnum

Type: Rimless (Belted), Necked, Center-
fire
Overall Length: 3.60"
Type Powder: Nitrocellulose
Type Primer: Boxer (Large Rifle)

BULLET

Type: (1) Soft Pt., (2) Hollow Pt., (3)
Pt'd Expanding, (4) Full Jacketed, (5)
Soft Pt.
Diameter: .3755"
Weight: (1) 270 grs., (2) 235 grs., (3) 300
grs., (4) 300 grs., (5) 270 grs.

Notes: Developed in England by Holland & Holland.

CARTRIDGE CASE
Length Overall: 2.85"
Length Head to Shoulder 2.41"
Length of Shoulder: .09"
Length of Neck: .35"
Diameter at Rim: .532"
Diameter at Belt: .513"
Diameter at Neck: .338"
Diameter at Shoulder: .430"

BALLISTICS (approximate)
Muzzle Velocity: (1) 2720 f.s., (2) 2860 f.s.,
     (3) 2540 f.s., (4) 2540 f.s., (5) 2750 f.s.
Normal Pressure Level: 53,000 lbs./sq. in.

.38-40 Winchester

Other Names: .38 W.C.F., .38 Winchester
Type: Rimmed, Necked, Centerfire
Overall Length: 1.59"
Average Wt.: 300 grs.
Type Powder: Black
Approximate Charge: 40 grs.
Type Primer: Boxer (Small Rifle)

BULLET

Type: (1) Lead, Flat Nose, (2) Soft Point,
(3) Hollow Point
Diameter: .401"
Weight: (1) 180 grs., (2) 180 grs., (3) 145
grs.

CARTRIDGE CASE
Length Overall: 1.30"
Length Head to Shoulder: .91"
Length of Shoulder: .09"
Length of Neck: .30"
Diameter at Rim: .525"
Diameter at Base: .469"
Diameter at Neck: .417"
Diameter at Shoulder: .430"

BALLISTICS (approximate)
Muzzle Velocity: (1) 1310 f.s., (2) 1770
f.s., (3) 2060 f.s

Normal Pressure Level: 22,000 lbs./sq. in.

Notes: 1. Modern cartridges are loaded with nitrocellulose powder and jacketed soft point bullets. Low velocity cartridges are loaded to a normal pressure level of 14,000 lbs./sq. in. and can also be used in .38-40 revolvers. The higher pressure cartridges are dangerous in revolvers.

.38-55 Winchester (For .38-56 W.C.F., see page 537.)

Type: Rimmed, Straight Taper
Overall Length: 2.50"
Average Wt.: 445 grs.
Type Powder: Black
Approximate Charge: 55 grs.
Type Primer: Boxer (large rifle)

BULLET

Type: Soft Point, Flat Nose
Diameter: .3775"
Weight: 255 grs.
Length: .97"

CARTRIDGE CASE

Length Overall: 2.13"
Diameter at Rim: .506"
Diameter at Base: .421"
Diameter at Neck: .392"

BALLISTICS (approximate)

Muzzle Velocity: 1320 f.s.
Normal Pressure Level: 30,000 lbs./sq. in.

.38-72 W.C.F.

Type: Rimmed, Necked, Centerfire
Overall Length: 3.175"
Average Wt.: 451 grs.
Type Powder: Black
Approximate Charge: 72 grs.
Type Primer: Boxer

BULLET

Type: Lead
Diameter: .377"
Weight: 275 grs.

CARTRIDGE CASE

Length Overall: 2.58"
Length Head to Shoulder: 1.85"
Length of Shoulder: .280"
Length of Neck: .455"
Diameter at Rim: .523"
Diameter at Base: .462"
Diameter at Neck: .400"
Diameter at Shoulder: .431"

BALLISTICS (approximate)

Muzzle Velocity: 1480 f.s.
Normal Pressure Level: 16,000 lbs./sq. in.

.401 Winchester Self-Loading

Type: Semi-rimmed, Straight Taper, Center-
fire
Overall Length: 2.00"
Average Wt.: 345 grs.
Type Powder: Nitrocellulose
Type Primer: Boxer (Large Rifle)

BULLET

Type: Jacketed, Soft Point
Diameter: .407"
Weight: 200 grs.

CARTRIDGE CASE

Length Overall: 1.50"
Diameter at Rim: .460"
Diameter at Base: .433"
Diameter at Mouth: .432"

BALLISTICS (approximate)

Muzzle Velocity: 2140 f.s.
Normal Pressure Level: 45,000 lbs./sq. in.

Notes: Used only in Win. autoloaders and a few European blowbacks.

.44-40 Winchester

Other Names: .44 WCF

Type: Rimmed, Straight Taper, Centerfire
Overall Length: 1.59"
Type Powder: Nitrocellulose
Type Primer: Boxer (Small Rifle)

BULLET

Type: Soft Point
Diameter: .4270"
Weight: 200 grs.

CARTRIDGE CASE

Length Overall: 1.30"
Diameter at Rim: .525"
Diameter at Base: .471"
Diameter at Neck: .443"

BALLISTICS (approximate)

Muzzle Velocity: 1300 f.s.
Normal Pressure Level: 13,000 lbs./sq. in.

Notes: 1. This cartridge was originally loaded with black powder. Name comes from its caliber plus the fact that the original load was 40 grains.

.40-60 Winchester

Other Names: .40-60 W.C.F.
Type: Rimmed, Centerfire
Overall Length: 2.25"
Average Wt.: 412 grs.
Type Powder: Black
Approximate Charge: 62 grs.
Type Primer: Boxer

BULLET

Type: (1) Lead, Flat Nose; (2) Soft Point
Diameter: .404"
Weight: (1) 210 grs., (2) 210 grs.
Length: .69"

CARTRIDGE CASE

Length Overall: 1.88"
Length Head to Shoulder: 1.22"
Length of Shoulder: .220"
Length of Neck: .438"
Diameter at Rim: .629"
Diameter at Base: .510"
Diameter at Neck: .426"
Diameter at Shoulder: .629"

BALLISTICS (approximate)

Muzzle Velocity: (1) 1533 f.s., (2) 1960 f.s.
Normal Pressure Level: 20,000 lbs./sq. in.

Notes: 1. The .40-60 Marlin cartridge has an overall length of 2.54" and a case length of 2.12". The Marlin cartridge is loaded with a 260 gr. lead bullet.

.40-65 WCF

Type: Rimmed, Straight Taper
Overall Length: 2.48"
Average Wt.: 437 grs.
Type Powder: Black
Approximate Charge: 65 grs.
Type Primer: Boxer

BULLET

Type: Lead
Diameter: .406"
Weight: 260 grs.

CARTRIDGE CASE

Length Overall: 2.10"
Diameter at Rim: .608"
Diameter at Base: .504"
Diameter at Neck: .427"

BALLISTICS (approximate)

Muzzle Velocity: 1360 f.s.
Normal Pressure Level: 35,000 lbs./sq. in.

.40-82 W.C.F.

Type: Rimmed, Necked, Centerfire
Overall Length: 2.76"
Average Wt.: 467 grs.
Type Powder: Black
Approximate Charge: 82 grs.
Type Primer: Boxer

BULLET

Type: Lead
Diameter: .406"
Weight: 260 grs.

CARTRIDGE CASE

Length Overall: 2.39"
Length Head to Shoulder: 1.67"
Length of Shoulder: .28"
Length of Neck: .42"
Diameter at Rim: .610"
Diameter at Base: .508"
Diameter at Neck: .427"
Diameter at Shoulder: .457"

BALLISTICS (approximate)

Muzzle Velocity: 1500 f.s.
Normal Pressure Level: 20,000 lbs./sq. in.

.405 Winchester

Other Names: .405 WCF 6
Type: Rimmed, Straight Taper
Overall Length: 3.15"
Average Wt.: 555 grs.
Type Powder: Nitrocellulose
Type Primer: Boxer (Large Rifle)

BULLET

Type: Soft Point
Diameter: .4115"
Weight: 300 grs.

CARTRIDGE CASE

Length Overall: 2.58"
Diameter at Rim: .543"
Diameter at Base: .461"
Diameter at Mouth: .436"

BALLISTICS (approximate)

Muzzle Velocity: 2200 f.s.
Normal Pressure Level: 40,000 lbs./sq. in.

Notes: Popular European hunting rifle caliber.

.44 Flat

Other Names: .44 Henry Flat
Type: Rimmed, Straight Taper, Rimfire
Overall Length: 1.35"
Average Wt.: 276 grs.
Type Primer: Rim

BULLET

Type: Lead
Diameter: .423"
Weight: 200 grs.

Notes: One of the earliest successful American metallics.

CARTRIDGE CASE

Length Overall: .914"
Diameter at Rim: .523"
Diameter at Base: .445"

BALLISTICS (approximate)

Muzzle Velocity: 1025 f.s.

.45-60 W.C.F.

Type: Rimmed, Necked, Centerfire
Overall Length: 2.25"
Average Wt.: 520 grs.
Type Powder: Black
Approximate Charge: 60 grs.
Type Primer: Boxer

BULLET

Type: Lead, Flat Nose
Diameter: .4575"
Weight: 300 grs.
Length: .76"

CARTRIDGE CASE

Length Overall: 1.89"
Length Head to Shoulder: 1.32"
Length of Shoulder: .12"
Length of Neck: .448"
Diameter at Rim: .629"
Diameter at Base: .507"
Diameter at Neck: .479"
Diameter at Shoulder: .488"

BALLISTICS (approximate)

Muzzle Velocity: 1315 f.s.

.45-70 Government

Other Names: .45-70-405 Carbine Load
Type: Rimmed, Straight Taper, Centerfire
Overall Length: 2.55"
Type Powder: Black
Type Primer: Boxer (Large Rifle)

BULLET

Type: Lead
Diameter: .458"
Weight: 405 grs.

CARTRIDGE CASE

Length Overall: 2.11"
Diameter at Rim: .605"
Diameter at Base: .502"
Diameter at Mouth: .475"

BALLISTICS (approximate)

Muzzle Velocity: 1310 f.s.
Normal Pressure Level: 28,000 lbs./sq. in.

Notes: 1. The present commercial cartridges are loaded with smokeless powder to a pressure safe for use in the old weapons.
2. The military cartridges were originally manufactured with 405 grain bullets for the Carbine and the 500 grain bullets for the rifle.

.45-75 Winchester

Other Names: .45-75 WCF
Type: Rimmed, Necked, Centerfire
Overall Length: 2.25"
Average Wt.: 600 grs.
Type Powder: Black
Approximate Charge: 75 grs.
Type Primer: Boxer

BULLET

Type: Lead, Flat Nose
Diameter: .4575"
Weight: 350 grs.
Length: .90"

CARTRIDGE CASE

Length Overall: 1.88"
Length Head to Shoulder: 1.03"
Length of Shoulder: .300"
Length of Neck: .553"
Diameter at Rim: .629"
Diameter at Base: .566"
Diameter at Neck: .483"
Diameter at Shoulder: .551"

BALLISTICS (approximate)

Muzzle Velocity: 1380 f.s
Pressure: 20,000 lbs./sq. in.

.458 Winchester Magnum

Type: Parallel sided, rimless, belted
Overall length: 3.346"
Type powder: Nitrocellulose
Type primer: Large rifle

BULLET

Type: Jacketed, soft point
Diameter: .459"
Weight: 500 gr.
   510 gr.

CARTRIDGE CASE

Length overall: 2.50"
Rim diameter: .532"
Base diameter: .513"
Belt diameter: .532"
Neck diameter: .4805"

BALLISTICS

Muzzle velocity: 500 gr.—2130 f.p.s.
      510 gr.—2130 f.p.s.
Normal pressure: Approx. 50,000 p.s.i.

7mm Remington Magnum

Type: Necked, rimless, belted
Overall length: 3.290"
Type powder: Nitrocellulose
Type primer: Large rifle

BULLET

Type: Jacketed, soft point
Diameter: .2845"
Weight: 150 gr.
   175 gr.

CARTRIDGE CASE

Length overall: 2.50"
Rim diameter: .532"
Base diameter: .5127"
Belt diameter: .532"
Neck diameter: .276"

BALLISTICS

Muzzle velocity: 150 gr.—3250 f.p.s
      175 gr.—3050 f.p.s.
Normal pressure: Approx. 51,750 p.s.i.

.50-95 Winchester

Other Names: .50-95 W.C.F.
Type: Lead, Flat Nose
Overall Length: 2.26"
Average Wt.: 598 grs.
Type Powder: Black
Approximate Charge: 86 grs.
Type Primer: Boxer (Large Rifle)

BULLET

Type: Lead, Flat Nose
Diameter: .512"
Weight: 300 grs.
Length: .74"

CARTRIDGE CASE

Length Overall: 1.93"
Length Head to Shoulder: 1.42"
Length of Shoulder: .110"
Length of Neck: .398"
Diameter at Rim: .627"
Diameter at Base: .568"
Diameter at Neck: .534"
Diameter at Shoulder: .553"

BALLISTICS (approximate)

Muzzle Velocity: 1520 f.s.

30·'06 Springfield
soft point.

30·'06 Springfield
soft point.

30·'06 Springfield
soft point.

30·'06 Springfield
"Silver Tip."

.30-'06 Springfield
hollow point.

.30-'06 Springfield
hollow point.

.30-'06 Springfield
full jacketed.

.22 Short.

.22 Long.

.22 Long Rifle.

.22 Long Rifle Shot.

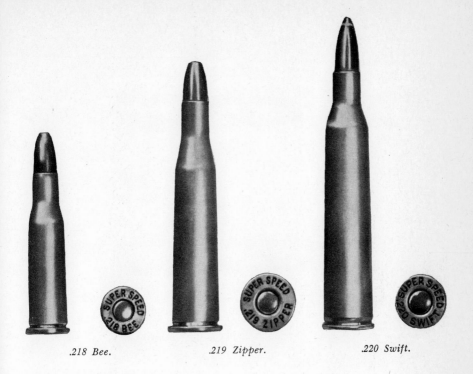

.218 Bee.   .219 Zipper.   .220 Swift.

.22 Hornet.   .22 Hornet.   .22 Savage.

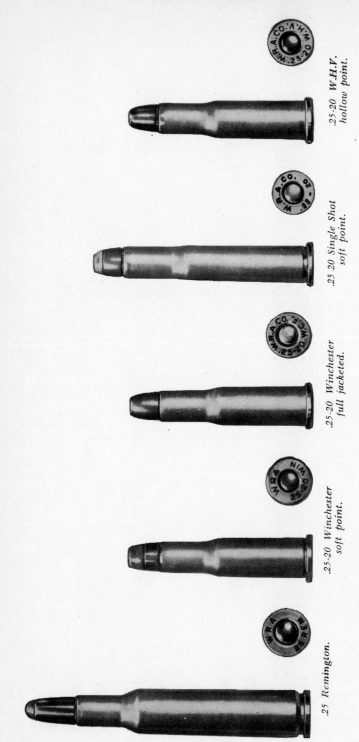

.25-20 W.H.V. hollow point.

.25-20 Single Shot soft point.

.25-20 Winchester full jacketed.

.25-20 Winchester soft point.

.25 Remington.

*.250-3000 Savage
soft point.*

*.250-3000 Savage
hollow point.*

.250 Savage.

*.25-35 Winchester
soft point.*

*.25-35 W.C.F.
full jacketed.*

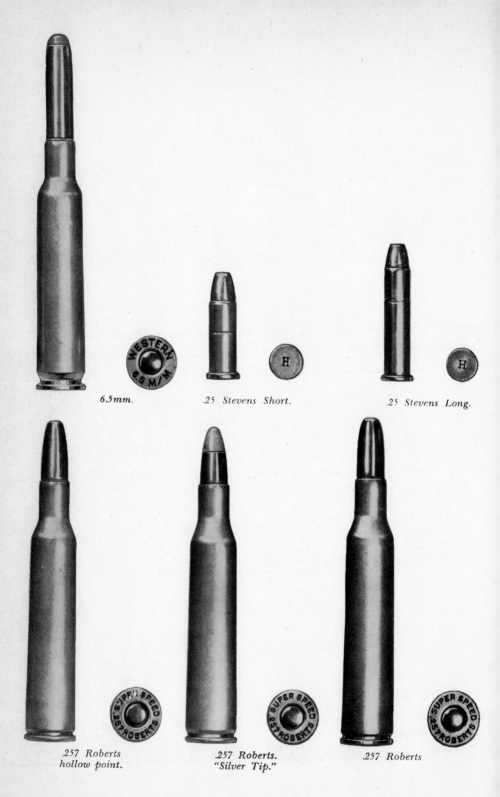

6.5mm.

.25 Stevens Short.

.25 Stevens Long.

.257 Roberts
hollow point.

.257 Roberts.
"Silver Tip."

.257 Roberts

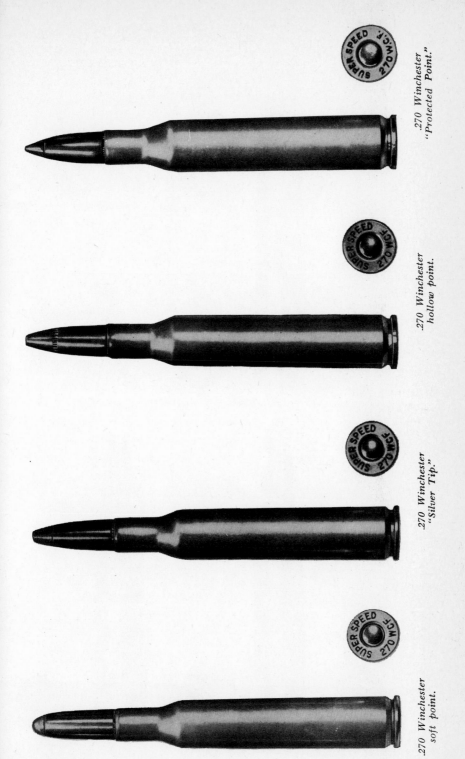

.270 Winchester
"Protected Point."

.270 Winchester
hollow point.

.270 Winchester
"Silver Tip."

.270 Winchester
soft point.

7mm.

.300 Savage
hollow point.

.300 Savage
soft point.

.300 Savage
"Silver Tip."

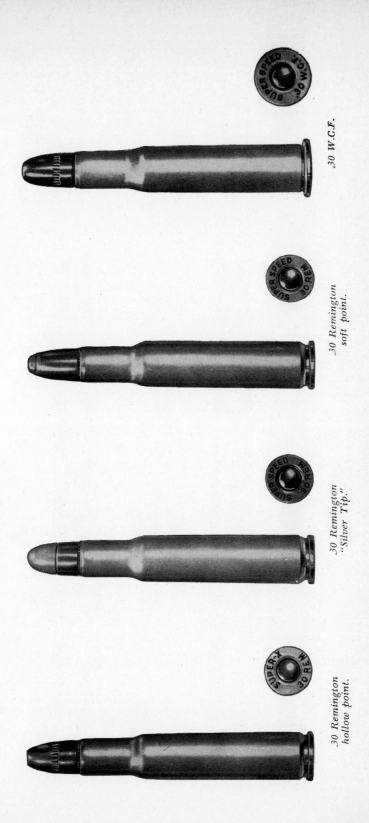

30 W.C.F.

*30 Remington
soft point.*

*30 Remington
"Silver Tip."*

*30 Remington
hollow point.*

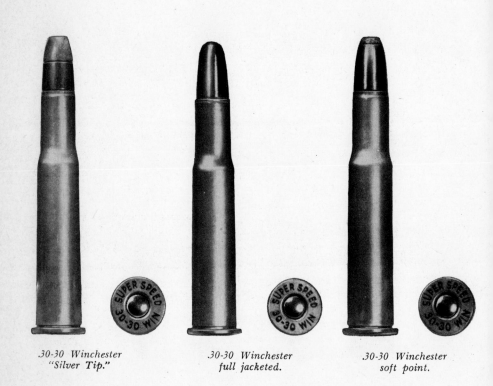

.30-30 Winchester
"Silver Tip."

.30-30 Winchester
full jacketed.

.30-30 Winchester
soft point.

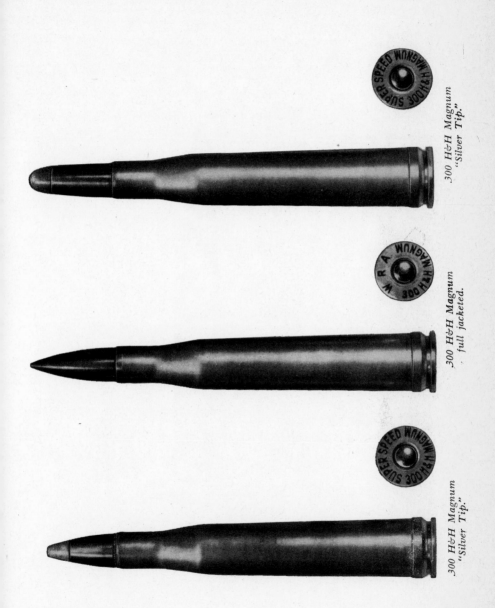

*300 H&H Magnum
"Silver Tip."*

*300 H&H Magnum
full jacketed.*

*300 H&H Magnum
"Silver Tip."*

.303 British.   7.62mm Russian.

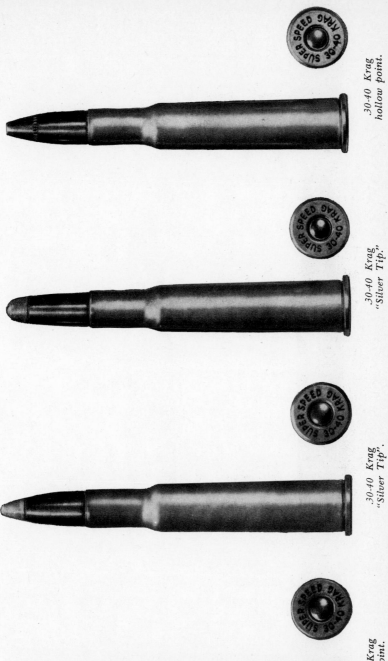

.30-40 Krag
hollow point.

.30-40 Krag
"Silver Tip."

.30-40 Krag
"Silver Tip."

.30-40 Krag
soft point.

8mm soft point.   8mm soft point.

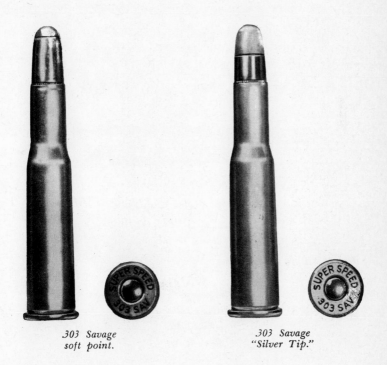

.303 Savage
soft point.

.303 Savage
"Silver Tip."

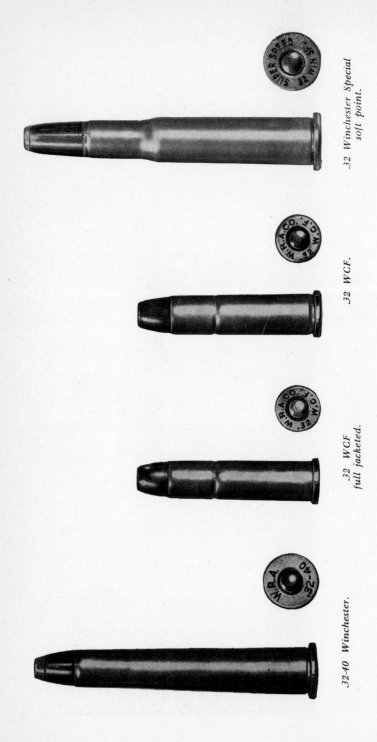

*.32 Winchester Special
soft point.*

.32 WCF.

*.32 WCF
full jacketed.*

.32-40 Winchester.

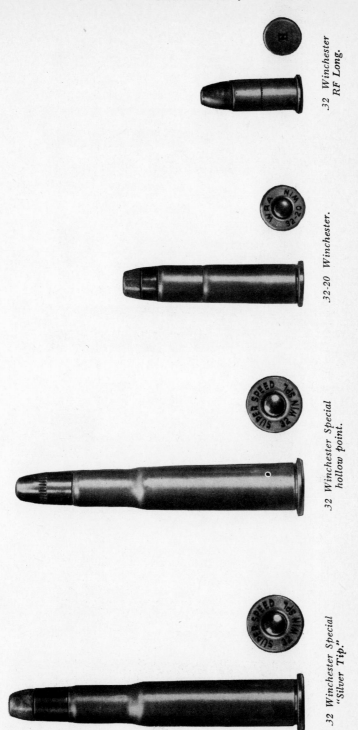

.32 Winchester RF Long.

32-20 Winchester.

.32 Winchester Special hollow point.

.32 Winchester Special "Silver Tip."

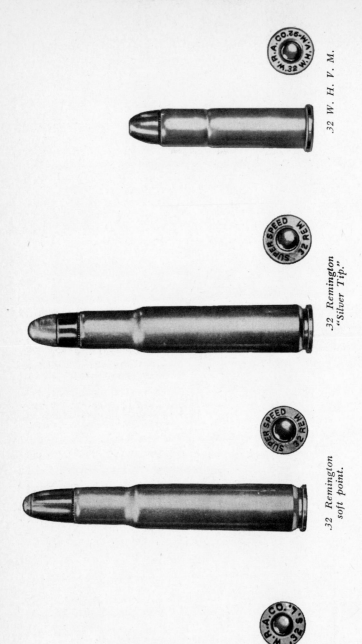

32 W. H. V. M.

32 Remington
"Silver Tip."

32 Remington
soft point.

32 Winchester
Self loading.

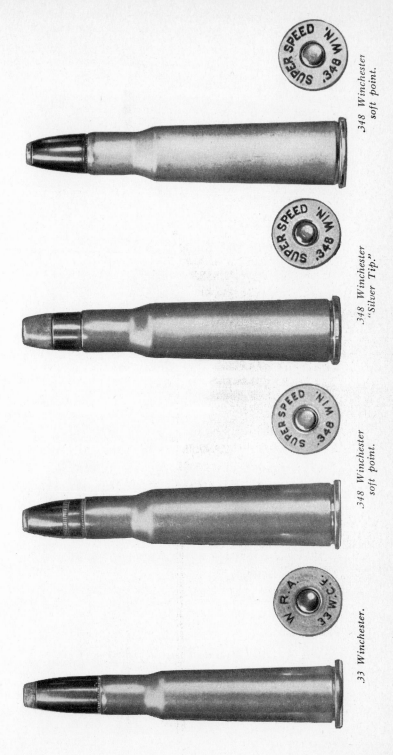

348 Winchester
soft point.

348 Winchester
"Silver Tip."

348 Winchester
soft point.

33 Winchester.

.35 Remington
hollow point

.35 Remington
"Silver Tip."

.35 Remington
soft point.

.35 Winchester.

.35 Winchester.

.351 Winchester
SL full jacketed.

.351 Winchester
SL soft point.

.375 H&H Magnum
hollow point.

.375 H&H Magnum
soft point.

.375 H&H Magnum
"Silver Tip."

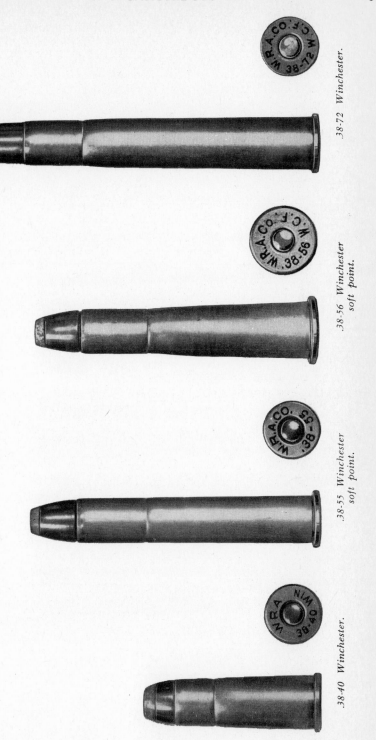

.38-72 Winchester.

.38-56 Winchester
soft point.

.38-55 Winchester
soft point.

.38-40 Winchester.

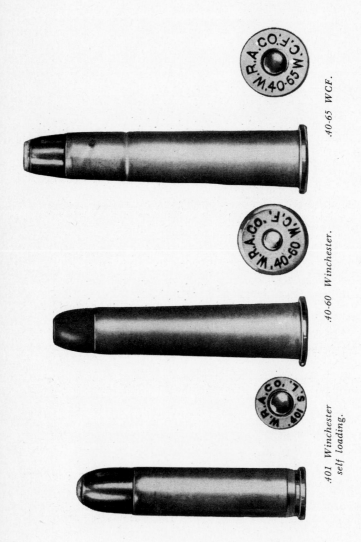

.40-65 WCF.

.40-60 Winchester.

.401 Winchester
self loading.

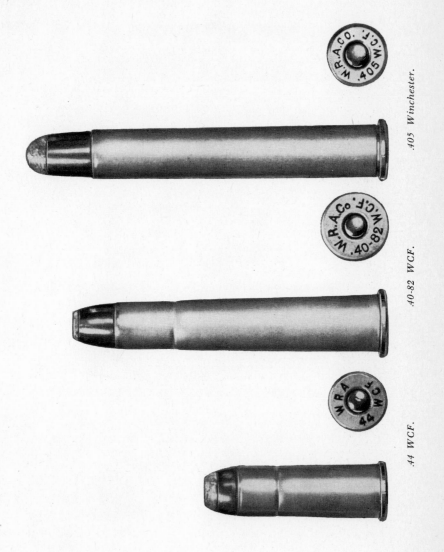

.405 Winchester.

.40-82 WCF.

.44 WCF.

.45-90 Winchester.

.45-75 WCF
full Jacketed.

.45-70 Government.

.45-60 WCF
full Jacketed.

50-95 Winchester.

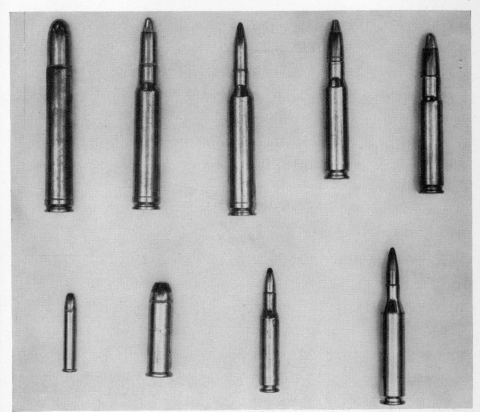

Cartridges Introduced Since World War II. Top row, left to right: *.458 Winchester Magnum, .338 Win. Magnum, .264 Win. Magnum, .308 Win. (7.62mm NATO), .358 Win.* Bottom row, left to right: *.22 Winchester Rimfire Magnum, .44 Magnum, .222 Remington, .243 Winchester.*

Chapter 58
URUGUAY
(Republica Oriental del Uruguay)

PRINCIPAL GOVERNMENT PLANTS: None.

PRINCIPAL PRIVATE PLANTS: Only minor custom makers.

PRINCIPAL MILITARY RIFLES: (1) Model 1895 Mauser, 7mm (Same as Spanish Model of that year). (2) F. N. (Belgian) Mauser 1924, 7mm. (3) Model 1927 Mauser, 7.92mm. Made by Oviedo Arsenal (Spain). This is a very slightly modified German 98 type.

The original 1895 equipment was made in Germany. The F. N. Models were purchased from Belgian because that country took over manufacture of Mauser military rifles after World War I when German manufacture was restricted. The switch to 7.92mm in 1927 on Spanish-made Mausers was in line with policy of other Latin American countries.

EARLIER OFFICIAL BREECHLOADERS: Spanish Remington Single Shot, 11mm.

Chapter 59
VENEZUELA
(Estados Unidos de Venezuela)

PRINCIPAL GOVERNMENT PLANTS: None.

PRINCIPAL PRIVATE PLANTS: None.

PRINCIPAL MILITARY RIFLES (1) 7.62mm F.N. "FAL" Rifle. (2) 7mm F.N. "SAFN"-M1949. (3) F. N. Mausers (Belgian) 1924 and 1924-30 in both 7mm and 7.92mm.

Chapter 60
YUGOSLAVIA
(Jugoslavija)

PRINCIPAL GOVERNMENT PLANTS: Kragujevac.

PRINCIPAL PRIVATE PLANTS: None.

PRINCIPAL MILITARY RIFLES: (1) 7.92mm M1948 Rifle. (2) Puska 7.9mm M24 (Yugoslav Model 1924), basically the same as Czech Model 24.

EARLIER OFFICIAL BREECHLOADERS: Models 1880 and 1881 (Mauser-Milanovic) bolt action single shot, caliber 10.15mm Serbian.

Yugoslav World War II Rifles

The Yugoslavs used every rifle they had or could obtain in World War II. Their standard rifle was the 7.92mm Model 24 and they had these rifles, in quantity, of both Yugoslav and Czech manufacture. In addition they had the Austrian M1890 and M1895 straight pull Mannlicher in the original caliber—8x50mm—and in 7.92mm—M95M. Older rifles such as the Serbian Mausers in 7mm, French M1886 Lebels, M1907/15, and M1916 rifles and carbines were also available. The rebarreled Turkish rifles—M1890, M1893, and later models, were also used by the Yugoslavs.

Since World War II, the Yugoslavs were initially equipped by the Soviets with 7.62mm Mosin Nagant rifles—mainly M1944 carbines and M1891/30 rifles. The Yugoslavs have continued the 7.92mm cartridge as standard and therefore their current standard rifles are the German 7.92mm Kar 98k and the Yugoslav M1948 rifles.

Yugoslav 7.92mm M48

The M48 is similar to the German 7.92mm Kar 98k, but has the M24 type handguard which covers the barrel from the receiver to the upper band.

Caliber: 7.92mm
Overall length (without bayonet): 42.9"
Weight: 8.62 lbs.
Type of action: Turnbolt
Barrel length: 23.3"

Type of magazine: Nondetachable, staggered column box, Capacity: 5 rounds
Sights—front: Hooded blade
rear: Tangent
Type of bolt: 1-piece, rotating head
Muzzle velocity: 2600 f.p.s. (approx.)

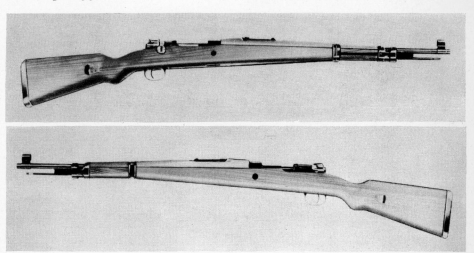

Yugoslav 7.92mm M48 Rifle. This is the current Yugoslav service rifle.

Yugoslavian (Serbia) 10.15mm Mauser M1881 Cartridge

Other Names: 10.15 Mauser Milanovic
Type: Rimmed, Necked, Centerfire, Type A Base
Overall Length: 3.1"

Average Wt.: 663 gr.
Type Powder: Black
Approximate Chg.: 74 gr.
Type Primer: Berdan

BULLET
Type: Lead, Paper Patched
Diameter: .405" (with) .402" (less patch)
Weight: 335.6 gr.
Length: 1.145"

CARTRIDGE CASE
Length Overall: 2.46"
Length Head to Shoulder: 1.65"
Length of Shoulder: .13"

Length of Neck: .68"
Diameter at Rim: .585"
Diameter at Base: .513"
Diameter at Neck: .432"
Diameter at Shoulder: .505"

BALLISTICS (approximate)
Muzzle Velocity: 1872 f.s.
Pressure: About 34,000 lbs./sq. in.

Yugoslavian (Serbian) Model 1878/80 Mauser Milanovic Single Shot (M1880)

Caliber: 10:15mm
Overall length, rifle without bayonet: 50.8"
Overall weight, rifle without bayonet: 9.9 lbs.
Type of action: Turnbolt
Barrel Length: 31.5"   *No. Grooves:* 4

Bore Diameter: .4"   *Groove Dia.:* .413"
Type of Bolt: 2 piece—Rotating Head
  Direction of Twist: Right
  Rate of Twist: 21.6"

Notes:

1. This rifle was listed by Mauser as the Model 78-80 and is essentially the same as the German Mauser Model 1871 with the exception of the bolt sleeve and cocking piece which differ somewhat. Later models were a magazine short rifle and carbine with 7 and 6 round tubular magazines, respectively. These weapons were later converted to 7mm and were known as Model 80/7C.

Other Serbian Mausers

The Serbs used the M1910, M1889, M99/07, M99/08 Mauser Rifles and the M1908 carbine—all in 7mm. The M1910 Mauser was similar to the M1910

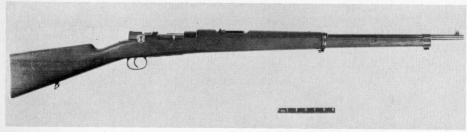

Serbian (Yugoslav) 7mm M99/08 Rifle.

Costa Rican in having a bolt head, barrel, and extractor design which completely enclosed the cartridge head. The other models were similar to the Chilean M95 and were more similar to the Spanish M93 than they were to the German M98. They did, however, have the thumb clearance cut in the left receiver wall to assist in charger loading.

Yugoslav Model 1924 (Puska 7·9mm M 24). (Note: This country was founded after World War I and modern production Mauser manufacture was undertaken in the early 1930's.)

Serbian Model 1910, caliber 7mm. These rifles were made in Germany and Austria.

Chapter 61

AMMUNITION

Introduction

Many military tacticians, Germans in particular, have become convinced that rifle cartridges, such as the .30-06 and 7.92mm, are far more powerful than required. This belief is based on modern battle observations where the rifleman seldom engages the enemy at ranges beyond 300 yards and the machine gunner seldom beyond 500 yards. Using this interpretation as a criterion, cartridges lower in power than the .30-06 and 7.92mm, which are ideal at ranges up to and beyond 500 yards, have been and are still being developed.

Medium-range cartridges, with their accompanying reduction in weight and size, have proved cheaper to manufacture and call for less massive construction in weapons, making feasible the design of assault rifles with a full automatic feature. Furthermore, the soldier is able to carry a proportionately larger quantity of ammunition. An added advantage of medium-range cartridges is lessened recoil permitting greater control during automatic fire and the hastening of marksmanship training of recruits.

Pistol and pistol-type cartridges offered a partial solution to the increased firepower demands. These cartridges permitted the design of the submachine gun which uses the simple blowback principle of operation—a design easy to produce. Even toy manufacturing plants can readily switch over to their production. But the submachine gun firing such cartridges is practical only for short-range work—approximately 50 yards—which is far short of the optimum of approximately 500 yards specified for medium-range cartridges.

During World War II Germany endeavored to give its soldiers greater firepower than the 7.92mm bolt action Mauser rifle delivered. The vast expanse of Russia dictated dispersion of German forces, leaving them particularly vulnerable to mass attack by the Russians. German ordnance technicians attempted to rectify the situation by designing a new medium-range cartridge (the 7.92mm Kurz) and an assault rifle capable of both semi- as well as full automatic fire (the Sturmgewehr). By this radical departure from hitherto conventional rifle and cartridge designs, with their new tactical implications, the Germans created military history, setting the pattern for future developments.

The MP43 cartridge which acquired fame as the 7.92mm Kurz (PP 43 m.e.) consisted of a shortened 7.92mm Mauser case. The Germans set its maximum effective range at 440 yards. The bullet has a gilding metal clad steel jacket, a lead inner sleeve, and a mild steel core.

STATISTICS ON THE GERMAN 7.92mm KURZ CARTRIDGE (pp 43 m.e.)
Length of cartridge: 1.88".
Weight of bullet: 122 grains.
Weight of cartridge: 266.97 grains.
Weight of powder: 24 grains.
Muzzle velocity: 2,247 f.p.s.

As a NATO nation, West Germany has committed herself to the 7.62mm NATO cartridge, but the German military have made no secret of their preference for a medium-type cartridge along the lines of the German 7.92mm Kurz round.

The Russians concurred with the German analysis, borne out by their own World War II experiences, and designed a new medium-range cartridge in 7.62 x 39mm.

In 1951 the United States propounded a contrary view:

"The Army is firmly opposed to the adoption of any less effective smaller caliber cartridge for use in either its present rifle or in the new weapons being developed. Any new rifle cartridge must have wounding power, penetration performance, and ballistics at least equal to that in use today. Battle experience has proven beyond question the effectiveness of the present rifle and ammunition, and there have been no changes in combat tactics that would justify a reduction of rifle caliber and power."

Admittedly, the high-powered cartridge develops stronger recoil and requires bulkier weapons but it has greater range and penetration. It also has much flatter trajectory and, consequently, eliminates to a great extent errors in judging distance by the individual soldier.

.280 vs. T65 Controversy

To understand the controversy which revolved around the .280 cartridge proposed for NATO standardization by the British and the .30 caliber round (experimentally called the T65 whose latest form, T65E3, became famous as the 7.62mm NATO cartridge) advocated by the United States military, it is important to know something of the background and events which affected the slightly different approach to the problem taken by the two countries. The United States' persistence in urging acceptance of the T65 cartridge was predicated on the belief that NATO standardization could best be served by a cartridge equal in power and performance to the U. S. .30 caliber M2 ball round. On the other hand, the English were convinced from their additional years of battle experience that modern warfare did not call for a cartridge superior ballistically to the .303 (best compared with the old U. S. .30-40 Krag round).

When the 1913 bolt action P13 Enfield rifle (known to U. S. shooters as the 1917 Enfield in caliber .30) was produced, it fired a newly-developed, high-velocity, magnum-type 7mm round which the British had designed because of the uneasy feeling that their .303 rimmed cartridge was not sufficiently powerful for military use. This new rifle and cartridge combination was shelved in view of the shaky European situation. A changeover at the time could have been disastrous. Their decision was justified because shortly thereafter England became involved in the First World War. Four years of fighting with the .303 cartridge demonstrated to the British that its power and ballistics were entirely adequate for modern warfare—a conclusion confirmed also by campaigns which followed.

The British would probably not have abandoned the .303 rimmed cartridge if its rimmed design had not proved unsuitable for automatic weapons. For this purpose, another round—the .280—was developed to meet the standards of the General Staff. Ballistically, the .280 proved eminently superior to the .303, giving greater penetration and improved velocity. The latest form uses the FN

Mauser 139-grain bullet with steel jacket, lead core, and flat base which produces a muzzle velocity of 2,530 f.p.s. as compared with 2440 f.p.s. of the .303 with a 174-grain bullet. It is also 18% lighter in weight: 100 rounds weighing 4.5 lbs. as against 5.43 lbs. for the .303. Its overall length of 2.54" is .53" shorter than the .303. The British arrived at the .280 case dimensions by shortening a .30-06 cartridge case to 1.71", necking it down for a 7mm bullet inasmuch as this particular .2856" diameter bullet has long been regarded by many experts as representing the optimum caliber for a military rifle. It develops pressures of approximately 52,000 lbs. per square inch, indicating that with present-day powders the cartridge is loaded to maximum.

The .280 proved more accurate, with light recoil, permitting a very efficient lightweight automatic assault rifle—the EM2—to be designed around it. With the 12-ounce heavier bolt action .30 caliber Lee Enfield rifle, 15 r.p.m. was the aimed rate of fire to be expected, while the .280 EM2 rifle delivered aimed fire of 30-40 r.p.m. With controlled full automatic fire, in aimed bursts of 2-3 shots, 60 r.p.m. was possible. The British were well pleased with the combined performance of the EM2 light automatic rifle and .280 round. The tolerable difference between their round and the U. S. T65 .30 caliber load (for which a weapon had yet to be perfected) made a change in caliber highly impractical for the British.

Comparisons were made between the .280 and the T65. The U. S. claimed flatter trajectory and superior muzzle velocity with its 150-grain bullet at 2,800 f.p.s.; the British 139-grain bullet produced a muzzle velocity of 2,530 f.p.s. From trajectory reports, it has been ascertained that the .30 caliber T65 cartridge with 150-grain, flat base bullet (or the 139-grain, boattail bullet existing at the time of the controversy) had flatter trajectory up to 1,000 yards than the .280 round. Beyond 1,000 yards the .280, because of its better ballistic bullet coefficient, gave superior results. However, the latest T65E3 ball load using 150-grain, boattail bullet (current NATO standard) surpasses the .280.

As a result of high-level conferences between Prime Minister Churchill, President Truman, and other NATO officials, and in the interest of NATO standardization, the adamant attitude of the British military on the subject of the .280 cartridge was reversed and the 7.62mm NATO cartridge was formally adopted September 15, 1955. Even at this late date, the English are reluctant to discuss the dispute to avoid opening old wounds and, consequently, classify detailed information on the .280 and .280/30 as Confidential.

Of special interest to reloaders, an article in the November 1951 issue of the *American Rifleman* magazine described experiments with the .280 round conducted by the capable Tom Florich, Bert Shay, and Phil Sharpe, its author.

Czechoslovakia

The Czech Brno factory, immediately after World War II, introduced a new 7.5mm medium-range cartridge, around which a series of assault-type automatic weapons was designed, the first of which was the ZK 472 rifle. In designing this new cartridge, the Czechs did not resort to shortening their standard 7.92mm Mauser cartridge case, as the Germans did for their 7.92mm Kurz cartridge. Instead, the Czechs produced a totally new case, shorter in length and smaller in diameter than their 7.92mm Mauser round. The smaller diameter

7mm Belgian
NATO case

.224E2
Winchester

.222 Remington
Special

7.92mm
CETME

.280
British

7.62x39mm
Russian M43

7.62x45mm
Czech M52

7.62mm
NATO

Modern Ammunition.

case permitted a reduction in the bulk or width of the weapon using it, something medium-type cartridges, based on standard rifle cartridges such as the .30 caliber U. S. and 7.92mm Mauser rounds, do not allow.

The later form, the Czech 7.62 x 45mm (or .30 caliber) cartridge case is 1.765" long and .443" in diameter, measured at its extreme near the extractor groove. It uses a 131-grain boattail bullet with mild steel core and has a muzzle velocity of approximately 2,450 feet per second. To facilitate smooth chambering of this round, the bullet is seated deeply into the case with a portion of the ogive extending into the neck of the case which is crimped and closed over to conform with the ogive of the bullet. The case is steel with a gray-green lacquered finish, typical of German World War II ammunition. Primer is the conventional European, Berdan-type, measuring 4.5mm in diameter. It has but one flash hole in place of the customary two in the primer pocket.

The 7.62 x 45mm cartridge was dropped in favor of the Soviet 7.62 x 39mm (actually 38.6) round, thus standardizing on ammunition with the Soviets in 1957. The Model 52 rifle and light machine guns were sold together with a large quantity of 7.62 x 45mm ammunition to Syria and figured prominently during the Suez crisis. The Czechoslovakians have been producing the 7.62 x 39mm Russian ammunition for the Model 58 Assault Rifle which is standard issue for Czechoslovakia.

For those reloaders who do not have a sufficient supply of original cases, Italian 6.5mm and 7.35mm brass cases or U. S. .276 Pedersen cases are recommended for reworking.

A careful analysis of ten Czech ball rounds in 7.62 x 45mm has been made which reveals the following data:

Primed case weight: 119.0 grains.
Bullet weight (boattail design, gliding metal clad steel jacket with mild steel core): 131.0 grains.
Powder weight: 27.6 grains
Powder: smokeless, single base, gray-colored, graphite-coated, cylindrical grains, measuring
in length: .018-.060".
in diameter: .015-.023".

Spain

German technicians, who went to work for the CETME organization in Spain, developed for them a lightweight assault rifle, known as the CETME, based on the German Mauser Stg 45 (M) system originating during World War II. Their primary problem was to develop a cartridge, equal ballistically to but with less recoil than the Spanish 7.92mm Mauser rifle and machine gun cartridge, so that the weapon would deliver controlled full automatic fire. The heavy bullet and high velocity of the Spanish 7.92mm Mauser cartridge generated such strong recoil (inherent in all powerful cartridges) as to make its use undesirable for the lightweight CETME Assault Rifle.

Dr. Voss, the noted German ballistician, felt the solution lay in a radically different cartridge. The result of his extensive experiments is the celebrated CETME 7.92mm short round. It has a very long (1.81") lightweight bullet, weighing only 105 grains, and producing a muzzle velocity of 2,689 feet per second. Overall length of the cartridge is 2.95" with short case of approximately 1⅝". The bullet core is aluminum with gilding metal jacket open at both ends.

Designers of this round claim it to be the equal of the Spanish 7.92mm Mauser load up to the range of 1,000 yards. When fired full automatically from the CETME rifle, the resultant light recoil has been compared with firing a 9mm submachine gun.

In 1958, Spain adopted the 7.62mm NATO cartridge, but makes it in a reduced charge for the CETME Assault Rifle. The cartridge in full charge with a long spire pointed bullet is used in the ALFA Model 55 and FAO Model 59 machine guns.

U.S.S.R.

The Russians were deeply impressed by the performance of the 7.92mm Kurz cartridge which the Germans used so effectively during World War II in their Sturmgewehr (assault rifle). The Russians lost little time in initiating experiments to develop a similar cartridge. The result was the rimless 7.62 x 39mm (actually 38.6mm) medium-type cartridge, known in Russian circles as the 7.62mm M43 cartridge. Wartime conditions prevented general issuance of the new cartridge, but shortly after the end of World War II it was introduced to replace their old rimmed 7.62 x 53mm Mosin-Nagant rifle and machine gun round.

The new 7.62 x 39mm cartridge is 27% lighter than its predecessor and is used in the SKS Semiautomatic and AK-47 Assault Rifles, and in the RPD light machine gun. The case is 38.6mm long and is of gilding metal clad, steel construction. For some time now the Russians have discontinued use of brass in rifle and machine gun cartridge cases; even the rimmed, 7.62mm Russian cartridge has a steel case. The case of the Russian 7.62 x 39mm cartridge is shorter than the Czech 7.62 x 45mm case, but both measure .443″ at the extreme diameter near the extractor groove and both have the same body taper. However, the rear of the Russian case has a smaller extractor groove and a larger rim diameter. (Attention: Reloaders—The cases most closely approximating the new Soviet round and best suited to re-working are the Italian 6.5mm and 7.35mm brass cases or the U. S. .276 Pedersen.)

The 7.62mm Russian boattail ball bullet weighs 122 grains and develops a muzzle velocity of 2,411 f.p.s. in the SKS Semiautomatic Rifle and 2,329 f.p.s. in the AK Assault Rifle. Greater velocity with the SKS is attributable to a 5″ longer barrel than on the AK. The ball cartridge has a mild steel core. The Soviets have designed outstanding special-purpose rounds, such as A.P.-Incendiary, Tracer, and Tracer-Incendiary; they are not only designed for maximum performance but also incorporate new features for ease in bullet manufacture.

As one indication of the stimulated interest in this new Russian short round, the SIG Company of Switzerland is offering its SG510 Assault Rifle in 7.62 x 39mm.

The CETME organization has also offered the CETME rifle in caliber 7.62 x 39mm.

The Finnish version of the Russian 7.62 x 39mm short round manufactured by the Lapua factory has a brass case. The bullet weighs 124 grains and has a gilding metal jacket with lead core. Bullet base is deeply concave. Powder charge weighs 26.5 grains. The cartridge develops a maximum chamber pressure of 45,500 pounds per square inch and attains a muzzle velocity of 2,374 f.p.s.

The Dutch firm of Nederlandsche Wapen en Munitiefabriek N.V. "De Kruithoorn" (NWM) is another European factory manufacturing 7.62 x 39mm Russian ammunition. It is produced in three different bullet weights: (1) a copy of the Russian ball round with soft steel core; (2) an A.P. round weighing 122.6 grains of their own design; and (3) another design of NWM, a ball round with lead core and gilding metal jacket weighing 151 grains (the resultant muzzle velocity of 2,428 exceeds 7.62 x 39mm cartridges manufactured elsewhere, including Russia).

Trajectory of Russian 7.62 x 39mm ball cartridge fired from an SKS rifle zeroed-in at 300 meters (or 328 yards):

METERS

Distance	At Muzzle	25	50	100	150	200	250	300
Trajectory (in inches)..	0	2.2	5.1	9.3	11.7	11.0	7.6	0

From this trajectory curve it is obvious that the Russian 7.62 x 39mm cartridge has been efficiently designed for medium ranges.

CHARACTERISTICS OF RUSSIAN 7.62 x 39mm M43 AMMUNITION

Type	Bullet Weight (in grains)	Length of Bullet (in inches)	Diameter (in inches)	Powder Weight (in grains)	Weight of Complete Rd. (in grains)	Length of Cartridge (in inches)	Color Identification on tip of Bullet	Type Designation
Ball	122.6	1.047	.310	24.2	256.79	2.18	none	Ps
Tracer	117.5	1.094	.310	24.5	240.74	2.18	green	T-45
Tracer-Incendiary	102.6	1.094	.310	24.7	239.81	2.18	red	Z
A.P.-Incendiary	118.7	1.078	.310	24.1	251.54	2.18	black & red	Bz

United States

Ballisticians and handloaders have long known that it is possible to reduce the M1906 cartridge case and load it with sufficient powder to give the U. S. .30 caliber M2 152-grain ball bullet the same velocity as achieved originally. The M1906 .30 caliber M2 ball cartridge with 152-grain bullet develops 2,800 f.p.s. at pressures as low as 42,000 pounds per square inch—a clear indication that this load is not at its usable potential inasmuch as bullet velocity could safely be increased to 3,000 f.p.s. at working pressures not exceeding 50,000 pounds per square inch.

The question has been asked, "Why not increase velocity?" Of course it can be done, but to do so would affect bullet trajectory, making necessary new sights for millions of rifles and machine guns which the United States has in service and in reserve. The task of changing these sights would be an enormous undertaking and very expensive. The U. S. Army is of the opinion that the ballistics of the M2 ball round in its present form are entirely adequate and, therefore, see no reason for increasing its velocity.

The cartridge which influenced the early designs leading to the eventual origination of the 7.62mm NATO round was the .300 Savage Sporting Cartridge. This shorter version of the .30-06 was developed back in the

20's by the Savage Company in an effort to approximate the ballistics of the
.30-06. It was advertised as achieving a muzzle velocity of 2,700 f.p.s. with a
150-grain bullet. A case similar to the Savage .300 formed the basis, late in 1946,
for initial U. S. experiments to develop a short .30 caliber round to replace the
M2 cartridge. As a ball load, it was called T65—the first in a series bearing this
designation. Since it has a .015" larger shoulder diameter than the .300 Savage,
resulting in less body taper, it cannot be chambered in the Savage rifle.

In time, a .30 caliber short round was developed by U. S. Ordnance which
was to become widely known as the 7.62mm NATO cartridge. It has an overall
length of 2.80" as compared to 3.34" of the M2 round, a difference of 1/2".
The length of the NATO case is 2.015" (51.18mm); the M2 case measures
2.5" (63.0mm). Considering the billions of rounds of rifle cartridges produced
for war, the shorter length of the 7.62mm NATO round represents a substantial
saving in a critical material, brass. Additionally, the shorter case permits a pro-
portionate reduction in the mechanism of the weapon and, of course, in its
weight.

Ordnance history will probably record the development of the 7.62mm
NATO round by Frankford Arsenal as one of the most concentrated scientific
efforts ever directed toward the development of a cartridge. Millions of rounds
were tested in experimental form before a final selection was made. It would
take volumes to describe the variations and experiments in bullets, loadings,
cases, etc., a chore for which only Frankford Arsenal is fitted, but their outstanding characteristics are represented by three distinct case lengths, the first
of which was, apparently, not given an experimental designation. However, as
a ball round, it was called the T65 (in A.P., T90, etc.) and, although T65 has
become a generic term when referring to the entire series of experimental
designs from which the NATO round evolved, this particular .300 Savage-type
case, for identification purposes, is being called the original T65.

The second distinct change in case length was the T65EI. Its case neck was
lengthened by .08" over the original T65 to give greater support to the bullet,
and extractor groove width was increased to .060".

The third and longest case was called the T65E3 developed in 1949. This
case was used for the famous NATO round. The M59 is a boat-tailed, mild
steel cored ball; its alternate is the M80, a boat tail with lead core. The muzzle
velocity of the M80 is 2,750 f.p.s. taken 78 feet from muzzle. The maximum
pressure is 50,000 lbs. per square inch. Ball powder is the propellant, the
average charge weighing 47 grains. Of course, the chief advantages of ball
powder are that it is cooler burning, cheaper and easier to produce, and increases
barrel life.

NATO-produced ammunition is distinguished by the manufacturer's mark
and year of manufacture; the headstamp also carries the NATO standardization
imprint in the form of a circle divided by a cross into four equal parts.

BULLET TIP MARKING

Ball: None	Incendiary: Blue
Tracer: Red	A.P.-Incendiary: Silver
A.P.: Black	Observing: Yellow

APPENDIX I.

GLOSSARY

A

ABRASION. In the bore: 1. Scratches caused by using improper cleaning materials, or by firing ammunition with bullets to which abrasive material was adhering. 2. Normal enlargement of the bore and wearing away of lands due to the abrasive action of the bullets. See *Corrosion, Erosion, Fouling,* and *Leading.*

ACCELERATOR. 1. A device used in some automatic and semiautomatic weapons to accelerate the rearward travel of the bolt or breechblock by applying leverage at the critical point in the bolt's travel. 2. Any device or linkage designed to speed the movement of some portion of the mechanical train.

ACTION. 1. The assembly of moving parts in a gun which (1) feed the cartridge into the chamber from the magazine (in a revolver, move a loaded chamber into position for firing), (2) seal and lock the chamber, (3) fire the cartridge, (4) unseal and unlock the chamber and extract the fired cartridge case, and (5) eject the empty case. The term is also loosely applied to the fixed housing: i. e., the *Receiver* or *Frame* in which the action operates.

2. SINGLE ACTION. A weapon in which the hammer must be cocked before pressure on the trigger will fire the gun. Each act (cocking hammer and pressing trigger) is distinct from the other.

3. DOUBLE ACTION. (1) A type of firing mechanism in a revolver by means of which a continuous pull on the trigger will (a) revolve the cylinder, placing a cartridge in position to fire, (b) cock the hammer, (c) release the hammer and fire the gun. The trigger must then be released and permitted to return fully forward; after which the cycle may be repeated. Alternatively, most double action arms may be cocked by drawing back the hammer (by pressing on the hammer itself, not on the trigger) to full-cock position, where it will remain until released by pressure on the trigger. (2) Some autoloading pistols are equipped with a type of double-action trigger which goes through the cycle of cocking and firing the first shot by continuous pressure on the trigger, but does not move a new cartridge from the magazine into the chamber.

4. BOLT ACTION. That type of breech closure which is accomplished by the longitudinal movement of the breech block (bolt) in line with the bore. Bolt actions are broadly classified as: A. TURN-BOLT ACTIONS. That type which is locked by the turning of one or more bolt locking lugs into locking recesses cut into the receiver. B. STRAIGHT-PULL ACTIONS. That type in which the rotary motion required to turn the bolt locking lugs into or out of engagement with their locking recesses is applied by the action of studs on the bolt sliding in helical grooves cut inside a bolt

cylinder. C. CAMMING-LUG BOLTS. That type which employs one or more bolt locking lugs which are cammed outward from the interior of the bolt cylinder to engage in their locking recesses and are retracted into the bolt cylinder to unlock the action. D. WEDGE-TYPE BOLTS. That type which employs a ramp or cam arrangement to raise, lower, or move to either side, one end of the bolt so that the end of the bolt or a lug thereon is wedged against a supporting surface in the receiver to lock the action.

5. RECOIL OPERATED. As pertains to automatic and semiautomatic arms, a weapon in which the barrel and breechblock are locked together at the instant of firing. As the bullet leaves the barrel, the rearward thrust of the powder gases starts the locked barrel and bolt to the rear. After a short travel, the barrel strikes an abutment, or is otherwise halted, and its locking device is withdrawn from the slide, breechblock, or bolt, which continues to the rear to eject the fired case and prepare for the reloading motion. (a) In short-recoil weapons the barrel travels to the rear, locked to the breech, only three-quarters of an inch or less. (b) In long-recoil weapons the barrel remains locked to the breech for the full distance of the recoil stroke. The barrel is then unlocked and thrust forward, the bolt is held back, ejection is accomplished, and the chamber is reloaded. Recoil-operated actions are not to be confused with blow-back actions, which are fired without the mechanical locking of the barrel and breechblock.

6. BLOWBACK. As pertains to automatic and semiautomatic arms, a weapon in which no mechanical locking system is employed. The breech is held closed at the moment of firing by the action of recoil springs and the weight of the slide, hammer, and other moving parts. The weight of these parts is so much greater than the weight of the bullet that the expanding powder gases drive the bullet out of the barrel before the inertia of the breech action has been appreciably overcome; then the breechblock action is blown backward by residual pressure.

7. DELAYED BLOWBACK. Sometimes called hesitation locking. The breech, although not positively locked, must overcome a mechanical disadvantage, such as a knuckle joint, to open.

8. BLOW FORWARD. An automatic or semiautomatic arm having a standing breech, in which the barrel is blown forward to open the action and eject the fired cartridge case. The barrel is then forced back against the standing breech by a powerful spring. The gun is cocked and reloaded as the barrel is forced to the rear.

9. SLIDE ACTION. That type of breech closure which is accomplished through an operating rod attached to a movable fore-end which is moved forward and backward along guideways paralleling the lower side of the barrel. The operating rod is properly linked to the breechblock to provide the desired opening and closing action.

10. PUMP ACTION. Popular term for slide action.

11. LEVER ACTION. That type of breech closure actuated by a lever suitably linked to the breechblock to provide the desired opening and closing action. The lever is usually mounted under the receiver so as to

form the triggerguard and is then extended to the rear along the small of the stock or pistol grip.

12. DROP-BLOCK ACTION. That type of action in which the breechblock rises and falls vertically in cuts in the receiver side walls. Lever actuated as a rule.

13. ROLLING BLOCK ACTION. That type of action in which the breechblock rotates about an axis pin downward and backward from the chamber. Actuated by a thumb lever on top of the rolling block or by a lever.

14. FALLING BLOCK ACTION. That type of action in which the breechblock is pivoted at the rear of the receiver so that the face of the breechblock swings down below the chamber to open the action. Lever actuated.

15. HINGED FRAME ACTION. That type of action utilizing a standing breech with the barrel or barrels carrying a fore-end and hinged to the receiver in such fashion that when the action is unlocked the barrel muzzle swings down, elevating the chamber above the line of the standing breech for extraction and loading. A variety of locking devices are employed to hold the rear of the chamber firmly against the standing breech when the action is closed. Generally actuated by a thumb lever on top of the frame at the rear of the standing breech. Finger levers sometimes used.

ADAPTER. A device designed to alter the use of functioning of a weapon usually to permit practice with less expensive ammunition of smaller caliber.

AMMUNITION. The bullet, propellant, igniter (primer), and cartridge case required to fire a gun. In modern small arms usage—cartridges.

ANVIL. A firm, fixed point against which the explosive primer mixture is compressed by the action of the firing pin or striker in a gun. In the Berdan-type primer, the anvil is in the head of the cartridge case, forming a projection in the center of the primer pocket. In the American-type (Boxer) primer, the anvil is a small arbor of metal fastened rigidly across the primer cup over the explosive pellet. In rim-fire cartridges there is no true anvil; the anvil is formed by the rear face of the barrel, which serves as the stop and resting place for the rim of the cartridge when it is inserted in the chamber. Thus, the anvil may be found (1) in the primer cup, (2) in the head of the cartridge case, or (3) in the gun.

APERTURE SIGHT. See *Sights* 2 (c).

ARMORY. 1. A manufacturing place for the production of weapons; as "Springfield Armory."

2. A building designed for the proper storage or display of weapons or both.

ARQUEBUS. See *Harquebus*

ARSENAL. A manufacturing place for the production of ordnance materiel, as "Frankford Arsenal." Often used interchangeably with Armory.

ASSEMBLY. Any collection of parts operating together which are housed to form a single unit; as "magazine assembly," "bolt assembly," etc.

AUTOLOADING. A weapon which, being manually loaded and fired for the first shot, will eject the fired cartridge case, load the next cartridge from the magazine, and cock the gun ready for refiring. Pressure on the trigger must be released after each shot and reapplied to fire the succeeding shot. The ejection and reloading operations are performed by utilizing the forces of gas expansion, recoil, and mechanical spring action. Semi-automatic. Self-loading.

AUTOMATIC. As applied to small arms, a weapon which, being manually loaded and fired for the first shot, will eject the fired case, load the next cartridge from the magazine, fire and eject that cartridge, and repeat the process indefinitely so long as the initial pressure is maintained on the trigger, or until the cartridge supply in the magazine has been exhausted. The ejection, loading, and firing operations are performed by utilizing the forces of gas pressure, recoil, and mechanical spring action.

The term is generally, though incorrectly, applied to semiautomatic or autoloading arms. The classic example of the misapplication of the term is the designation of the Colt, caliber .45, Model 1911, as the "Automatic Colt Pistol" (".45 A.C.P.")

AUTOMATIC SAFETY. See *Mechanical Safety.*

B

BACKLASH. 1. Excess motion in linked mechanical parts. Generally applied to the continued rearward travel of the trigger beyond the point where the firing pin, or hammer, has been released to fire the weapon.

2. Also commonly referred to in connection with the failure of sight-adjusting screws to move the sight positively the proper distance for each rotation of the adjusting screw.

BALL. A bullet. A hangover from the days when a round ball was the only projectile used in firearms. Today, ball ammunition is any ammunition loaded with a single projectile, regardless of the shape of that projectile. See *Cartridge 2.*

BALLISTIC DRIFT. See *Drift 2.*

BALLISTICS. The study of bullets in flight and of the action of their propellants.

1. Exterior ballistics cover the flight of the bullet after it leaves the muzzle of the gun.

2. Interior ballistics have to do with the explosion of the primer, the ignition and burning of the propellant powder, internal pressures, and the stresses, strains, and torques resulting as the bullet is forced through the barrel.

BARLEYCORN. An inverted "V" type front sight.

BARREL. 1. The steel tube in a gun through which the bullet is driven by the explosion of the propellant charge.

2. Subcaliber Barrel. A barrel of smaller caliber inserted down the bore or mounted over the barrel of a large-caliber gun, permitting it to be used for practice work with less powerful, cheaper ammunition. Generally called a "sub-caliber tube."

BARREL BAND. A metal band holding together the barrel and stock.

BATTERY CUP. The pocket in the head of center-fire cartridge cases in which the primer seats. See *Anvil* and *Cartridge 5.*

BLACK POWDER. See *Powder 2.*

BLANK CARTRIDGE. See *Cartridge 3.*

BLOWBACK. 1. A term commonly used to describe the backward escape of powder or primer gases from the chamber around the breechblock or bolt due to a split or fractured cartridge case or punctured primer. 2. A type of action. See *Action 6.*

BLOW FORWARD. See *Action 8.*

BLOWN PRIMER. A primer blown loose from its seat in the battery cup by the action of the powder or primer gases. Sometimes improperly applied to a punctured primer.

BOLT. As applied to bolt-action weapons the bolt is the cylindrical or oblong block of steel which is so designed that it may be pushed forward and locked (or held in its closed position by spring action) so as to seal the breech for firing, then withdrawn so as to permit the ejection of the fired cartridge case and the loading of another cartridge. A type of breechblock which opens and closes the breech by moving forward and backward in the receiver. See *Action 4.* The rear section of a pistol slide.

BOLT ACTION. See *Action 4.*

BOLT CYLINDER. 1. In a two-piece bolt the rear, cylindrical portion into which the bolt head slides and to which the bolt handle is attached. 2. In a one-piece bolt the main body of the bolt carrying the locking lugs and bolt handle and enclosing the mainspring and striker.

BOLT FACE. The forward end of the bolt against which the base of the chambered cartridge rests.

BOLT SLEEVE. That unit of the bolt assembly which fits into, or over the rear of the bolt cylinder, the firing pin or striker passing from the bolt cylinder through the bolt sleeve to its anchorage in the cocking piece.

BOLT STOP. A projecting metal surface which halts the rearward travel of the bolt.

BOMBARDELLE. One of the earliest forms of hand arms (about 1380) consisting of a short, muzzle loading barrel with touch hole, attached to a short, straight rod longitudinal with the bore.

BORE. 1. The hole bored lengthwise through the gun barrel from the chamber to the muzzle. 2. Sometimes used descriptively in lieu of gauge or caliber as "a 12-bore gun," "a .410 bore gun."

BORE DIAMETER. In a rifled arm the diameter of the bore prior to rifling, i.e., the diameter of the bore measured from the top of a land to the top of the opposite land.

BORE SIGHTING. Adjusting the gunsights by sighting through the gun bore at a target, holding the gun rigidly in that position, then aligning the gunsights.

BOTTLENECK. See *Case 2.*

BREECH. 1. The rear face of the barrel. 2. Often loosely applied to the entire chamber, breech and receiver portion of a gun as "open the breech," "there is a cartridge stuck in the breech" etc.

3. STANDING BREECH. When a receiver is not cut away at its rear to a point below the line of the gun bore the solid rear wall of the receiver is the "standing breech." In the case of hinged frame weapons

the solid rearward portion of the frame (receiver) against which the heads of the chambered cartridges rest after the gun has been closed and locked is the "standing breech." In a revolver or single shot pistol that section of the frame which supports the head of the cartridges in the cylinder or chamber is the "standing breech."

BREECHBLOCK. That part of the action which, being moved into position and locked by any one of several means, supports the head of the cartridge in the chamber of the gun so that the case may form an effective gas seal when the weapon is fired. Although the bolt is a "breechblock" it is not generally so called. In modern usage the term is generally reserved for breech closures which swing up, down or to the side or slide up and down in the receiver.

BREECHLOADER. A gun loaded from the rear, or breech end. All modern weapons are breechloaders.

BREECH PRESSURE. See *Pressure 2*.

BROWNING. A chemical process for coloring barrels and receivers. Often used to mean bluing.

BUFFER. A part intended to absorb shock or check recoil.

BULLET. 1. A projectile fired from a gun.

2. ARMOR-PIERCING BULLET. A bullet having a hard metal core so supported by a short metal envelope and by the bullet jacket that, when the bullet strikes armor, stopping the jacket and envelope, the armor-piercing core continues forward and penetrates the armor.

3. DUMDUM BULLET. "Dumdum" is an out-moded and generally misused term. It was an unofficial name first applied to hollow point bullets made at the British Arsenal at Dumdum, India. Gradually, the term came to be applied to any expanding-point bullet. None of today's expanding-point bullets are properly called dumdum.

4. HOLLOW POINT. A bullet with a cavity in the nose designed to increase the expansion when it hits. Now mostly obsolete except in .22 rim-fire cartridges.

5. INCENDIARY BULLET. A bullet containing an incendiary mixture or compound, which will create a fire on impact.

6. JACKETED bullets have a gilding metal, soft steel, cupro-nickel, or other tough metal envelope surrounding the lead core.

7. LEAD bullets are actually a mixture of lead and one or more hardening ingredients.

8. METAL-CASED BULLET. Colloquially used to indicate either a metal-patched or full-metal-patched bullet.

9. METAL PATCHED BULLET. Loosely, any metal-jacketed bullet. (a) Technically, a bullet having a metal cup over the base and extending forward over that portion of the bullet which bears against the rifling, the lead core being exposed at the nose of the bullet. The term "metal patched" originated when thin metal was substituted for the parchment-paper patches first used on lead bullets to protect the base from the heat of heavy charges of black powder or the early smokeless loads. There have been exceptions to the above rule in which the metal patch covered only the nose of the bullet and did not engage the rifling. (b) A bullet

on which the metal jacket covers the nose and is crimped over the core at the base is technically a full-metal patched (F.M.P.) bullet.

10. MUSHROOM BULLET. Colloquially, any bullet designed to expand on impact. Technically, a metal-patched bullet with exposed rounded nose. Suitable only for use in weapons of comparatively low velocity.

11. STEEL JACKETED BULLET. Bullets having a soft steel jacket, often clad or plated with gilding metal to prevent rusting and reduce frictional resistance in the bore.

12. TRACER BULLET. A bullet containing a substance inside the jacket at the base of the bullet which is ignited when fired showing a brilliant "taillight" during its flight. Tracer bullets have an incendiary effect if they strike before the "taillight" has burned out.

13. WAD-CUTTER bullets are bullets with a square shoulder at or near the nose, to cut a clean round hole in paper targets.

BUSHING. A detachable metal lining. In a gun, a bushing is commonly a very thin metal ring used around another part to provide a better fit than direct machining can readily accomplish; or to provide a bearing surface.

BUTT. 1. In a shoulder arm the rearmost face of the stock. Often used to indicate the butt stock. 2. In a handgun the bottom of the grip. Thus some revolvers are said to have a "square butt" others a "round butt." Often used to indicate that entire part of the handgun which is held in the hand. See *Grip* and *Stock*.

BUTT PLATE. A protective plate fastened to the butt.

BUTT STOCK. That portion of the stock extending from the receiver rearward and ending in the butt.

BUTTS. 1. In target shooting, a term now generally applied to the entire area in which the targets are mounted, including the parapet or pit protecting the markers, the targets, and the target frames. To "go down to the butts" is to go to the end of the range where the targets are mounted.

2. In its ancient form, the painted wooden target and the earthen bank against which the target was placed.

C

CALIBER. 1. The distance across the bore of a weapon, measured from land to land. In the United States and Great Britain, usually measured in hundredths or thousandths of an inch; as "caliber .22," "caliber .455." In Europe and Asia, normally expressed in millimeters; as "8mm." The caliber used to designate the weapon commercially may be, and usually is, a somewhat arbitrary figure not necessarily within several thousandths of an inch of the real diameter.

2. Ballistically, the term caliber is also used as a convenient means of expressing comparative dimensions. A bullet may be said to have a length of "three calibers," meaning that its length is three times its diameter.

CANNELURE. An indented ring or groove around a cartridge case or bullet.

CAP. See *Primer 2*.

CARBINE. A short rifle, usually with a barrel length of less than 22 inches.

CARTRIDGE. 1. In small-arms parlance, a complete round of fixed ammunition (see *Ammunition*) consisting of (1) the case, in which are inserted (2) the primer, (3) the powder, and (4) the bullet.

2. A BALL CARTRIDGE is any cartridge loaded with a single projectile.

3. A BLANK CARTRIDGE is a cartridge consisting of the case with its primer, a charge of powder, and a wad to retain the powder. No bullet is contained in this type of cartridge, but the wads will cause painful injuries or death at short range.

4. BELTED CARTRIDGE. A cartridge which has a raised belt before the extractor groove. The cartridge seats on this belt; most "Magnum" cartridges are belted.

5. CENTER-FIRE CARTRIDGE. A cartridge in which the primer is contained in a small metal cup placed in a receptacle in the center of the head of the cartridge case.

6. GUARD CARTRIDGE is one loaded with buckshot, or a reduced charge ball.

7. RIM-FIRE CARTRIDGE. A cartridge made of soft ductile metal, often copper, in which the priming mixture is inserted inside the rim at the head of the case. The powder is then loaded into the case, abutting the primer. Thus, when the firing pin strikes the rim of the cartridge at any point on its circumference, the priming is exploded and the powder ignited.

8. SEMI-RIMMED CARTRIDGE. A cartridge having a shallow extractor groove and a rim projecting only slightly beyond the diameter of the body of the cartridge case. A compromise between rimmed and rimless cartridge cases.

9. RIMLESS CARTRIDGE. A cartridge having an extraction groove, or cannelure, around its circumference near the head, so that the head of the case is of the same diameter as the body, with no projecting rim, or flange. Rimless cartridges are all of the center-fire type.

10. RIMMED CARTRIDGE. A cartridge having a head larger than its body, forming a rim or flange around the circumference. This rim serves as a means of preventing the cartridge from entering too deeply into the chamber, and provides a surface which can be gripped by the extractor claw. Rimmed cartridges may be either of the rim-fire or center-fire type.

11. A SHOT CARTRIDGE is a metallic cartridge loaded with small shot.

12. A SIGNAL CARTRIDGE is one containing vari-colored luminous balls of the "roman candle" variety.

CARTRIDGE CLIP. 1. A sheet-metal box, open top and bottom, of the proper size to fit into the magazine well of a repeating arm. It is filled with cartridges and inserted into the magazine well. The cartridges are fed directly from the clip into the chamber of the gun. The clip is automatically ejected from the weapon as the last cartridge feeds into the chamber. This is the Mannlicher system.

2. A CLIP of spring metal, usually brass, so formed as to grip the rims of the exact number of cartridges required to fill the magazine of the weapon. A loaded cartridge clip is placed in proper guides at the

top of the magazine and the cartridges are stripped from the clip into the magazine by steady downward pressure of the thumb or fingers. The empty clip in some cases is manually removed and in other cases is knocked away by the closing of the bolt as the first round is fed into the chamber. Technically, this type of cartridge clip is a "charger" but American usage labels it a "cartridge clip." This is the Mauser system.

3. A spare magazine for weapons having a removable magazine into which cartridges are manually loaded by the shooter. This is an improper use of the term clip, as such accessories are, in fact, magazines; but the improper usage is a common one.

4. Revolver Clips are not common but two types are used to a limited extent. The more important is the half-moon-shaped piece of flat metal used to hold the rims of three caliber .45 model 1911 rimless cartridges so that the rimless cartridges may be used in the U. S. Model 1917 revolver. The extractor grooves of three cartridges are slipped into semi-circular cutouts on the inner circumference of the half-moon strip which holds the cartridges friction tight. Each clip holds the cartridges for one half the cylinder, two clips being required each time the gun is loaded. The second type of revolver clip is also a flat metal strip but is a complete circle with holes properly spaced and of the correct diameter to hold a cylinder full of rimmed cartridges. The idea was to speed up loading by inserting all six cartridges at one time. This clip never worked well and is almost never seen. Linked flexible clips exist but are not common or practical.

CASE. 1. The main body of the cartridge; the container in which the other elements of the cartridge are held. Cases may be of steel or aluminum but are usually of copper in rim-fire cartridges, of brass in center-fire cartridges. Often improperly called the "shell."

2. A Bottleneck Case has a body larger in diameter than the caliber of the arm, the forward portion of the case being reduced in diameter (necked down) to hold the bullet. Shaped like a bottle.

3. Ruptured Case. (1) A cartridge from which the head has been ripped during discharge. (2) Loosely, any cartridge case which has been split in firing so that gas has escaped. See *Crimp* and *Cartridge*.

CENTER-FIRE CARTRIDGE. See *Cartridge 5*.

CHAMBER. That portion of the rear end of the barrel which receives and supports the cartridge when the breech has been closed. The chamber must aline the bullet with the bore, and the primer with the firing pin.

CHAMBER PRESSURE. See *Pressure 2*.

CHARGE. Generally means the weight and type of powder in the cartridge cases. Can also mean the weight and type of explosive in the primer.

CHARGER. See *Cartridge Clip 2*.

CHRONOGRAPH. An instrument for measuring and recording the time required for a projectile to pass between two predetermined points thereby indicating the average velocity between those two points.

CLIP. See *Cartridge Clip*.

CLIP GUIDES. Slots machined into the slides of some weapons (like the Military Steyr) or in the barrel extension (as in the Military Mauser) or in the receiver (as in the U. S. Springfield rifle) to permit the insertion of the edges of the cartridge clip or charger and to hold it firmly for loading.

COMB. The upper edge of the buttstock rearward from the grip.

COCK. 1. To draw back the hammer or firing pin against the compression of the mainspring. When at "full cock," the trigger mechanism engages the hammer or firing pin, holding it against the tension of the mainspring. Pressure on the trigger will then release the hammer or firing pin and the mainspring drives it against the primer, firing the weapon. 2. Some weapons are provided with a "half-cock" arrangement which permits drawing back the hammer and engaging it in a notch far enough to the rear to prevent the hammer from accidentally firing the primer. In this position, the hammer does not engage the trigger mechanism, and pressure on the trigger will not fire the gun. The "half-cock" is, therefore, a sort of safety device. (In some revolvers, it frees the cylinder to turn for convenience in loading and unloading.)

COCKING PIECE. That part of the firing mechanism which is attached to the rear of the striker or firing pin and carries the cocking stud. The cocking piece may, or may not, be fitted with a knob or spur to permit drawing it back and cocking the piece with the fingers.

COCKING STUD. A projection on the underside of the cocking piece which engages with the trigger or sear to hold the firing pin in the cocked position.

COMPENSATOR. See *Muzzle Brake.*

CORDITE. A double based nitroglycerine propellant used principally in Britain. So called because of the cord-like shape of the powder.

CORE. The material inside the bullet's outer metal jacket; ordinarily lead. See *Bullet.*

CORROSION. In the bore of a gun; rust, and the resulting pitting. See *Abrasion, Erosion, Fouling,* and *Leading.*

CREEP. In the trigger mechanism, a dragging action which prevents the trigger releasing the hammer immediately when the proper pressure is applied. See *Slack.*

CRIMP. 1. Rolled Crimp: One in which the mouth of the cartridge case is turned inward into a cannelure on the bullet all around its circumference, to retain the bullet at the proper seating depth.

2. STAB CRIMP, or INDENTCRIMPS: a series of small indents at intervals around the cartridge case, engaging a cannelure in the bullet jacket. Both types of crimp are also used on high-pressure cartridges to hold the primer in the primer pocket.

CUPRONICKEL. A copper-nickel alloy once widely used as a material for bullet jackets. Because of its tendency to deposit lumpy metal fouling in the bore, it has been largely superseded in American ammunition by gilding metal.

CUT-OFF. A device mounted in the receiver in such position as to utilize it to prevent cartridges from feeding from the magazine. Cartridges in the magazine are thus held in reserve while single cartridges are loaded into the chamber.

D

DEMIHAG or **DEMIHAQUE**. A small harquebus. Widely used in France in the 16th Century.

DISCONNECTOR. A device incorporated in the action of a semiautomatic weapon to prevent the firing of more than one shot with each pull of the trigger.

DOUBLE. 1. As pertains to scoring in target shooting; two bullet holes so closely overlapping as to look like one bullet hole on casual examination.

2. As pertains to firing a gun see *Doubling*.

DOUBLE ACTION. See *Action 3*.

DOUBLING. 1. The failure of the disconnector in a semiautomatic weapon to function properly, with the result that two or more shots are fired automatically with only one continuing pressure on the trigger.

2. In double-barrel guns, the unintentional firing of both barrels simultaneously or in rapid succession due to accidental pressure on both triggers, or to the jarring off of the second hammer by the shock of recoil from the first shot.

DOUBLE SET TRIGGERS. See *Trigger 2*.

DRIFT. The movement of a bullet to the left or right of the straight line from gun muzzle to target. There are two kinds of drift:

1. WINDAGE, or drift due to the pressure of prevailing winds. See *Windage*.

2. BALLISTIC DRIFT, which is due to the precessional rotation of the bullet's nose around the curve of the trajectory (a gyroscopic phenomenon), plus the tendency of the bullet to "roll" on the air.

DUMDUM BULLET. See *Bullet 3*.

E

EFFECTIVE RANGE. See *Range 3*.

EJECTOR. 1. A small cam or projection inside the receiver against which the cartridge case strikes and is thrown clear of the gun when it has been pulled out of the chamber by the extractor.

2. On hinge-frame guns, a spring arrangement working in conjunction with the extractor which snaps the extractor violently to the rear after the barrels have been swung into a position which will allow the ejected cartridge to be thrown clear of the gun.

3. On hand-ejector models, the extractor is manually pressed to the rear until the cartridge case is clear of the chamber.

4. In rifles like the Garand, the ejector is a spring-loaded pin in the bolt face which constantly exerts pressure on the head of the case. When the action opens enough for the case or cartridge to clear the receiver opening, the pin ejects it.

5. In some auto pistols and foreign rifles the striker pin acts to eject near the close of the rearward stroke.

EROSION. The washing away of the bore by the action of the hot powder gases. Should not be, but often is confused with abrasion and corrosion. See also *Abrasion, Corrosion, Fouling* and *Leading*.

EXTERIOR BALLISTICS. See *Ballistics 1.*

EXTRACTOR. 1. A spring-steel claw attached to the bolt or breechblock, which slips over the head of the cartridge case, engaging in the rim or extractor groove, as the breech is closed. When the breech is opened, the claw withdraws the cartridge case from the chamber.

2. A movable part forming a segment of the rear face of the barrel. When the breech is closed, the cartridge rim is forced against the rear face of the barrel, including this extractor segment. When the breech is opened, a cam or spring forces the extractor smartly to the rear, withdrawing the cartridge case from the chamber.

3. In a revolver, the extractors form a segment of the rear face of the cylinder, the rims of the cartridge cases fitting against the extractors when the cylinder is closed. The extractors for all chambers are attached to the extractor rod, which is manually operatable only when the cylinder is open. See *Ejector.*

EXTREME RANGE. See *Range 4.*

F

FACE OF BREECH. See *Breech 2.*

FEEDING. The mechanical action of forcing cartridges from the magazine successively into the chamber.

FEEDING GUIDES. 1. Surfaces formed within the receiver at the top of the magazine well to guide the cartridges from the magazine into the chamber.

2. Lips formed at the top of the magazine to guide the cartridges from the magazine into the chamber.

FIELD STRIP. See *Stripping.*

FIRE. To discharge a firearm. To shoot a gun.

FIREARM. A gun from which the projectile is expelled by the action of expanding powder gases.

FIRELOCK. A term often used to mean a matchlock. In British usage, a flintlock.

FIRING LINE. 1. National Rifle Association of America definition, for competitive purposes: "The firing line is that part of the range immediately in rear of an imaginary line drawn through the several firing points."

2. In general, a line of shooters.

FIRING MECHANISM. Those parts of a gun which operate together to detonate the primer and so fire the weapon. Normally, the trigger, sear, hammer, firing pin, mainspring, and the necessary pins, bolts, screws, auxiliary springs, etc.

FIRING PIN. 1. That part of the firing mechanism which strikes the primer to discharge the gun. It may be (1) integral with the hammer or striker, (2) separately mounted within the forward face of the hammer, or separably attached to the forward end of the striker, (3) a separate unit mounted in the standing breech or in the breechblock or bolt, free to move forward when struck by the hammer or striker and to rebound when the primer fires. Obsolete designs may not have the desirable rebounding or retracting feature.

2. FLYING FIRING PIN. A firing pin shorter than the length of its travel in the breechblock. A spiral spring coiled around the pin retains it in position in the breechblock. When the impact of the hammer drives the firing pin forward, compressing the spring and exploding the primer, the compressed spring immediately draws the firing pin back into the breechblock. This is a safety feature, since the firing pin is not in contact with the primer except when driven forward by the hammer at the instant of firing. Also known as a rebound type firing pin.

Examples: Colt Government Model .45; Tokarev 7.62mm.

3. INERTIA FIRING PIN. A firing pin assembled into the breechblock and free to move forward or backward. It is impelled forward by the blow of the hammer or striker, and backward by the explosion of the primer. See *Hammer* and *Striker*.

FIRING POINT. 1. For competitive purposes, a firing position properly graded and marked with a numbered marker.

2. In general, any position selected as a vantage point for shooting.

FLASH HIDER. A device attached to the muzzle of a rifle to reduce muzzle flash. Mis-named because its function is to reduce, not to hide, muzzle flash.

FLASH SUPPRESSOR. A prong type arrangement fitted to the muzzle of weapons which reduces muzzle flash.

FLINT. A piece of silica cut to proper size and shape to be clamped into the hammer (or cock) of a flintlock firearm. When the hammer falls, the projecting flint strikes the steel frizzen, showering sparks into the priming powder exposed in the pan.

FLINTLOCK. A type of ignition system for firearms representing one of the notable advances in the development of small arms. The muzzle-loading barrel is pierced with a touchhole on the side, near the breech. On the outside of the barrel and lying adjacent to the touchhole, a pan is fixed to hold a small quantity of priming powder. A suitably shaped hinged cover, called the frizzen, protects the priming powder from wind and light rain. When the trigger is pulled, the hammer carrying the flint strikes in a downward arc, knocking the frizzen forward on its hinge and showering sparks into the priming pan. The flash from the burning priming powder is transmitted through the touchhole into the main charge inside the barrel, and the gun is discharged.

Flintlocks were used as late as the American Civil War, but their period of greatest popularity extended from about 1670 to about 1835.

FOLDING TRIGGER. See *Trigger 3*.

FOLLOWER. The small metal platform atop the magazine spring, on which the bottom cartridge of the stack rests. The follower transmits the thrust of the magazine spring to the stack of cartridges, so that they will feed at the proper angle into the feed guides for delivery into the chamber of the gun.

FORE-END. That portion of the stock extending under the barrel forward from the receiver.

FORESIGHT. See *Sight 2(a)*.

FOULING. Foreign matter in the bore.

1. Ordinarily refers to burned powder grains, gummy matter, and light rust.

2. Lumpy metal deposits from bullet jackets are usually designated as metal fouling, or leading.

3. Heavy rusting is usually called CORROSION rather than fouling. See also *Abrasion, Corrosion, Erosion* and *Leading.*

FRAME. 1. Applied to American revolvers, the heavy forging which usually consists of the grip straps, the section carrying the lockwork, and the support for the cylinder, together with the section for screwing in the barrel in swing-out cylinder and solid-frame revolvers. In hinge-frame revolvers (see 2), the frame consists of the grip section, the section carrying the lockwork, and a forward extension above the trigger at whose forward end the barrel with its extension and the cylinder are hinged. The frame in a revolver roughly corresponds to the receiver in an automatic pistol.

2. HINGE (D) FRAME. A weapon in which the barrel or barrels (including the cylinder, in the case of a revolver) are pivoted to the forward end of the frame. Closing the gun swings the barrel (s) into firing position, where the chambers are firmly locked against the standing breech. A manually operated latch unlocks the barrel (s), the muzzle (s) being swung downward, pivoting the chambers above the top of the standing breech for unloading and loading. (In a few instances, the barrel (s) pivots to the right or left.)

3. SOLID FRAME. (a) In a revolver, a swing-out-cylinder or rod-ejector type. There is no break, or hinge, in the frame. Popularly used to indicate a revolver in which cartridges must be ejected singly, or in which the cylinder must be removed from the frame by withdrawing the axis pin. (b) In a rifle, a gun in which the barrel and stock cannot be quickly "taken down," *i. e.,* separated for ease in packing.

FRIZZEN. That steel or iron section of the flintlock against which the flint strikes to provide sparks to ignite the priming powder.

FRONT SIGHT. See *Sight 2.*

FUSEE. An obsolete light musket of flintlock type.

FUSIL. 1. An ancient flintlock, lighter than the musket, introduced about 1635. 2. In French, a rifle.

G

GAIN TWIST. See *Pitch.*

GALLERY RANGE. See *Range 5.*

GAS CHECK. A copper cup placed over the base of a lead-alloy bullet to protect the base of the bullet from the action of the powder gases.

GAS CYLINDER. In semiautomatic, gas operated weapons, the gas expansion chamber in which the piston or tappet which functions the action is mounted.

GAS PORT. In semiautomatic, gas operated weapons, the hole drilled from the bore to the outside of the barrel to carry the powder gases into the gas cylinder.

GUARD SCREW. A screw or bolt extending from the triggerguard upward through the stock and threaded into the underside of the receiver firmly securing the receiver to the stock.

GAUGE. The bore diameter of a shotgun, originally roughly determined by the number of lead balls of a particular diameter required to weigh a pound avoirdupois—12 balls to the pound, 12 gauge, etc.

GEWEHR. In German, a rifle.

GILDING METAL. An alloy of copper and zinc which gives excellent performance as a bullet jacket. See *Cupronickel.*

GRIP. 1. That portion of the gun which is gripped by the hand that fires the weapon. 2. On pistols and revolvers, the handle. Commonly but improperly called the butt. 3. On rifles and shotguns, that portion of the stock immediately behind the breech: "the small of the stock." See *Stocks.*

GROOVES. The spiral cuts in the bore which impart a spinning motion to the bullet as it travels through the barrel.

GROOVE DIAMETER. The inside diameter as measured from the bottom of one groove to the bottom of the opposite groove.

GUN. A gun is any weapon designed to expel a projectile (or projectiles) through a tube (gun barrel) directing the projectile (bullet) toward the target.

GUN METAL. The dark blue or black finish generally used on the metal parts of firearms. (A grayish finish, called Parkerizing, is widely used today.)

GUNPOWDER. Technically, the propellant which is a mechanical mixture of charcoal, saltpetre, and sulphur, known as black powder. Present-day propellant powders are chemical compounds, not merely mechanical mixtures. Loosely, the propelling agent in any cartridge. See *Powder.*

H

HAGBUT. A harquebus with its buttstock bent or hooked for easier holding.

HAIR TRIGGER. See *Trigger 4.*

HALF COCK. See *Cock.*

HAMMER. 1. A type of firing mechanism which pivots around an axis, (i.e., swings through an arc, hammer-fashion), to deliver the impulse to its firing pin. Thus, the hammer-type firing mechanism differs from the striker type which moves straight forward in line with the firing pin. The hammer may be visible, or it may be entirely inside the gun, as it is in many so-called "hammerless" guns. The hammer may carry the firing pin into contact with the primer, or it may strike a blow against a separate firing pin which is thereby impelled forward to strike the primer.

2. Burr Hammer. An exposed hammer having a serrated knob at the top to provide a gripping surface for cocking.

3. Spur Hammer. A hammer having a cocking spur. (See *Hammer Spur.*)

4. Straightline Hammer. A metal plunger forced straight back by bolt action during bolt reciprocation to cocked position. When released it drives straight ahead to fire. Found on Reising and similar guns.

HAMMER HOOKS. In that type of weapon employing a concealed hammer which is rocked backward and downward into cocked position by an overriding bolt or breechblock, the finely machined projection at the top of the hammer which is engaged by the trigger and/or sear in such fashion as to hold the hammer in full cocked position and to prevent doubling.

HAMMERLESS. Loosely applied to any weapon in which the hammer or striker is concealed within the metal frame. (Examples: Smith & Wesson .32 Hammerless; Colt .32 Automatic.) The only truly hammerless weapons are those in which a striker is used instead of a hammer. (Examples: Colt .25 Automatic; Luger.)

HAMMER SPUR. On exposed-hammer weapons, the spur, or projection rearward, which provides a gripping surface and leverage to cock the hammer. See *Hammer 3*.

HANDGUARD. That portion of the stock covering the top of the barrel forward from the receiver. Intended to protect the hand supporting the piece from being burned on a barrel heated by rapid firing, the handguard is usually provided on military rifles, seldom on sporting rifles. In some cases the handguard has been made of ventilated metal during recent years.

HANDGUN. 1. A pistol or a revolver.

2. In the early stages of firearms development, handgun was used to mean small arms as distinct from cannon.

HANGFIRE. Delayed ignition of the powder charge. Unpredictable, usually unexplainable, often dangerous. A hangfire may last many seconds from the time the firing pin strikes the primer until the gun discharges. Not to be confused with *Misfire*.

HARQUEBUS. Originally a smooth-bore matchlock fired from a forked rest and introduced in the middle of the 15th century. The name persisted through wheel-lock and flintlock designs. Other names—Arbalest, Arbalist, Arcubugio, Archobugio, Arquebus, Hack, Hackbush, Hackbutt, Hagenbüsche, Hagbut, Haquebut, and Hookbut.

HEAD SPACE. Loosely, the distance from the head of the case to the face of the supporting bolt when action is locked. On every cartridge there is either a flange on the head of the case (rimmed cartridge) or a shoulder where the neck of the case joins the body (rimless cartridge) which by coming in contact with a stop in the chamber, prevents the cartridge from entering the chamber deeper than the correct distance. When the halting flange is on the case body, it constitutes a "belted case."

a. HEAD SPACE in the chamber of a gun using rimmed cartridges is measured from the face of the breechblock to the surface at the rear of the chamber on which the forward surface of the rim of the cartridge case rests. Calibrated shims may be used to measure head space in a chamber built for rimmed cases. "Belted" cases are rimmed variants.

b. HEAD SPACE in a chamber for a rimless cartridge is the distance from the front face of the breechblock or bolt to some predetermined point on the shoulder of the chamber, where it slopes down from the body of the case to the neck. Head space of this kind cannot be measured with ordinary measuring devices, so a standard head space gauge of hardened and seasoned steel is deposited in the gauge laboratory of the factory. The working gauges used in manufacture are controlled in size by comparison with this standard.

c. HEAD SPACE in a chamber for rimless straight-bodied cartridges, such

as the Caliber .45 Colt Auto cartridge and the Caliber .30 Army Carbine
is measured from the squared shoulder of the chamber just in rear of the
throat to the face of the breechblock.

HEEL of the BUTT.   The upper corner of the butt, the portion which is to
the rear when the butt is on the ground, the soldier standing at "Order
Arms."

HOLLOW POINT.   See *Bullet 4.*

I

IGNITION.   Setting fire to the powder charge in a gun.

INERTIA FIRING PIN.   See *Firing Pin 3.*

INERTIA LOCK.   See *Action 6* and *8.*

INSTRUMENTAL VELOCITY.   See *Velocity 1.*

INTERIOR BALLISTICS.   See *Ballistics 2.*

J

JACKET.   The tough metal envelope covering the outside of a bullet.

JUMP.   The extent to which the axis of the bore rises while the bullet is
traveling down the barrel. See *Recoil; Kick.*

K

KEYHOLING.   The failure of a bullet to remain gyroscopically balanced,
with the result that it gyrates and eventually tumbles end over end. A
tumbling bullet leaves an elongated hole in a target; hence "keyholing."

KICK.   Shooters' term for recoil. Actually, the "kick" felt by a shooter is
vastly different from the recoil measured by the ballistician. "Kick" includes recoil plus muzzle blast, torque, and varying thrusts imposed by
the shape of the stock. Thus, a gun which seems to one shooter to have a
vicious "kick" may seem to another shooter a very comfortable gun to fire.
See *Recoil; Jump.*

L

LANDS.   The raised portion of the spiral rifling in the bore of a rifled firearm;
the metal standing between the grooves.

LEADING.   Small bits of the lead bullet which adhere to the barrel from the
bullet as a result of heat, friction, etc. See *Abrasion, Corrosion, Erosion,*
and *Fouling.*

LEAF SIGHT.   See *Sight 2 (c).*

LINE OF SIGHT.   The straight line from the shooter's eye through (or over)
the sights of the gun to the target.

LIVE AMMUNITION.   Loaded cartridges. See *Ammunition.*

LOAD.   1.   To insert a cartridge (or loading components) into a gun.

2.   To insert primer, powder, and bullet into a cartridge case so as
to make a complete cartridge.

3.   Colloquially, a cartridge; as, "the revolver holds six loads."

LOADING GATE.   1.   A hinged cover giving access to the magazine.

2.   In revolvers, a hinged segment of the standing breech, found only

on revolvers having a cylinder which does not swing away from the standing breech for loading.

LOCK. 1. Originally, on muzzle-loading weapons, the firing mechanism.

2. With the introduction of hinge-frame breech-loading weapons, the term was broadened to include the hinge and the mechanism which locks the barrels firmly in position against the standing breech.

LOCK TIME. The interval of time between the release of the sear notch (on the hammer or cocking stud) by the sear and the impact of firing pin on the primer in the chambered cartridge.

LOCKING LUG (S). Carefully machined lugs on the bolt which engage in suitable recesses in the receiver to securely hold the breech closed when the gun is fired.

LOCKWORK. See *Action*.

M

MAGAZINE. As pertains to small arms, that operating assembly in which cartridges are stored and which feeds those cartridges one at a time into position so that the closing of the bolt or breechblock will force a new cartridge into the chamber ready for firing. The magazine may be built into the gun or may be a separate part. Magazines are of many types; tubular, box, rotary-box, drum, etc. (The cylinder of a revolver is, in effect, a magazine, but is not so called.) See *Cartridge Clip*.

MAINSPRING. That spring which provides the energy actuating the hammer or striker. Not to be confused with the operating spring or recoil spring found in semiautomatic weapons as a part of the breech closing mechanism.

MATCH. A cord of slow-burning material used in early matchlock guns to ignite the priming charge. One end was placed in the jaws of the moving section of the lock (the cock or serpentine). This end was lighted and when the "trigger" was pulled, the lighted end descended into contact with the priming powder in the pan.

MATCH, SLOW. A slow-burning fuse, often of twisted cotton soaked in a solution of saltpetre, or hemp twine soaked in lead acetate and wood ash, used for ignition on matchlock weapons.

MATCHLOCK. An early form of muzzle-loading firearm in which the priming charge was ignited by a slow burning match. See *Match*.

MAYNARD. See *Percussion Cap 2*.

MECHANICAL SAFETY. The mechanical arrangement built into the action which prevents firing the piece until the action is fully closed and locked. Sometimes referred to as the "automatic safety."

METAL FOULING. See *Fouling*.

METAL PATCHED BULLET. See *Bullet 9*.

MIQUELET. One of the earliest forms of flintlock.

MISFIRE. Absolute failure of the cartridge to fire after the primer has been struck by the firing pin. Not to be confused with hangfire.

MOUTH. Of the cartridge case; the open end of a cartridge case into which the bullet is inserted.

MOUSQUET FUSIL. A flintlock arm invented in France by Marshal Vauban about 1640.

MOUSQUETON. French artillery carbine.

MUSHROOM BULLET. See *Bullet 10*.

MUSHROOMING. The round, fairly regular expansion caused by impact of a bullet outward from the nose and flowing back toward the base, the bullet remaining mostly in one piece and retaining most of its original weight. A bullet which breaks into numerous pieces on impact does not mushroom. A bullet of any type may mushroom. There is no necessary connection between a mushroom bullet and one which has mushroomed or which exhibits good mushrooming qualities. See *Bullet 10*.

MUSKET. A term originally applied to a smoothbore arm invented about 1540 which succeeded the *Harquebus*. Later applied to all military smoothbores of the long type with fore-ends extending the length of the barrel. Still later during the transition from single-shot to magazine rifles the term "rifled musket" or "rifle musket" was applied to single-shot military rifles apparently to distinguish them from repeating rifles.

MUZZLE. The forward end of the gun barrel from which the bullet emerges.

MUZZLE BLAST. Atmospheric disturbance at the muzzle following the emergence of the bullet, caused by the expansion of the powder gases in the air.

MUZZLE BRAKE. A device attached to the muzzle of a gun, designed to deflect the propelling gases emerging from the muzzle behind the bullet, and to utilize the energy of these gases to pull the gun forward to counter the recoil of the weapon.

MUZZLE ENERGY. The computed energy of the bullet as it leaves the muzzle of the gun. Usually measured in foot pounds. A function of bullet weight and velocity.

MUZZLE FLASH. The incandescent flash in the air at the muzzle of the gun following the departure of the bullet; caused by the expansion of powder gases, the ignition of oxygen in the air and the expulsion of burning powder grains.

MUZZLE-LOADER. A gun which can be loaded only from the muzzle.

MUZZLE VELOCITY. See *Velocity 2*.

N

NECK. Pertaining to bottleneck cartridge cases, that forward portion of the case which is reduced in diameter to hold the bullet. See *Case 2*.

NIPPLE. In percussion-lock weapons, a small tube screwed into the breech and projecting sufficiently on the outside to permit seating the percussion cap (primer) over the end of the tube. When the primer is exploded by the hammer, the resulting flame passes down through the tube into the chamber, igniting the propelling charge.

O

OGIVE. In ballistics, the radius of the curve of the nose of the bullet.

OPEN SIGHTS. See *Sights 2 (d)*.

OPERATING HANDLE. The projection from the operating rod or bolt of a gas or recoil operated semiautomatic weapon which is grasped to manually open the action.

OPERATING ROD. In gas operated semiautomatic weapons the rod which extends from the gas piston to the receiver where it engages and operates the breech mechanism.

OPERATING SPRING. In automatic and semiautomatic weapons the spring which closes the action. Also called recoil spring, retracting spring, etc.

OPTICAL SIGHTS. See *Sights 3*.

OVER AND UNDER GUN. A double-barrelled, hinged frame gun with one barrel superimposed on the other. Occasionally found with three barrels.

P

PAN. The small pan on the side of a flintlock weapon in which the priming powder is placed. The priming pan.

PARKERIZE. A grey rust-preventive finish for metal.

PASTER. A sticker of suitable size and color used to cover a bullet hole in a target.

PATCH. 1. As used in connection with muzzle loading rifles, a piece of leather, cloth or paper, usually greased and placed over the muzzle of the rifle under the bullet so that it practically encases the ball as the latter is rammed into the rifle. 2. As used in connection with more modern bullets see *Bullet 9*.

PENETRATION. The distance a bullet will travel through a given substance. For testing purposes ⅞-inch pine boards at given distances are commonly used.

PERCUSSION ARM. A weapon designed to fire by the use of a percussion cap.

PERCUSSION CAP. 1. An early form of small arms primer consisting of a small metal cup containing an explosive, weatherproofed on its open end. In use, the cap is placed, open end down, over the nipple and exploded by the blow of the hammer.

2. The Maynard primer was another form of percussion cap. Explosive pellets were sealed at proper intervals between two strips of paper. This primer tape was then rolled and inserted in guns of suitable design. The action of cocking the hammer pulled the primer tape until a primer pellet lay under the hammer and over the ignition vent into the chamber, ready for firing. Similar forms are used in cap pistols today.

PERCUSSION LOCK. The type of action designed for the use of a percussion cap.

PIECE. Any firearm under discussion. The origin of this term in its application to guns is unknown.

PISTOL. 1. A firearm designed to be fired using one hand only, and having a chamber integral with or permanently aligned with, the bore. Pistols may be single shot or magazine type.

2. Popularly, but improperly, used to designate any weapon designed to be fired using one hand only; i.e., both pistols and revolvers. See also *Autoloading* and *Automatic*.

PITCH. 1. As pertains to rifling, the angle at which the rifling spiral is cut in relation to the axis of the bore. For convenience, usually expressed as the number of inches of bore required for one complete spiral as "one turn in sixteen inches." Commonly referred to as the "twist" of the rifling. Usually, the spiral is maintained at a uniform rate throughout the length of the barrel. Sometimes, the pitch is increased steadily from chamber to muzzle. The spiral may start at one turn in twenty inches, and increase to one turn in ten inches at the muzzle. This is called gain-twist rifling.

2. As pertains to pistol and revolver grips, the angle at which the grip slants in relation to the axis of the bore.

3. As pertains to rifle and shotgun stocks the angle at which the butt plate slopes in relation to the axis of the bore.

POINT BLANK. See *Range 6.*

POWDER. 1. As pertains to small arms, any propellant explosive.

2. Black Powder. A mechanical mixture of charcoal, sulphur and saltpetre. Burns with considerable white smoke.

3. Smokeless Powder, a progressive explosive which ignites and burns with a minimum of ash and smoke. A chemical compound normally built around nitrated cellulose. Often surface-coated mechanically.

PRESSURE. 1. The thrust of the powder gases expanding in the gun. In the United States, recorded in pounds per square inch.

2. Chamber Pressure, the pressure generated within the chamber, erroneously called breech pressure.

3. Residual Pressure is the pressure remaining in the chamber after the bullet has left the barrel. Generally used with reference to automatic weapons.

PRIMER. 1. The small charge which is detonated by the firing pin or striker, and which ignites the propelling powder.

2. A metal cap containing a priming charge. See *Percussion Cap.*

PROPELLANT. 1. Progressive explosive used to propel a projectile from a gun.

2. The powder charge in a cartridge.

PROJECTILE. A bullet. Ballistically, a bullet does not become a projectile until it is in flight.

PISTOL GRIP. On shoulder weapons, an extension below the small of the stock shaped like the grip of a pistol or revolver. Actual design and dimensions vary widely. If the pistol grip curves downward sharply and comes in close behind the triggerguard it is referred to as a "full pistol grip." If the downward curve or slant is slight, merely forming a protuberance below the small of the stock it is referred to as a "half-pistol grip" or "semi-pistol grip."

PUMP GUN. A weapon having a pump action. See *Action 10.*

PYRITES. Sulphide of iron. When brought sharply into contact with iron or steel, it gives off a shower of sparks. This mineral was used in the ignition system of early wheel-lock guns. It was also used in the first form of flintlock. It is not as satisfactory as flint for this purpose.

R

RAMMER. Pertaining to small arms, usually a ramrod attached to the weapon with a hinged arm and pivot, in such fashion as to permit the use of the rammer without detaching it from the gun.

RAMROD. 1. A metal or wood rod used to ram the wad and bullet (or shot) down the barrel of a muzzle-loader, into position on the powder charge.

2. Colloquially, a cleaning rod.

RAMP. A sloping surface connecting a lower level with a higher level. (See *Sight.*)

RANGE. 1. A place where target shooting is practiced.

2. ACCURACY RANGE. The maximum distance at which a particular gun and cartridge will consistently place all shots in the standard target for that distance. A comparative term only.

3. EFFECTIVE RANGE. The maximum distance at which a bullet may reasonably be expected to travel accurately and kill a particular type of game. A comparative term only.

4. EXTREME RANGE. The greatest distance the bullet will travel when the cartridge is fired.

5. GALLERY RANGE. An indoor target range. National Rifle Association of America gallery rules require a distance from firing point to target of 50 feet or 75 feet for .22 rim-fire rifles; 50 feet or 60 feet for .22 rim-fire pistols. On properly constructed indoor ranges, firing may be conducted with center-fire pistols and revolvers at ranges of 25 yards and 50 yards. Such installations are generally referred to as "indoor ranges," the term "gallery" being applied usually only to short-range .22-caliber installations.

6. POINT-BLANK RANGE. Popularly used to indicate the distance the bullet will travel before it drops enough to require sight adjustment. A shot fired so close to the target that no sighting is necessary for effective aiming. All bullets begin to drop as soon as they emerge from the barrel.

REAR SIGHT. See *Sight 2(b)*.

RECEIVER. 1. That metal portion of a gun in which the breech action and firing mechanism are housed, and to which the barrel and stocks are assembled.

2. In revolvers and hinge-frame shotguns, called the "frame."

3. In some types of autoloading pistols, the terms "frame" and "receiver" are used synonymously.

RECEIVER BRIDGE. The rearward portion of the receiver which forms an arch over the rear of the bolt race-way. If there is an opening cut through the receiver bridge to permit the passage of the bolt handle the construction is referred to as a "split bridge" receiver.

RECEIVER RING. The circular forward portion of the receiver into which the barrel is threaded.

RECOIL. The backward thrust of the gun caused by the expansion of the powder gases which act to thrust the bullet forward and react to thrust the gun rearward. Ballistically, recoil is computed or measured (in foot pounds) as the rearward thrust in the line of the axis of the bore. This line of thrust is usually above the point of resistance to the thrust, which is the point where the hand grips the stocks of a handgun or where the shoulder rests against the butt of a shotgun or rifle. Hence, the muzzle of the gun tends to swing upward in an arc around the point of resistance. Different methods of holding the gun change the point of resistance, therefore change the apparent recoil. Several other factors also affect the reaction of the gun; so that simple ballistic recoil is not necessarily a measure of the recoil as it is felt by the shooter. (See *Kick and Jump*.)

RECOIL LUG. A projection on the underside of the receiver projecting down into the wood of the stock to distribute the shock of recoil through the portion of the stock best able to take the shock without cracking.

RECOIL OPERATED. See *Action*.

RECOIL SHOULDER. See *Recoil Lug*.

RECOIL SPRING. See *Operating Spring*.

REPEATER. Any arm equipped with a magazine. Colloquial.

RESIDUAL PRESSURE. See *Pressure 3*.

REVOLVER. 1. A firearm designed to be fired using one hand only and having a series of chambers in a cylinder, mounted coaxially with the barrel. A mechanism revolves the cylinder so that the chambers are successively aligned with the bore. Only the cartridge in the particular chamber which is in alignment with the bore is fired.

Colloquially, a "six gun."

2. DOUBLE-ACTION REVOLVERS are those in which continuous pressure on the trigger (a) revolves the cylinder to align a chamber with the bore, (b) cocks and then releases the hammer, discharging the piece. Generally, but not always such revolvers are designed to permit thumb cocking also if desired.

3. SINGLE-ACTION REVOLVERS are those in which the hammer must be manually cocked; i.e., it cannot be cocked by trigger pressure. Cocking the hammer revolves the cylinder, aligning a chamber ready for firing. Pressure is then applied to the trigger, which performs the single function (action) of releasing the hammer to discharge the piece.

4. SEMI-AUTOMATIC REVOLVERS are those in which the recoil from one shot plus spring action revolves the cylinder, aligns a chamber, and cocks the hammer ready for firing the next shot. Pressure must then be applied to the trigger to discharge the piece. Not to be confused with a "Hammerless Revolver" or semi-automatic pistol. Example: Webley-Fosberry .455 Revolver.

RICOCHET. A bullet which has struck and glanced off; or the act of so doing. The very rapid spinning motion of a bullet causes it to ricochet very easily and without much loss of forward velocity.

RIFLING. The spiral cut into the bore to impart a spinning motion to the bullet, to establish gyroscopic stability. Normally, the rifling consists of "grooves" and "lands," the latter being the metal left standing between the grooves. Through the years of firearms development, every conceivable form of boring the barrel to impart a rotary motion to the projectile has been tried, but the land and groove has survived as the most practicable type. See *Pitch*.

RIM-FIRE. *See Cartridge 7.*

RIMLESS CARTRIDGE. See *Cartridge 9.*

RIMMED CARTRIDGE. See *Cartridge 10.*

RUPTURED CASE. See *Case 3.*

S

SAFETY. Any mechanism which blocks the hammer, sear, or trigger (or any combination of the three) to prevent the accidental discharge of a weapon. Ordinarily of two types.

    1. GRIP OR AUTOMATIC SAFETIES. Flat levers or plungers, normally protruding from some portion of the grip in such position that, when the hand firing the piece is squeezed around the grip, the safety lever is pressed inward without conscious attention by the firer, automatically releasing the firing mechanism. In most cases, when pressure on the grip is relaxed the safety automatically resets itself. In a few instances, it must be manually reset.

    2. THUMB SAFETIES. Small levers or sliding buttons situated within comfortable reach of the thumb of the hand firing the gun. They must be deliberately set in the "safe" or "ready" position.

SCHUETZEN RIFLE. An American term derived from the German-American shooting societies (Schuetzenverein) which were the first organized target shooting clubs in America. The "Schuetzen" rifle is a typical Continental European type target rifle. Custom built, it is fitted with double set triggers, heavy barrel, palm rest, cheek piece and heavy butt-plate having a prong extending to the rear to fit under the arm-pit. Frequently a top prong is also provided so that the butt plate fits well around the firer's shoulder. In Europe the actions are generally various forms of the Martini. In America, England and the Scandinavian countries some "Schuetzen" rifles have been custom built using various bolt actions. Officially designated by the Union Internationale de Tir (International Shooting Union) and by the national rifle associations of the various nations as the "Free Rifle."

SEAR. One or more levers operating between the trigger and the hammer or firing pin to provide additional controlled leverage to improve trigger action while transmitting that action to the hammer.

SEAR SPRING. A small spring operating in connection with the sear.

SELF-LOADING. See *Autoloading.*

SEMIAUTOMATIC. See *Autoloading.*

SEMI-RIMMED CARTRIDGE. See *Cartridge 8.*

SERPENTINE. 1. On matchlock weapons, the S-shaped lever, centrally pivoted, which holds in its upper jaws the slow match. Its lower portion, extending below the stock, serves as a trigger.

    2. A gun using the matchlock type of ignition.

SETSCREW. 1. A screw so located as to secure another screw which might become loosened in the normal use of the weapon.

    2. A screw which regulates the amount of pressure necessary to release the trigger.

SET TRIGGER. See *Trigger 5.* (For some unknown reason sometimes written "sett" trigger.)

SHELL. As pertains to small-arms ammunition.

    1. A loaded shotgun cartridge.

    2. An empty metallic cartridge case.

    3. Colloquially, a loaded metallic cartridge.

SIDE ARMS. Small arms which are designed to be carried on the belt and used in one hand. Includes edged weapons as well as pistols and revolvers.

SIGHT. 1. An aiming device. Gun sights are of two general types: metallic and optical.

    2. METALLIC SIGHTS normally consist of a pair; a front sight and a rear sight.

    (a) FRONT SIGHT. A protrusion or attachment above the barrel near the muzzle. It may be integral with the barrel, or separate. It may be fixed or adjustable. Foresight.

    (b) REAR SIGHT. The rearmost of a pair of metallic gun sights. It may be mounted on the barrel, receiver, frame, slide, tang, cocking-piece, bolt sleeve, or stock; may be fixed or adjustable. It may contain a haze filter or a single corrected lens in lieu of the shooter wearing eyeglasses. (A telescopic sight is not a rear sight, although mounted at the rear of the gun, because the complete aiming system is contained in the telescope.) Called "back sight" in English publications.

    (c) LEAF SIGHT. Any metallic sight which is hinged at the base to permit raising it to a vertical position for sighting, and lowering it to a horizontal position to avoid damage in carrying or shipping. The leaf-sight principle is usually applied to rear sights only. The leaf sight may consist of a series of leaves, each designed for a particular range, to be raised and lowered individually as needed, or it may consist of a single arborlike leaf in which is mounted a sliding member containing the sighting notch or aperture. This sliding member may be moved up or down to set it at the desired range. The adjustment is manual on some sights, mechanical (by means of a vernier screw) on others. Leaf sights may or may not be adjustable for windage.

    Metallic sights may be open (post or notch), or aperture. Both open and aperture sights may be "hooded," i.e., covered to keep the direct rays of the sun off the sight. Unhooded post sights may be equipped with some light-reflecting material to improve visibility in dim light; hence "gold bead," et cetera. Whenever an optical system is incorporated, the sights become "optical" sights.

    (d) OPEN SIGHT. Any sight in which there is no tube or aperture through which aim is taken.

    (e) VERNIER SIGHTS. Metallic sights which may be adjusted for elevation or windage by the action of a vernier screw; i.e., a screw having a head calibrated (marked with a scale) to indicate the amount of movement transmitted to the sight. Also called a micrometer sight.

    (f) POST SIGHT. A front sight resembling a post or one of generally rectangular or quadrilateral design.

    (g) PYRAMIDAL SIGHT. A front sight of generally pyramidal design.

    (h) RAMP SIGHT. 1. A front sight mounted at the top of a ramp which inclines upward and forward. 2. A rear sight having a sliding member which may be moved up and down a ramp to change the elevation of the sight.

(i) RECEIVER SIGHT. Any type (commonly aperture) fastened to the receiver bridge.

(j) TUBE SIGHT. A tube in which front and rear sights are mounted. It resembles a telescopic sight externally, but it contains no optical system.

3. OPTICAL SIGHTS are sights containing a series of lenses to form an optical system, the entire aiming system being contained in one unit. Optical sights do not necessarily have telescopic properties. The optical system may merely include range-indicating, or range-estimating devices, plus the necessary means of adjusting for elevation and windage. Most optical sights as used on small arms are of the telescopic type.

(a) TELESCOPIC SIGHT. An optical sight employing the principle of the telescope to enlarge the image, i.e., the target.

SHOULDER. Pertaining to bottle-necked cartridge cases, that sharply sloping portion of the case which joins the neck and the body of the case.

SLACK. As pertains to small arms, the free travel, against spring tension only, of a trigger before it begins to disengage the hammer or firing pin. Slack is not provided in target weapons or in most sporting arms. It is a form of safety device used mostly in military weapons. Not to be confused with "creep," which occurs while the trigger is disengaging the hammer or striker.

SLIDE. 1. In slide action weapons, the operating rod. 2. In semiautomatic pistols, a metal sleeve covering part or all of the barrel and/or top of the action. It usually forms the breechblock. Driven back by recoil, it is returned to its forward position by spring action.

SLIDE ACTION. See *Action 9.*

SLING. A leather or webbing strap detachably fastened to a weapon and used to assist in carrying and to steady the piece in firing.

SLING SWIVELS. Metal loops fastened to barrel or fore-end and to the butt-stock for the purpose of attaching the sling.

SLOW MATCH. See *Match.*

SMALL ARMS. Weapons which may be carried on the person and fired from one or two hands. In military usage, also machine guns. (Apparently because the Navy is essentially big-gun minded, U. S. naval usage includes 20 mm. and 40 mm. automatic weapons in the category of "small arms.") Any weapon caliber .60 and below by Army definition.

SMALL BORE. 1. As applied to American target shooting, a .22 caliber, rim fire cartridge using a lead-alloy bullet. 2. As popularly employed by American hunters, any center-fire rifle of less than .25 caliber or shotgun under 16-gauge. In England and on the Continent rifles of 7 mm caliber and less are frequently called "small bore" rifles. To the African and Indian big game hunter any rifle of less than .450 caliber is "small bore."

SMALL OF THE STOCK. That portion of the stock customarily gripped by the shooting hand. It lies between the receiver and the comb of the stock. Its underside may be straight or may be formed into a "pistol grip" or "half-pistol grip."

SMOKELESS POWDER. See *Powder.*

SMOOTH BORE. A gun in which the barrel is not rifled. Formerly, a "musket," "fowling piece," "blunderbuss," loosely, a shotgun.

SNAPHANCE. The earliest form of flintlock. In British usage "snaphaunce."

SPANNER. In connection with wheel-locks, a small wrench used to wind up the action spring.

SPLIT BRIDGE. See *Receiver Bridge.*

SPUR HAMMER. See *Hammer* and *Hammerspur.*

STACKING SWIVEL. An open metal loop swiveled near the muzzle end of the fore-end to permit engaging with the stacking swivels of other weapons so that the rifles will support one another and stand on their butt-stocks with the barrels and actions clear of the ground.

STANDING BREECH. See *Breech.*

STAR GAUGE. A precision gauge used to measure the inside diameter of a gun bore.

STAR GAUGED. A rifle which has been star gauged and found to meet the tolerances for bore diameter established by the manufacturer. Measurements are taken at one inch intervals along the length of the bore. Star gauging checks the regularity of the bore diameter but is not, of itself, a guarantee of accuracy.

STOCKS. 1. Those parts, attached to the receiver or frame of a weapon, which make it possible to hold, aim, and fire the gun. The stocks, normally made of wood, may also be made of metal, plastic, or other rigid materials. Pistol and revolver stocks are attached to the rear frame or handle, to form the grip.

2. Rifle and shotgun stocks consist of (a) the buttstock, extending from the breech to the butt which is held into the shoulder and on the upper edge of which (the comb) the cheek rests in aiming the weapon, (b) the fore-end, which extends forward from the breech under the barrel to provide a comfortable grasp for the hand upholding the barrel, (c) on military weapons, the handguard, which extends forward from the receiver on top of the barrel to protect the hand from the heated barrel. The fore-end and buttstock may be made in one piece.

STRIKER. 1. A rod type of firing pin which travels inside the bolt or breechblock and is directly actuated by its own spiral spring when released by the action of the trigger. It is not actuated by being struck by a hammer. The actual firing pin may be integral with the striker or may be a separate piece fastened to the forward end of the striker rod.

2. Sometimes loosely and improperly used to indicate any firing pin.

STRIPPING. 1. As pertains to weapons, disassembling. (a) Field stripping is disassembling as far as necessary for normal cleaning and care.

2. As pertains to bullets, failure of the bullet jacket to properly grip the rifling so that the bullet fails to acquire the proper spin and bits of bullet jacket are stripped off and left in the bore.

3. As pertains to loading a magazine weapon, pressing the cartridges out of the charger clip into the magazine.

T

TAKE-DOWN. That design of rifle or shotgun which permits the quick disassembly of the fore-end and barrel from the buttstock and receiver and their rapid re-assembly by the shooter in the field without the use of tools. In some designs (such as the Marlin 39) the takedown joint may be in the receiver itself.

TANG. The rearward projecting arms of the receiver into which the buttstock is fastened.

THROAT. 1. The forward section of the chamber where it tapers to meet the diameter of the barrel bore.

2. In a revolver the enlargement of the bore at the breech end to permit the centering of the bullet in the barrel when it jumps from the cylinder into the barrel.

TOE OF THE BUTT. The lower corner of the butt. The portion which is to the front when the butt is on the ground, the soldier standing at "Order Arms."

TOUCH HOLE. In early weapons, the hole through which the priming flash passed into the powder charge inside the barrel.

TRAJECTORY. 1. The path of the bullet in flight.

2. Flat Trajectory. A comparative term used to indicate very little curvature in the flight of the bullet from muzzle to point of impact. When the velocity is high, comparatively flat trajectory is achieved. There is no such thing as perfectly flat trajectory.

TRIGGER. 1. The finger-actuated lever, usually projecting below the receiver, used to release the firing mechanism and so discharge the gun.

2. DOUBLE-SET TRIGGERS. A pair of triggers so arranged that pressure on one trigger engages the sears in such fashion that the slightest touch on the second trigger will then discharge the gun.

3. FOLDING TRIGGER. A trigger hinged so that it can be folded forward close to the under side of the frame. Example: Italian 10.35 mm. Bodego.

4. HAIR TRIGGER. A term loosely applied to any trigger which can be released by very light pressure.

5. SET TRIGGER. An adjustable trigger designed to operate reliably with a very light trigger pull. Colloquially a "hair trigger."

6. SHEATH TRIGGER. An obsolete form of trigger in which no trigger guard was used. The trigger was mounted in and projected only slightly from the frame just forward of the grip.

7. THUMB TRIGGER. A button design on or near the tang. It fires the rifle when depressed, normally by thumb pressure.

TRIGGER BAR. A connecting bar used in some types of actions to transmit the pressure from the trigger to the sear.

TRIGGERGUARD. The metal loop which partially protects the trigger from damage and from being pressed by accident.

TWIST. See *Pitch.*

V

VELOCITY. 1. INSTRUMENTAL VELOCITY. The velocity of a projectile measured by scientific instruments at a specified point on its trajectory. In America usually measured in feet per second. Instrumental velocity figures always indicate the range at which the readings were made. In attempting to compare instrumental velocity figures for different cartridges or loads it is essential that comparisons be made only of those figures which were taken at identical ranges.

2. MUZZLE VELOCITY. The computed velocity at which a projectile leaves the muzzle. In America usually given in feet per second (abbreviation f.s.).

VERNIER SIGHT. See *Sights.*

W

WADCUTTER. See *Bullet 13.*

WHEEL-LOCK. 1. An ancient ignition system consisting of a toothed wheel driven by a coil spring wound up by a key or "spanner" and a piece of pyrites held stationary in contact with the rim of the wheel, with a priming pan below the pyrites. Pressure on the trigger unlatches the wheel, which rotates its serrated edge rapidly against the pyrites, showering sparks into the priming pan to ignite the main charge and fire the piece.

2. A weapon using the wheel-lock system of ignition. These weapons followed the matchlock and preceded the flintlock.

WINDAGE. 1. The lateral drift of a bullet in flight due to the effect of wind.

2. Generally applied to all lateral drift, including ballistic drift.

3. The movement of sights to compensate for the lateral drift. To "take left windage" means to move the rear sight to the left.

Z

ZERO. The point at which sights are set so that, with a given load, a given range, and no wind, the bullet will strike the center of a target. The marksman uses this "zero sight setting" as the base point from which to adjust his sights for different loads, different ranges, and different weather conditions. A gun may be "zeroed in" at any range and with any ammunition. Hence the term is relative only.

APPENDIX II

THE WILLIAMS FLOATING CHAMBER

While the modern American forms of blcwback .22 rifles will handle .22 short, long and long rifle cartridges when *manually* operated, it has not yet been possible to adjust the timing to give satisfactory semiautomatic performance with all three cartridges.

To accomplish this result, David M. Williams, inventor of the floating chamber, adapted a rifle on the design of the ones already described to employ his device. This rifle was produced in small quantity as the Remington 550 in 1941 and was catalogued and sold by gun dealers at that time.

The Williams "floating chamber" consists of a small steel block containing the cartridge chamber, inserted in the breech section of the barrel where the regular chamber would normally be drilled. This "floating chamber" is so mounted in the rear of the barrel as to be free to move forward and backward a small fraction of an inch. In the normal blowback design the rearward push which operates the breechblock is derived from the pressure pushing backward on the inside of the head of the cartridge case after the case has contracted enough to let go its grip on the walls of the chamber.

Using the floating chamber the entire chamber-block is free to move to the rear as soon as the pressure has built up sufficiently to overcome the inertia of the steel floating chamber. The walls of the cartridge case may be still tightly adhering to the walls of the chamber but the entire chamber moves rearward. As the floating chamber slides to the rear a gap opens between the forward face of the chamber and the rear face of the barrel. The expanding powder gases rush into this space and press hard against the entire face of the floating chamber. Thus the amount of rearward thrust is vastly increased over the amount of thrust which the same pressure would deliver on the much smaller area of the internal head of the cartridge case. The comparatively low pressure from the .22 short is given enough working area to enable it to drive open the breech mechanism originally designed to operate safely with the .22 long rifle cartridge.

In the Remington 550 Model, the floating chamber is just long enough to hold the .22 short cartridge. If a .22 long or a .22 long rifle cartridge is inserted in this arm, the cartridge case extends *beyond the forward end of the floating chamber* and into the barrel. The result is that when the cartridge is fired the cartridge case expands against the walls of both the floating chamber and barrel chamber, completely sealing the joint between floating chamber and barrel until the residual pressure has dropped to the point where the cartridge case can contract, let go its grip on the chamber walls and allow the normal thrust from the head of the cartridge case to drive open the action. The physicist and mechanical engineer will recognize that there are numerous forces which have to be carefully computed and which are not specifically mentioned here because of the effort to explain this action in as simple terms as possible. One weakness of the floating chamber design is the tendency of the lead bullets to deposit lead scrapings in the gap between the floating chamber and the barrel face. Sometimes the combination of scrapings, heat and pressure "solders" the floating chamber to the barrel so that a malfunction results. Clearing such jams is not very difficult and intelligent cleaning will eliminate the trouble by eliminating the "soldering" element.

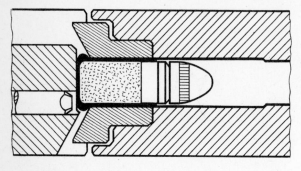

REMINGTON MODEL 550, showing floating chamber. Chamber loaded with .22 short cartridge. The short case extends to the forward end of the chamber, which "floats."

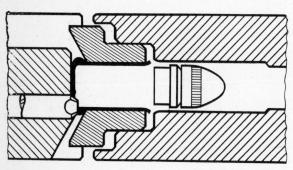

Rifle firing .22 short cartridge. In this design the gas exerts added pressure on the front end of the chamber as well as against the head of the cartridge case, providing sufficient energy to operate the rifle. The chamber is forced back against an abutment which halts it, while the remaining breech members continue to the rear.

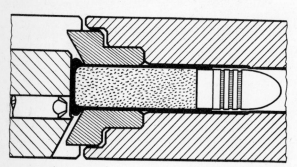

Rifle ready to fire with chamber loaded with a long rifle cartridge. The case extends well forward of the end of the chamber, sealing it off. When the cartridge is fired, there is sufficient gas pressure from the long rifle cartridge, working against the head of the cartridge case, to operate the rifle.

APPENDIX III

DOUBLE BARRELED AND THREE BARRELED RIFLES

The term "double barreled" rifle may be applied either to (a) guns having two barrels superimposed or two barrels side by side. (b) Those with parallel

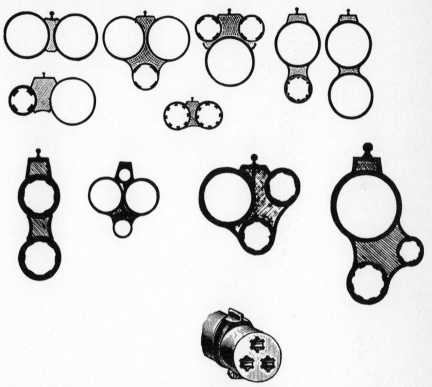

Types of Multibarrel Weapons

barrels commonly called "side-by-side." A separate firing lock for each barrel is the rule but there are exceptions.

In general appearance, breech locking systems, and firing mechanisms, these rifles are practically identical with double barreled shotguns made by the same manufacturers.

While double barreled rifles are found to shoot small caliber low powered cartridges, they are neither common nor of any practical value. Double barreled rifles are not usually made on a production line basis in the United States. Some have been made to order by custom gunsmiths.

Three barreled rifles are seldom encountered but 3-barreled combination rifles and shotguns are very common on the Continent. They are usually of German though sometimes of English manufacture.

These weapons ordinarily have two parallel shotgun barrels with the rifle barrel mounted in the center below the two upper ones.

APPENDIX IV

PARADOX GUNS

G. B. Fosbery originally patented in England the idea of the rifled-shotgun, in which the barrel of an ordinary choke bored shotgun is rifled for the last few inches at the muzzle. It is sometimes called "ratchet rifled." The rifling is a sharp spiral. The solid ball load for these guns carries a heavily cannelured, conical, lead alloy slug. This design has been much imitated abroad under various trade names. Fosbery used originally the trade name "Paradox," to indicate this type of arm.

APPENDIX V

RIFLE-SHOTGUN COMBINATIONS

These arms resemble standard double barreled shotguns or double barreled rifles in all respects except that one barrel (usually the left) is rifled to handle a standard metallic cartridge of almost any European caliber (and a few American calibers), while the other barrel is shotgun bored. Arms of this type have never been very highly esteemed by either American, African or Asiatic shooters. They were most popular in Middle Europe. To a limited degree these weapons were mass manufactured in Suhl, Germany before World War II for export trade. The quality varies from fair to excellent. However, such weapons have rather bad balance and are much too heavy for standard field shotgun use. Beautiful custom built specimens are encountered, usually German or Belgian.

APPENDIX VI

RIFLED SHOTGUN SLUGS

Special "rifled" slugs of the German Brenneke type are designed for standard shotgun use. These slugs have slanting "lands and grooves" around the body of the projectile intended to impart a spinning motion to the round nosed slug and thereby improve its accuracy. As a matter of fact, ordinary shotguns using Brenneke slugs give fairly good hunting accuracy up to 100 yards.

Literally scores of varieties of these slugs have been manufactured. Rifled slugs are also made by American manufacturers.

APPENDIX VII

MORRIS TUBE GUNS

The Morris tube is a device well known in England and on the Continent. It is seldom encountered in the United States. The "tube" is a rifled barrel having an exterior diameter small enough to permit it to be fitted into the barrel of a rifle of larger caliber or of a shotgun. The tubes are designed to utilize the regular sights and the firing and extracting system of the arm in which each is to be used. Germany and Spain were also seats of manufacture of various types of similar adapter tubes.

While scores of such devices have been made here and abroad (notably the Marble devices and the conversion units used by the Germans for permitting use of .22 cartridges in their service rifles), they have not achieved acceptance in the United States. Generally speaking, a fair grade American .22 rifle will cost less and be more efficient than an average conversion insert assembly.

APPENDIX VIII

THE RIFLES OF PETER PAUL MAUSER

In the long course of history few men indeed have left greater marks on the world of their time than Peter Paul Mauser, last of the thirteen children of the humble German gunsmith, Franz Andreas Mauser.

Mauser rifles and pistols are known in every corner of the earth; yet no writer, no economist, no politician has ever correctly assayed the tremendous influence Mauser and his successors wielded throughout the world. Where Mauser arms have gone, there too German ideology has gone, whether for good or ill. Our own concern however, is primarily with the inventor and the arms themselves.

The first basic Mauser design was a product of such great genius, simple though it seems today, that developing the entire future line of Mauser rifles was essentially but a matter of adapting the improvements indicated by mechanical, metallurgical and chemical advances in the course of firearms evolution. In our own country at a later day John M. Browning, by a parallel stroke of genius, evolved his famous Winchester 1886, a lever action arm so absolutely correct in principle that only elementary changes in its basic design have given us an entire line of the finest hunting rifles to this very day. Where Browning was the product of a free country interested in the preservation of peace, Mauser was born and raised—and died—in an atmosphere of the rankest militarism. Therein lies the difference between the developments of the arms of these two geniuses.

Peter Paul was working in the Government firearms factory in his native Oberndorf at the age of 14. That was in 1852 when he graduated from elementary school. The family record shows that two years before that he was already receiving instructions in mechanical matters from his father and the four older brothers who worked in the factory, which had once been a peaceful Augustine cloister.

When he was drafted for the army in 1859, young Mauser the riflesmith was assigned as an artilleryman, a procedure which would indicate that the general military mind then was much the same as now. However, in his spare time he was able to study closely the Dreyse needle gun and to weigh its values and its defects.

When placed on inactive status he returned to work at Oberndorf. His father died, his brother Franz emigrated to America, later to join the Remington organization. Paul was close only to his brother Wilhelm, the next older of the Mausers. Wilhelm was the businessman and to some extent a mechanical helper. Paul was the designer and the finished workman. Paul developed a breech loading cannon—his very first invention—and very soon found there was no prospect for him in the big money field of heavy ordnance.

The brothers fell out for a time and Paul himself devoted all his spare hours to improving the Dreyse. In 1865 he worked out the system of cam cocking by raising and lowering the bolt handle. This was a tremendous step forward, as one of the real dangers of the first bolt actions was accidental fire on bolt closing. The other danger, gas escape at the breech from the paper cartridge, had already been solved by the metallic cartridge which had wide sporting use and limited military use in Europe by then.

Wilhelm rejoined Paul and managed to obtain a Government loan to buy machinery. Their native Württemberg had just bought new arms for its troops and wasn't interested in their rifle; the Prussians rejected the first Mauser because the Dreyse "was so excellent that a change could not even be considered" to quote the Royal Prussian Ambassador at Stuttgart; Austria would have been definitely interested except that it was already changing over to the Wänzl. However, the Austrian Ambassador interested an American, Samuel Norris of Springfield, Mass., in the Mauser. Norris, a representative of Remington, saw the great military potential of the new design and undertook to back the two brothers. His contract called for him to finance them at Luttich (Liege) in Belgium, the great arms center of that day, and to pay them a royalty on arms sold. The patents were to be taken out in the United States.

And so it happens that the first Mauser rifle, the Mauser-Norris, was actually patented (No. 78603) in the U. S. Patent Office on June 2, 1868.

Remington was incensed at the actions of their employee, Norris, to put it mildly. Norris was unable to obtain the financial backing he needed, and his contract with the Mausers was invalidated, though he did succeed in having the Prussian Government consider the new rifle. It is useless to speculate here on what changes in history might have occurred had Norris been able to raise capital; but soon after Norris parted with the brothers, Wilhelm was summoned to Spandau, and negotiations were underway for the first German Army metallic cartridge arm, the famous "Infanteriegewehr M. 71." This arm was officially adopted December 2, 1871 but changes made by Mauser held up manufacture until the following year.

The personal inventions specifically set forth by Mauser in this design are:

automatic cam cocking; bolt head design; elastic extractor; ejector; primary extraction and manual safety.

The M. 71 started the Mauser empire throughout the military and later the sporting world. The following chronology of development, taken directly from the personal Mauser records, shows graphically the evolution and development of the German rifle. Its effects on world history, both evident and hidden, may be gauged from the way the Mauser arms were spread abroad from the still-existing manufacturing liaisons started early in the life of the Mauser firm.

1872. M. 71 made at Spandau by Prussian Government on royalty basis. Mauser Brothers given order for parts, opened workshop. Foundation laid for new plant.

1872. New plant opened in August. Burned down in 1874. Württemberg ordered 100,000 M. 71's and sold Government Firearms Factory at Oberndorf to the Mauser brothers. Mauser Brothers & Co. was formed with financial help of Württembergische Vereinsbank of Stuttgart.

1876. 26,000 Model 71's sold to China.

1878. Experimental work on magazines for attachment to M. 71.

1880. Magazine tube below barrel added to M. 71.

1881. Improved Mauser single shot, M. 78/80 produced. 120,000 sold in caliber 10.15mm to Serbia by Wilhelm.
Tube magazine rifle demonstrated to Kaiser Wilhelm I in September. 2000 ordered for field tests.

1882. Wilhelm Mauser died.

1884. Prussian High Command accepted tube magazine loader in caliber 11mm for re-equipping army. Designated "M. 71/84."
Serbia bought 4000 of these magazine arms as 7-shot cavalry carbines and 4000 more as longer 8-shot artillery rifles.
Württemberg ordered 19,000 M. 71/84 rifles.
April 1st the firm changed structure and name was changed from Gebruder Mauser & Cie. to Waffenfabrik Mauser and became a stock company.

1887. Turkey ordered 500,000 rifles and 50,000 cavalry carbines in 9.5mm black powder caliber. This arm introduced dual locking lugs on the Mauser design to stand increased pressure. The firm of Ludwig Loewe & Co. of Berlin was a 50% partner in this contract.
Vertical and revolving box magazines for M. 71 issued.

1889. Belgium adopted Mauser 7.65mm with projecting vertical box magazine and Mauser strip-in clip loading system. Two hundred seventy-five thousand supplied by Fabrique Nationale d'Armes de Guerre at Herstal, by Fabrique d'Armes de l'Etat at Lüttich (Liege).
Arms made to Mauser's specifications and by payment of royalty. This deal marks the first step in continued Mauser manufacture in Belgium through the years.

1890. Turkey renegotiated with Mauser after receiving 220,000 on her order for black powder 9.5mm tube repeaters.
280,000 improved vertical box magazine rifles delivered to Turkey as M. 90, in caliber 7.65mm Mauser rimless.

1891. Argentina adopted vertical box Mauser in caliber 7.65mm Mauser.

Bolivia adopted vertical box Mauser in caliber 7.65mm Mauser.

Columbia adopted vertical box Mauser in caliber 7.65mm Mauser.

Ecuador adopted vertical box Mauser in caliber 7.65mm Mauser.

Spain ordered 1840 rifles and many carbines for field tests. Cal. 7.65mm.

1893. Spain adopted improved Mauser with first staggered built-in box magazine in new caliber 7mm. Spain received 251,800 rifles and 27,500 carbines. All but 30,000 were made by Loewe at Berlin.

Turkey ordered an additional 150,000 M. 90 rifles.

Turkey ordered 201,000 new models (modifications of Spanish) in caliber 7.65mm Mauser. These had a magazine cut off.

1894. Sweden adopted the improved Mauser in the caliber 6.5mm carbine, 5000 purchased in 1894, 7185 in the following year. Manufacturing under German patents and specifications continued on royalty basis at Carl Gustavs Stads Firearms Factory at Eskilstuna, Sweden.

Brazil adopted the new Mauser in caliber 7mm.

1894. Congo Free State adopted the New Mauser in caliber 7.65mm.

1895. Germany ordered 2000 new model Mausers with barrel jackets for tests. Cal. 7.9mm.

Chile adopted Mauser in caliber 7mm.

Mexico adopted Mauser in caliber 7mm.

Uruguay adopted Mauser in caliber 7mm, also Transvaal and the Orange Free State.

1896. Germany ordered 2185 Mausers without barrel jackets for tests. Cal. 6mm. Mauser demonstrated his new 7.63mm Military Automatic Pistol for Kaiser Wilhelm II and promised to develop an automatic rifle within 5 years. Sweden adopted Mauser rifle in 6.5mm.

Luxemburg adopted the Mauser in caliber 6.5mm.

Modified Spanish Model 93 rifles delivered to Cuba and Spain.

1898. The improved Mauser in caliber 7.9mm adopted for entire German army under designation "Infanteriegewehr M. 98." This rifle is the basis for all Mausers since that date.

1899. Sweden purchased 45,000 Mausers in cal. 6.5mm from Oberndorf.

Serbia adopted Mauser in cal. 7mm.

1902. Mexico adopted improved Mauser in caliber 7mm.

1903. Turkey adopted modified pattern in cal. 7.65mm Turkish.

1904. Modified 1904 pattern introduced having rear safety lug on bolt as in Model 98 and a rib to guide bolt travel.

1904. Brazil adopted Model 1904, cal. 7mm.

Chile adopted Model 1904, cal. 7mm.

Portugal adopted Model 1904 with modified bolt handle and safety (Mauser-Vergueiro pattern), cal. 6.5mm. (Special split-bridge receiver.)

1906. Sweden adopted new Mauser in caliber 6.5mm.

1908. Model 98 rifle shortened and modified. Short rifle renamed, "Kar. 98." No further changes until 1916 when bushed holes were provided in stock. Sporting rifles introduced. Modifications of military pattern.

1914. Austria tentatively adopted 7mm Mauser. Manufacture halted by World War I.

1914-1918. War manufacture.

1918. Mauser introduced its famous antitank rifle.
1920. Mauser sporting weapons again in production.
Mauser rifle manufactured in Poland.
1922. Name changed from Waffenfabrik Mauser A.G. to Mauser-Werke A.-G.
1924. Fabrique Nationale in Belgium manufactured Mauser for export.
These and later minor modifications used by: Arabia, Argentina, Brazil, Belgian Armed Forces and Gendarmerie, China, Columbia, Costa Rica, Ethiopia, Greece, Iran, Liberia, Lithuania, Mexico, Peru, Paraguay, Poland, Uruguay, Venezuela and Yugoslavia. Note: Though F. N. is a Belgian plant, the European manufacturer of Browning arms, its Mauser rifles have always been made to finest Mauser specifications.
Mausers manufactured by Czechs at Brno. Also by Yugoslavia.
1930. Mausers manufactured at new Berlin plant.
1935-1945. War production.
1941. Gas operated semiautomatic rifle, unsuccessful. (The 41-M.)

THE RIFLES OF THE RITTER VON MANNLICHER

In the entire history of firearms no inventor even approaches, for prolific originality and mechanical wizardry, the great Austrian, Ferdinand Ritter von Mannlicher; though our own J. M. Browning created more designs which were actually quantity produced.

Beginning his career when the breech-sealing metallic cartridge was still in its infancy, Baron von Mannlicher actually produced bolt rifles, magazine types and semiautomatic arms which correctly forecast every successful magazine and semiautomatic arm since marketed.

His amazing semiautomatic rifle in 1895 quite accurately forecast our Garand, and his short stroke piston arm of 1900 was to some degree a forerunner of our M1 (Winchester) Carbine.

At present we must concern ourselves with his *successful* bolt actions and magazines. The word "successful" is used advisedly, since von Mannlicher *actually produced* over 150 different types of weapons. Some great inventors like Maxim worked out enough details on paper to file patent specifications for a score of designs which were never to reach even the model stage. Other great inventors like Browning actually made crude operating models which had to be completely factory engineered before a firing model could be produced. Still others like Mauser worked to *evolve* a single basic arm to a higher state of efficiency, and only secondarily to introduce new designs.

The Austrian genius actually produced, manufactured and tested his more than 150 types, some being evolutions of his own designs, some being improvements of basic ideas already known—but most being strictly original creations. Why did so few survive, why are so few generally known? Because von Mannlicher was far ahead of his time—politically, economically, militarily, mechanically. The cartridges of his day, the machinery and the metals were not far enough advanced to utilize many of his mechanical designs. The bugbear of *cost* was always uppermost in the minds of the European War Office heads: it would cost too much to issue certain types; the troops would waste ammunition needlessly employing other types. Thus went the reasoning. The German government was whole-heartedly behind Mauser, and every effort was lent to spread his superior arms throughout the world. The Austrian government, having no such militaristic ambitions on a broad scale, failed to lend the support it might have to the wider spread of the output of the Steyr Armoury.

Where a chronology of Mauser discloses primarily a pattern of the evolution of a single design and of its spread across the earth, the Mannlicher chronology of but a fraction of his designs discloses primarily the *creative genius* of the Austrian. It must be noted that the years given are the actual *years of introduction*. Many types were designed long before they appeared.

Selected Mannlicher Arms

1880. Turning bolt rifle with 3 tubes within buttstock for Austrian M. 77 cartridge (4 tubes in design tested by Germany). Tubes were revolved and cartridge fed successively from each tube as bolt was operated. Magazine capacities 15 and 20 cartridges.

1881. Turning bolt rifle with new bolt design. Special slanting steel box magazine inserted from below. Special system to prevent double-loading. Cal. 11mm (.433) Model Austrian 77.

1882. Simplified turning bolt lock. Magazine tube below barrel. Cal. 11mm. Positive single feeder action.

1882. Turning bolt lock rifle. Gravity feed magazine of box type mounted on top right side of receiver. Cal. 11mm. (With magazine spring added, this system is used on some modern European light machine guns.)

1884. Straight pull rifle with revolving bolt, lugs locked to rear of magazine. Top gravity feed on left side of receiver from box magazine. Cal. 11mm. This bolt design was the precursor of the famous M. 95 Austrian service.

1885. Straight pull bolt with hinged wedge lock to rear of magazine. Cal. 11mm. This lock was the first form of the famous 1888-90 Mannlicher straight pull. The magazine was a fixed box loaded with a special clip through the top of the open action, the clip forming part of the magazine system. When bolt was pulled back to eject last empty case, the clip was thrown out *the top* of the rifle. (This principle is used on the modern U.S. Garand.)

1886. Officially adopted by Austria in cal. 11mm. Straight pull, wedge locked bolt. This was the first successful "multiple loader" arm. A clip loaded with cartridges is inserted through the top of the open action and may be removed at any time the action is open by pressing a release catch. The spring-controlled follower arm rising between the side walls of the clip feeds cartridges up for chambering. When the last cartridge is chambered the empty clip falls through the opening in the bottom of the receiver. (This is the perfected form of the noted Mannlicher packet-loading magazine principle.)

1887. Special turning bolt action with *revolving box* magazine. This evolved from the Spitalsky box introduced at Steyr in 1879, which was further modified by Schulhof in 1885. Cal. 11mm. Magazine capacity 8 cartridges. Mannlicher claimed several modifications. This magazine was loaded with individual cartridges, not with a clip.

1887/88. The first Mannlicher-Schoenauer. 1884 type turning bolt. Radically improved revolving box magazine loaded through top of open action either with single cartridges or with special strip-in clip. Cartridge release provided for emptying magazine.

1888. Austrian service rifle. Identical with 1886 straight pull except as modified to take 8mm compressed black powder cartridge. When later slightly modified to take 8mm smokeless powder cartridge in 1890, the Model was listed as "M. 1888/90."

1888. The German Army rifle for the new 7.9mm rimless cartridge. Only *the magazine system* and a few receiver details were Mannlicher. The arm was actually designed from a modified Mauser bolt by a German Army Commission. This weapon was made in quantity at Steyr as well as in Germany and Belgium. It was also made as a carbine.

1890. The M. 1890 official Austrian carbine introduced in this year was a straight pull action with the locking lugs at the forward end of the revolving bolt head. This bolt design had been patented several years earlier. Except for length and minor characteristics, this rifle is identical with the famous Austrian service rifle of 1895.

1891. The new Italian service rifle of this year generally designed by Parraviccini and Carcano (respectively director and arms controller of the Turin Arsenal) was built around a Mannlicher patent magazine.

1890/92. The French carbines in several styles introduced in these years were essentially the old Lebel bolt action with a Mannlicher 3-shot magazine. Modifications of the Lebel (or 1886 Model) French rifles between 1907 and 1916 also used the Mannlicher packet-loading magazine system instead of the old Lebel tube system.

1893. This year marked the official adoption by Rumania of a new **Mannlicher** rifle actually designed three years earlier. The Rumanian Mannlicher is a turning bolt rifle with typical packet-loading magazine. The dual bolt lugs are at the *forward end* of the bolt head. A carbine model of this arm was also produced.

1894. The Swiss Cavalry Carbine of this year employs a Mannlicher breech system practically identical with the Austrian Model 1890 Straight Pull. The magazine system is radically different, consisting of a 6-shot detachable staggered box inserted from below. The magazine may be loaded through the top of the open action with a special clip. Note that while this is an official Swiss arm, it is not the famous Swiss Schmidt-Rubin straight pull. The Mannlicher was adopted as a lighter and more practical cavalry arm than its heavy Swiss counterpart.

1894. The Model 1894 Mannlicher designed for 6mm rimless cartridges was a turning bolt design using the special clip-loading staggered box magazine of the Swiss 1894 Model mentioned above.

1895. Austrian service rifle. This is probably the most widely known Mannlicher design, the famous straight pull with revolving bolt head and packet-loading magazine. When introduced this was the lightest service rifle made (8.05 pounds), yet in field tests it took terrific punishment. In endurance tests it fired 50,000 fully loaded service charges and was in usable but worn condition at the end of the tests. The first breakage occurred only after firing 13,016 rounds. Total breakages during tests were 1 extractor hook, 1 carrier spring and 2 trigger springs. The rifle was not lubricated throughout the tests, which included thousands of rounds at rapid fire.

The carbine of this year differs from the earlier M. 90 chiefly in having a wooden upper forestock for hand protection and a differently shaped striker nut and feeder.

The Stutzen (short rifle) of this year and pattern forecast the much later adoption of the short-rifle principle of the American Springfield and the German Kar. 98 series.

1895. The Dutch Rifle and Gendarmerie and Cavalry Carbines of this year differ from each other in details only. The bolt system is the turning type, the magazine is the typical Mannlicher packet loading. The design closely resembles the Romanian Mannlichers. The rifle of this type is noted for long range accuracy even today.

1896. The Mannlicher Model 1896 employed an entirely new design of turning bolt. Eight small lugs were provided at the forward end of the long bolt body, 4 on each side. The magazine was packet loading. The breech and firing action was completely new.

1900. The official Greek rifle of this year, the Mannlicher-Schoenauer, is the basic design on which all later M-S sporting rifles are based. This design used the revolving box magazine perfected by Schoenauer from the earlier designs of Spitalsky (a Steyr engineer), Schulhof and von Mannlicher. The turning bolt action with front lugs is the Mannlicher design. Schoenauer was an engineer at Steyr Armoury under Mannlicher. The special loading clip was designed by Pieper in Belgium. (All Mannlicher rifles were extensively made by Belgian firms.) Practically all the Mannlicher sporting type rifles, whether made in Austria, Belgium, Germany, or England, use but very minor modifications of this original system. Many employ double set triggers, special stock designs and the like, but the basic mechanism does not differ materially.

APPENDIX X

GERMAN SMALL ARMS MANUFACTURERS' CODES

A

aak-Waffenfabrik Brunn A. G., Prague

ac-Carl Walther, Zella-Mehlis, Thuringia

aek-F. Dusek Waffenerzeugung, Opoczno bei Nachod

amn-Mauser Works, Waldeck bei Kassel

ar-Mauser Works Borsigwalde, Berlin

asb-Deutsche-Waffen und Munitions Fabriken A. G., Borsigwalde, Berlin

auc-Mauser Works A. G., Ehrenfeld, Cologne

awt-Wurttembergische Metallwarenfabrik A. G., Geislingen

axs-Berndorfer Metallwarenfabrik Arthur Krupp A. G., Berndorf, Niederdonau

ayf-B. Geipel, G. m. b. H., Waffenfabrik "Erma"

azg-Siemens-Schuckert Works A. G., Berlin

B

bed-Gustloff Co., Weimar Works, Weimar

be-Berndorfer Metallwarenfabrik Arthur Krupp A. G., Berndorf, Neiderdonau

bh-Brunner Waffenfabrik A. G., Brunn (Brno, Czechoslovakia)

bjv-Bohm-Mahrische Kolben-Danek A. G., Prague, Vysocan Works

bkp-Gewehrfabrik H. Burgsmüller and Sons G. m. b. H., Kreiensen, Harz

bkq-Rohrenfabrik Johannes Surmann G. m. b. H., Arnsberg

bky-Bohmische Waffenfabrik A. G., of Prague, Ung-Brod Works, Ung Brod, (Moravia)

bmv-Rheinmetall-Borsig A. G., Sömmerda Works, Sömmerda

bmz-Minerva Nahmaschinenfabrik A. G., Boscowitz

bnd-M. A. N., A. G., Nürnberg Works, Nürnberg

bnz-Steyr-Daimler Puch A. G., Steyr Works, Steyr, Austria

bod-Teudloff Vamag Dreinigte Armaturen & Maschinen Fabriken A. G., Wien

bpr-Johannus Grossfuss Metall and Locierwarenfabrik, Dobeln, Saxony

br-Mathias Bauerle Laufwerke G. m. b. H., St. Georgen, Schwarzwald

bvl-Th. Bergmann & Co. Abteilung Automaten u. Metallwarenfabrikation, Altona, Hamburg

bxb-Skoda Works, Pilsen

byf-Mauser Works, Oberndorf

bym-Genossenschafts Maschinenhaus der Buchsenmacher, Ferlach, Carinthia, Austria

byq-Pohlman & Co., Hammerwerke, Wetterburg, Hessen-Nassau

bzt-Fritz Wolf Gewehrfabrik, Zella-Mehlis, Thuringia

C

ce-J. P. Sauer and Sons Gewehrfabrik, Suhl, Saxony

cdo-Th. Bergmann & Co. A. G., Waffen u. Munitionfabrik, Veltem Works, Veltem am Main

ch-Fabrique Nationale d'Armes de Guerre, Herstal, Liege, Belgium
chd-Berlin Industrie Werke A. G., Spandau, Berlin
cl-Metschke, Carl, Auto and Maschinen Repair Werk, Berlin
cyq-Spreewerk GmbH, Metallwaren Fabrik, Berlin, Spandau
cof-Carl Eickhorn, Waffenfabrik Solingen
con-Franz Stock Maschinen u. Werkzeufabrik, Berlin
cos-Merz Brothers, Frankfurt am Main
cpo-Rheinmetall-Borsig A. G., Marienfeld Works, Marienfeld, Berlin
cpp-Rheinmetall-Borsig A. G., Guben Works
cpq-Rheinmetall-Borsig A. G., Breslau Works
crs-Paul Weyersberg & Co. Waffenfabrik, Solingen
cvl-WKC Waffenfabrik G. m. b. H., Solingen
cxq-Spreewerk G. m. b. H., Metallwarenfabrik, Spandau, Berlin

D

dfb-Gustloff Co., Suhl Gun Works, Suhl, Saxony
dgl-Remo Gewehrfabrik, Rempt Brothers, Suhl, Saxony
dnz-Schwarzwalder Apparates Bauanstalt, Aug. Schwek Sohne, Villingen/
Schwarz Wald
dot-Waffenwerke Brunn A. G., Brunn (Brno, Czechoslovakia)
dou-Waffenwerke Brunn A. G., Bystrica Works
dov-Waffenwerke Brunn A. G., Vsetin Works Czechoslovakia
dow-Opticotechna, (formerly Waffenfabrik Brunn A. G.), Prerau, Czechoslovakia
dph-Interessen Gemeinschaft Farbenindustrie A. G., Autogen Works, Gries-
heim, Frankfurt am Main
dsh-Engineer F. Janecek, Gun Works, Prague
duv-Berliner-Lubecker Maschinenfabriken, Lubeck Works
duw-Deutsche Rohrewerke A. G., Thyssen Works, Mulheim

E

egy-Engineer Fr. August Pfeffer, Oberlind, Thuringia

F

fnh-Bomische Waffenfabrik A. G. of Prague, Strakonitz Works
fue-Mechanische Werkstatt A. G., (formerly Dubnica Works of Skoda Co.),
Dubnica
fwh-Norddeutsche Maschinenfabrik G. m. b. H., Hauptverwalting, Berlin
fxa-Eisenacher Karosseriefabrik Assmann G. m. b. H., Eisenach
fxo-C. G. Haenel Waffen u. Fahrrad Fabrik, Suhl, Saxony
fze-F. W. Holler Waffenfabrik, Solingen
fzs-Heinrich Krieghoff Waffenfabrik, Suhl, Saxony

G

ghf-Fritz Kiess & Co., G. m. b. H, Waffenfabrik, Suhl, Saxony
gsb-Rheinmetall-Borsig A. G., (formerly S. A. des Ateliers de la Dyle), Louvain,
Belgium
gsc-S. A. Belge de Mécanique et de l'Armement, Monceau-sur-Sambre, Belgium

guy-Werkzeugmaschinenfabrik Oerlikon, Buhrle & Co., Oerlikon Zurich, Switzerland

H

hew-Engineer F. Janecek, Gun Works, Prague
hhg-Rheinmetall-Borsig A. G., Tegel Works, Tegel, Berlin
hhv-Steyr-Daimler Puch A. G., Nibelungen Works, St. Valentin, Austria
hla-Metallwaren Fabrik Treuenbrietzen, GmbH, Werk Sebaldushoff

J

jhv-Metallwaren Waffen u. Maschinenfabrik A. G., Budapest
jkg-Kong. Ungar. Staatlische Eisen, Stahl u. Maschinenfabrik, Budapest
jlj-Heeres Zeugamt, Ingoldstadt
jua-Danuvia Waffen u. Munitionsfabrik A. G., Budapest
jwa-Manufacture d'Armes Chatellerault, Chatellerault, France

K

kfk-Dansk Industrie Syndicat, Copenhagen, Denmark
kls-Steyr-Daimler Puch A. G., Warsaw
ksb-Manufacture Nationale d'Armes de Levallois, Levallois, Paris, France
kur-Steyr-Daimler Puch A. G., Graz Works
kwn-S. A. Fiat, Turın, Italy

L

lza-Mauser Werke A. G., Werk Karlsruhe

M

moc-Johann Springer's Erben Gewehrfabrikanten, Vienna
mpr-S. A. Hispano Suiza, Geneva, Switzerland
mrb-Aktiengesellschaft, (formerly Prague Works of Skoda Co.), Prague
myx-Rheinmetall-Borsig A. G., Sömmerda Works, Sömmerda, Thuringia

N

nb-Wappenfabrik Kongsberg, Kongsberg, Norway
nec-Waffenwerke Brunn A. G., Prague
nhr-Rheinmetall-Borsig A. G., Sömmerda Works, Sömmerda, Thuringia
nyv-Rheinmetall-Borsig A. G., Werk Unterluss
nyw-Gustloff Co., Meiningen

This list is by no means a complete list of German Small Arms Manufacturers during World War II. It is a list of the largest and most commonly encountered markings on standard weapons. The German World War II Ordnance Markings Code which ran from A-Z and AA-ZZ would occupy a volume twice the size of this book; few complete copies of this code exist in the United States.

APPENDIX XI

FOREIGN RIFLE MARKINGS

In the following pages are some typical identifying markings found on foreign military rifles. U. S. military rifles are usually easily identified by markings, since it is U. S. custom to stamp the full nomenclature on the receiver of the rifle. Rifles made in certain European countries during and since World War II are more difficult to identify by markings, since model designation is frequently not stamped on the weapon and the place of manufacture may be designated by a numerical or alphabetical· code. This is the result of an appreciation that designation of manufacturer by name and geographical location may result in an unwelcome visit by enemy bombers.

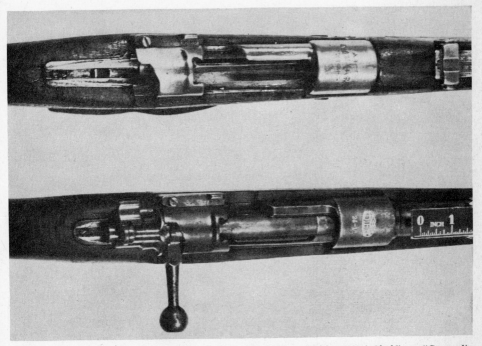

Top: *Chinese 7.92mm Chinese Mauser.* Bottom: *Chinese "Chiang Kai Shek" or "Generalissimo" 7.92mm Mauser.*

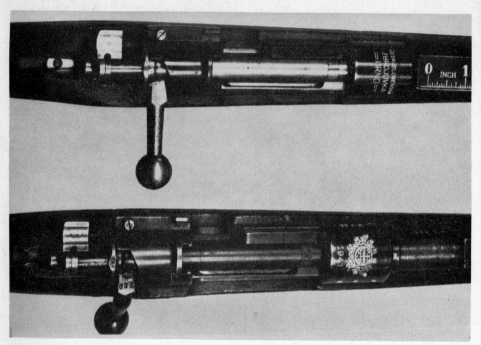

Top: *Czech 7.92mm Model 24 Mauser*. Bottom: *Portuguese 7.92mm M937 Mauser (Kar 98k)*.

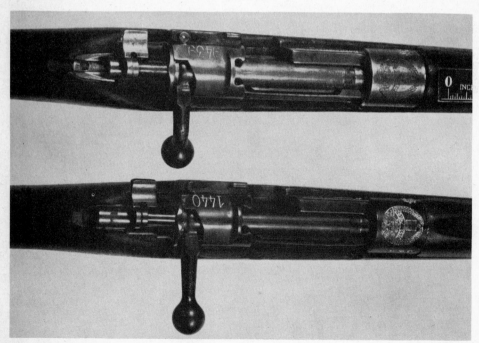

Top: *Ethiopian 7.92mm FN Model 24 Rifle*. Bottom: *Ethiopian 7.92mm FN Model 24 Carbine*.

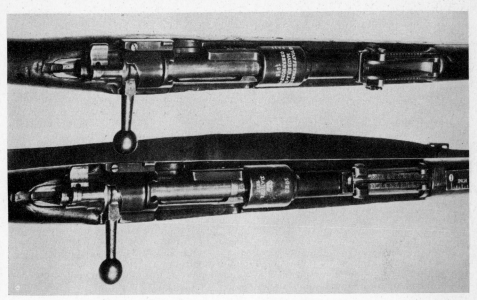

Top: *German 7.92mm Rifle M98 made at Mauser.* Bottom: *German Rifle M98 Modified.*

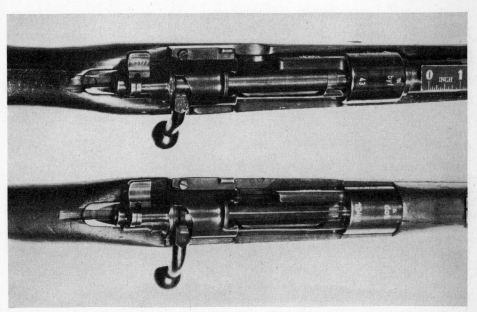

Top: *German 7.92mm Kar 98k made at Mauser in 1943.* Bottom: *German/Czech Model 33/40 7.92mm made at Brno in 1942.*

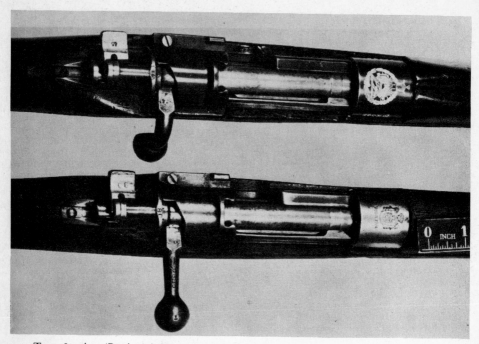

Top: *Iranian (Persian) 7.92mm Mauser.* Bottom: *Yugoslav 7.92mm M1924 Mauser.*

Japanese 7.7mm Type 99 Rifle.

Japanese 6.5mm Type 38 Rifle.

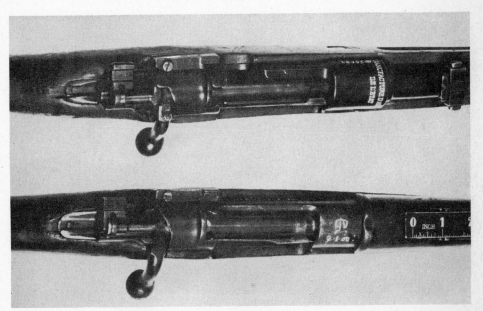

Top: *7.65mm Belgian Mauser made by Manufacture D'Armes De L'Etat (Government Arms Factory).* Bottom: *German-made Mauser M1893, made by DWM.*

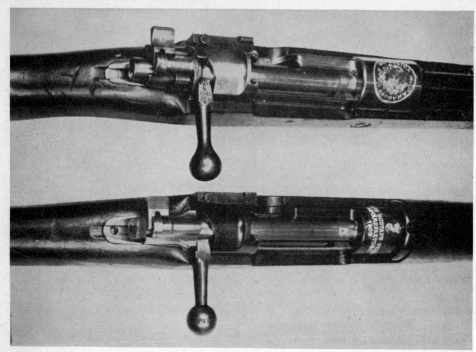

Top: *7.65mm M1907 Paraguayan Mauser.* Bottom: *6.5mm M1896 Swedish Mauser.*

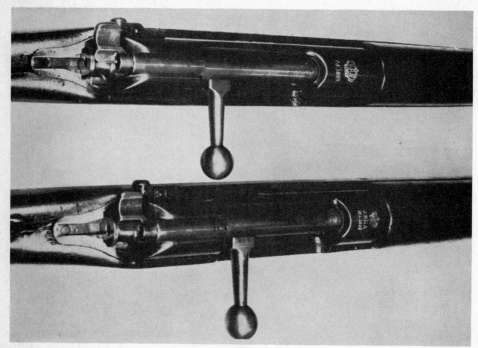

Top: *Roumanian 6.5mm Mannlicher M1893.* Bottom: *6.5mm Roumanian Mannlicher Model 1892.*

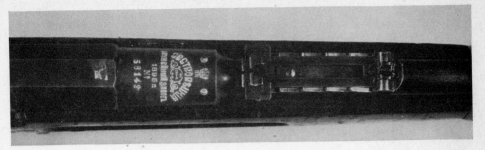

Russian 7.62mm M1891 Mosin Nagant made at Sestroretsk in 1895.

Russian 7.62mm M1891 Mosin Nagant made at Schweiz Industrie Gesellschaft (SIG), Neuhausen, Switzerland.

Soviet 7.62mm M1938 Mosin Nagant Carbine.

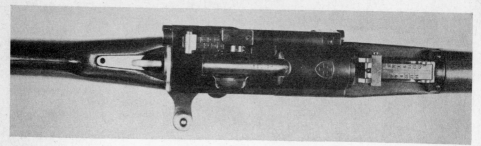

Swiss 7.5mm M31/42 Sniper Rifle.

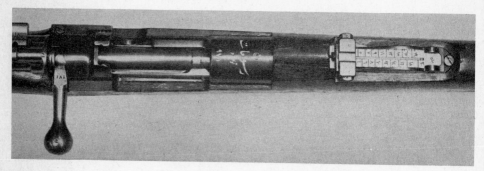

Turkish 7.65mm M1903 Mauser.

INDEX